Howard Pyle

His Life—His Work

When All the World Was Young, 1908, oil on canvas, Delaware Art Museum purchase, 1912

Howard Pyle
His Life—His Work

A Comprehensive Bibliography and Pictorial Record of
Howard Pyle: Illustrator, Author, Teacher

Father of American Illustration
America's Foremost Illustrator

VOLUME II

Compiled, Indexed, and Edited by
Paul Preston Davis

Preface by Steve Bruni, Director, Delaware Art Museum

Foreword by Howard Pyle Brokaw

Computer/Technical Assistance by George W. Peacock

Oak Knoll Press
New Castle, Delaware, USA

Delaware Art Museum
Wilmington, Delaware, USA

2004

First Edition, 2004

Published by **Oak Knoll Press**
310 Delaware Street, New Castle, Delaware, 19720, USA
Web: http://www.oakknoll.com
and the **Delaware Art Museum**
3201 Kentmere Parkway, Wilmington, Delaware, 19806, USA
Web: http://www.delart.org

Support for this publication has been provided, in part, by Helen Farr Sloan,
the Wyeth Foundation for American Art, and the Cawley Family Foundation.

ISBN: 1-58456-133-5

Title: Howard Pyle: His Life—His Work
Editor/Compiler: Paul Preston Davis
Typographers: George W. Peacock and Michael Höhne Design
Publication Director: J. Lewis von Hoelle
Project Coordinator: Kraig Binkowski
Art Director: Deborah Mackie
Cover Design: Megan Erin Paar

Library of Congress Cataloging-in-Publication

Pyle, Howard, 1853–1911.
    Howard Pyle : His Life—His Work / compiled, indexed, & edited by Paul Preston Davis:
Foreword by Howard Pyle Brokaw.--1st ed.
      p. cm.
    Includes bibliographical references and index.
    ISBN 1-58456-133-5
    1. Pyle, Howard, 1853–1911-Bibliography. 2. Pyle, Howard, 1853–1911--Catalogues
raisonnês. I. Davis, Paul Preston. II. Title

Z8720.P954 2004
[N6537.P94]
016.7416'4'092--dc22

                            2003069107

This work was printed and bound in China on archival, acid-free paper
meeting the requirements of the American Standard for Permanence of
Paper for Printed Library Materials.

Contents

Acknowledgments i
Preface iii
Foreword v
Introduction ix

Volume I

Section I   BIBLIOGRAPHY OF HOWARD PYLE'S WORK
Periodicals 1
Books 129
Murals 257
Unpublished Art and Writing 259
Other Miscellaneous:
    Advertising:
        Catalogue 265
        Leaflet 271
    Bookplate 274
    Catalogue:
        Auction; School 276
    Collectible:
        Game; Plate 277
    Ephemera:
        Bookmark; Calendar 277
        Christmas Seal; Cigar Box Label; Invitation 278
    Etching 279
    Exhibition 281
    Illustration/Art Incorrectly Attributed to Howard Pyle 318
    Lecture/Speech/Talk 319
    Photo Portraits 322
    Portfolio 325
    Poster 326
    Print 328
    Programme 341
    Unique/Special 347

Section II   INDEXES TO THE BIBLIOGRAPHY
Pyle's Writing Published in Books 349
Alphabetical Listing of All Books 353
Year Published Listing of All Books 361
Pyle's Writing Published in Periodicals 369
Alphabetical Listing of All Periodicals 375
Writing and References About Pyle 381
Pyle Portraits Publication Record 389
Pyle's Published Work — PM Numbers 391

Volume II

Section III   PICTURE RECORD OF ALL KNOWN WORKS OF HOWARD PYLE
        3,382 PLATES IN COLOR AND BLACK & WHITE 401
Photograph Credits 613

Section IV   INDEXES TO THE PICTURE TITLE AND PUBLICATION HISTORY
Titles and Alternate Titles of Pyle's Art 615
Titles of Pyle's Art In Chronological Sequence 671
Publication and Exhibition History of Pyle's Art 713

Howard Pyle

His Life—His Work

Book II

Illustration titles are listed as they were first published.

MBPI0001

Ye Pirate Bold

MBPI0002

"I saw him pass his sword through the mate's body"

MBPI0003

"He put the glass to his lips and drank at one gulp"

MBPI0004

"Will you forgive my having followed you?"

MBPI0005

"The gigantic monster dragged the hacked and headless corpse of his victim up the staircase"

MBPI0006

"A man in it, standing upright, and something lying in a lump at the bow"

MBPI0007

The Rivals

MBPI0008

The First Sketch

MBPI0009

Illustrated initial A for The First Sketch

MBPI0010

The Second Sketch

MBPI0011

Illustrated initial A for The Second Sketch

MBPI0012

The Third Sketch

MBPI0013

Illustrated initial T for The Third Sketch

MBPI0014

The Fourth Sketch

MBPI0015

Illustrated initial T for The Fourth Sketch

MBPI0016

The Fifth Sketch

MBPI0017
ILLUSTRATED INITIAL A FOR THE FIFTH SKETCH

MBPI0018
THE SIXTH SKETCH

MBPI0019
ILLUSTRATED INITIAL T FOR THE SIXTH SKETCH

MBPI0020
THE SURRENDER OF CAPTAIN PEARSON ON THE DECK OF THE "BONHOMME RICHARD"

MBPI0021
THE BONHOMME RICHARD AND YE SERAPIS

MBPI0022
HEADPIECE WITH TITLE AND INITIAL T FOR PAUL JONES

MBPI0023
PAUL JONES RAISING THE RATTLESNAKE FLAG ON THE "ALFRED"

MBPI0024
TAILPIECE FOR PAUL JONES

MBPI0025
"THE ADMIRAL CAME IN HIS GIG OF STATE"

MBPI0026
HEADPIECE WITH TITLE FOR THE CONSTITUTION'S LAST FIGHT

MBPI0027
THE CONSTITUTION'S LAST FIGHT

MBPI0028
TAILPIECE FOR THE CONSTITUTION'S LAST FIGHT

MBPI0029
MAID MARIAN'S SONG WITH TITLE

MBPI0030
MAID MARIAN'S SONG

MBPI0031
"DIDST THOU TELL THEM I TAUGHT THEE?"

MBPI0032
"I WILL TEACH THEE TO ANSWER THY ELDERS"

MBPI0033
"There was instant silence"

MBPI0034
In Aunt Gainor's Garden

MBPI0035
Aunt Gainor

MBPI0036
In the presence of Washington

MBPI0037
In the Prison

MBPI0038
"Here, André! A Spy!"

MBPI0039
The visit to André

MBPI0040
Arnold and his wife

MBPI0041
The Duel

MBPI0042
"Is it Yes or No, Darthea?"

MBPI0043
Headpiece for The Battle of Copenhagen

MBPI0044
Nelson sealing his letter to the Crown Prince of Denmark

MBPI0045
Tailpiece for The Battle of Copenhagen

MBPI0046
The Mizzen Top of the "Redoubtable"

MBPI0047
Don Quixote's Encounter with the Windmill

MBPI0048
Headpiece with title and decorated border for Hope and Memory

MBPI0049
HOPE AND MEMORY

MBPI0050
HEADPIECE FOR HOPE AND MEMORY

MBPI0051
TAILPIECE FOR HOPE AND MEMORY

MBPI0052
MARGINAL DECORATION FOR HOPE AND MEMORY

MBPI0053
MARGINAL DECORATION FOR HOPE AND MEMORY

MBPI0054
THE WICKET OF PARADISE

MBPI0055
IN THE MEADOWS OF YOUTH

MBPI0056
IN THE VALLEY OF THE SHADOWS

MBPI0057
AT THE GATES OF LIFE

MBPI0058
TITLE PAGE DECORATION FOR THE TRAVELS OF THE SOUL

MBPI0059
HEADPIECE WITH TITLE THE TRAVELS OF THE SOUL

MBPI0060
ILLUSTRATED INITIAL T FOR THE TRAVELS OF THE SOUL

MBPI0061
HEADPIECE WITH TITLE IN THE MEADOWS OF YOUTH

MBPI0062
ILLUSTRATED INITIAL O FOR IN THE MEADOWS OF YOUTH

MBPI0063
TAILPIECE FOR IN THE MEADOWS OF YOUTH

MBPI0064
HEADPIECE WITH TITLE IN THE VALLEY OF THE SHADOWS

MBPI0065
Illustrated initial N for In the Valley of the Shadows

MBPI0066
Tailpiece for In the Valley of the Shadows

MBPI0067
Headpiece with title At the Gates of Life

MBPI0068
Illustrated initial A for At the Gates of Life

MBPI0069
Tailpiece for At the Gates of Life

MBPI0070
Christmas Morn

MBPI0071
Decoration with title for Poisoned Ice

MBPI0072
Headpiece for Poisoned Ice

MBPI0073
On the edge of the ring, guarded, stood Brother Bartholome and the Carmelite

MBPI0074
Tailpiece for Poisoned Ice

MBPI0075
Upon the last stage of the journey they stopped for dinner at a tavern

MBPI0076
Headpiece with title for The Price of Blood

MBPI0077
Illustrated initial I for The Price of Blood

MBPI0078
Tailpiece, Introduction for The Price of Blood

MBPI0079
Illustrated initial T for The Price of Blood

MBPI0080
Headpiece for The Price of Blood

MBPI0081
HEADPIECE, CHAPTER II FOR THE PRICE OF BLOOD

MBPI0082
ILLUSTRATED INITIAL A FOR THE PRICE OF BLOOD

MBPI0083
HEADPIECE, CHAPTER III FOR THE PRICE OF BLOOD

MBPI0084
ILLUSTRATED INITIAL O FOR THE PRICE OF BLOOD

MBPI0085
HEADPIECE, CHAPTER IV FOR THE PRICE OF BLOOD

MBPI0086
ILLUSTRATED INITIAL E FOR THE PRICE OF BLOOD

MBPI0087
HEADPIECE, CHAPTER V FOR THE PRICE OF BLOOD

MBPI0088
ILLUSTRATED INITIAL T FOR THE PRICE OF BLOOD

MBPI0089
DEAD MEN TELL NO TALES

MBPI0090
THE FLYING DUTCHMAN

MBPI0091
COLUMBIA SPEAKS

MBPI0092
HEADPIECE FOR A SAHIB'S WAR

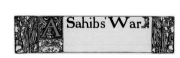

MBPI0093
DECORATION WITH TITLE FOR A SAHIB'S WAR

MBPI0094
ILLUSTRATED INITIAL P FOR A SAHIB'S WAR

MBPI0095
UMR SINGH

MBPI0096
"THEN APPEARED SUDDENLY, A LITTLE BEYOND THE LIGHT OF THE LAMP, THE SPIRIT OF KURBAN SAHIB"

MBPI0097
Tailpiece for A Sahib's War

MBPI0098
Song of Peace

MBPI0099
Whither?

MBPI0100
The Burning Ship

MBPI0101
"Why Seek Ye the Living Among the Dead?"

MBPI0102
The Minute Man

MBPI0103
The Nation Makers

MBPI0104
"In the Garden"

MBPI0105
"They stood and looked across the chasm at him"

MBPI0106
"He turned the slab-like leaves rapidly"

MBPI0107
"The young fellow lounged in a rattan chair"

MBPI0108
"Their first meeting happened at the club"

MBPI0109
"DuMoreau was leaning part way across the table"

MBPI0110
"He glared at the girl in the dim light"

MBPI0111
"Then there was a crash and clatter of an overturned chair"

MBPI0112
"His Majesty would furnish no more money for treasure hunting"

MBPI0113
THE SETTLER

MBPI0114
"HE FELL IN LOVE"

MBPI0115
"A FAIR BRICK HOUSE IN THE GREEN LANE OF NORTH BOSTON"

MBPI0116
"STAND OFF, YE WRETCHES"

MBPI0117
"HE HAD SEEN GREAT GUNS IN THE BOTTOM OF THE SEA"

MBPI0118
"SOBERLY JOINED HIMSELF TO THE NORTH CHURCH"

MBPI0119
"THE SHIPS ROLLED AND WALLOWED IN THE RIVER"

MBPI0120
"WHY, WHAT IS THIS? WHENCE CAME THIS?"

MBPI0121
"AN 'EMINENT PERSON FROM WHITEHALL' VISITED HIM IN HIS CHAMBERS"

MBPI0122
"THE VICTIMS OF THE WITCHCRAFT DELUSION"

MBPI0123
"THE QUEEN GRANTED HIM AN AUDIENCE"

MBPI0124
HE HAD LOST THE SOUL OF M. FOURNIER

MBPI0125
OVER HER GLEAMING SHOULDER HER CHALKY FACE LOWERED AT HIM, WITH A LOOK OF SULLEN HATRED

MBPI0126
IN THE BOOKSELLER'S SHOP

MBPI0127
"THE REJECTION"

MBPI0128
DAISIES

MBPI0129
A Quaker Wedding

MBPI0130
The Flight of the Swallow

MBPI0131
Illustrated initial T for The Flight of the Swallow

MBPI0132
Tailpiece for The Flight of the Swallow

MBPI0133
"He was a tall dark gentleman dressed in black from head to foot"

MBPI0134
"He suddenly began an uncouth grotesque dance"

MBPI0135
"At that moment she looked up"

MBPI0136
"'I am thy Uncle,' said the strange gentleman"

MBPI0137
"He lighted a match and dropped it into the vase"

MBPI0138
"Oliver gave a piping cry"

MBPI0139
"At the open doorway stood Gaspard and his master"

MBPI0140
"Creeping cautiously forward, Oliver came to the chimney-place"

MBPI0141
"'Good day, Monsieur,' said a familiar voice"

MBPI0142
"The question was so sudden and so startling that Oliver sank back in his seat"

MBPI0143
"They saw Arnold de Villeneuve, the great master, lying upon the floor"

MBPI0144
"Such was the workshop in which the two labored together"

MBPI0145
"She held the book to the flames whilest talking, her eyes fixed intently upon it"

MBPI0146
"He leaned over and looked into her face"

MBPI0147
"He saw within an oval mirror, set in a heavy frame of copper"

MBPI0148
"And stripped the false body off of him as you would strip off a man's coat"

MBPI0149
"The innkeeper served him in person"

MBPI0150
"'Mad!' said Oliver, 'why am I mad?'"

MBPI0151
"Oliver spread out the gems upon the table with his hand"

MBPI0152
"He is clad in a loose dressing-robe of figured cloth and lies in bed reading his book"

MBPI0153
"'Do you know,' said the Marquis, 'what a thing it is that you ask?'"

MBPI0154
"He sank upon his knees beside her"

MBPI0155
"She drew her down until the girl kneeled upon the floor beside the sofa"

MBPI0156
"Monsieur the Count de St. Germaine"

MBPI0157
"The Count de St. Germaine, without removing his eyes from his victim, took another deep, luxurious pinch of snuff"

MBPI0158
"Oliver fixed his gaze upon the smooth brilliant surface of the glass"

MBPI0159
"He saw a dull heavy yellow smoke arise to the ceiling"

MBPI0160
"They beheld their master lying upon his face under the table"

MBPI0161
"Suddenly someone touched Oliver lightly upon the shoulder"

MBPI0162
"He found in his clinched hand a lace cravat"

MBPI0163
"'Celeste!' breathed Oliver through the crack in the door"

MBPI0164
"Over his shoulder he carried something limp, like an empty skin, or a bundle of clothes tied together"

MBPI0165
Headpiece with title for The First Thanksgiving

MBPI0166
Illustrated initial O for The First Thanksgiving

MBPI0167
Carnival, Philadelphia, 1778

MBPI0168
"The little pink finger and the huge black index came to a full stop under this commandment"

MBPI0169
At Daddy Bayne's

MBPI0170
"She walked on after saying this, musing"

MBPI0171
"She went by without looking at him"

MBPI0172
Fermina opens the casket

MBPI0173
"Well, dat nigger cheat de burer—he s-t-o-l-e, Massa!"

MBPI0174
"Then came the tug of war"

MBPI0175
Dinner-bell at an Eastville Tavern

MBPI0176
The Country Clerk, Eastville

MBPI0177
OLD RECORDS

MBPI0178
AUNT SABER

MBPI0179
PEACE AND WAR

MBPI0180
OYSTER SHUCKERS

MBPI0181
DREDGING FOR OYSTERS

MBPI0182
STRAWBERRY PICKING

MBPI0183
COOKING SHANTY

MBPI0184
AUNT SALLY

MBPI0185
FISHING SHANTY

MBPI0186
GEORGE, THE COOK

MBPI0187
INTERIOR OF FISHING STATION

MBPI0188
IN THE NORTHERN MARKET—"PEACHES, ONE CENT"

MBPI0189
A FARM "PLUCK"

MBPI0190
GROUP OF NOMADIC "PLUCKS"

MBPI0191
THE PEELING-ROOM

MBPI0192
RAISING CYPRESS LOGS IN THE DISMAL SWAMP

MBPI0193
Making shingles

MBPI0194
The Phantom Horseman

MBPI0195
The Captain of the Yacht "Delaware"

MBPI0196
A bit of sentiment

MBPI0197
"Who stuffed that white owl?"

MBPI0198
"I'm an owl; you're another"

MBPI0199
"As she spoke, she took his hand, and then paused one moment"

MBPI0200
"Laying the old violin tenderly beneath his chin"

MBPI0201
Peter plays the fiddle for the Tavern Folk

MBPI0202
Tacy Kelp

MBPI0203
Representing the manner of Peter's Courtship

MBPI0204
Jonathan Quidd

MBPI0205
"The little boys cheered vigorously as he pushed off"

MBPI0206
"Here it turned, and said 'Knowest thou who I am?'"

MBPI0207
Tailpiece for The Last Revel in Printz Hall

MBPI0208
A complimentary Address to Old Hickory–Interior of Ben Bean's ("Barton") House

MBPI0209
Arrival of the Coach at an Old Stage Station

MBPI0210
An Old Government Toll-Gate, with Westward-Bound Express

MBPI0211
An Old Stager

MBPI0212
Ruins of Old Post Tavern

MBPI0213
Old National Pike Bridge

MBPI0214
Leander

MBPI0215
Uncle Sam

MBPI0216
Preparing for Highwaymen

MBPI0217
An Old Smithy

MBPI0218
Old Way-Side Tavern

MBPI0219
An Old Mile-Stone

MBPI0220
Old Hempstead House

MBPI0221
A Revolutionary Recruiting Office–Privateersmen in New London

MBPI0222
A Garden Party given to General Washington

MBPI0223
Portrait Gallery in Shaw Mansion

MBPI0224
An Old Time Cup of Coffee

MBPI0225
Patty Hempstead in her Gran'ther's
waistcoat

MBPI0226
Ye Antient Gunne

MBPI0227
Old tiled Fire Place, Winthrop House

MBPI0228
Mather Byles preaching to Quakers

MBPI0229
Captain Kidd's gift to Mercy
Redmond

MBPI0230
The Song of Captain Kidd

MBPI0231
The Old Chimney-Corner

MBPI0232
The Botanist

MBPI0233
The Old Bartram Homestead

MBPI0234
Old Corner Cupboard

MBPI0235
Old Inscription

MBPI0236
The Christ Thorn

MBPI0237
The Garden Path

MBPI0238
Departure for New York

MBPI0239
"The Clang of the Yankee Reaper, on
Salisbury Plain!"

MBPI0240
Along the Chester Valley

MBPI0241
OLD VALLEY FORGE BRIDGE

MBPI0242
WASHINGTON'S PRIVATE PAPERS, 1777

MBPI0243
WASHINGTON'S HEAD-QUARTERS, VALLEY FORGE

MBPI0244
GENERAL WAYNE'S GRAVE

MBPI0245
OLD ST. DAVID'S CHURCH

MBPI0246
DRAWING-ROOM, WAYNE HOMESTEAD

MBPI0247
PAOLI MONUMENT

MBPI0248
MELISSY

MBPI0249
JOHN DUBOIS'S DRIVE TO NEWBURGH

MBPI0250
SUNDAY IN OLD CATSKILL

MBPI0251
DINNER AT CORNELIUS DUBOIS'S

MBPI0252
"PERHAPS SHE SAT THERE WHILE SHE STONED HER RAISINS"

MBPI0253
"IT IS ALL A MISTAKE, MY FRIEND, A GRIEVOUS MISTAKE"

MBPI0254
HALE RECEIVING INSTRUCTIONS FROM WASHINGTON

MBPI0255
"I ONLY REGRET THAT I HAVE BUT ONE LIFE TO LOSE FOR MY COUNTRY"

MBPI0256
"I SAW HER FACE WHITE EVEN IN ALL THAT IMMENSE RUDDY GLARE"

MBPI0257
OLD SWEDES CHURCH, WILMINGTON

MBPI0258
GOING TO CHURCH

MBPI0259
AT EVENING

MBPI0260
THE UMBRELLA–A CURIOUS PRESENT

MBPI0261
WILLIAM COBBETT'S SCHOOL

MBPI0262
THE DESTRUCTION OF THE SIGN

MBPI0263
THE BRITISH IN WILMINGTON

MBPI0264
"I NEVER HAD WOOD THAT I LIKED HALF
SO WELL–DO SEE WHO HAS NICE CROOKED
FUEL TO SELL"

MBPI0265
NEW-YEAR'S HYMN TO ST. NICHOLAS

MBPI0266
MYNHEER'S MORNING HORN

MBPI0267
"HE STOPS AT THE SIGN OF THE
WEATHERVANE"

MBPI0268
"THEN HE TELLS HIS NEWS, IN THE RUDDY
GLOW"

MBPI0269
A MOUNTAIN FARM-HOUSE

MBPI0270
THE LOWLAND BROOK

MBPI0271
AN AUTUMN EVENING

MBPI0272
THE MOUNTAIN ORCHARD

MBPI0273
The Corn Fields on the Hill-Side

MBPI0274
Isaac Sears addressing the Mob

MBPI0275
The Press-Gang in New York

MBPI0276
Theophylact Bache saving Graydon from the Mob in 1776

MBPI0277
Spine design for Men of Iron

MBPI0278
"I often took my Bible and sat in hollow trees"

MBPI0279
"The Word of the Lord came to me, saying 'Cry, Woe to the bloody City of Litchfield!'"

MBPI0280
"I sat in a hay-stack, and said nothing for some hours"

MBPI0281
"They led me, taking hold of my collar, and by my arms"

MBPI0282
"The Admiral lost all control of himself, and in a rage ordered his son to quit the house"

MBPI0283
Quaker and King at Whitehall 1681

MBPI0284
The Departure of the "Welcome"

MBPI0285
A burial at sea on board the "Welcome"

MBPI0286
William Penn and his Commissioners in the cabin of the "Welcome"

MBPI0287
"Thomas Moon began to lay about him with his Sword"

MBPI0288
Drake's Attack on San Domingo

MBPI0289
"Jacques Cartier setting up a Cross at Gaspé"

MBPI0290
Dominique de Gourgues avenging the Murder of the Huguenot Colony

MBPI0291
"He brought both Catholic Priests and Huguenot Ministers, who disputed heartily on the Way"

MBPI0292
"He rested his Musket"

MBPI0293
The Landing of the Pilgrims

MBPI0294
Arrival of the Young Women at Jamestown

MBPI0295
Endicott cutting the cross out of the English flag

MBPI0296
Death of King Philip

MBPI0297
Governor Andros and the Boston People

MBPI0298
A Quaker Exhorter in New England

MBPI0299
Arresting a Witch

MBPI0300
Peter Stuyvesant tearing the Letter demanding the Surrender of New York

MBPI0301
The "Boston Massacre"

MBPI0302
An out-of-door Tea Party in Colonial New England

MBPI0303
Washington refusing a Dictatorship

MBPI0304
Washington and his Generals in Consultation March 15, 1783

MBPI0305
Lexington Green–"If they want a War, let it begin here"

MBPI0306
Sergeant Jasper at the Battle of Fort Moultrie

MBPI0307
The last boat-load of the British leaving New York

MBPI0308
The civil procession, headed by General Washington and Governor Clinton

MBPI0309
"The Master caused vs to haue some Beere"

MBPI0310
The Puritan Governor interrupting the Christmas sports

MBPI0311
The French Officers at Newport

MBPI0312
Shay's Mob in possession of a Court House

MBPI0313
At Mrs. Washington's Reception

MBPI0314
Impressment of American Seamen

MBPI0315
Among the Daffodillies

MBPI0316
"So saying, she turned and left me"

MBPI0317
"Bringing in the May"

MBPI0318
President Johnson teaching his first class

MBPI0319
Hamilton addressing the mob

MBPI0320
The Search for Toinette

MBPI0321
Headpiece for Witchcraft

MBPI0322
Witchcraft, 1692

MBPI0323
Witchcraft, 1884

MBPI0324
Spring Blossoms

MBPI0325
Rescue of Sevier

MBPI0326
"The Cherokees Are Coming"

MBPI0327
Death of the Indian Chief Alexander

MBPI0328
"Roger Feverel had kindled it for the first time"

MBPI0329
"Her glance fell, under his steady gaze"

MBPI0330
Traveling in the Olden Time

MBPI0331
Governor Huntington attacked by wolves

MBPI0332
Paul Revere bringing news to Sullivan

MBPI0333
Surrender of Fort William and Mary

MBPI0334
Transporting powder from the Fort

MBPI0335
Bringing the powder to Bunker Hill

MBPI0336
The Landing of Cadillac

MBPI0337
The Ojibway Maiden disclosing Pontiac's Plot

MBPI0338
"The woman turned fiercely upon the Chieftain"

MBPI0339
Joseph Brown leading his company to Nicojack

MBPI0340
"I sat gazing upon her as she leaned forward"

MBPI0341
"Thereupon, lifting up his eyes again, he began once more wrestling with the spirit in prayer"

MBPI0342
"Still she looked upon me, though silently and pale as death"

MBPI0343
"Then came Mistress Margaret unto me and put a letter into my hand"

MBPI0344
Capture of Elizabeth and Frances Callaway and Jemima Boone

MBPI0345
Defence of the Station

MBPI0346
On the Tortugas

MBPI0347
Capture of the Galleon

MBPI0348
Henry Morgan Recruiting for the Attack

MBPI0349
The Sacking of Panama

MBPI0350
Avary sells his jewels

MBPI0351
Marooned

MBPI0352
Blackbeard buries his treasure

MBPI0353
WALKING THE PLANK

MBPI0354
AARON BURR'S WOOING

MBPI0355
"THEY PLOUGHED THEIR FIELDS WITH AN ARMED SENTRY BESIDE THEM"

MBPI0356
FINDING THE BODY OF JOSEPH HAY IN THE TRAIL

MBPI0357
COUREURS DE BOIS

MBPI0358
MORGAN AT PORTO BELLO

MBPI0359
WASHINGTON MET BY HIS NEIGHBORS ON HIS WAY TO THE INAUGURATION

MBPI0360
THE INAUGURATION

MBPI0361
CELEBRATION ON THE NIGHT OF THE INAUGURATION

MBPI0362
AN OLD LANCASTER HOUSE

MBPI0363
A DORMITORY IN THE SISTERS' HOUSE, EPHRATA

MBPI0364
THE KLOSTER

MBPI0365
GOING TO MEETING

MBPI0366
THE KISS OF PEACE

MBPI0367
MY CICERONE

MBPI0368
"IT WAS TO REPRESENT THE NARROW WAY"

MBPI0369

"It was along this wall that the wounded soldiers sat"

MBPI0370

Interior of Chapel

MBPI0371

"She stood like a bronze. Gabriel was beside her, his naked cutlass in his hand"

MBPI0372

"And you would not give me a chance to tell you,'—she repeated, pleadingly,—touching his arm"

MBPI0373

Illustrated initial I for Jamaica, New and Old

MBPI0374

"Popping ineffectual round-shot after her"

MBPI0375

"The dim, shadowy forms of vessels riding at anchor in the night"

MBPI0376

"A hot, broad, all-pervading glare of sunlight"

MBPI0377

"A lodging-house very well known to all Jamaica travellers"

MBPI0378

Spanish Galleon

MBPI0379

"That prince or potentate of the old sugar king period"

MBPI0380

"A turbaned coolie and his wife"

MBPI0381

"Where they sit in long rows with baskets of oranges"

MBPI0382

"Sitting with piles of great pots and bowls and queer jars of red earthenware"

MBPI0383

"A curious group traveling along a hot dusty road"

MBPI0384

In the market place

MBPI0385
"In mid-harbor the tainted crafts were burned in sight of all"

MBPI0386
Gallows Point

MBPI0387
"The beautiful sweeping curve of harbor"

MBPI0388
"Squatted on a log, and talked in a sad, melancholy manner"

MBPI0389
"The abbot and the town major personating conquered Spain"

MBPI0390
The Mangrove

MBPI0391
"One time it was alive with the great lumbering coaches"

MBPI0392
"Around the archways and the square stone pillars, buzzing like angry hornets"

MBPI0393
"It is the Cathedral of St. Katherine"

MBPI0394
"Sic transit gloria mundi"

MBPI0395
Headpiece for Jamaica, New and Old

MBPI0396
Illustrated initial P for Jamaica, New and Old

MBPI0397
"The Governor was among the very first to set foot upon the deck"

MBPI0398
"The embrasures are blind and empty"

MBPI0399
"Here and there one comes upon an old house"

MBPI0400
"They were dressed in loose sackcloth shirt and drawers"

MBPI0401
"A store stood with open front toward the road"

MBPI0402
"An old man, lean and naked"

MBPI0403
"An ancient sibyl-like figure"

MBPI0404
"A crowd gathered around"

MBPI0405
"Plantation houses standing back from the roadside"

MBPI0406
"It is the leader, and all the others follow it"

MBPI0407
"The long straggling aqueduct"

MBPI0408
"A turbaned negro woman sat with her knitting"

MBPI0409
"The crooked winding road that leads into the village"

MBPI0410
"He sat down by the garden gate"

MBPI0411
"And thither children brought donkeys every morning"

MBPI0412
"In all houses one finds the filter and the water jar"

MBPI0413
"Coffee mill, surrounded by flat stone terraces"

MBPI0414
"A great section of bamboo trunk balanced upon her head"

MBPI0415
"Two negro women stood gossiping and cooling their feet"

MBPI0416
"The only picturesque object in the whole horrid expanse"

MBPI0417
THE BUGLE CALL

MBPI0418
ILLUSTRATED INITIAL A FOR OLD NEW YORK TAVERNS

MBPI0419
THE OLD-TIME LANDLORD

MBPI0420
"THE KING'S HEAD, KEPT BY ONE ROGER BAKER"

MBPI0421
"ELIZABETH JOURDAIN, WHO LODGED HER MAJESTY'S SOLDIERS"

MBPI0422
GAME OF BOWLS

MBPI0423
"'THE DOG'S HEAD IN THE POT' (OF GREAT ANTIQUITY)"

MBPI0424
"IT CROSSED THE RIVER TO THE LONG ISLAND SIDE OF THE BROOKLYN FERRY"

MBPI0425
BROWNEJOHN'S WHARF

MBPI0426
"EACH TO BE HONORED WITH BUMPERS INNUMERABLE OF RICH WINE AND PUNCH"

MBPI0427
IN THE READING-ROOM

MBPI0428
"THE RIVAL EDITORS"

MBPI0429
"JOHN STILL, 'AN HONEST BARBER AND PERUKE-MAKER FROM LONDON'"

MBPI0430
"THE BALL BEGAN WITH FRENCH DANCES"

MBPI0431
"THE CHAIR WAS CARRIED BY HAND AND THE HARNESS WAS WORN BY THE BEARERS"

MBPI0432
"CARDS AND GAMING WERE FEATURES"

MBPI0433
The ferry

MBPI0434
"Cargoes of favorite vintages"

MBPI0435
"The drum beat in the streets of the city"

MBPI0436
"The first violin would be played by a 'gentleman lately arrived'"

MBPI0437
At the Vauxhall

MBPI0438
"Exchanged thrusts with the merciless Junius"

MBPI0439
"The variety and fatigues of his business"

MBPI0440
Meeting of Captain Tollemache and Captain Pennington at the New York Arms

MBPI0441
"John Cape takes down the quaint old sign"

MBPI0442
"The men who met at Hampden Hall"

MBPI0443
Tailpiece for Old New York Taverns

MBPI0444
The Chapman

MBPI0445
Claude DuVal proposes a Dance on the Heath

MBPI0446
Sir James Thornhill painting Jack Sheppard's portrait

MBPI0447
Turpin and King

MBPI0448
Jonathan in the Wood Street Compter Prison

MBPI0449
JONATHAN AS AN ENEMY ARRESTING A
THIEF

MBPI0450
JONATHAN AND A CLIENT—THE LADY WITH
THE GREEN POCKET-BOOK

MBPI0451
ON THE WAY TO TYBURN

MBPI0452
HEADPIECE WITH TITLE FOR THE QUAKER
LADY

MBPI0453
VIGNETTE FOR THE QUAKER LADY

MBPI0454
VIGNETTE FOR THE QUAKER LADY

MBPI0455
VIGNETTE FOR THE QUAKER LADY

MBPI0456
VIGNETTE FOR THE QUAKER LADY

MBPI0457
VIGNETTE FOR THE QUAKER LADY

MBPI0458
VIGNETTE FOR THE QUAKER LADY

MBPI0459
VIGNETTE FOR THE QUAKER LADY

MBPI0460
VIGNETTE FOR THE QUAKER LADY

MBPI0461
VIGNETTE FOR THE QUAKER LADY

MBPI0462
VIGNETTE FOR THE QUAKER LADY

MBPI0463
VIGNETTE FOR THE QUAKER LADY

MBPI0464
VIGNETTE FOR THE QUAKER LADY

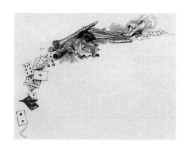

MBPI0465
VIGNETTE FOR THE QUAKER LADY

MBPI0466
VIGNETTE FOR THE QUAKER LADY

MBPI0467
VIGNETTE FOR THE QUAKER LADY

MBPI0468
VIGNETTE FOR THE QUAKER LADY

MBPI0469
THE MAGIC FLUTE

MBPI0470
"HE HAD BEAUTIFUL MANNERS"

MBPI0471
"HIS LONG NIGHTLY LABORS"

MBPI0472
THE WIDOW SPURLOCK

MBPI0473
OLD ARSENA

MBPI0474
"WITH THEIR HEADS CLOSE TOGETHER"

MBPI0475
"HE BEGAN TO PLAY"

MBPI0476
HANGING THE VIOLIN

MBPI0477
DAVID

MBPI0478
"HE PRAYED WITH UNUSUAL FERVOR"

MBPI0479
MR. LEUBA

MBPI0480
"EXECUTING AN INTRICATE PASSAGE"

MBPI0481

"A SMALL CROWD HAD COLLECTED AROUND THE ENTRANCE TO THE MUSEUM"

MBPI0482

"THE WIDOW DROPPED HER EYES"

MBPI0483

"IT WAS A VERY GAY DINNER"

MBPI0484

THE PARSON CAME DOWN THE STREET DRIVING HIS FLOCK OF BOYS

MBPI0485

BEFORE THE PICTURE

MBPI0486

"TOILED HOMEWARD WITH HIS TREASURE"

MBPI0487

"BURIED HIS HEAD ON HER BOSOM"

MBPI0488

AT DAVID'S BEDSIDE

MBPI0489

"HIS HEAD BOWED ON HIS FOLDED ARMS"

MBPI0490

A MAID'S CHOICE

MBPI0491

VERSE 1. YE JOVIAL HUNTSMAN

MBPI0492

VERSE 2. YE FAT, RICH MAN

MBPI0493

VERSE 3. YE GALLANT SOLDIER

MBPI0494

VERSE 4. YE JOLLY COUNTRY BOY

MBPI0495

TAILPIECE FOR THE BIRDS OF CIRENCESTER

MBPI0496

VIGNETTE, THE OLD NATICK CHURCH

MBPI0497
Vignette, Sam Lawson's House

MBPI0498
Sam Lawson telling stories

MBPI0499
The fields around lay bare to the moon

MBPI0500
Then Winfried told the story of Bethlehem

MBPI0501
Reading the Declaration before Washington's Army, New York, July 9, 1776

MBPI0502
Headpiece with title for How the Declaration was Received in the Old Thirteen

MBPI0503
At Philadelphia, Pennsylvania

MBPI0504
At Princeton, New Jersey

MBPI0505
At Dover, Delaware

MBPI0506
In New York (At Headquarters)

MBPI0507
At Boston, Massachusetts

MBPI0508
At Portsmouth, New Hampshire

MBPI0509
At Newport, Rhode Island

MBPI0510
In Connecticut

MBPI0511
At Williamsburg, Virginia

MBPI0512
At Halifax, North Carolina

MBPI0513
At Baltimore, Maryland

MBPI0514
At Charleston, South Carolina

MBPI0515
At Savannah, Georgia

MBPI0516
Headpiece with title and decorative border for Two Moods

MBPI0517
Headpiece for Among the Sand Hills

MBPI0518
Illustrated initial T for Among the Sand Hills

MBPI0519
Vignette for Among the Sand Hills

MBPI0520
Illustrated initial S for Among the Sand Hills

MBPI0521
Vignette for Among the Sand Hills

MBPI0522
Illustrated initial T for Among the Sand Hills

MBPI0523
The Sand Hills

MBPI0524
Vignette for Among the Sand Hills

MBPI0525
Illustrated initial F for Among the Sand Hills

MBPI0526
Vignette for Among the Sand Hills

MBPI0527
Illustrated initial B for Among the Sand Hills

MBPI0528
Vignette for Among the Sand Hills

MBPI0529
VIGNETTE FOR AMONG THE SAND HILLS

MBPI0530
ILLUSTRATED INITIAL S FOR AMONG THE SAND HILLS

MBPI0531
VIGNETTE FOR AMONG THE SAND HILLS

MBPI0532
THE WRECK

MBPI0533
ILLUSTRATED INITIAL C FOR AMONG THE SAND HILLS

MBPI0534
VIGNETTE FOR AMONG THE SAND HILLS

MBPI0535
ILLUSTRATED INITIAL B FOR AMONG THE SAND HILLS

MBPI0536
VIGNETTE FOR AMONG THE SAND HILLS

MBPI0537
VIGNETTE FOR AMONG THE SAND HILLS

MBPI0538
VIGNETTE FOR AMONG THE SAND HILLS

MBPI0539
ILLUSTRATED INITIAL T FOR AMONG THE SAND HILLS

MBPI0540
VIGNETTE FOR AMONG THE SAND HILLS

MBPI0541
VIGNETTE FOR AMONG THE SAND HILLS

MBPI0542
ILLUSTRATED INITIAL N FOR AMONG THE SAND HILLS

MBPI0543
VIGNETTE FOR AMONG THE SAND HILLS

MBPI0544
THE LILY LAKE

MBPI0545
"This is no courting night"

MBPI0546
"Hey, black cat! hey, my pretty black cat"

MBPI0547
"There is a flock of yellow birds around her head"

MBPI0548
"Father, Father!"

MBPI0549
Question

MBPI0550
Headpiece with title for Monochromes

MBPI0551
Illustrated initial S for Question

MBPI0552
Tailpiece for Question

MBPI0553
Living

MBPI0554
Illustrated initial H for Living

MBPI0555
To-Morrow

MBPI0556
Illustrated initial O for To-Morrow

MBPI0557
Tailpiece for Friends and Foes

MBPI0558
From Generation to Generation

MBPI0559
Illustrated initial I for From Generation to Generation

MBPI0560
Tailpiece for From Generation to Generation

MBPI0561
The Bewildered Guest

MBPI0562
Illustrated initial I for The Bewildered Guest

MBPI0563
Hope

MBPI0564
Illustrated initial Y for Hope

MBPI0565
Tailpiece for Hope

MBPI0566
Illustrated initial D for Respite

MBPI0567
Respite

MBPI0568
"He sat down beside her on the bench"

MBPI0569
"Thereupon the poor woman screamed aloud, and cried out that he was a murderer"

MBPI0570
Along the Canal in Old Manhattan

MBPI0571
Headpiece with title and illustrated initial T for The Evolution of New York

MBPI0572
On the River Front

MBPI0573
Tailpiece for The Evolution of New York

MBPI0574
Headpiece, In 1776, The Conflagration

MBPI0575
A Privateersman Ashore

MBPI0576
Opening of the Erie Canal

MBPI0577
Tailpiece for The Evolution of New York

MBPI0578
Headpiece with title and illustrated initial T for The Cocklane Ghost

MBPI0579
Vignette for The Cocklane Ghost

MBPI0580
Vignette for The Cocklane Ghost

MBPI0581
Vignette for The Cocklane Ghost

MBPI0582
Vignette for The Cocklane Ghost

MBPI0583
Vignette for The Cocklane Ghost

MBPI0584
Vignette for The Cocklane Ghost

MBPI0585
Vignette for The Cocklane Ghost

MBPI0586
Vignette for The Cocklane Ghost

MBPI0587
Vignette for The Cocklane Ghost

MBPI0588
Vignette for The Cocklane Ghost

MBPI0589
Vignette for The Cocklane Ghost

MBPI0590
Tailpiece for The Cocklane Ghost

MBPI0591
Headpiece with initial O for A Soldier of Fortune

MBPI0592
Vignette for A Soldier of Fortune

MBPI0593
Vignette for A Soldier of Fortune

MBPI0594
A Night in the Village Street

MBPI0595
Vignette for A Soldier of Fortune

MBPI0596
Vignette for A Soldier of Fortune

MBPI0597
Dragging the Duke out of the Coach

MBPI0598
Vignette for A Soldier of Fortune

MBPI0599
Vignette for A Soldier of Fortune

MBPI0600
Vignette for A Soldier of Fortune

MBPI0601
Vignette for A Soldier of Fortune

MBPI0602
The Fight for the Crown

MBPI0603
Vignette for A Soldier of Fortune

MBPI0604
Vignette for A Soldier of Fortune

MBPI0605
Vignette for A Soldier of Fortune

MBPI0606
Vignette for A Soldier of Fortune

MBPI0607
"He had found the Captain agreeable and companionable"

MBPI0608
Headpiece with title and illustrated initial T for The Sea Robbers of New York

MBPI0609
"Pirates used to do that to their Captains now and then"

MBPI0610
Kidd at Gardiner's Island

MBPI0611
Tailpiece for The Sea Robbers of New York

MBPI0612
Illustration for Stops of Various Quills

MBPI0613
Headpiece with title for Stops of Various Quills

MBPI0614
Illustrated initial W for Sphinx

MBPI0615
Tailpiece for Twelve P.M.

MBPI0616
Time

MBPI0617
Illustrated initial D for Time

MBPI0618
Society

MBPI0619
Illustrated initial Y for Society

MBPI0620
Tailpiece for Society

MBPI0621
Heredity

MBPI0622
Illustrated initial T for Heredity

MBPI0623
In the Dark

MBPI0624
Solitude

MBPI0625
ILLUSTRATED INITIAL A FOR SOLITUDE

MBPI0626
CHANGE

MBPI0627
ILLUSTRATED INITIAL S FOR CHANGE

MBPI0628
TAILPIECE FOR CHANGE

MBPI0629
MIDWAY

MBPI0630
ILLUSTRATED INITIAL S FOR MIDWAY

MBPI0631
CALVARY

MBPI0632
ILLUSTRATED INITIAL I FOR CALVARY

MBPI0633
"SOME OF THE BY-STANDERS SAID 'SHE IS DRUNK, IT WILL SOON PASS AWAY'"

MBPI0634
"THE CHOICEST PIECES OF HER CARGO WERE SOLD AT AUCTION"

MBPI0635
"WE ESCAPED IN THE BOAT"

MBPI0636
"AND AGAIN MY CAPTAIN TOOK THE BIGGEST"

MBPI0637
HEADPIECE WITH TITLE AND ILLUSTRATED INITIAL O FOR NEW YORK COLONIAL PRIVATEERS

MBPI0638
"BARBAROUSLY MURDERED THE FIRST, AND GRIEVOUSLY WOUNDED THE LATTER"

MBPI0639
TAILPIECE FOR NEW YORK COLONIAL PRIVATEERS

MBPI0640
HEADPIECE WITH TITLE FOR SOCIETY

MBPI0641
MARGINAL DECORATION FOR SOCIETY

MBPI0642
TAILPIECE FOR SOCIETY

MBPI0643
FRONTISPIECE FOR PEBBLES

MBPI0644
HEADPIECE WITH TITLE FOR PEBBLES

MBPI0645
ILLUSTRATED INITIAL I FOR THE BURDEN

MBPI0646
HOPE

MBPI0647
SYMPATHY

MBPI0648
ILLUSTRATED INITIAL F FOR SYMPATHY

MBPI0649
REWARD AND PUNISHMENT

MBPI0650
PARABLE

MBPI0651
ILLUSTRATED INITIAL T FOR PARABLE

MBPI0652
STATISTICS

MBPI0653
ILLUSTRATED INITIAL S FOR STATISTICS

MBPI0654
TAILPIECE FOR STATISTICS

MBPI0655
IN THE WOOD-CARVER'S SHOP

MBPI0656
HEADPIECE WITH TITLE FOR BY LAND AND SEA

MBPI0657
Tailpiece, Sketch Four for By Land and Sea

MBPI0658
Tailpiece, Sketch One for By Land and Sea

MBPI0659
A Sailor's Sweetheart

MBPI0660
Headpiece, Sketch Two for By Land and Sea

MBPI0661
Illustrated initial I, Sketch Two for By Land and Sea

MBPI0662
Tailpiece, Sketch Two for By Land and Sea

MBPI0663
The Sailor's Wedding

MBPI0664
Headpiece, Sketch Three for By Land and Sea

MBPI0665
Illustrated initial T, Sketch One for By Land and Sea

MBPI0666
Tailpiece, Sketch Three for By Land and Sea

MBPI0667
A Wreck from the Sea

MBPI0668
Headpiece, Sketch Four for By Land and Sea

MBPI0669
Illustrated initial E, Sketch Four for By Land and Sea

MBPI0670
Cap'n Goldsack

MBPI0671
Headpiece with title and illustrated initial G for In Washington's Day

MBPI0672
A Virginia Plantation Wharf

MBPI0673
"Even Sir William Berkeley, the redoubtable Cavalier Governor, saw he must yield"

MBPI0674
"They read only upon occasion, when the weather darkened"

MBPI0675
Ye Virginia Gentleman of the Olden Time

MBPI0676
Washington's Retreat from Great Meadows

MBPI0677
Headpiece for Colonel Washington

MBPI0678
The Burial of Braddock

MBPI0679
Washington and Mary Philipse

MBPI0680
Tailpiece for Colonel Washington

MBPI0681
Leaving Mount Vernon for the Congress of the Colonies

MBPI0682
The Old Capitol at Williamsburg

MBPI0683
In the Old Raleigh Tavern

MBPI0684
Head and sidepiece with illustrated initial T for Through Inland Waters

MBPI0685
Vignette for Through Inland Waters

MBPI0686
Vignette for Through Inland Waters

MBPI0687
A Floating Town

MBPI0688
Headpiece with subtitle for Through Inland Waters

MBPI0689
Vignette for Through Inland Waters

MBPI0690
Vignette for Through Inland Waters

MBPI0691
Vignette for Through Inland Waters

MBPI0692
Vignette for Through Inland Waters

MBPI0693
Vignette for Through Inland Waters

MBPI0694
Vignette for Through Inland Waters

MBPI0695
Vignette for Through Inland Waters

MBPI0696
Vignette for Through Inland Waters

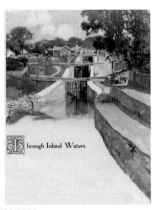

MBPI0697
Vignette for Through Inland Waters

MBPI0698
Vignette for Through Inland Waters

MBPI0699
Tailpiece for Through Inland Waters

MBPI0700
Headpiece with title and initial T
for Through Inland Waters

MBPI0701
Vignette for Through Inland Waters

MBPI0702
Vignette for Through Inland Waters

MBPI0703
Vignette for Through Inland Waters

MBPI0704
Vignette for Through Inland Waters

MBPI0705
Vignette for Through Inland Waters

MBPI0706
Illustration for Through Inland Waters

MBPI0707
Vignette for Through Inland Waters

MBPI0708
Vignette for Through Inland Waters

MBPI0709
Vignette for Through Inland Waters

MBPI0710
Vignette for Through Inland Waters

MBPI0711
Vignette for Through Inland Waters

MBPI0712
Illustration for Through Inland Waters

MBPI0713
Vignette for Through Inland Waters

MBPI0714
Vignette for Through Inland Waters

MBPI0715
Tailpiece for Through Inland Waters

MBPI0716
Headpiece with title for General Washington

MBPI0717
Washington and Steuben at Valley Forge

MBPI0718
Lady Washington's Arrival at Headquarters, Cambridge

MBPI0719
The Escape of Arnold

MBPI0720
Carpenter's Hall, Philadelphia

MBPI0721
WASHINGTON IN THE GARDEN AT MOUNT VERNON

MBPI0722
HEADPIECE WITH TITLE FOR FIRST IN PEACE

MBPI0723
WASHINGTON BRINGING HIS MOTHER INTO THE BALLROOM, FREDERICKSBURG

MBPI0724
MUSTERED OUT—A REST ON THE WAY HOME

MBPI0725
TAILPIECE FOR FIRST IN PEACE

MBPI0726
WASHINGTON AND NELLY CUSTIS

MBPI0727
HEADPIECE WITH TITLE FOR THE FIRST PRESIDENT OF THE UNITED STATES

MBPI0728
THOMPSON, THE CLERK OF CONGRESS, ANNOUNCING TO WASHINGTON, AT MOUNT VERNON, HIS ELECTION TO THE PRESIDENCY

MBPI0729
THE DEATH OF WASHINGTON

MBPI0730
TAILPIECE FOR THE FIRST PRESIDENT OF THE UNITED STATES

MBPI0731
CHRISTMAS 1896, COVER DESIGN

MBPI0732
HEADPIECE WITH TITLE FOR THE ROMANCE OF AN AMBROTYPE

MBPI0733
ILLUSTRATED INITIAL T FOR THE ROMANCE OF AN AMBROTYPE

MBPI0734
VIGNETTE FOR THE ROMANCE OF AN AMBROTYPE

MBPI0735
VIGNETTE FOR THE ROMANCE OF AN AMBROTYPE

MBPI0736
VIGNETTE FOR THE ROMANCE OF AN AMBROTYPE

MBPI0737
Vignette for The Romance of an Ambrotype

MBPI0738
Vignette for The Romance of an Ambrotype

MBPI0739
Vignette for The Romance of an Ambrotype

MBPI0740
Vignette for The Romance of an Ambrotype

MBPI0741
Vignette for The Romance of an Ambrotype

MBPI0742
Vignette for The Romance of an Ambrotype

MBPI0743
Vignette for The Romance of an Ambrotype

MBPI0744
Vignette for The Romance of an Ambrotype

MBPI0745
Tailpiece for The Romance of an Ambrotype

MBPI0746
The Assembly Ball

MBPI0747
Headpiece with title for The Assembly Ball

MBPI0748
Illustrated initial I for The Assembly Ball

MBPI0749
Tailpiece for The Assembly Ball

MBPI0750
Love and Death

MBPI0751
Headpiece for Love and Death

MBPI0752
Tailpiece for Love and Death

MBPI0753
A Banquet to Genet

MBPI0754
Headpiece, Arrival of Genet at Gray's Ferry

MBPI0755
The News of the Execution of Louis XVI

MBPI0756
Citizen Genet formally presented to Washington

MBPI0757
Tailpiece for Washington and the French Craze of '93

MBPI0758
Decoration with title for Old Chester Tales

MBPI0759
Headpiece for "The Promises of Dorthea"

MBPI0760
"She seemed 'a tall white lily,' he said"

MBPI0761
"'Change it? My name?' she said"

MBPI0762
Headpiece for "Good For the Soul"

MBPI0763
Headpiece for "Miss Maria"

MBPI0764
"And who's going to support 'em?' demanded Mrs. Barkley"

MBPI0765
"Judge Morrison read these harmless jingles, chuckling and sneering"

MBPI0766
Headpiece for "The Thief"

MBPI0767
Headpiece for "The Child's Mother"

MBPI0768
"Mary turned white, then she dropped down at his feet"

MBPI0769
HEADPIECE FOR "JUSTICE AND THE JUDGE"

MBPI0770
"'SO YOU'RE HANGING THE LOCUSTS?'
INQUIRED THE JUDGE, CONTEMPTUOUSLY"

MBPI0771
HEADPIECE FOR "WHERE THE LABORERS
ARE FEW"

MBPI0772
"I HAD ENEMIES IN MY LINE"

MBPI0773
HEADPIECE FOR "SALLY"

MBPI0774
"THEY TOLD EACH OTHER ABOUT IT"

MBPI0775
HEADPIECE FOR "THE UNEXPECTEDNESS
OF MR. HORACE SHIELDS"

MBPI0776
"MR. HORACE LOOKED AT HER WITH
INSTANT SYMPATHY"

MBPI0777
"AND YOU SHALL NOT HINDER ME"

MBPI0778
HEADPIECE FOR OLD CAPTAIN

MBPI0779
ILLUSTRATION FOR OLD CAPTAIN

MBPI0780
ILLUSTRATION FOR OLD CAPTAIN

MBPI0781
ILLUSTRATION FOR OLD CAPTAIN

MBPI0782
ILLUSTRATION FOR OLD CAPTAIN

MBPI0783
ILLUSTRATION FOR OLD CAPTAIN

MBPI0784
ILLUSTRATION FOR OLD CAPTAIN

MBPI0785
Illustration for Old Captain

MBPI0786
Illustration for Old Captain

MBPI0787
Tailpiece for Old Captain

MBPI0788
Frontispiece for The Body to the Soul

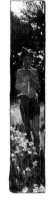

MBPI0789
Headpiece with title for The Body to the Soul

MBPI0790
Marginal decoration for The Body to the Soul

MBPI0791
Decoration for The Body to the Soul

MBPI0792
Marginal decoration for The Body to the Soul

MBPI0793
Marginal decoration for The Body to the Soul

MBPI0794
Tailpiece for The Body to the Soul

MBPI0795
Headpiece with title with illustrated initial T for A Puppet of Fate

MBPI0796
Vignette for A Puppet of Fate

MBPI0797
Chapter heading with illustrated initial N for A Puppet of Fate

MBPI0798
Vignette for A Puppet of Fate

MBPI0799
Vignette for A Puppet of Fate

MBPI0800
Vignette for A Puppet of Fate

MBPI0801

VIGNETTE FOR A PUPPET OF FATE

MBPI0802

CHAPTER HEADING WITH ILLUSTRATED
INITIAL F FOR A PUPPET OF FATE

MBPI0803

VIGNETTE FOR A PUPPET OF FATE

MBPI0804

ILLUSTRATION FOR A PUPPET OF FATE

MBPI0805

CHAPTER HEADING WITH ILLUSTRATED
INITIAL A FOR A PUPPET OF FATE

MBPI0806

VIGNETTE FOR A PUPPET OF FATE

MBPI0807

HEADPIECE WITH TITLE FOR A PRELUDE

MBPI0808

ILLUSTRATED INITIAL T FOR A PRELUDE

MBPI0809

IN SPRINGTIME

MBPI0810

TAILPIECE FOR A PRELUDE

MBPI0811

HEADPIECE FOR THE YELLOW OF THE LEAF

MBPI0812

TITLE WITH DECORATIONS FOR THE
YELLOW OF THE LEAF

MBPI0813

ILLUSTRATED INITIAL T FOR THE YELLOW
OF THE LEAF

MBPI0814

THE FALLING LEAF IS AT THE DOOR; THE
AUTUMN WIND IS ON THE HILL

MBPI0815

TAILPIECE FOR THE YELLOW OF THE LEAF

MBPI0816

TRUTH LEAVES THE FAIRIES' WONDERLAND

MBPI0817
TRUTH BEFORE THE KING

MBPI0818
TRUTH IN THE TEMPLE

MBPI0819
TRUTH BEFORE THE SEER

MBPI0820
TRUTH WENT ON HER WAY ALONE

MBPI0821
TRUTH IN THE FOOL'S LODGE

MBPI0822
HEADPIECE WITH TITLE FOR THE
PILGRIMAGE OF TRUTH

MBPI0823
ILLUSTRATED INITIAL F FOR THE
PILGRIMAGE OF TRUTH

MBPI0824
TAILPIECE FOR THE PILGRIMAGE OF TRUTH

MBPI0825
ILLUSTRATED INITIAL T FOR THE
PILGRIMAGE OF TRUTH

MBPI0826
TAILPIECE FOR THE PILGRIMAGE OF TRUTH

MBPI0827
ILLUSTRATED INITIAL T FOR THE
PILGRIMAGE OF TRUTH

MBPI0828
HEADBAND FOR THE PILGRIMAGE OF
TRUTH

MBPI0829
HEADBAND FOR THE PILGRIMAGE OF
TRUTH

MBPI0830
ILLUSTRATED INITIAL B FOR THE
PILGRIMAGE OF TRUTH

MBPI0831
ILLUSTRATED INITIAL O FOR THE
PILGRIMAGE OF TRUTH

MBPI0832
ILLUSTRATED INITIAL H FOR THE
PILGRIMAGE OF TRUTH

MBPI0833
Headpiece with decoration and title for Colonies and Nation

MBPI0834
Landing negroes at Jamestown from Dutch man-of-war, 1619

MBPI0835
Anne Hutchinson preaching in her house in Boston

MBPI0836
Arrival of Stuyvesant in New Amsterdam

MBPI0837
The Burning of Jamestown

MBPI0838
Ships loading in Albemarle Sound

MBPI0839
On the War-Path

MBPI0840
A Pennsylvania Cave-Dwelling XVIIth Century

MBPI0841
An interview between Sir Edmund Andros and James Blair

MBPI0842
Phips recovering the sunken treasure

MBPI0843
Sloughter signing the death warrant of Leisler

MBPI0844
Colonel Rhett and Pirate Stede Bonnet

MBPI0845
The Capitulation of Louisbourg

MBPI0846
After the Massacre; Samuel Adams demanding of Governor Hutchinson the instant withdrawal of British Troops

MBPI0847
Burning of the "Gaspee"

MBPI0848
The Boston Tea Party

MBPI0849
VIEWING THE BATTLE OF BUNKER'S HILL

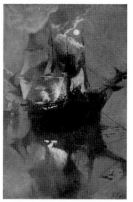

MBPI0850
FIGHT BETWEEN "BONHOMME RICHARD" AND "SERAPIS"

MBPI0851
WASHINGTON AND ROCHAMBEAU BEFORE THE TRENCHES AT YORKTOWN

MBPI0852
TORY REFUGEES ON THEIR WAY TO CANADA

MBPI0853
A POLITICAL DISCUSSION

MBPI0854
A DREAM OF YOUNG SUMMER

MBPI0855
HEADPIECE FOR KING CUSTOM

MBPI0856
ILLUSTRATED INITIAL M FOR KING CUSTOM

MBPI0857
MARGINAL DECORATION FOR KING CUSTOM

MBPI0858
VIGNETTE FOR KING CUSTOM

MBPI0859
MY LADY OF BREDE

MBPI0860
HEADPIECE FOR MARGARET OF CORTONA

MBPI0861
THE SEA MAN

MBPI0862
FRONTISPIECE FOR NORTH FOLK LEGENDS OF THE SEA

MBPI0863
DECORATION WITH TITLE FOR NORTH FOLK LEGENDS OF THE SEA

MBPI0864
ILLUSTRATED INITIAL T FOR NORTH FOLK LEGENDS OF THE SEA

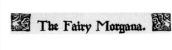

MBPI0865

DECORATION WITH TITLE FOR NORTH FOLK LEGENDS OF THE SEA

MBPI0866

THE FISHING OF THOR AND HYMIR

MBPI0867

HEADPIECE FOR NORTH FOLK LEGENDS OF THE SEA

MBPI0868

TITLE WITH DECORATIONS, THE FAIRY MORGANA

MBPI0869

THE FAIRY MORGANA

MBPI0870

HEADPIECE FOR NORTH FOLK LEGENDS OF THE SEA

MBPI0871

TITLE WITH DECORATIONS, SAINT BRENDAN'S ISLAND

MBPI0872

SAINT BRENDAN

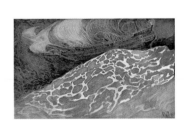

MBPI0873

HEADPIECE FOR NORTH FOLK LEGENDS OF THE SEA

MBPI0874

TITLE WITH DECORATIONS, MOTHER CAREY'S CHICKENS

MBPI0875

MOTHER CAREY

MBPI0876

HEADPIECE FOR NORTH FOLK LEGENDS OF THE SEA

MBPI0877

TITLE WITH DECORATIONS, THE FLYING DUTCHMAN

MBPI0878

HEADPIECE FOR THE VOICE

MBPI0879

AN AUTUMN FIELD OF WHICH SHE HAD DREAMED

MBPI0880

SHE CRIED OUT

MBPI0881

She felt her blood tingling in every vein

MBPI0882

Headpiece for The True Captain Kidd

MBPI0883

Title with decoration for The True Captain Kidd

MBPI0884

Illustrated initial W for The True Captain Kidd

MBPI0885

Kidd on the Deck of the "Adventure Galley"

MBPI0886

Burning the Ship

MBPI0887

Buried Treasure

MBPI0888

The Chantey-Man

MBPI0889

"Small heed had we of the fleet, sweet hours"

MBPI0890

"'Twas a strange tale she had ended"

MBPI0891

Lady Adeliza came wondering to the balcony

MBPI0892

He thought of his love

MBPI0893

In the night

MBPI0894

"Nothing harms me all the day"

MBPI0895

At the gate of the Castle

MBPI0896

Vidal—Poet and Satirist

MBPI0897
IN THE TRAIN OF KING ALFONZO

MBPI0898
HER WHISPER WAS SO SOFT HE ONLY GUESSED THE WORDS

MBPI0899
THIS LAST PICTURE

MBPI0900
HE STRETCHED OUT HIS HAND TO THE CURTAINS

MBPI0901
HE FOUND MELITE ALONE

MBPI0902
HE SANG FOR HER AS THEY SAT IN THE GARDENS

MBPI0903
HE CLIMBED THE STAIRS SLOWLY, FOR HE WAS GROWING FEEBLE

MBPI0904
ESTERCEL

MBPI0905
"THERE IS A CHARM," SAID THE NURSE AT LAST

MBPI0906
EILEEN SLIPPED THE RING INTO THE NEST

MBPI0907
THE BATTLE OF THE STAIRS

MBPI0908
THE DARK FOLK TROOPED TO MEET THEM ON THE SHORE

MBPI0909
BERTHA, THE MUCH BELOVED

MBPI0910
THE DRAWING OF THE SWORD

MBPI0911
THE RESCUE OF AZILICZ

MBPI0912
HER HEAD AND SHOULDERS HUNG OVER THE SPACE WITHOUT

MBPI0913
"She tricked me, little maid"

MBPI0914
Catherine de Vaucelles, in her garden

MBPI0915
"Villon—The singer Fate fashioned to her liking"

MBPI0916
"The King himself hauled me out of gaol"

MBPI0917
The charge

MBPI0918
They brought in their dead and wounded on hay wagons

MBPI0919
"I thought of you, when I was falling," he said vaguely

MBPI0920
She believed that she had daily speech with angels

MBPI0921
The triumphal entry into Rheims

MBPI0922
Guarded by rough English soldiers

MBPI0923
A lithe, young, slender figure

MBPI0924
Parson Rawson spoke to her with a pleasant chiding

MBPI0925
Catherine Duke quickened her steps

MBPI0926
Melicent stood motionless like a wild thing at gaze

MBPI0927
A man lay prone there, half turned upon his face

MBPI0928
Sir John shook his spear at the ladies who sneered

MBPI0929
LA SALLE CHRISTENING THE COUNTRY "LOUISIANA"

MBPI0930
LA SALLE PETITIONS THE KING FOR PERMISSION TO EXPLORE THE MISSISSIPPI

MBPI0931
SHE DREW BRIDLE, LISTENING—THERE WAS NO SOUND

MBPI0932
"ARE YOU EVER LONELY HERE?" HE INQUIRED

MBPI0933
"COME, COME, YOUR FUTURE MAJESTY! CHEER UP!"

MBPI0934
I KNELT BY THE WHISPERING, MUTTERING OLD MAN

MBPI0935
THEY STOOD STARING AT THE VIOLENT SKY

MBPI0936
WITH A CRY, SHALLUM FLUNG UP HIS ARMS AND JUMPED

MBPI0937
THE CROWN-PRINCE KARL, DEAD BY HIS OWN HAND

MBPI0938
CARLOTTA—TALL, WHITE, QUEENLY—A CLUSTER OF FLOWERS IN HER ARMS

MBPI0939
HER OUTSTRETCHED ARMS SEEMED TO CLOSE UPON SOMETHING

MBPI0940
OLD IMMORTALITY

MBPI0941
"I LOVED THE HUSK OF A MAN"

MBPI0942
HEADPIECE WITH TITLE FOR THE FOX BRUSH

MBPI0943
SO FOR A HEART-BEAT SHE SAW HIM

MBPI0944
HE CAME TO HER—IN HIS HELMET A FOX BRUSH SPANGLED WITH JEWELS

MBPI0945
HEADBAND FOR THE FOX BRUSH

MBPI0946
MARGINAL DECORATION, FEMALE WITH
OUTSTRETCHED ARM

MBPI0947
MARGINAL DECORATION, MALE WITH
SWORD AND SHIELD

MBPI0948
THE DOGE SAT ALONE IN A GREAT CARVEN
CHAIR

MBPI0949
HE LAID THE MANTLE OVER THE GIRL'S
SHOULDERS

MBPI0950
"HE LAY AWHILE CONSCIOUS OF GREAT
COMFORT"

MBPI0951
"SHE HUNG DROOPING IN THE GREAT
CHAIR OF STATE"

MBPI0952
THE BUCCANEER WAS A PICTURESQUE FEL-
LOW

MBPI0953
AN ATTACK ON A GALLEON

MBPI0954
SO THE TREASURE WAS DIVIDED

MBPI0955
EXTORTING TRIBUTE FROM THE CITIZENS

MBPI0956
HEADBAND FOR THE FATE OF A TREASURE
TOWN

MBPI0957
HEADPIECE FOR THE FATE OF A TREASURE
TOWN

MBPI0958
ILLUSTRATED INITIAL A FOR THE FATE OF A
TREASURE TOWN

MBPI0959
MARGINAL DECORATION, FEMALE WITH
SHIP

MBPI0960
MARGINAL DECORATION, MALE WITH TREE

MBPI0961

A NEAT AND SHRIVELLED GENTLEMAN SAT
AT A DESK

MBPI0962

THEY WERE OVERTAKEN BY FALMOUTH
HIMSELF

MBPI0963

BEATRIX AND ESMOND

MBPI0964

BECKY SHARP AND LORD STEYNE

MBPI0965

A FIGURE TO PROVOKE TEARS

MBPI0966

PENDENNIS

MBPI0967

"WHO IS THE LUCKY MISS, MY LITTLE VIL-
LAIN?"

MBPI0968

THE DUEL BETWEEN JOHN BLUMER AND
CAZAIO

MBPI0969

"THE BASTILLE IS NOT A VERY HEALTHY
PLACE"

MBPI0970

THE DEATH OF CAZAIO

MBPI0971

THE KING GLARED DOWN AT HER

MBPI0972

SUDDENLY THEIR COMEDY TURNED TRAGIC

MBPI0973

"I AM THE DAUGHTER OF THAT UNFORTU-
NATE CAPTAIN KEITT!"

MBPI0974

TAILPIECE, TABLE OF CONTENTS FOR
TWILIGHT LAND

MBPI0975

ILLUSTRATED INITIAL T FOR THE RUBY OF
KISHMOOR

MBPI0976

JONATHAN RUGG

MBPI0977

THE NEGRESS BECKONED HIM TO DRAW
NEARER

MBPI0978

THE LITTLE GENTLEMAN WITH ONE EYE

MBPI0979

WITH GREAT AMITY THE TWO WALKED OFF
TOGETHER

MBPI0980

THE LITTLE GENTLEMAN IN BLACK EMIT-
TED A PIERCING SCREAM

MBPI0981

THE MAN WITH THE SILVER EARRINGS

MBPI0982

THE STRANGER THREW HIMSELF UPON
JONATHAN WITH THE FURY OF A MADMAN

MBPI0983

THE MAN WITH THE BROKEN NOSE

MBPI0984

THE ARMS OF HIS CAPTOR HELD HIM AS IN
A VISE

MBPI0985

THE LADY WITH THE SILVER VEIL

MBPI0986

JONATHAN RUGG WAS MARRIED TO
MARTHA DOBBS THE FOLLOWING YEAR

MBPI0987

CAPTAIN KEITT

MBPI0988

ABRAHAM LINCOLN

MBPI0989

SHE BECAME AS FAMOUS FOR SPEED AS HER
SHORT CAREER ALLOWED

MBPI0990

HER CAPTAIN WAS A CUBAN

MBPI0991

THE CRUISER PILED ON ALL SAIL

MBPI0992

THEY HAVE A SO-CALLED NATIVE KING

MBPI0993
They carried fruit and vegetables

MBPI0994
'Tween decks of the slaver

MBPI0995
The rest were shot and thrown over-board

MBPI0996
The mate elevated and sighted the gun

MBPI0997
The lighters were soon alongside

MBPI0998
She was a solid mass of flame

MBPI0999
Meregrett, daughter of Philippe the Bold

MBPI1000
Then sang Sire Edward

MBPI1001
"Others have lived through greater woes than ours"

MBPI1002
"Take care, my friend, take care"

MBPI1003
The officers would be waiting until she should appear

MBPI1004
The passing of Dona Victoria

MBPI1005
Rosamund and Sir Gregory

MBPI1006
Queen Ysabeau in her carven chair

MBPI1007
She arrayed herself in silence

MBPI1008
Horse and man plunged heavily after her

MBPI1009

THE COMING OF LANCASTER

MBPI1010

BRANWEN

MBPI1011

THE NEWCOMES

MBPI1012

THE DARK, SMILING SALIM, WITH HIS
MAGIC PACK, WAS WELCOME

MBPI1013

EDRIC THE SINGER

MBPI1014

MARGINAL DECORATION WITH TITLE FOR
EDRIC AND SYLVAINE

MBPI1015

MARGINAL DECORATION FOR EDRIC AND
SYLVAINE

MBPI1016

MARGINAL DECORATION FOR EDRIC AND
SYLVAINE

MBPI1017

MARGINAL DECORATION FOR EDRIC AND
SYLVAINE

MBPI1018

MARGINAL DECORATION FOR EDRIC AND
SYLVAINE

MBPI1019

MARGINAL DECORATION FOR EDRIC AND
SYLVAINE

MBPI1020

MARGINAL DECORATION FOR EDRIC AND
SYLVAINE

MBPI1021

MARGINAL DECORATION FOR EDRIC AND
SYLVAINE

MBPI1022

MARGINAL DECORATION FOR EDRIC AND
SYLVAINE

MBPI1023

MARGINAL DECORATION FOR EDRIC AND
SYLVAINE

MBPI1024

MARGINAL DECORATION FOR EDRIC AND
SYLVAINE

MBPI1025
Marginal decoration for Edric and Sylvaine

MBPI1026
Marginal decoration for Edric and Sylvaine

MBPI1027
Marginal decoration for Edric and Sylvaine

MBPI1028
Marginal decoration for Edric and Sylvaine

MBPI1029
Tailpiece for Edric and Sylvaine

MBPI1030
"I will have him between these hands"

MBPI1031
In an instant those long fingers closed on the Governor

MBPI1032
"The American captain with his mate boarded us"

MBPI1033
Then the real fight began

MBPI1034
Diana Sherley

MBPI1035
"Go, Madam, and leave the Prodigal among his husks"

MBPI1036
Old Jacob Van Kleek had never favored our hero's suit

MBPI1037
Decorative title with illustrated initial U for The Mysterious Chest

MBPI1038
The skeletonlike stranger entered

MBPI1039
It was his belief that the chest was certainly haunted

MBPI1040
Swinging his lanthorn and followed by his laboring assistants

MBPI1041

THE REVEREND EBENEZER DOOLITTLE

MBPI1042

"D'YE SEE WHAT THE WRETCHES HAVE LEFT?"

MBPI1043

GAZED DOWN UPON THE DREADFUL OBJECT

MBPI1044

HE WAS GREATLY ADDICTED TO LITTLE SUPPER PARTIES OF HIS OWN SEX

MBPI1045

A DREADFUL SPECTACLE

MBPI1046

OLD JACOB VAN KLEEK THE MONEY-LENDER

MBPI1047

ILLUSTRATION FOR THE MYSTERIOUS CHEST

MBPI1048

OUR YOUNG GENTLEMAN OF THE LAW

MBPI1049

HE PERUSED THE INSCRIPTION WITH GREAT PARTICULARITY

MBPI1050

"IF THIS DREADFUL THING IS NOT TAKEN AWAY I SHALL GO MAD"

MBPI1051

LUGGED THE MYSTERIOUS CHEST TO THE LAWYER'S HOUSE

MBPI1052

TAILPIECE FOR THE MYSTERIOUS CHEST

MBPI1053

THE SHELL

MBPI1054

"THE DANCER"

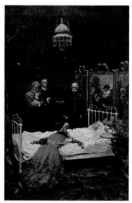

MBPI1055

HIS EYES FELL ON THE DANCER IN HER SHIMMERING SCARLET

MBPI1056

IN PLACE OF THE APPLE HUNG A LITTLE GILDED SKULL

MBPI1057

THE PRECIOUS MINUTES FLEW PAST, BUT SHE WAS SILENT

MBPI1058

"HE WATCHED ME AS A CAT WATCHES A MOUSE"

MBPI1059

"HE LOST HIS HOLD AND FELL, TAKING ME WITH HIM"

MBPI1060

THE DUKE OF GLOUCESTER SENT FOR EDWARD MAUDELAIN

MBPI1061

THE QUEEN READ THE SCRIPTURES IN THE VULGAR TONGUE

MBPI1062

DIM AND FADED PICTURES AT TIMES CAME BEFORE THEM

MBPI1063

VITIA AND THE GOVERNOR

MBPI1064

SHERIDAN'S FIRST INTERVIEW WITH ROWAND

MBPI1065

A LONELY DUEL IN THE MIDDLE OF A GREAT, SUNNY FIELD

MBPI1066

WHEN ALL THE WORLD WAS YOUNG

MBPI1067

THE MIDNIGHT COURT MARTIAL

MBPI1068

SHE PUT THE SILVER CORONET UPON HER HEAD

MBPI1069

SHE SAW HERSELF FOR WHAT HE HAD SAID, AND SWOONED

MBPI1070

THEIRS WAS A SPIRITED ENCOUNTER UPON THE BEACH OF TEVIOT BAY

MBPI1071

"WHO ARE WE THAT HEAVEN SHOULD MAKE OF THE OLD SEA A FOWLING NET?"

MBPI1072

IT WAS A COMRADE FROM HIS OWN REGIMENT

MBPI1073

"They talked it over—with me sitting on the horse"

MBPI1074

A wolf had not been seen at Salem for thirty years

MBPI1075

Decorative title with illustrated initial T for The Salem Wolf

MBPI1076

Once it chased Dr. Wilkinson into the very town itself

MBPI1077

Marginal illustration for The Salem Wolf

MBPI1078

Vignette for The Salem Wolf

MBPI1079

Vignette for The Salem Wolf

MBPI1080

Marginal illustration for The Salem Wolf

MBPI1081

Marginal illustration for The Salem Wolf

MBPI1082

Vignette for The Salem Wolf

MBPI1083

Vignette for The Salem Wolf

MBPI1084

Headpiece for The Salem Wolf

MBPI1085

Vignette for The Salem Wolf

MBPI1086

The nation is at war and must have men

MBPI1087

They awaited the order for the charge

MBPI1088

"I grow old, having no son but Randver"

MBPI1089
THEREAFTER SHE CLUNG ABOUT RANDVER

MBPI1090
"I FOUND HIM AND HE WASN'T ALONE"

MBPI1091
"MY BOY WANTED TO DO THE DIVIN', BUT 'TWAS ME THAT WENT DOWN"

MBPI1092
THE WHOLE WORLD GOES AFIELD TODAY

MBPI1093
FLAGGINGLY THE REED PEN WENT UP AND DOWN THE VELLUM

MBPI1094
SHE TOLD HIM HER ADVENTURES IN A BREATH

MBPI1095
WRITING ON SOME LOOSE SHEETS OF PAPER THAT HE HELD ON HIS KNEE

MBPI1096
"I HAVE BROKEN IT," SHE WAILED

MBPI1097
"AND SEE THAT YOU WATCH WELL," HE SNARLED

MBPI1098
"THEY QUESTIONED HIM WITH MALEVOLENT PERSISTENCE"

MBPI1099
THE SEA BOILED OVER THE WRECKAGE IN STREAKY WHITE

MBPI1100
PAGE WAS AT THE WHEEL, STEERING

MBPI1101
THERE STOOD THE FAERY PRINCE

MBPI1102
DECORATIVE TITLE WITH ILLUSTRATED INITIAL T FOR YSOBEL DE CORVEAUX

MBPI1103
MARGINAL ILLUSTRATION FOR YSOBEL DE CORVEAUX

MBPI1104
MARGINAL ILLUSTRATION FOR YSOBEL DE CORVEAUX

MBPI1105
MARGINAL ILLUSTRATION FOR YSOBEL DE CORVEAUX

MBPI1106
MARGINAL ILLUSTRATION FOR YSOBEL DE CORVEAUX

MBPI1107
MARGINAL ILLUSTRATION FOR YSOBEL DE CORVEAUX

MBPI1108
MARGINAL ILLUSTRATION FOR YSOBEL DE CORVEAUX

MBPI1109
MARGINAL ILLUSTRATION FOR YSOBEL DE CORVEAUX

MBPI1110
MARGINAL ILLUSTRATION FOR YSOBEL DE CORVEAUX

MBPI1111
MARGINAL ILLUSTRATION FOR YSOBEL DE CORVEAUX

MBPI1112
MARGINAL ILLUSTRATION FOR YSOBEL DE CORVEAUX

MBPI1113
HEADPIECE FOR YSOBEL DE COREAUX

MBPI1114
WHICH SHALL BE CAPTAIN?

MBPI1115
"'TIS AN UNFAIR RACE, O MASTER," CRIED EPHIALTES

MBPI1116
"COME HITHER, LADS," SHE SAID

MBPI1117
GENERAL LEE ON HIS FAMOUS CHARGER "TRAVELER"

MBPI1118
HIS ARMY BROKE UP AND FOLLOWED HIM, WEEPING AND SOBBING

MBPI1119
SO LONG AS GANN WOULD FOLLOW, HIS MASTER WOULD LEAD

MBPI1120
MAN AND STAFF SANK INTO THE PEAT MUD

MBPI1121

Jocelin, with many encomiums, displayed his emeralds

MBPI1122

"I have loved you for a great while, fair Mervisaunt"

MBPI1123

She was continually beset by spies

MBPI1124

The secret room

MBPI1125

The Virginians

MBPI1126

"Everything you wish for shall be yours"

MBPI1127

Decorative title for The Dead Finger

MBPI1128

So Beppo's first wish was fulfilled

MBPI1129

The two rode away together

MBPI1130

Beppo sat in the Notary's house talking about the will

MBPI1131

He saw a great coach approaching

MBPI1132

The grand duke gave him a golden chain

MBPI1133

He thrust the cobbler back against the door

MBPI1134

He was poor as ever

MBPI1135

The last of the "Naronic"

MBPI1136

Stefano and Serafina at the well

MBPI1137
Decorative title for The Painted Pitcher

MBPI1138
Montofacini, the Magician

MBPI1139
The shopman

MBPI1140
The bear would stand upon his hind legs and dance

MBPI1141
Nicolo, the tallow chandler

MBPI1142
Serafina was leaning from the window

MBPI1143
Cassacinci and the runaway horse

MBPI1144
Decorative title for The Evil Eye

MBPI1145
He was engaged to Caterina

MBPI1146
She pointed her finger at Caterina

MBPI1147
One of the horses fell dead in the field

MBPI1148
While she stood looking the cow died

MBPI1149
The vines were dying

MBPI1150
"The Evil Eye," he said

MBPI1151
Montofacini, the Magician

MBPI1152
"I am a ruined man"

MBPI1153
THAT NIGHT HIS STRAW STACK CAUGHT
FIRE

MBPI1154
HE KNEW NOT WHAT AILED HER OR WHAT
TO DO

MBPI1155
HE WAS LYING ON THE LIBRARY FLOOR IN
THE MORNING

MBPI1156
THE TRAVELLER FOUND THE STONE BEHIND
THE HEDGE A RESTING-PLACE

MBPI1157
NICOLO AND THE ROBBER

MBPI1158
HERR VOLLMER QUIETLY STEPPED OUT
INTO THE STREET

MBPI1159
SHE BEGAN TO TALK TO HUNTFORD ABOUT
HIMSELF

MBPI1160
THE LITTLE MAN RACED DOWN THE STAIRS
AND OUT INTO THE STREET

MBPI1161
HEADBAND WITH TITLE FOR TOM CHIST
AND THE TREASURE BOX

MBPI1162
SUCH A WRECK WAS A GODSEND TO THE
POOR AND NEEDY SETTLERS

MBPI1163
"AND TWENTY ONE AND TWENTY TWO"

MBPI1164
THE PIRATE CAPTAIN LOOKED IMPASSIVELY
ON

MBPI1165
OVER THE NEXT RISE HE RAN, AND SO ON
OVER THE SLIDING, SHIFTING GROUND,
PANTING AND GASPING

MBPI1166
"'TIS ENOUGH TO MAKE US BOTH RICH
MEN"

MBPI1167
"I KNEW IT, I KNEW IT," EXCLAIMED THE
GREAT MAN

MBPI1168
HEADPIECE WITH TITLE FOR THE
BUCCANEERS

MBPI1169
HE ASKED THIS FIGURE OF WAR TO STEP
ASIDE FOR HIM

MBPI1170
THE CROWD SCATTERED

MBPI1171
HE LEAPED TO THE WHEEL

MBPI1172
THEY WOULD STAND HOURS TOGETHER

MBPI1173
DECORATION WITH TITLE FOR THE MAN
WITH THE HOE

MBPI1174
ST. VALENTINE'S DAY IN MERRIE OLD
ENGLAND

MBPI1175
QUEEN OF THE MAY–UNPROPITIOUS SKIES

MBPI1176
"ONE OF THOSE CITY FELLOWS"–A
HUNDRED YEARS AGO

MBPI1177
ENTANGLED

MBPI1178
"WRECK IN THE OFFING!"

MBPI1179
LOST IN THE SNOW

MBPI1180
A MATRIMONIAL DIFFICULTY–LEGAL
INTERVENTION

MBPI1181
THE ROBIN'S VESPER, WITH TITLE AND
POEM INSERTED

MBPI1182
A LOVE AFFAIR OF THE OLDEN
TIME–CONSULTING THE WISE WOMAN

MBPI1183
THE MILKMAID'S SONG, WITH TITLE AND
POEM INSERTED

MBPI1184
THE DANCE OF THE VETERANS

MBPI1185
"Breaking the News"

MBPI1186
The Outcast's Return

MBPI1187
The Song of the Whip-poor-Will,
with title and poem inserted

MBPI1188
Illustrated initial E for The Song of
The Whip-poor-Will

MBPI1189
Illustrated initial B for The Song of
The Whip-poor-Will

MBPI1190
The First Public Reading of the
Declaration of Independence

MBPI1191
An Interrupted Performance

MBPI1192
Women at the Polls in New Jersey in
the Good Old Times

MBPI1193
Christmas Morning in Old New York

MBPI1194
New Year's Day Seventy Years
Ago–The Last Evening Caller

MBPI1195
St. Valentine's Day in the Morning

MBPI1196
Politics in the Olden Times–General
Jackson, President-elect, on his way
to Washington

MBPI1197
Shad-Fishing on the Lower Delaware
at Night–The Last Haul Before Dawn

MBPI1198
The Surrender of Cornwallis

MBPI1199
"He was doubtless a tramp"

MBPI1200
"Suppose you let me take care of this
young lady in future?"

MBPI1201

"'Thee hasn't killed him?' timidly inquired the girl"

MBPI1202

The Christmas Tree, title inserted

MBPI1203

"Holding forth the missive, he stood by, breathless and speechless"

MBPI1204

"Heart of gold! kindest of men!"

MBPI1205

"Hilda, airily mounting a high pair of steps, proceeded to catalogue the various articles that she now dropped one by one into Grettel's wide-spread apron"

MBPI1206

"Glancing at the white-robed girlish figure before him, with evident admiration, he made a becoming obeisance"

MBPI1207

"They sat down and chatted in an easy, friendly fashion"

MBPI1208

"Then the Hofrath emerged from the balcony, and etiquette forbade a longer interview"

MBPI1209

Washington's Birth-Day, with title and verses inserted

MBPI1210

"The old man's face changed suddenly, and he pressed his hand hard upon the arm of the hair-cloth sofa"

MBPI1211

"Breaking from her companions with an excited exclamation, Mlle. Bland grasped the old woman by the wrists"

MBPI1212

The Dead Stowaway

MBPI1213

The Sea-Gull's Song

MBPI1214

Headpiece with initial D for Christmas Time Two Hundred Years Ago

MBPI1215

Christmas presents for the Squire

MBPI1216

The Arrival at the Blue Boar Inn

MBPI1217
The stirrup-cup

MBPI1218
The Mummers

MBPI1219
The Snapdragon

MBPI1220
Bringing in the Yule-Log

MBPI1221
The Glee Singers

MBPI1222
The Return from Church, Christmas Morning

MBPI1223
Christmas Pudding

MBPI1224
The Contra-Dance

MBPI1225
The Duel

MBPI1226
The Elopement

MBPI1227
A Valentine to Phillis

MBPI1228
A Love Feast Among the Dunkers

MBPI1229
Scene in a Tavern on the Old Albany Post Road

MBPI1230
A Conference with the Colonists

MBPI1231
"Autumn Leaves"

MBPI1232
Evacuation Day One Hundred Years Ago—The Continental Army Marching Down the Old Bowery, New York, November 25, 1783

MBPI1233
Headpiece with title for Ye True Story of Granny Greene of Salem Town

MBPI1234
Illustrated initial S for Ye True Story of Granny Greene of Salem Town

MBPI1235
Vignette for Ye True Story of Granny Greene of Salem Town

MBPI1236
Granny Greene seeketh the Life of ye Hen

MBPI1237
Dame Charity Greene meeteth Ye Strange Little Man

MBPI1238
Granny Greene Falleth Into Ill Repute

MBPI1239
The Arrest

MBPI1240
Ye End for Ye True Story of Granny Greene of Salem Town

MBPI1241
Washington Taking Leave of His Officers, Dec. 4, 1783

MBPI1242
"The Ant and the Grasshopper"

MBPI1243
"He seized and held the treasure near the light"

MBPI1244
Vignette with illustrated initial C for The Strange Adventures of Carl Spich

MBPI1245
"Maybe the snow deadened his foot-steps, maybe it was the Devil"

MBPI1246
"The tall stranger with the club-foot stood before her"

MBPI1247
"He stopped when he had come close to Carl"

MBPI1248
"I am going to run away with you"

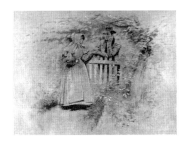

MBPI1249
"SHE CAME CLOSE TO HIM AND LAID HER HAND LOVINGLY ON HIS ARM"

MBPI1250
"THE SQUIRE WENT ON AS THOUGH HE HAD NOT HEARD"

MBPI1251
"HE HELD HIS HAMMER POISED FOR A MOMENT"

MBPI1252
"THE FINGERS OF THE HAND WERE CLUTCHED LIKE A CLAW"

MBPI1253
"MR. LONGWAYS LOOKED UP UNDER HIS BROWS AT ME WITH A VERY CURIOUS LEER"

MBPI1254
"'BOAT AHOY!' I CRIED OUT, AND THEN LEVELLED MY PISTOL AND FIRED"

MBPI1255
"'CAPTAIN MACKRA,' SAID HE, COLDLY, 'YOU WERE PLEASED TO PUT UPON ME LAST NIGHT A GROSS AND UNCALLED FOR INSULT.'"

MBPI1256
"SO SOON AS THEY SAW ME THEY FELL TO SCREAMING AND CLUNG TO ONE ANOTHER"

MBPI1257
"'I AM CAPTAIN JOHN MACKRA,' SAID I, AND I SAT DOWN UPON THE GUNWALE OF THE BOAT"

MBPI1258
"I ROSE SLOWLY FROM MY CHAIR, AND STOOD WITH MY HAND LEANING UPON THE TABLE"

MBPI1259
"THE THREE FELLOWS WERE BROUGHT AFT TO THE QUARTERDECK, WHERE CAPTAIN CROKER STOOD, JUST BELOW THE RAIL OF THE DECK ABOVE"

MBPI1260
"THERE, IN THE CORNER, I BEHELD THE FAMOUS PIRATE, CAPTAIN EDWARD ENGLAND"

MBPI1261
HEADPIECE FOR THE TWO CORNETS OF MONMOUTH

MBPI1262
"ON SPED THE LIGHT CHESTNUT, WITH THE LITTLE OFFICER BENDING ALMOST TO THE SADDLE-BOW"

MBPI1263
HEADPIECE FOR A THREAD WITHOUT A KNOT

MBPI1264
STOPPING THE CHRISTMAS STAGE

MBPI1265

ILLUSTRATION FOR STAMFORD'S SOPRANO

MBPI1266

SCENE IN THE TOWN JAIL

MBPI1267

"'AUSTIN,' SHE SAID, 'I HAVE COME TO TELL YOU OUR ENGAGEMENT IS AT AN END'"

MBPI1268

"I WAS CONSCIOUS ONLY OF HER OWN EYES LOOKING DOWN AT ME, GRAY, DEEP, INSCRUTABLE"

MBPI1269

"I STOPPED, FOR THE WOMAN'S HEAD HAD FALLEN BACK—SHE HAD FAINTED"

MBPI1270

ILLUSTRATION FOR THE PARASITE

MBPI1271

HEADPIECE WITH TITLE FOR SAILORS AND LANDSMEN, A STORY OF 1812

MBPI1272

VIGNETTE FOR SAILORS AND LANDSMEN, A STORY OF 1812

MBPI1273

VIGNETTE FOR SAILORS AND LANDSMEN, A STORY OF 1812

MBPI1274

VIGNETTE FOR SAILORS AND LANDSMEN, A STORY OF 1812

MBPI1275

VIGNETTE FOR SAILORS AND LANDSMEN, A STORY OF 1812

MBPI1276

VIGNETTE FOR SAILORS AND LANDSMEN, A STORY OF 1812

MBPI1277

VIGNETTE FOR SAILORS AND LANDSMEN, A STORY OF 1812

MBPI1278

VIGNETTE FOR SAILORS AND LANDSMEN, A STORY OF 1812

MBPI1279

VIGNETTE FOR SAILORS AND LANDSMEN, A STORY OF 1812

MBPI1280

VIGNETTE FOR SAILORS AND LANDSMEN, A STORY OF 1812

MBPI1281
An Unwelcome Toast

MBPI1282
"Captain Malyoe shot Captain Brand
through the head"

MBPI1283
Headpiece with title for The Ghost
of Captain Brand

MBPI1284
Illustrated initial B for The Ghost
of Captain Brand

MBPI1285
Headpiece for The Ghost of Captain
Brand

MBPI1286
Headpiece for The Ghost of Captain
Brand

MBPI1287
Headpiece for The Ghost of Captain
Brand

MBPI1288
"She would sit quite still, permitting
Barnaby to gaze"

MBPI1289
Headpiece for The Ghost of Captain
Brand

MBPI1290
"I've kept my ears open to all your
doings"

MBPI1291
How the Devil Haunted the Meeting-
House, Part I.

MBPI1292
How the Devil Stole the Collector's
Snuff Box, Part II.

MBPI1293
The Strange Adventures of a Young
Gentleman of Quality, Part III.

MBPI1294
A Romantic Episode in the Life of a
Young Lady, Part IV.

MBPI1295
How the Devil Was Cast Out of the
Meeting-House, Part V.

MBPI1296
Tailpiece for A True History of the
Devil at New Hope

MBPI1297
Small Game Better Than None

MBPI1298
How the Buccaneers Kept Christmas

MBPI1299
"Here is all I have to give thee—It is the King's Jewel"

MBPI1300
"I know thy heart, that thou dost love me well"

MBPI1301
"Not for myself do I seek this vengeance"

MBPI1302
So may the future bring its wreath of roses and of bay to you.

MBPI1303
Preliminary study for MBPI3240 The Landing of Carteret

MBPI1304
Miss Nancy takes leave of the officers

MBPI1305
Early settlers going to meeting

MBPI1306
Isaac Bradley carrying Joseph into the settlement

MBPI1307
The escape of Hannah Dustin

MBPI1308
"Lieutenant Wyman, creeping up, put a bullet through him"

MBPI1309
"Crack! Crack! went the guns of the Indians"

MBPI1310
Cutting off a queue to bind a wound

MBPI1311
Franklin on his way to France

MBPI1312
Battle between the "Bon Homme Richard" and the "Serapis"

MBPI1313
Decatur and his men boarding the gun-boat

MBPI1314
A Christmas Carol, with title, illustrations, and verse

MBPI1315
"There's something in there"

MBPI1316
Paul Revere at Lexington

MBPI1317
"And blew as he'd not blown since he was born"

MBPI1318
"What a racket they made at the gate"

MBPI1319
"It seemed to lie sound asleep, with a snow blanket all over its roof"

MBPI1320
"I'm Bijah"

MBPI1321
"Do you live with Santa Claus in his own house?"

MBPI1322
"With a plate of mince-pie in his lap, and Bush, the big house-dog, sitting beside him"

MBPI1323
"Grandfather came in with a back-load of sleds"

MBPI1324
"He crawled forward, and looked down through the scuttle hole"

MBPI1325
"Then Uncle Tom lifted her in his big, strong arms"

MBPI1326
Robin on his way to Nottingham

MBPI1327
Robin meets a fair lady

MBPI1328
Robin encounters John Little

MBPI1329
Ye Romantic Adventures of Three Tailors, with title, illustrations and verse

MBPI1330
Two Opinions, with title, illustrations and verse

MBPI1331
A Victim to Science, with title, illustrations and verse

MBPI1332
Headpiece with title for The Revolt of the Holidays

MBPI1333
Fred

MBPI1334
Dora–Dorothy

MBPI1335
Thanksgiving Day (entering politely)

MBPI1336
Enter Fourth of July bowing and followed by Washington's Birthday

MBPI1337
The Chorus of the Six Jolly Feeders

MBPI1338
The Military Ballet dance

MBPI1339
Easter & Saturday

MBPI1340
Four Pages armed with spears attendant

MBPI1341
Enter New Years Day saluting

MBPI1342
Santa Claus bursts into the room from the chimney followed by the Elves & Fairies. Tableau

MBPI1343
A Disappointment, with title, illustrations and verse

MBPI1344
The Accident of Birth, with title, illustrations and verse

MBPI1345

A Verse with a Moral but No Name, with title, illustrations and verse

MBPI1346

"I am the Grand Duke"

MBPI1347

A Tale of a Tub, with title, illustrations and verse

MBPI1348

Pride in Distress, with title, illustrations and verse

MBPI1349

Moral Blindness, with title, illustrations and verse

MBPI1350

Serious Advice, with title, illustrations and verse

MBPI1351

Three Fortunes, with title, illustrations and verse

MBPI1352

The Young Baron leaves his Home

MBPI1353

An old woman & a young girl coming towards the Castle

MBPI1354

Instantly there appeared before her a strange being

MBPI1355

Blow ye horn for ye ferry man

MBPI1356

Ye School for Men

MBPI1357

Then they began to pull

MBPI1358

Instantly there stood by her side a School Trustee

MBPI1359

Fitting a long arrow to his bow he sent it directly through the foremost horseman

MBPI1360

They sat down under a tree in a quiet corner of the palace grounds

MBPI1361
TO ZISK, I

MBPI1362
TO ZISK, II

MBPI1363
YE SONG OF YE GOSSIPS, WITH TITLE,
ILLUSTRATIONS AND VERSE

MBPI1364
VENTURESOME BOLDNESS, WITH TITLE,
ILLUSTRATIONS AND VERSE

MBPI1365
YE SONG OF YE FOOLISH OLD WOMAN,
WITH TITLE, ILLUSTRATIONS AND VERSE

MBPI1366
YE SONG OF YE RAJAH & YE FLY, WITH
TITLE, ILLUSTRATIONS AND VERSE

MBPI1367
YE TWO WISHES, WITH TITLE, ILLUSTRA-
TIONS AND VERSE

MBPI1368
SUPERFICIAL CULTURE, WITH TITLE, ILLUS-
TRATIONS AND VERSE

MBPI1369
PLAY & EARNEST, WITH TITLE, ILLUSTRA-
TIONS AND VERSE

MBPI1370
HEADPIECE WITH INITIAL T FOR THE
SWORD OF HILDEBRAND

MBPI1371
VIGNETTE FOR THE SWORD OF
HILDEBRAND

MBPI1372
VIGNETTE FOR THE SWORD OF
HILDEBRAND

MBPI1373
VIGNETTE FOR THE SWORD OF
HILDEBRAND

MBPI1374
VIGNETTE FOR THE SWORD OF
HILDEBRAND

MBPI1375
VIGNETTE FOR THE SWORD OF
HILDEBRAND

MBPI1376
THE FORCE OF NEED, WITH TITLE, ILLUS-
TRATIONS AND VERSE

MBPI1377
Ye Story of a Blue China Plate, with title, illustrations and verse

MBPI1378
Ye sad story concerning one innocent little Lamb and four wicked Wolves, with title, illustrations and verse

MBPI1379
Overconfidence, with title, illustrations and verse

MBPI1380
Title and illustrated initial H for Hans Hecklemann's Luck

MBPI1381
Hans Hecklemann

MBPI1382
Catherine

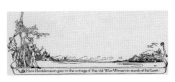

MBPI1383
Hans Hecklemann goes to the cottage of the Old Wise-Woman in search of his Luck

MBPI1384
Hans Hecklemann and the Old Wise-Woman

MBPI1385
Hans finds his Luck

MBPI1386
Hans Hecklemann ploughs for Gold

MBPI1387
Profession & Practice, with title, illustrations and verse

MBPI1388
Title and illustrated initial H for How Dame Margery Twist saw more than was good for her

MBPI1389
Dame Twist drinketh tea

MBPI1390
The Little Man and the Great Horse

MBPI1391
Dame Twist visits a Strange Patient

MBPI1392
Dame Margery Twist goeth to see the merry doings at the Fair

MBPI1393
Dame Twist drives away the Little Folks

MBPI1394
Dame Twist sees the Little Man in Green for the last time

MBPI1395
A Newspaper Puff, with title, illustrations and verse

MBPI1396
Headpiece with title for Clever Peter & the Two Bottles

MBPI1397
Clever Peter & the Little Gentleman in Black

MBPI1398
Clever Peter rides to the King's Palace upon his fine Horse

MBPI1399
Peter Eats With the King and Princess

MBPI1400
Clever Peter and the Unlucky Bottle

MBPI1401
Clever Peter opens the Unlucky Bottle for the King and Princess

MBPI1402
Fancy and Fact, with title, illustrations and verse

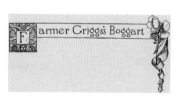

MBPI1403
Headpiece with title and initial F for Farmer Griggs's Boggart

MBPI1404
Farmer Georgie Griggs

MBPI1405
Dame Mally Griggs

MBPI1406
Farmer Griggs and the Boggart

MBPI1407
The Departure

MBPI1408
Farmer Griggs and the Wise Man

488

MBPI1409
THE BOGGART REJOICES

MBPI1410
HEADPIECE WITH TITLE AND ILLUSTRATED
INITIAL O–THE SKILLFUL HUNTSMAN

MBPI1411
JACOB'S MOTHER & THE HERR MAYOR

MBPI1412
JACOB AND THE RED ONE

MBPI1413
JACOB SHOOTS AT–

MBPI1414
–THE MAGPIE

MBPI1415
JACOB AND THE MAGIC PLOUGH

MBPI1416
JACOB AND THE RED ONE GO HUNTING
TOGETHER

MBPI1417
JACOB AND GRETCHEN GET THE BEST OF
THE RED ONE AND GO HOME TOGETHER
HAPPILY

MBPI1418
HEADPIECE WITH TITLE FOR CLAUS & HIS
WONDERFUL STAFF

MBPI1419
CLAUS AND THE WHITE SNAKE

MBPI1420
CLAUS AND THE MASTER OF BLACK-ARTS

MBPI1421
THE MASTER IS ANGRY

MBPI1422
CLAUS LISTENS TO THE TALK OF THE TWO
RAVENS

MBPI1423
CLAUS AND THE MANIKIN

MBPI1424
HANS DISCOVERS CLAUS'S LUCK

MBPI1425
Headpiece with title and initial T for The Apple of Contentment

MBPI1426
The little man asks for his cap

MBPI1427
Christine's Mother and Sisters wish for the Apple

MBPI1428
Christine and the Apple

MBPI1429
The King talks with the Wise Man

MBPI1430
The King reaches for the Apple

MBPI1431
The King's Steward and Christine

MBPI1432
Christine gives the Apple to the King

MBPI1433
Headpiece with title for The Bird in the Linden Tree

MBPI1434
Ye King

MBPI1435
Prince John

MBPI1436
The Prince aids the Old Woman

MBPI1437
The Great Ugly Troll finds the Prince by the Fire

MBPI1438
The Gooseherd & her Daughter meet the Princess at the Roadside

MBPI1439
The Prince looks through the Magic Key

MBPI1440
The Old King Rejoices at His New Daughter-in-Law

MBPI1441

HEADPIECE WITH TITLE FOR THE SWAN
MAIDEN

MBPI1442

THE SWAN CARRIES THE PRINCE AWAY

MBPI1443

THE PRINCE AND THE OLD WITCH WITH
THREE EYES

MBPI1444

YE PRINCE & YE SWAN MAIDEN

MBPI1445

THE WITCH & THE WOMAN OF HONEY &
BARLEY MEAL

MBPI1446

HEADPIECE WITH ILLUSTRATED INITIAL K
FOR THE BOOK OF BALBO

MBPI1447

THE CHILDREN ARE SENT TO THE ASYLUM

MBPI1448

THE JOLLY RED-FACED MAN COMES TO
TOWN

MBPI1449

RAMBUSTIUS READS THE BOOK OF BALBO

MBPI1450

THE KING FINDS HIS CHILDREN

MBPI1451

HEADPIECE WITH TITLE FOR HOW ONE
TURNED HIS TROUBLE TO SOME ACCOUNT

MBPI1452

THE SOLDIER AND HIS TROUBLE

MBPI1453

THE SOLDIER BRINGS HIS TROUBLE BEFORE
THE KING

MBPI1454

THE THREE GIANTS COME TO BLOWS

MBPI1455

THE RICH MAN FINDS MONEY AND
TROUBLE

MBPI1456

HEADPIECE WITH TITLE FOR HOW BOOTS
BEFOOLED THE KING

MBPI1457

PETER GOES TO BEFOOL THE KING

MBPI1458

PAUL GOES HOME AGAIN

MBPI1459

THE OLD WOMAN BREAKS THINGS

MBPI1460

THE COUNCILOR FINDS THE WISDOM SACK

MBPI1461

BOOTS TRICKS THE PRINCESS INTO SHOW-ING HERSELF

MBPI1462

HEADPIECE WITH TITLE FOR HOW THREE WENT OUT INTO THE WIDE WORLD

MBPI1463

THE GRAY GOOSE MEETS THE SAUSAGE

MBPI1464

THE FOX CALLS ON THE COCK

MBPI1465

THE FOX CALLS ON THE SAUSAGE

MBPI1466

THE FOX'S WIFE MAKES HIS BED

MBPI1467

HEADPIECE WITH TITLE FOR THE PRINCESS GOLDEN-HAIR AND THE GREAT BLACK RAVEN

MBPI1468

THE KING MEETS THE GREAT BLACK RAVEN IN THE FOREST

MBPI1469

THE PRINCESS DRINKS FROM THE GOLDEN CUP

MBPI1470

THE PRINCESS COMES TO GRUFF'S DOOR

MBPI1471

THE PRINCESS FINDS HER DEAR PRINCE AGAIN

MBPI1472

HEADPIECE WITH TITLE FOR THE CLEVER STUDENT AND THE MASTER OF BLACK ARTS

MBPI1473
THE PRINCESS WALKING BESIDE THE SEA

MBPI1474
THE STUDENT AND THE PRINCESS

MBPI1475
THE MASTER OF BLACK ARTS WITH A HEN

MBPI1476
WHAT HAPPENED TO THE MASTER

MBPI1477
HEADPIECE WITH TITLE FOR PETERKIN AND THE LITTLE GRAY HARE

MBPI1478
PETERKIN'S BROTHERS MARVEL AT HIS FINE TRAPPINGS

MBPI1479
PETERKIN MAKES OFF WITH THE GIANT'S GOOSE

MBPI1480
PETERKIN BRINGS THE SILVER BELL TO THE KING

MBPI1481
PETERKIN DRESSED AS A LASS, AND THE GIANT

MBPI1482
HEADPIECE WITH TITLE FOR HOW THE GOOD GIFTS WERE USED BY TWO

MBPI1483
SAINT NICHOLAS AT THE RICH MAN'S DOOR

MBPI1484
SAINT NICHOLAS AT THE POOR MAN'S HOUSE

MBPI1485
THE POOR MAN AND ST. CHRISTOPHER

MBPI1486
THE RICH MAN AND THE TWO SAINTS

MBPI1487
HEADPIECE WITH TITLE FOR MOTHER HILDEGARDE

MBPI1488
MOTHER HILDEGARDE AND THE PRINCESS

MBPI1489
The Princess peeped into the Jar

MBPI1490
The Princess and the Pigeons

MBPI1491
Mother Hildegarde carries away the Baby

MBPI1492
Headpiece with title for Master Jacob

MBPI1493
Master Jacob brings his Pig to Market

MBPI1494
Master Jacob goes to Town with his Goat

MBPI1495
The little tin horn has no effect

MBPI1496
Master Jacob and the three Cronies meet in the Woods

MBPI1497
Headpiece with title for How Three Little Pigs Had the Best of the Great Wicked Ogre

MBPI1498
"Have you a roasted apple to put in my mouth?"

MBPI1499
"Do you find the hole?" asked the Little Pig

MBPI1500
"The Ogre shut his eyes and began to count"

MBPI1501
"Here comes the farmer and his men to see what all the stir is about"

MBPI1502
Headpiece with title for The Staff and the Fiddle

MBPI1503
"Give the poor old Woman a penny or two"

MBPI1504
"'Rub-a-dub-dub!' says the Fiddler"

MBPI1505

A Princess as pretty as a ripe Apple

MBPI1506

"What do you want, Master?"

MBPI1507

Headpiece with title for The Simpleton and his Little Black Hen

MBPI1508

Caspar and the cunning Landlord

MBPI1509

Caspar finds the Gold in the Willow-Tree

MBPI1510

The Two Brothers and the Landlord divide the money

MBPI1511

Caspar and the Three rascals go to see the King

MBPI1512

Headpiece with title for King Stork

MBPI1513

The Drummer carries the Old Man across the River

MBPI1514

The Princess starts for the Witch's House

MBPI1515

The Drummer with his Cap of Darkness in the Witch's House

MBPI1516

The Drummer captures the one-eyed Raven

MBPI1517

Headpiece with title for How the Princess's Pride was Broken

MBPI1518

The Gooseherd plays with a Golden Ball

MBPI1519

The King peeps over the hedge

MBPI1520

The Princess goes to Market with her Eggs

MBPI1521
King Florimel greets the Princess

MBPI1522
Dame Bridget's Prophecy

MBPI1523
Headpiece with title for How Two Went into Partnership

MBPI1524
The Great Red Fox at the Store-house

MBPI1525
"What are you doing here, Father Goat?"

MBPI1526
"Which shall it be first—Sausages or Pudding?"

MBPI1527
Uncle Bear and the Great Red Fox after Farmer John's Apples

MBPI1528
Headpiece with title for Bearskin

MBPI1529
The basket with the baby in it drifted down the river

MBPI1530
Bearskin and the Princess

MBPI1531
The Princess wept and wept

MBPI1532
Bearskin and the Swineherd had a fine feast together

MBPI1533
Illustration for Hugo Grotius and His Book Chest

MBPI1534
Headpiece with title for Cousin Greylegs, Ye Great Red Fox and Grandfather Mole

MBPI1535
"The Great Red Fox and Cousin Greylegs were great cronies"

MBPI1536
Cousin Greylegs steals away with the bag of nails

MBPI1537
Brother Fox comes near tramping on the Mole's House

MBPI1538
The Great Red Fox shut his teeth and grinned

MBPI1539
Headpiece and title for Which is Best?

MBPI1540
So the Rich Man left him in his blindness

MBPI1541
He touched the lock with the little black stone

MBPI1542
The Poor Brother opens the chest

MBPI1543
The Rich Brother takes the diamond from the statue's hand

MBPI1544
Headpiece with title for The Best that Life Has to Give

MBPI1545
"'So you are stealing my pine cones,' said he"

MBPI1546
He snatched it and ran

MBPI1547
The Blacksmith carries the Golden Tree to the Queen

MBPI1548
And that was the end of the Dwarf

MBPI1549
Headpiece with title for The Water of Life

MBPI1550
A Stranger shows the King the portrait of a beautiful Princess

MBPI1551
The Faithful Servant is borne on the wings of the North Wind

MBPI1552
The King gives the Water of Life to the beautiful Princess

MBPI1553
The King goes to cut off the Faithful Servant's arm

MBPI1554
Headpiece with title for The Step-mother

MBPI1555
The Step-daughter follows the Golden Ball

MBPI1556
The King rescues the Maiden from a deep pit

MBPI1557
The Step-mother changes the Queen into a White Dove

MBPI1558
The King caresses the White Dove

MBPI1559
Headpiece with title for The White Bird

MBPI1560
The door was opened by a poor man

MBPI1561
There sat three terrible giants

MBPI1562
The Prince takes the Sword of Brightness

MBPI1563
The White Bird recognizes the Prince

MBPI1564
Headpiece with title for One Good Turn Deserves Another

MBPI1565
The Fisher Lad catches a strange fish

MBPI1566
The Fisher Lad comes to the Gray Master's house

MBPI1567
The Gray Master is caught in the stream and is swept away

MBPI1568
The Princess finds the Fisher Lad with the key of Wish-House

MBPI1569
HEADPIECE WITH TITLE FOR THE THREE FORTUNES

MBPI1570
HE WAS AN OLD MAN NO LONGER, BUT A BLESSED ANGEL

MBPI1571
THE ANGEL AND THE YOUNGEST BROTHER SAID "GOOD-BYE" AND TRUDGED AWAY

MBPI1572
A GREAT, UGLY, POISONOUS SNAKE CREPT OUT OF A HOLE IN THE WALL

MBPI1573
THEY SET BEFORE HIM A LOAF OF BREAD AND A BOWL OF MILK

MBPI1574
HEADPIECE WITH ILLUSTRATED INITIAL T FOR THE PRINCESS ON THE GLASS HILL

MBPI1575
THE PRINCE POURS WATER INTO THE BARREL

MBPI1576
THE PRINCE BATHES IN THE FOUNTAIN

MBPI1577
THE PRINCE KILLS THE DRAGON

MBPI1578
THE PRINCE WINS THE GOLDEN APPLE AND THE SILVER PEAR

MBPI1579
HEADPIECE WITH TITLE AND ILLUSTRATED INITIAL T FOR THAT WHICH IS DONE NEVER DIES

MBPI1580
"A GOLDEN SWAN LEAPED INTO THE AIR"

MBPI1581
"AS IT SANG IT SANG SO SWEETLY AND SO SADLY"

MBPI1582
"THE PRINCESS SITS IN THE WINDOW AND SINGS"

MBPI1583
"THE KING OPENED THE CLOSET DOOR AND BROUGHT FORTH THE TRUE BRIDE"

MBPI1584
"THERE SPRANG FROM THE MIDST OF THE SMOKE A BEAUTIFUL BIRD"

MBPI1585
HEADPIECE WITH TITLE FOR ILL-LUCK AND THE FIDDLER

MBPI1586
VIGNETTE FOR ILL-LUCK AND THE FIDDLER

MBPI1587
VIGNETTE FOR ILL-LUCK AND THE FIDDLER

MBPI1588
VIGNETTE FOR ILL-LUCK AND THE FIDDLER

MBPI1589
VIGNETTE FOR ILL-LUCK AND THE FIDDLER

MBPI1590
VIGNETTE FOR ILL-LUCK AND THE FIDDLER

MBPI1591
VIGNETTE FOR ILL-LUCK AND THE FIDDLER

MBPI1592
HEADPIECE WITH TITLE FOR WISDOM'S WAGES AND FOLLY'S PAY

MBPI1593
VIGNETTE FOR WISDOM'S WAGES AND FOLLY'S PAY

MBPI1594
VIGNETTE FOR WISDOM'S WAGES AND FOLLY'S PAY

MBPI1595
VIGNETTE FOR WISDOM'S WAGES AND FOLLY'S PAY

MBPI1596
VIGNETTE FOR WISDOM'S WAGES AND FOLLY'S PAY

MBPI1597
VIGNETTE FOR WISDOM'S WAGES AND FOLLY'S PAY

MBPI1598
VIGNETTE FOR WISDOM'S WAGES AND FOLLY'S PAY

MBPI1599
VIGNETTE FOR WISDOM'S WAGES AND FOLLY'S PAY

MBPI1600
HEADPIECE WITH TITLE FOR THE SALT OF LIFE

MBPI1601
"Away with you, and never let me see your face again"

MBPI1602
"An old man looked down into the water"

MBPI1603
"The Queen raised the veil and looked at the Prince"

MBPI1604
"Away the boat went, swifter than the wind"

MBPI1605
"Beat the statue with her steel-tipped whip"

MBPI1606
"The raven spread his wings and flew"

MBPI1607
"At last they dashed against one another"

MBPI1608
"The statue became flesh and blood"

MBPI1609
"He had a noble feast set for them"

MBPI1610
Headpiece with title for Empty Bottles

MBPI1611
"Making strange figures upon the table"

MBPI1612
"Now,' said the Master, 'take me by the belt'"

MBPI1613
"He gazed and gazed until his heart melted within him"

MBPI1614
"The dragon leaped into the air"

MBPI1615
"He raised the dagger to strike"

MBPI1616
Headpiece with title for Where to Lay the Blame

MBPI1617
"The old man began to utter strange spells"

MBPI1618
"He caught something that weighed heavily as lead"

MBPI1619
"They kissed one another"

MBPI1620
"The chief treasurer emptied a bag of money into the fur cap"

MBPI1621
"Down fell the fisherman"

MBPI1622
Headpiece with title for Not a Pin to Choose

MBPI1623
"He was like one bereft of wits"

MBPI1624
"A wise man stopped to enquire the cause of his sorrow"

MBPI1625
"A great crowd of horses laden with balls and bundles of rich stuffs"

MBPI1626
"There was a passageway yawning before him"

MBPI1627
"Out leaped a great hideous Genie"

MBPI1628
"Bread as white as snow, and a piece of cheese"

MBPI1629
"Blazing with diamonds and rubies and emeralds"

MBPI1630
"The Princess looked over the edge of the balcony"

MBPI1631
"'Sire,' said the Ambassador, 'I will answer now for my master'"

MBPI1632
Headpiece with title for Woman's Wit

MBPI1633

"A box of adamant"

MBPI1634

"The little man set him to work on the bench"

MBPI1635

"It was the King's daughter passing by"

MBPI1636

"The young man prostrated himself in the dust"

MBPI1637

"Then prepare to die"

MBPI1638

Tailpiece for Woman's Wit

MBPI1639

Headpiece with title for Good Gifts and a Fool's Folly

MBPI1640

"An old man with a beard as white as snow"

MBPI1641

"Away flew the carpet swifter than the wind"

MBPI1642

"Every day there was feasting and dancing and singing"

MBPI1643

"He balanced the earthen jar on his head"

MBPI1644

"Around and around they spun and whirled"

MBPI1645

"He lay there sighing and groaning"

MBPI1646

Headpiece with title for All Things Are as Fate Wills

MBPI1647

"Three men seized him"

MBPI1648

"The King and the beggar feasted"

MBPI1649
"He knocked upon the brazen gate"

MBPI1650
"The beggar crawled out"

MBPI1651
"He was seated upon a throne"

MBPI1652
Headpiece with title for Much Shall Have More and Little Shall Have Less

MBPI1653
"He spread the money out on the table"

MBPI1654
"Sat down by the road-side to eat his pie"

MBPI1655
"He met a poor woman coming home from market"

MBPI1656
"'Keep the bag of money for yourself,' said the King"

MBPI1657
Headpiece with title for The Stool of Fortune

MBPI1658
"If the shot had cracked the sky he could not have been more frightened"

MBPI1659
"Away flew the stool"

MBPI1660
"The prettiest princess the sun ever shone upon"

MBPI1661
"Riding in his gilded coach"

MBPI1662
"What are my lord's commands?"

MBPI1663
Tailpiece for The Stool of Fortune

MBPI1664
Headpiece with title for The Fruit of Happiness

MBPI1665
"He came to the cross-roads and the stone cross"

MBPI1666
"He drew out his pipe, and began to play"

MBPI1667
"In came the gang of thieves"

MBPI1668
"All was a red blaze behind them"

MBPI1669
"Went whirling over rocks and waterfalls"

MBPI1670
The Flight from Falworth Castle

MBPI1671
"Myles as in a dream kneeled, and presented the letter"

MBPI1672
Illustration for Men of Iron

MBPI1673
"At last they had the poor boy down"

MBPI1674
"Myles pushed the door further open"

MBPI1675
In the "Eyry"

MBPI1676
"They bore him away to a bench at the far end of the room"

MBPI1677
"But tell me, Robin Ingoldsby, dost know aught more of this matter?"

MBPI1678
"'Belike thou sought to take this lad's life,' said Sir James"

MBPI1679
"Stories and jests recited by some strolling mummer or minstrel"

MBPI1680
Myles entertains the Lady Anne and the Lady Alice with his adventures

MBPI1681
"Myles found himself standing beside the bed"

MBPI1682
The Earl of Mackworth receives King Henry IV

MBPI1683
"Lord George led him to where the King stood"

MBPI1684
"There he watched and guarded while the others slept"

MBPI1685
Illustration for Men of Iron

MBPI1686
Illustration for Men of Iron

MBPI1687
Prior Edward and Myles in the Priory Garden

MBPI1688
The Challenge

MBPI1689
Illustration for Men of Iron

MBPI1690
"He held tightly to the saddle-bow of the fallen man's horse"

MBPI1691
Headpiece with title for The Enchanted Island

MBPI1692
"Selim the Fisherman finds a leaden box"

MBPI1693
"The old man rapped on the door three times"

MBPI1694
"There was feasting and merrymaking"

MBPI1695
"The men brought Selim up in front of the statue"

MBPI1696
"Selim the Baker lands on the desert island"

MBPI1697

"'Come with me,' said the little old man"

MBPI1698

"He called the wisest men of the island to him"

MBPI1699

"Down she came from the pedestal where she stood"

MBPI1700

Tailpiece for The Enchanted Island

MBPI1701

"Zadok and his master"

MBPI1702

"An old man who had a curious necklace for sale"

MBPI1703

"A vessel of brass full of money"

MBPI1704

"A great tall Demon"

MBPI1705

"He fell on his face and kissed the ground"

MBPI1706

"The Demon leaped from the earth"

MBPI1707

"A basin filled with jewels"

MBPI1708

"A palace of marble and gold"

MBPI1709

"'I think everybody has gone mad,' said the young man"

MBPI1710

"They entered the vestibule of the palace"

MBPI1711

"The young man fell upon his knees"

MBPI1712

"Drew a circle upon the ground with his finger-tip"

MBPI1713
"'This is my daughter,' said the merchant"

MBPI1714
"There sat an old woman at a wheel spinning"

MBPI1715
"Thou art a wonder of wonders"

MBPI1716
"A dense cloud of blue smoke rose in the air"

MBPI1717
"'I am ready,' said the young man steadily"

MBPI1718
"Flew away swifter than the wind"

MBPI1719
Headpiece with title for A Piece of Good Luck

MBPI1720
"They danced around and around the chest"

MBPI1721
"'What will you have?' said the Genie"

MBPI1722
"Close your doors! close your doors! her Highness the Princess comes to ride"

MBPI1723
"The Genie had flown with her through the air"

MBPI1724
"Next morning the Prime Minister looked like a shorn sheep"

MBPI1725
"Jacob's magnificent court suit"

MBPI1726
"As for the King, he could not believe his eyes when he saw it"

MBPI1727
"Jacob and the King left in the desert by the Genie"

MBPI1728
"The Genie snatched the Minister up and flew away with him"

MBPI1729
Headpiece with title for The Good of
a Few Words

MBPI1730
"Feasting and drinking and junketing
and merry-making"

MBPI1731
"'Look at yonder poor man,' said she
to her nurse"

MBPI1732
"The tall man in black knocked upon
the gate"

MBPI1733
"'Now,' said the King, 'now you are
married'"

MBPI1734
"Then Beppo carried the Princess
ashore"

MBPI1735
"Again Sebastian served a feast"

MBPI1736
"Beppo offers the King milk"

MBPI1737
"'Alas, my poor friend!' said he"

MBPI1738
"The King laid his hands on Beppo's
shoulders"

MBPI1739
"'Do you not know me?' said she; 'I am
the Queen'"

MBPI1740
"The werewolf...skulked for a
moment in the shadow of the yews,
and...Yseult plucked old Siegfried's
spear from her girdle"

MBPI1741
"My dear," said General Washington,
"Captain Prescott's behavior was
inexcusable"

MBPI1742
Spirit of Spring

MBPI1743
George and Martha Washington
entertaining their friends on the
lawn at Mount Vernon

MBPI1744
"He called on Franklin and received
the necessary recognition"

MBPI1745

"The good, aged Doctor, the appearance of whose rotund figure on the streets was the signal for the Parisians to doff their hats"

MBPI1746

"At the same time he extended toward King Louis the precious Memorial"

MBPI1747

The Death of Colonel John Laurens

MBPI1748

Cover design for McClure's Magazine

MBPI1749

Headband for At the Turn of the Glass

MBPI1750

At the Turn of the Glass

MBPI1751

Marginal decoration for At the Turn of the Glass

MBPI1752

Uncle Sammy and Joe

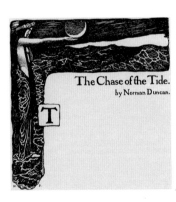

MBPI1753

Headpiece with title and initial T for The Chase of the Tide

MBPI1754

Marginal illustration for The Chase of the Tide

MBPI1755

Vignette for The Chase of the Tide

MBPI1756

Illustration for The Chase of the Tide

MBPI1757

"The Sea—He've cotched us!"

MBPI1758

"The tall man was lying at his feet, huddled hideously on the floor"

MBPI1759

Headband for The Second-Class Passenger

MBPI1760

"I have been reserved for this—to free the land from spiritual tyranny"

MBPI1761
"The Lord hath sent me here to die like Stephen at the feet of Saul"

MBPI1762
"At her appearing the multitude was hushed, awed by that air she wore"

MBPI1763
Headpiece with title for The Captain's Well

MBPI1764
Illustration for The Captain's Well

MBPI1765
Illustration for The Captain's Well

MBPI1766
Illustration for The Captain's Well

MBPI1767
Illustration for The Captain's Well

MBPI1768
"He lay silent and still, with his face half buried in the sand"

MBPI1769
"He struck once and again at the bald, narrow forehead beneath him"

MBPI1770
"A child, sunburned, and with many fluttering shreds of raiment"

MBPI1771
"She hadn't on anything but a little nightgown, the same as if they'd snatched her out o' the berth, with no time to dress her"

MBPI1772
"Then turned to the table where master and pupil sat absorbed"

MBPI1773
Sylvia's troubles

MBPI1774
"She wasn't no kin when I marr'ed her, but we've lived together over thirty year"

MBPI1775
The fight in the fog

MBPI1776
The Gosling states his opinion of the Cock

MBPI1777
The Gosling is punished

MBPI1778
The Fox and the Tablet

MBPI1779
The Swineherd who knew curious things

MBPI1780
Gottenlieb's music works a charm

MBPI1781
Pictorial Puzzle

MBPI1782
The King and his Prime Minister

MBPI1783
Fritz guides the Baron

MBPI1784
"I have brought you the Baron's head"

MBPI1785
The Princess and her Pigs

MBPI1786
"Poor Piggy led the way"

MBPI1787
The Royal Bodyguard

MBPI1788
Tailpiece for Drummer Fritz and His Exploits

MBPI1789
Kitty and Turkish Merchant

MBPI1790
"A very little old man seated in a very large chair"

MBPI1791
"He examined with astonishment and delight"

MBPI1792
"A page was appointed to escort it"

MBPI1793
"The king sat upon a chair of state, with a learned judge at each side"

MBPI1794
An Old-time May-Day in "Merrie England"

MBPI1795
Illustration for How Willy-Wolly Went A-Fishing

MBPI1796
Illustration for How Willy-Wolly Went A-Fishing

MBPI1797
Illustration for How Willy-Wolly Went A-Fishing

MBPI1798
The Fox, the Monkey, and the Pig

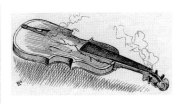

MBPI1799
"As good as new"

MBPI1800
Tailpiece for The Origin of the Jumping-Jack

MBPI1801
The Gourd and the Oak

MBPI1802
Front cover design for The Price of Blood

MBPI1803
Bluetree declines Lord Diddledaddle's offer

MBPI1804
A Bowl of Milk for Robin Goodfellow

MBPI1805
A Great Black Bear came out of the Woods

MBPI1806
Gretelein and the Elf King

MBPI1807
Back cover design for The Price of Blood

MBPI1808
"A Person of Consequence, carefully fed and attended to"

MBPI1809

"Edmund Burton, you are a genius!"

MBPI1810

The Boys consult Jack-in-the-Box

MBPI1811

Jupiter and the Philosopher

MBPI1812

"One of the policemen produced a bull's-eye lantern"

MBPI1813

"The clown counted the money"

MBPI1814

"They used to drill every evening"

MBPI1815

Headpiece with title and initial W for The Soldiering of Beniah Stidham

MBPI1816

Vignette for The Soldiering of Beniah Stidham

MBPI1817

Vignette for The Soldiering of Beniah Stidham

MBPI1818

Vignette for The Soldiering of Beniah Stidham

MBPI1819

Vignette for The Soldiering of Beniah Stidham

MBPI1820

Vignette for The Soldiering of Beniah Stidham

MBPI1821

Vignette for The Soldiering of Beniah Stidham

MBPI1822

Vignette for The Soldiering of Beniah Stidham

MBPI1823

Vignette for The Soldiering of Beniah Stidham

MBPI1824

Uncle and Nephew—"Well, Jacky, you shall have that hundred pounds, you shall"

MBPI1825

"'He'll come to by and by; he's only stunned a trifle,' said the Captain"

MBPI1826

"'Now then, Gentlemen, how much do you bid for this boy?' said the auctioneer"

MBPI1827

"'Speak up, boy,—speak up,' said the gentleman"

MBPI1828

"Mr. Parker stood looking at his visitor with his usual calm reserve"

MBPI1829

"I don't want to be anybody's servant, lady, and wouldn't if I could help it"

MBPI1830

"He picked up the bird and held it out at arm's length"

MBPI1831

"He led Jack up to a man who sat on a barrel"

MBPI1832

"Jack followed the Captain and the young lady up the crooked path to the house"

MBPI1833

"They found her still sitting in the same place"

MBPI1834

Governor Spottiswood visits Colonel Parker

MBPI1835

Jack and Dred rescue Eleanor–The Start

MBPI1836

The pirates fire upon the fugitives

MBPI1837

"Colonel Parker reached out and laid his hand upon Jack's shoulder; 'Ay,' said he, 'tis a good, honest face'"

MBPI1838

Blackbeard's last fight

MBPI1839

"'Then I will come,' said he"

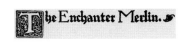

MBPI1840

Title with illustrated initial T for The Story of King Arthur and His Knights

MBPI1841
The Enchanter Merlin

MBPI1842
Headpiece for The Story of King Arthur and His Knights

MBPI1843
Illustrated initial A for The Story of King Arthur and His Knights

MBPI1844
Title with illustrated initial H for The Story of King Arthur and His Knights

MBPI1845
How one clad all in black did a wonder before King Leodegrance of Camilard

MBPI1846
Sir Kay overthroweth his Enemies

MBPI1847
Illustrated initial I for The Story of King Arthur and His Knights

MBPI1848
Title with illustrated initial S for The Story of King Arthur and His Knights

MBPI1849
Sir Kay breaketh his sword at ye Tournament

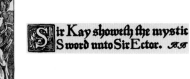

MBPI1850
Headpiece for The Story of King Arthur and His Knights

MBPI1851
Title with illustrated initial S for The Story of King Arthur and His Knights

MBPI1852
Sir Kay showeth the mystic Sword unto Sir Ector

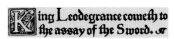

MBPI1853
Title with illustrated initial K for The Story of King Arthur and His Knights

MBPI1854
King Leodegrance cometh to the assay of the Sword

MBPI1855
Title with illustrated initial K for The Story of King Arthur and His Knights

MBPI1856
How Arthur drew forth Ye Sword

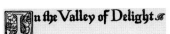

MBPI1857
HEADPIECE FOR THE STORY OF KING ARTHUR AND HIS KNIGHTS

MBPI1858
TITLE WITH ILLUSTRATED INITIAL K FOR THE STORY OF KING ARTHUR AND HIS KNIGHTS

MBPI1859
KING ARTHUR OF BRITAIN

MBPI1860
ILLUSTRATED INITIAL S FOR THE STORY OF KING ARTHUR AND HIS KNIGHTS

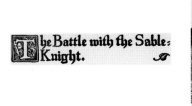

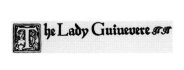

MBPI1861
TITLE WITH ILLUSTRATED INITIAL I FOR THE STORY OF KING ARTHUR AND HIS KNIGHTS

MBPI1862
IN THE VALLEY OF DELIGHT

MBPI1863
TITLE WITH ILLUSTRATED INITIAL T FOR THE STORY OF KING ARTHUR AND HIS KNIGHTS

MBPI1864
THE BATTLE WITH THE SABLE KNIGHT

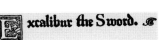

MBPI1865
THE WINNING OF A SWORD AND A QUEEN

MBPI1866
TITLE WITH ILLUSTRATED INITIAL E FOR THE STORY OF KING ARTHUR AND HIS KNIGHTS

MBPI1867
EXCALIBUR THE SWORD

MBPI1868
TITLE WITH ILLUSTRATED INITIAL T FOR THE STORY OF KING ARTHUR AND HIS KNIGHTS

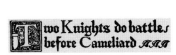

MBPI1869
THE LADY GUINEVERE

MBPI1870
TITLE WITH ILLUSTRATED INITIAL T FOR THE STORY OF KING ARTHUR AND HIS KNIGHTS

MBPI1871
TWO KNIGHTS DO BATTLE BEFORE CAMELIARD

MBPI1872
HEADPIECE FOR THE STORY OF KING ARTHUR AND HIS KNIGHTS

MBPI1873

Title with illustrated initial T for The Story of King Arthur and His Knights

MBPI1874

The White Champion meets two Knights at the Mill

MBPI1875

Title with illustrated initial F for The Story of King Arthur and His Knights

MBPI1876

Four Knights serve the Gardener Lad

MBPI1877

Headpiece for The Story of King Arthur and His Knights

MBPI1878

Title with illustrated initial T for The Story of King Arthur and His Knights

MBPI1879

The Gardener Lad takes off his Cap

MBPI1880

Title with illustrated initial K for The Story of King Arthur and His Knights

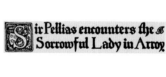

MBPI1881

King Arthur meets the Lady Guinevere

MBPI1882

Headpiece for The Story of King Arthur and His Knights

MBPI1883

Title with illustrated initial S for The Story of King Arthur and His Knights

MBPI1884

Sir Pellias encounters the Sorrowful Lady in Arroy

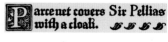

MBPI1885

Title with illustrated initial S for The Story of King Arthur and His Knights

MBPI1886

Sir Pellias, the Gentle Knight

MBPI1887

Headpiece for The Story of King Arthur and His Knights

MBPI1888

Title with illustrated initial P for The Story of King Arthur and His Knights

MBPI1889
Parcenet covers Sir Pellias with a cloak

MBPI1890
Title with illustrated initial T for The Story of King Arthur and His Knights

MBPI1891
The Lady of the Lake sits by the Fountain in Arroy

MBPI1892
Headpiece for The Story of King Arthur and His Knights

MBPI1893
Title with illustrated initial S for The Story of King Arthur and His Knights

MBPI1894
Sir Gawaine sups with ye Lady Ettard

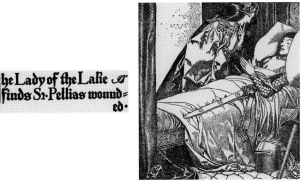

MBPI1895
Title with illustrated initial T for The Story of King Arthur and His Knights

MBPI1896
The Lady of the Lake finds Sir Pellias wounded

MBPI1897
Headpiece for The Story of King Arthur and His Knights

MBPI1898
Title with illustrated initial S for The Story of King Arthur and His Knights

MBPI1899
Sir Percival of Gales

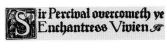

MBPI1900
Title with illustrated initial S for The Story of King Arthur and His Knights

MBPI1901
Sir Percival and Sir Pellinore ride together

MBPI1902
Headpiece, Vivien for The Story of King Arthur and His Knights

MBPI1903
Title with illustrated initial S for The Story of King Arthur and His Knights

MBPI1904
Sir Percival overcometh ye Enchantress Vivien

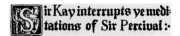

MBPI1905
Title with illustrated initial S for The Story of King Arthur and His Knights

MBPI1906
Sir Kay interrupts ye meditations of Sir Percival

MBPI1907
Title with illustrated initial T for The Story of King Arthur and His Knights

MBPI1908
The Lady Yvette the Fair

MBPI1909
Gambetta Proclaiming the Republic of France

MBPI1910
Looking into the Prussian Lines from the Chateau de la Muette

MBPI1911
"Then faced her the leonine chief"

MBPI1912
"A moment later there was a great hammering on the oak door"

MBPI1913
"Five red-coated soldiers on horseback, with another cloaked to the eyes… Clustering about these, a motley score of poor people, young and old"

MBPI1914
Within sound of the shouting waters

MBPI1915
"We men-folk thought the music as sweet as that of the Cherubim"

MBPI1916
"This is Enoch Wade, gentlemen," said the baronet

MBPI1917
"Good-by, big brother," she said softly

MBPI1918
"He told them, when we chanced to sit around the fires of an evening, most remarkable stories of field and forest"

MBPI1919
"At sight of me the good soul gave a guttural exclamation, and stared at me open-mouthed"

MBPI1920
"The negro boy, arms whirling wide in air, shot over the side of the cliff"

MBPI1921
"The blow—the whole crushing series of blows—had fallen!"

MBPI1922
"She was silent for a moment, her eyes seeking the floor"

MBPI1923
"The dignified sober figure of Abraham Ten Broeck appeared in our wrathful circle"

MBPI1924
"While his eyes still glowed fiery wrath, the trembling lips became piteous in their inability to form words"

MBPI1925
"Then a great mashing blow on my face ended my fight"

MBPI1926
"'Who are you? and off with your hat!' I said to the man, sharply"

MBPI1927
"Is your hanging-party ready?" he said

MBPI1928
"I turned the sheet over and over in my hands, re-reading lines here and there"

MBPI1929
"'I wish to God we were well out of this all,' he said, almost gloomily"

MBPI1930
"There, half stretched on the wet blood-stained grass, lay Philip Cross"

MBPI1931
"My hatred of him seemed suddenly to have taken to itself wings"

MBPI1932
Breton Peasants at a Wayside Cross

MBPI1933
Decorative title for A Pastoral Without Words

MBPI1934
Subtitle, A Pastoral Without Words

MBPI1935
Decorative title, Verse I for A Pastoral Without Words

MBPI1936
Verse I, A Pastoral Without Words

MBPI1937
Decorative title, Verse II for A Pastoral Without Words

MBPI1938
Verse II, A Pastoral Without Words

MBPI1939
Decorative title, Verse III for A Pastoral Without Words

MBPI1940
Verse III, A Pastoral Without Words

MBPI1941
Decorative title, Verse IV for A Pastoral Without Words

MBPI1942
Verse IV, A Pastoral Without Words

MBPI1943
Decorative title, L'Envoy for A Pastoral Without Words

MBPI1944
L'Envoy, A Pastoral Without Words

MBPI1945
The First Christmas Tree

MBPI1946
"It poised for an instant above the child's fair head—death cruel and imminent"

MBPI1947
Headpiece with title for Peter Rugg Ye Bostonian

MBPI1948
Vignette for Peter Rugg Ye Bostonian

MBPI1949
Vignette for Peter Rugg Ye Bostonian

MBPI1950
Vignette for Peter Rugg Ye Bostonian

MBPI1951
Vignette for Peter Rugg Ye Bostonian

MBPI1952
Vignette for Peter Rugg Ye Bostonian

MBPI1953
Vignette for Peter Rugg Ye Bostonian

MBPI1954
Vignette for Peter Rugg Ye Bostonian

MBPI1955
Vignette for Peter Rugg Ye Bostonian

MBPI1956
Vignette for Peter Rugg Ye Bostonian

MBPI1957
Vignette for Peter Rugg Ye Bostonian

MBPI1958
Vignette for Peter Rugg Ye Bostonian

MBPI1959
"Seeing no enemy, and themselves falling every moment from the fire"

MBPI1960
The Death of Braddock

MBPI1961
"For a while no one said a word"

MBPI1962
January and May

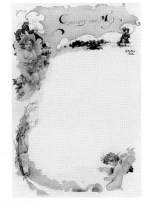

MBPI1963
Decorative border with title for January and May

MBPI1964
Illustration with illustrated initial M for McAndrew's Hymn

MBPI1965
Illustration for McAndrew's Hymn

MBPI1966
Headpiece for McAndrew's Hymn

MBPI1967
Illustrated initial L for McAndrew's Hymn

MBPI1968
"I heard a land-breeze ca'"

MBPI1969
Headpiece for McAndrew's Hymn

MBPI1970
Tailpiece for McAndrew's Hymn

MBPI1971
Illustration for A Forgotten Tale

MBPI1972
Illustration for A Forgotten Tale

MBPI1973
The Brooks Forces evacuating the State House at Little Rock

MBPI1974
The rush from the New York Stock Exchange on September 18, 1873

MBPI1975
Dennis Kearney being drawn through the streets of San Francisco after his release from the House of Correction

MBPI1976
November, 1776

MBPI1977
The Enemy at the Door

MBPI1978
Esmond and the Prince

MBPI1979
Undergraduate Life in 1679

MBPI1980
"Bringing fire and terror to roof tree and bed"

MBPI1981
Headpiece with title and illustrated initial T for The Birds of Cirencester

MBPI1982
Illustrated initial D for The Birds of Cirencester

MBPI1983
Illustrated initial A for The Birds of Cirencester

MBPI1984
Illustrated initial A for The Birds of Cirencester

MBPI1985
ILLUSTRATED INITIAL F FOR THE BIRDS OF CIRENCESTER

MBPI1986
ILLUSTRATED INITIAL S FOR THE BIRDS OF CIRENCESTER

MBPI1987
ILLUSTRATED INITIAL H FOR THE BIRDS OF CIRENCESTER

MBPI1988
ILLUSTRATED INITIAL S FOR THE BIRDS OF CIRENCESTER

MBPI1989
ILLUSTRATED INITIAL F FOR THE BIRDS OF CIRENCESTER

MBPI1990
ILLUSTRATED INITIAL Y FOR THE BIRDS OF CIRENCESTER

MBPI1991
THE FIGHT ON LEXINGTON COMMON, APRIL 19, 1775

MBPI1992
THE BATTLE OF BUNKER HILL

MBPI1993
THOMAS JEFFERSON WRITING THE DECLARATION OF INDEPENDENCE

MBPI1994
THE RETREAT THROUGH THE JERSEYS

MBPI1995
THE BURIAL OF GENERAL FRASER

MBPI1996
THE ATTACK UPON THE CHEW HOUSE

MBPI1997
CLARK ON HIS WAY TO KASKASKIA

MBPI1998
THE MEETING OF GREENE AND GATES AT CHARLOTTE, N.C.

MBPI1999
THE EVACUATION OF CHARLESTON BY THE BRITISH DECEMBER 14, 1782

MBPI2000
ARNOLD TELLS HIS WIFE OF THE DISCOVERY OF HIS TREASON

MBPI2001
Washington Firing the First Gun at the Siege of Yorktown

MBPI2002
Benjamin Franklin and Richard Oswald Discussing the Treaty of Peace at Paris

MBPI2003
His niece had found him lying dead

MBPI2004
Another rush of breakers pitching the boat, cork-like, into the air

MBPI2005
He looked down and sang out, "Lower away!"

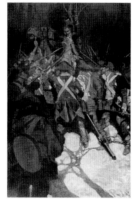

MBPI2006
General Wayne endeavoring to quell the mutiny of the Pennsylvania Regiments at Morristown, N.J.

MBPI2007
General Andrew Jackson receiving the plaudits of his motley army after the victory of New Orleans

MBPI2008
Queen Esther inciting the Indians to attack the settlers at Wyoming

MBPI2009
The Connecticut Settlers entering the Western Reserve

MBPI2010
We started to run back to the raft for our lives

MBPI2011
The boat and I went by him with a rush

MBPI2012
Decorative title with illustrated initial S for Sindbad on Burrator

MBPI2013
I began to play

MBPI2014
I sat at her feet while she drilled the island language into me

MBPI2015
"If I catch you here again you'll need someone to sew you up"

MBPI2016
I clutched at his ankle

MBPI2017
"There is a time to fight and that time has now come"

MBPI2018
"Humility is the fountain of all wirtue"

MBPI2019
"'Ah me!' said the Parson, 'I wish I were young'"

MBPI2020
"Alas! he had turned to a terrible boy"

MBPI2021
Peter asks the fatal question

MBPI2022
Grief and indignation

MBPI2023
"I'll do it!"

MBPI2024
"Do you see this knife?"

MBPI2025
The Notary beckons

MBPI2026
"She's yours"

MBPI2027
"Why don't you show him?"

MBPI2028
The reconciliation

MBPI2029
The Sailor from Constantinople

MBPI2030
"Horror! Devastation! Agony!"

MBPI2031
The Sailor is saved

MBPI2032
The End

MBPI2033

CATCHING A PONY

MBPI2034

A SON OF THE SOIL

MBPI2035

THE LADY OF THE HOUSE

MBPI2036

UNCLE KEN

MBPI2037

OLD DAN TUCKER

MBPI2038

THE MAJESTY OF THE LAW

MBPI2039

CROSSING TO ASSATEAGUE

MBPI2040

UNCLE BENNY

MBPI2041

THE PONY PEN

MBPI2042

J. A. M. WHEALTON

MBPI2043

FAMILY CARES

MBPI2044

BLISS

MBPI2045

IN THE PARK

MBPI2046

A QUOTATION FROM "KING LEAR"

MBPI2047

SPEARING EELS IN EEL BAY

MBPI2048

FRENCH CANADIAN

MBPI2049
RUINS OF OLD FORT, CARLETON'S ISLAND

MBPI2050
CATCHING MUSKALLONGE

MBPI2051
CAMPING OUT

MBPI2052
BILLY PATTERSON

MBPI2053
JOSEPH GLADD

MBPI2054
McCUE

MBPI2055
COOKING A CAMP DINNER

MBPI2056
GEORGE CAMPBELL

MBPI2057
YOUNG DE LESKEN

MBPI2058
MISTRESS BETTY

MBPI2059
DIETRICH EXAMINES THE DISASTER FROM
A DISTANCE

MBPI2060
"HE KISSED THE LITTLE HAND"

MBPI2061
KOBUS AND HIS PUPIL

MBPI2062
JAN'S COURTSHIP

MBPI2063
DE LESKEN ENTERTAINING

MBPI2064
KOBUS BRINGS NEWS OF MYNHEER JAN

MBPI2065
JAN RETURNS

MBPI2066
TAILPIECE FOR THE STORY OF LESKEN

MBPI2067
ANTHONY VON CORLEAR, THE TRUMPETER OF NEW AMSTERDAM

MBPI2068
PRINCE CHARLES SPRANG TO HIS SIDE: "IF HE GOES, SO DO I!"

MBPI2069
WAS THIS...KING HENRY'S SELF? MARGERY DROPPED TO HER KNEE

MBPI2070
YOUNG WILLIAM PENN MEETS THE DISAPPROVAL OF HIS FATHER, THE ADMIRAL

MBPI2071
ON THE GREAT TERRACE OF DONEGAL CASTLE

MBPI2072
"TO SEA IN A BOWL!" EXCLAIMED THE PUZZLED PEMBROKE

MBPI2073
THE YOUNG EMPEROR'S ENTRANCE TO THE CIRCUS MAXIMUS

MBPI2074
"THE DARK AND SHADOWY OUTLINE OF A MAN"

MBPI2075
"A GREAT DAY THIS, MY YOUNG FRIEND," SAID MR. JOHN ADAMS OF MASSACHUSETTS

MBPI2076
HEADPIECE FOR THE LITTLE MAID AT THE DOOR

MBPI2077
ILLUSTRATED INITIAL J FOR THE LITTLE MAID AT THE DOOR

MBPI2078
"I SEE NAUGHT BUT A LITTLE MAID AT THE DOOR"

MBPI2079
SURPRISED BY THE HERO OF SEVENTY FIGHTS–THE GOOD LORD JAMES OF DOUGLAS

MBPI2080
WASHINGTON REFUSES THE COLT

MBPI2081
THE STAR BEARER

MBPI2082
MARGINAL DECORATION WITH TITLE FOR
THE STAR BEARER

MBPI2083
MARGINAL DECORATION FOR THE STAR
BEARER

MBPI2084
MARGINAL DECORATION FOR THE STAR
BEARER

MBPI2085
THE SAVING OF KING INGÉ

MBPI2086
HALF-TITLE DECORATION FOR THE MERRY
ADVENTURES OF ROBIN HOOD

MBPI2087
THE MERRY FRIAR CARRIETH ROBIN
ACROSS THE WATER

MBPI2088
TITLE PAGE DECORATION FOR THE MERRY
ADVENTURES OF ROBIN HOOD

MBPI2089
HEADPIECE, PREFACE FOR THE MERRY
ADVENTURES OF ROBIN HOOD

MBPI2090
TAILPIECE, PREFACE FOR THE MERRY
ADVENTURES OF ROBIN HOOD

MBPI2091
HEADPIECE, TABLE OF CONTENTS FOR THE
MERRY ADVENTURES OF ROBIN HOOD

MBPI2092
HEADPIECE, LIST OF ILLUSTRATIONS FOR
THE MERRY ADVENTURES OF ROBIN HOOD

MBPI2093
TAILPIECE, LIST OF ILLUSTRATIONS FOR
THE MERRY ADVENTURES OF ROBIN HOOD

MBPI2094
ROBIN HOOD MEETETH THE TALL
STRANGER ON THE BRIDGE

MBPI2095
YOUNG ROBIN GOES TO THE SHOOTING
MATCH

MBPI2096
ILLUSTRATED INITIAL I FOR THE MERRY
ADVENTURES OF ROBIN HOOD

MBPI2097
TAILPIECE, PROLOGUE FOR THE MERRY
ADVENTURES OF ROBIN HOOD

MBPI2098
ROBIN AND THE TINKER AT THE BLUE
BOAR INN

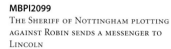

MBPI2099
THE SHERIFF OF NOTTINGHAM PLOTTING
AGAINST ROBIN SENDS A MESSENGER TO
LINCOLN

MBPI2100
ILLUSTRATED INITIAL N FOR THE MERRY
ADVENTURES OF ROBIN HOOD

MBPI2101
THE SHERIFF OF NOTTINGHAM COMETH
BEFORE THE KING AT LONDON

MBPI2102
THE AGED PALMER GIVES YOUNG DAVID OF
DONCASTER NEWS OF WILL STUTELY

MBPI2103
TAILPIECE, PART I FOR THE MERRY
ADVENTURES OF ROBIN HOOD

MBPI2104
ROBIN TURNS BUTCHER AND SELLS HIS
MEAT IN NOTTINGHAM

MBPI2105
ROBIN BUYS THE BUTCHER'S MEAT

MBPI2106
ILLUSTRATED INITIAL N FOR THE MERRY
ADVENTURES OF ROBIN HOOD

MBPI2107
LITTLE JOHN OVERCOMES ERIC O' LINCOLN

MBPI2108
THE MIGHTY FIGHT BETWIXT LITTLE
JOHN AND THE COOK

MBPI2109
THE STOUT BOUT BETWEEN LITTLE JOHN
AND ARTHUR A BLAND

MBPI2110
LITTLE JOHN KNOWETH NOT WHICH ROAD
TO TAKE

MBPI2111
ILLUSTRATED INITIAL I FOR THE MERRY
ADVENTURES OF ROBIN HOOD

MBPI2112
MERRY ROBIN STOPS A STRANGER IN
SCARLET

MBPI2113
The Four Yeomen have Merry Sport with a Stout Miller

MBPI2114
Tailpiece, Part III for The Merry Adventures of Robin Hood

MBPI2115
Allan a Dale lieth beside the Fountain

MBPI2116
Allan a Dale tells his Story

MBPI2117
Illustrated initial I for The Merry Adventures of Robin Hood

MBPI2118
The Merry Friar sings a goodly song

MBPI2119
Robin Hood steps betwixt Sir Stephen and his Bride

MBPI2120
Tailpiece, Part IV for The Merry Adventures of Robin Hood

MBPI2121
Merry Robin stops a Sorrowful Knight

MBPI2122
The young Knight of the Lea overcomes the Knight of Lancaster

MBPI2123
Illustrated initial S for The Merry Adventures of Robin Hood

MBPI2124
Sir Richard pleadeth before the Prior of Emmet

MBPI2125
Tailpiece, Part V for The Merry Adventures of Robin Hood

MBPI2126
Little John in ye guise of a Friar stops three Lasses

MBPI2127
Little John journeys in Holy Company

MBPI2128
Illustrated initial C for The Merry Adventures of Robin Hood

MBPI2129

Merry Robin clad as a Beggar stops the Corn Engrosser by the Cross nigh Ollerton

MBPI2130

Tailpiece, Part VI for The Merry Adventures of Robin Hood

MBPI2131

Allan a Dale Singeth Before Our Good Queen Eleanor

MBPI2132

Young Richard Partington cometh to seek Merry Robin Hood

MBPI2133

Illustrated initial T for The Merry Adventures of Robin Hood

MBPI2134

Stout Robin hath a narrow escape

MBPI2135

Tailpiece, Part VII for The Merry Adventures of Robin Hood

MBPI2136

Robin Hood slayeth Guy of Gisbourne

MBPI2137

Robin and Little John go their ways in search of Adventure

MBPI2138

Illustrated initial A for The Merry Adventures of Robin Hood

MBPI2139

Merry Robin hath the worst of a Bargain

MBPI2140

Tailpiece, Part VIII for The Merry Adventures of Robin Hood

MBPI2141

Robin shooteth his Last Shaft

MBPI2142

So Ye Great Reaper reapeth among the Flowers

MBPI2143

Illustrated initial A for The Merry Adventures of Robin Hood

MBPI2144

Finis for The Merry Adventures of Robin Hood

MBPI2145
COVER DESIGN FOR THE MERRY ADVENTURES OF ROBIN HOOD

MBPI2146
SPINE DESIGN FOR THE MERRY ADVENTURES OF ROBIN HOOD

MBPI2147
FRONT COVER DESIGN FOR PEPPER & SALT

MBPI2148
BACK COVER DESIGN FOR PEPPER & SALT

MBPI2149
HALF-TITLE DECORATION FOR PEPPER & SALT

MBPI2150
THIS IS THE WAY THAT ONE IN CAP AND MOTLEY STOPS FOR AWHILE ALONG THE STONY PATH OF LIFE TO MAKE YOU LAUGH

MBPI2151
TITLE PAGE DECORATION FOR PEPPER & SALT

MBPI2152
HEADPIECE, PREFACE FOR PEPPER & SALT

MBPI2153
TAILPIECE, PREFACE FOR PEPPER & SALT

MBPI2154
HEADPIECE, TABLE OF CONTENTS FOR PEPPER & SALT

MBPI2155
TAILPIECE, TABLE OF CONTENTS FOR PEPPER & SALT

MBPI2156
HEADPIECE, LIST OF ILLUSTRATIONS FOR PEPPER & SALT

MBPI2157
TAILPIECE, LIST OF ILLUSTRATIONS FOR PEPPER & SALT

MBPI2158
HOW HANS WAS CAUGHT

MBPI2159
DECORATION FOR PEPPER & SALT

MBPI2160
DECORATION FOR PEPPER & SALT

MBPI2161
DECORATION FOR PEPPER & SALT

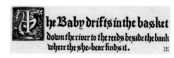

MBPI2162
DECORATION FOR PEPPER & SALT

MBPI2163
COVER DESIGN FOR THE WONDER CLOCK

MBPI2164
HALF-TITLE DECORATION FOR THE
WONDER CLOCK

MBPI2165
FRONTISPIECE FOR THE WONDER CLOCK

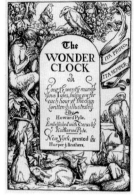

MBPI2166
TITLE PAGE DECORATION FOR THE
WONDER CLOCK

MBPI2167
HEADPIECE, PREFACE FOR THE WONDER
CLOCK

MBPI2168
ILLUSTRATED INITIAL I, PREFACE FOR THE
WONDER CLOCK

MBPI2169
HEADPIECE, TABLE OF CONTENTS FOR THE
WONDER CLOCK

MBPI2170
TAILPIECE, TABLE OF CONTENTS FOR THE
WONDER CLOCK

MBPI2171
HEADPIECE, LIST OF ILLUSTRATIONS FOR
THE WONDER CLOCK

MBPI2172
TAILPIECE, LIST OF ILLUSTRATIONS FOR
THE WONDER CLOCK

MBPI2173
ILLUSTRATED INITIAL T FOR BEARSKIN

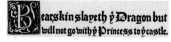

MBPI2174
ILLUSTRATED INITIAL T WITH HEADING
FOR BEARSKIN

MBPI2175
ILLUSTRATED INITIAL B WITH HEADING
FOR BEARSKIN

MBPI2176
ILLUSTRATED INITIAL O FOR THE WATER
OF LIFE

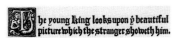

MBPI2177
ILLUSTRATED INITIAL T WITH HEADING FOR THE WATER OF LIFE

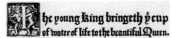

MBPI2178
ILLUSTRATED INITIAL T WITH HEADING FOR THE WATER OF LIFE

MBPI2179
ILLUSTRATED INITIAL T WITH HEADING FOR THE WATER OF LIFE

MBPI2180
ILLUSTRATED INITIAL T FOR HOW ONE TURNED HIS TROUBLE TO SOME ACCOUNT

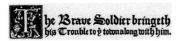

MBPI2181
ILLUSTRATED INITIAL T WITH HEADING FOR HOW ONE TURNED HIS TROUBLE TO SOME ACCOUNT

MBPI2182
ILLUSTRATED INITIAL H WITH HEADING FOR HOW ONE TURNED HIS TROUBLE TO SOME ACCOUNT

MBPI2183
ILLUSTRATED INITIAL T FOR HOW THREE WENT OUT INTO THE WIDE WORLD

MBPI2184
ILLUSTRATED INITIAL T WITH HEADING FOR HOW THREE WENT OUT INTO THE WIDE WORLD

MBPI2185
ILLUSTRATED INITIAL T WITH HEADING FOR HOW THREE WENT OUT INTO THE WIDE WORLD

MBPI2186
ILLUSTRATED INITIAL T FOR THE CLEVER STUDENT AND THE MASTER OF BLACK ARTS

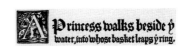

MBPI2187
ILLUSTRATED INITIAL A WITH HEADING FOR THE CLEVER STUDENT AND THE MASTER OF BLACK ARTS

MBPI2188
ILLUSTRATED INITIAL T WITH HEADING FOR THE CLEVER STUDENT AND THE MASTER OF BLACK ARTS

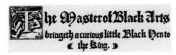

MBPI2189
ILLUSTRATED INITIAL T WITH HEADING FOR THE CLEVER STUDENT AND THE MASTER OF BLACK ARTS

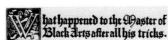

MBPI2190
ILLUSTRATED INITIAL W WITH HEADING FOR THE WONDER CLOCK

MBPI2191
DECORATION FOR THE WONDER CLOCK

MBPI2192
ILLUSTRATED INITIAL O FOR THE PRINCESS GOLDEN-HAIR AND THE GREAT BLACK RAVEN

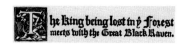

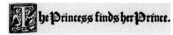

MBPI2193
ILLUSTRATED INITIAL T WITH HEADING FOR THE PRINCESS GOLDEN-HAIR AND THE GREAT BLACK RAVEN

MBPI2194
ILLUSTRATED INITIAL P WITH HEADING FOR THE PRINCESS GOLDEN-HAIR AND THE GREAT BLACK RAVEN

MBPI2195
ILLUSTRATED INITIAL P WITH HEADING FOR THE PRINCESS GOLDEN-HAIR AND THE GREAT BLACK RAVEN

MBPI2196
ILLUSTRATED INITIAL T WITH HEADING FOR THE PRINCESS GOLDEN-HAIR AND THE GREAT BLACK RAVEN

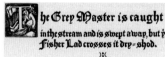

MBPI2197
ILLUSTRATED INITIAL I FOR COUSIN GREYLEGS, YE GREAT RED FOX AND GRANDFATHER MOLE

MBPI2198
ILLUSTRATED INITIAL C WITH HEADING FOR COUSIN GREYLEGS, YE GREAT RED FOX AND GRANDFATHER MOLE

MBPI2199
ILLUSTRATED INITIAL C WITH HEADING FOR COUSIN GREYLEGS, YE GREAT RED FOX AND GRANDFATHER MOLE

MBPI2200
ILLUSTRATED INITIAL O FOR ONE GOOD TURN DESERVES ANOTHER

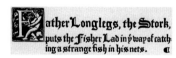

MBPI2201
ILLUSTRATED INITIAL F WITH HEADING FOR ONE GOOD TURN DESERVES ANOTHER

MBPI2202
ILLUSTRATED INITIAL T WITH HEADING FOR ONE GOOD TURN DESERVES ANOTHER

MBPI2203
ILLUSTRATED INITIAL T WITH HEADING FOR ONE GOOD TURN DESERVES ANOTHER

MBPI2204
ILLUSTRATED INITIAL T WITH HEADING FOR ONE GOOD TURN DESERVES ANOTHER

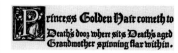

MBPI2205
ILLUSTRATED INITIAL O FOR THE WHITE BIRD

MBPI2206
ILLUSTRATED INITIAL T WITH HEADING FOR THE WHITE BIRD

MBPI2207
ILLUSTRATED INITIAL T WITH HEADING FOR THE WHITE BIRD

MBPI2208
ILLUSTRATED INITIAL T WITH HEADING FOR THE WHITE BIRD

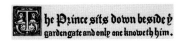

MBPI2209
ILLUSTRATED INITIAL T WITH HEADING FOR THE WHITE BIRD

MBPI2210
ILLUSTRATED INITIAL T FOR HOW THE GOOD GIFTS WERE USED BY TWO

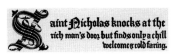

MBPI2211
ILLUSTRATED INITIAL S WITH HEADING FOR HOW THE GOOD GIFTS WERE USED BY TWO

MBPI2212
ILLUSTRATED INITIAL S WITH HEADING FOR HOW THE GOOD GIFTS WERE USED BY TWO

MBPI2213
ILLUSTRATED INITIAL T WITH HEADING FOR HOW THE GOOD GIFTS WERE USED BY TWO

MBPI2214
DECORATION FOR THE WONDER CLOCK

MBPI2215
ILLUSTRATED INITIAL O FOR HOW BOOTS BEFOOLED THE KING

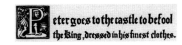

MBPI2216
ILLUSTRATED INITIAL P WITH HEADING FOR HOW BOOTS BEFOOLED THE KING

MBPI2217
ILLUSTRATED INITIAL P WITH HEADING FOR HOW BOOTS BEFOOLED THE KING

MBPI2218
ILLUSTRATED INITIAL T WITH HEADING FOR HOW BOOTS BEFOOLED THE KING

MBPI2219
ILLUSTRATED INITIAL T WITH HEADING FOR HOW BOOTS BEFOOLED THE KING

MBPI2220
DECORATION FOR THE WONDER CLOCK

MBPI2221
ILLUSTRATED INITIAL O FOR THE STEP-MOTHER

MBPI2222
ILLUSTRATED INITIAL T WITH HEADING FOR THE STEP-MOTHER

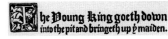

MBPI2223
ILLUSTRATED INITIAL T WITH HEADING FOR THE STEP-MOTHER

MBPI2224
ILLUSTRATED INITIAL T WITH HEADING FOR THE STEP-MOTHER

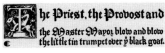

MBPI2225
ILLUSTRATED INITIAL O FOR MASTER JACOB

MBPI2226
ILLUSTRATED INITIAL M WITH HEADING FOR MASTER JACOB

MBPI2227
ILLUSTRATED INITIAL T WITH HEADING FOR MASTER JACOB

MBPI2228
ILLUSTRATED INITIAL M WITH HEADING FOR MASTER JACOB

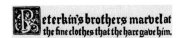

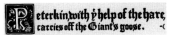

MBPI2229
ILLUSTRATED INITIAL T FOR PETERKIN AND THE LITTLE GREY HARE

MBPI2230
ILLUSTRATED INITIAL P WITH HEADING FOR PETERKIN AND THE LITTLE GREY HARE

MBPI2231
ILLUSTRATED INITIAL P WITH HEADING FOR PETERKIN AND THE LITTLE GREY HARE

MBPI2232
ILLUSTRATED INITIAL P WITH HEADING FOR PETERKIN AND THE LITTLE GREY HARE

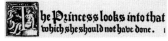

MBPI2233
ILLUSTRATED INITIAL O FOR MOTHER HILDEGARDE

MBPI2234
ILLUSTRATED INITIAL T WITH HEADING FOR MOTHER HILDEGARDE

MBPI2235
ILLUSTRATED INITIAL T WITH HEADING FOR MOTHER HILDEGARDE

MBPI2236
ILLUSTRATED INITIAL T WITH HEADING FOR MOTHER HILDEGARDE

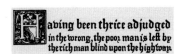

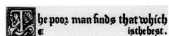

MBPI2237
ILLUSTRATED INITIAL M WITH HEADING FOR MOTHER HILDEGARDE

MBPI2238
ILLUSTRATED INITIAL T FOR WHICH IS BEST?

MBPI2239
ILLUSTRATED INITIAL H WITH HEADING FOR WHICH IS BEST?

MBPI2240
ILLUSTRATED INITIAL T WITH HEADING FOR WHICH IS BEST?

MBPI2241
ILLUSTRATED INITIAL T WITH HEADING
FOR WHICH IS BEST?

MBPI2242
DECORATION FOR THE WONDER CLOCK

MBPI2243
ILLUSTRATED INITIAL T FOR THE
SIMPLETON AND HIS LITTLE BLACK HEN

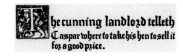

MBPI2244
ILLUSTRATED INITIAL T WITH HEADING
FOR THE SIMPLETON AND HIS LITTLE
BLACK HEN

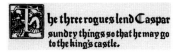

MBPI2245
ILLUSTRATED INITIAL T WITH HEADING
FOR THE SIMPLETON AND HIS LITTLE
BLACK HEN

MBPI2246
ILLUSTRATED INITIAL O FOR THE SWAN
MAIDEN

MBPI2247
ILLUSTRATED INITIAL T WITH HEADING
FOR THE SWAN MAIDEN

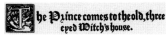

MBPI2248
ILLUSTRATED INITIAL T WITH HEADING
FOR THE SWAN MAIDEN

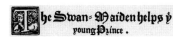

MBPI2249
ILLUSTRATED INITIAL T WITH HEADING
FOR THE SWAN MAIDEN

MBPI2250
ILLUSTRATED INITIAL T FOR THE THREE
LITTLE PIGS AND THE OGRE

MBPI2251
ILLUSTRATED INITIAL T WITH HEADING
FOR THE THREE LITTLE PIGS AND THE
OGRE

MBPI2252
ILLUSTRATED INITIAL T WITH HEADING
FOR THE THREE LITTLE PIGS AND THE
OGRE

MBPI2253
DECORATION FOR THE WONDER CLOCK

MBPI2254
ILLUSTRATED INITIAL T FOR THE STAFF
AND THE FIDDLE

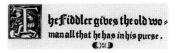

MBPI2255
ILLUSTRATED INITIAL T WITH HEADING
FOR THE STAFF AND THE FIDDLE

MBPI2256
ILLUSTRATED INITIAL T WITH HEADING
FOR THE STAFF AND THE FIDDLE

  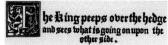

MBPI2257
ILLUSTRATED INITIAL T WITH HEADING
FOR THE STAFF AND THE FIDDLE

MBPI2258
ILLUSTRATED INITIAL T FOR HOW THE
PRINCESS'S PRIDE WAS BROKEN

MBPI2259
ILLUSTRATED INITIAL T WITH HEADING
FOR HOW THE PRINCESS'S PRIDE WAS BRO-
KEN

MBPI2260
ILLUSTRATED INITIAL T WITH HEADING
FOR HOW THE PRINCESS'S PRIDE WAS BRO-
KEN

MBPI2261
ILLUSTRATED INITIAL T FOR HOW TWO
WENT INTO PARTNERSHIP

MBPI2262
ILLUSTRATED INITIAL T WITH HEADING
FOR HOW TWO WENT INTO PARTNERSHIP

MBPI2263
ILLUSTRATED INITIAL U WITH HEADING
FOR FOR HOW TWO WENT INTO
PARTNERSHIP

MBPI2264
ILLUSTRATED INITIAL T FOR KING STORK

  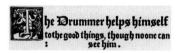

MBPI2265
ILLUSTRATED INITIAL T WITH HEADING
FOR KING STORK

MBPI2266
ILLUSTRATED INITIAL T WITH HEADING
FOR KING STORK

MBPI2267
ILLUSTRATED INITIAL T WITH HEADING
FOR KING STORK

MBPI2268
ILLUSTRATED INITIAL T FOR THE BEST
THAT LIFE HAS TO GIVE

MBPI2269
ILLUSTRATED INITIAL T WITH HEADING
FOR THE BEST THAT LIFE HAS TO GIVE

MBPI2270
ILLUSTRATED INITIAL T WITH HEADING
FOR THE BEST THAT LIFE HAS TO GIVE

MBPI2271
ILLUSTRATED INITIAL T WITH HEADING
FOR THE BEST THAT LIFE HAS TO GIVE

MBPI2272
TAILPIECE, THE END FOR THE WONDER
CLOCK

MBPI2273
Cover design for Otto of the Silver Hand

MBPI2274
Half-title decoration for Otto of the Silver Hand

MBPI2275
In the Belfry

MBPI2276
Headpiece, Contents for Otto of the Silver Hand

MBPI2277
Tailpiece, Contents for Otto of the Silver Hand

MBPI2278
Headpiece, List of Illustrations for Otto of the Silver Hand

MBPI2279
Tailpiece, List of Illustrations for Otto of the Silver Hand

MBPI2280
Headpiece, Foreword for Otto of the Silver Hand

MBPI2281
Illustrated initial B, Foreword for Otto of the Silver Hand

MBPI2282
Tailpiece, Foreword for Otto of the Silver Hand

MBPI2283
Headpiece, Chapter I for Otto of the Silver Hand

MBPI2284
Illustrated initial U for Otto of the Silver Hand

MBPI2285
There they sat, just as little children of the town might sit upon their father's doorstep

MBPI2286
Tailpiece, Chapter I for Otto of the Silver Hand

MBPI2287
Headpiece, Chapter II for Otto of the Silver Hand

MBPI2288
Illustrated initial B for Otto of the Silver Hand

MBPI2289

AWAY THEY RODE WITH CLASHING HOOFS AND RINGING ARMOR

MBPI2290

TAILPIECE, CHAPTER II FOR OTTO OF THE SILVER HAND

MBPI2291

HEADPIECE, CHAPTER III FOR OTTO OF THE SILVER HAND

MBPI2292

ILLUSTRATED INITIAL B FOR OTTO OF THE SILVER HAND

MBPI2293

NO ONE WAS WITHIN BUT OLD URSELA, WHO SAT CROONING OVER A FIRE

MBPI2294

TAILPIECE, CHAPTER III FOR OTTO OF THE SILVER HAND

MBPI2295

HEADPIECE, CHAPTER IV FOR OTTO OF THE SILVER HAND

MBPI2296

ILLUSTRATED INITIAL W FOR OTTO OF THE SILVER HAND

MBPI2297

ABBOT OTTO OF ST. MICHAELSBURG WAS A GENTLE, PATIENT, PALE-FACED OLD MAN

MBPI2298

"WHILE I LAY THERE WITH MY HORSE UPON ME, BARON FREDERICK RAN ME DOWN WITH HIS LANCE"

MBPI2299

TAILPIECE, CHAPTER IV FOR OTTO OF THE SILVER HAND

MBPI2300

HEADPIECE, CHAPTER V FOR OTTO OF THE SILVER HAND

MBPI2301

ILLUSTRATED INITIAL S FOR OTTO OF THE SILVER HAND

MBPI2302

THE POOR SIMPLE BROTHER SITTING UNDER THE PEAR TREE CLOSE TO THE BEE-HIVES, ROCKING THE LITTLE BABY IN HIS ARMS

MBPI2303

ALWAYS IT WAS ONE PICTURE THAT LITTLE OTTO SOUGHT

MBPI2304

TAILPIECE, CHAPTER V FOR OTTO OF THE SILVER HAND

MBPI2305
Headpiece, Chapter VI for Otto of the Silver Hand

MBPI2306
Illustrated initial T for Otto of the Silver Hand

MBPI2307
Poor Brother John came forward and took the boy's hand

MBPI2308
Otto lay close to her feet upon a bear-skin

MBPI2309
Tailpiece, Chapter VI for Otto of the Silver Hand

MBPI2310
Headpiece, Chapter VII for Otto of the Silver Hand

MBPI2311
Illustrated initial T for Otto of the Silver Hand

MBPI2312
The grim Baron sat silent with his chin resting upon his clenched fist

MBPI2313
Slowly raising himself upon the narrow foot-hold, he peeped cautiously within

MBPI2314
Schwartz Carl, holding his arbelast in his hand, stood silently watching

MBPI2315
He strode forward into the room and laid his hand heavily on the boy's shoulder

MBPI2316
Tailpiece, Chapter VII for Otto of the Silver Hand

MBPI2317
Headpiece, Chapter VIII for Otto of the Silver Hand

MBPI2318
Illustrated initial A for Otto of the Silver Hand

MBPI2319
"Then dost thou not know why I am here?" said the Baron

MBPI2320
Headpiece, Chapter IX for Otto of the Silver Hand

MBPI2321
ILLUSTRATED INITIAL F FOR OTTO OF THE SILVER HAND

MBPI2322
FRITZ, THE SWINEHERD, SAT EATING HIS LATE SUPPER OF PORRIDGE

MBPI2323
HANS HELD UP A NECKLACE OF BLUE AND WHITE BEADS

MBPI2324
TAILPIECE, CHAPTER IX FOR OTTO OF THE SILVER HAND

MBPI2325
HEADPIECE, CHAPTER X FOR OTTO OF THE SILVER HAND

MBPI2326
ILLUSTRATED INITIAL H FOR OTTO OF THE SILVER HAND

MBPI2327
"THOU UGLY TOAD," SAID THE WOMAN

MBPI2328
THE MAN WAS LONG JACOB, THE BOWMAN

MBPI2329
IN AN INSTANT HE WAS FLUNG BACK AND DOWN

MBPI2330
TAILPIECE, CHAPTER X FOR OTTO OF THE SILVER HAND

MBPI2331
HEADPIECE, CHAPTER XI FOR OTTO OF THE SILVER HAND

MBPI2332
ILLUSTRATED INITIAL L FOR OTTO OF THE SILVER HAND

MBPI2333
THE NEXT MOMENT THEY WERE HANGING IN MID-AIR

MBPI2334
TAILPIECE, CHAPTER XI FOR OTTO OF THE SILVER HAND

MBPI2335
HEADPIECE, CHAPTER XII FOR OTTO OF THE SILVER HAND

MBPI2336
ILLUSTRATED INITIAL B FOR OTTO OF THE SILVER HAND

MBPI2337
HE WAS GAZING STRAIGHT BEFORE HIM WITH A SET AND STONY FACE

MBPI2338
TAILPIECE, CHAPTER XII FOR OTTO OF THE SILVER HAND

MBPI2339
HEADPIECE, CHAPTER XIII FOR OTTO OF THE SILVER HAND

MBPI2340
ILLUSTRATED INITIAL A FOR OTTO OF THE SILVER HAND

MBPI2341
IN THE MIDDLE OF THE NARROW WAY STOOD THE MOTIONLESS, STEEL-CLAD FIGURE

MBPI2342
FOR A MOMENT THEY STOOD SWAYING BACKWARD AND FORWARD

MBPI2343
TAILPIECE, CHAPTER XIII FOR OTTO OF THE SILVER HAND

MBPI2344
HEADPIECE, CHAPTER XIV FOR OTTO OF THE SILVER HAND

MBPI2345
ILLUSTRATED INITIAL T FOR OTTO OF THE SILVER HAND

MBPI2346
IT WAS THE GREAT EMPEROR RUDOLPH

MBPI2347
TAILPIECE, CHAPTER XIV FOR OTTO OF THE SILVER HAND

MBPI2348
HE TOOK HER HAND AND SET IT TO HIS LIPS

MBPI2349
HEADPIECE, AFTERWORD FOR OTTO OF THE SILVER HAND

MBPI2350
ILLUSTRATED INITIAL T FOR OTTO OF THE SILVER HAND

MBPI2351
COVER DESIGN FOR MEN OF IRON

MBPI2352
"ENTER OLIVER AND MADEMOISELLE CELESTE"

MBPI2353

Cover design for The Garden Behind the Moon

MBPI2354

In the garden behind the moon

MBPI2355

Headband for The Garden Behind the Moon

MBPI2356

Headband, Illustrations for The Garden Behind the Moon

MBPI2357

Headpiece, Foreword for The Garden Behind the Moon

MBPI2358

Tailpiece, Foreword for The Garden Behind the Moon

MBPI2359

Headpiece, Chapter I for The Garden Behind the Moon

MBPI2360

Headband, Chapter II for The Garden Behind the Moon

MBPI2361

Headband, Chapter III for The Garden Behind the Moon

MBPI2362

Headband, Chapter IV for The Garden Behind the Moon

MBPI2363

David looked up into Hans Krout's face

MBPI2364

Headband, Chapter V for The Garden Behind the Moon

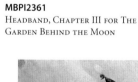

MBPI2365

Suddenly a half-door opened and there stood a little man

MBPI2366

Headband, Chapter VI for The Garden Behind the Moon

MBPI2367

David sat down on the wooden bench and took up a big blue star

MBPI2368

Headband, Chapter VII for The Garden Behind the Moon

MBPI2369
He was standing at an open window

MBPI2370
"Where did you come from, little boy?" she said

MBPI2371
Headband, Chapter VIII for The Garden Behind the Moon

MBPI2372
Headband, Chapter IX for The Garden Behind the Moon

MBPI2373
Headband, Chapter X for The Garden Behind the Moon

MBPI2374
Headband, Chapter XI for The Garden Behind the Moon

MBPI2375
Headband, Chapter XII for The Garden Behind the Moon

MBPI2376
Quick as a flash, David leaped out and upon it

MBPI2377
Headband, Chapter XIII for The Garden Behind the Moon

MBPI2378
Headband, Chapter XIV for The Garden Behind the Moon

MBPI2379
Headband, Chapter XV for The Garden Behind the Moon

MBPI2380
Fast flew the black winged horse

MBPI2381
Headband, Chapter XVI for The Garden Behind the Moon

MBPI2382
The giant fell crashing upon the stones

MBPI2383
Cover design for Stops of Various Quills

MBPI2384
Headband, Chapter XVIII for The Garden Behind the Moon

MBPI2385
HEADBAND, CHAPTER XIX FOR THE
GARDEN BEHIND THE MOON

MBPI2386
SHE PLACED HER HANDS ON HIS SHOUL-
DERS

MBPI2387
COVER DESIGN FOR TWILIGHT LAND

MBPI2388
ITA PRIMO ITA SEMPER

MBPI2389
DEDICATION FOR TWILIGHT LAND

MBPI2390
HEADPIECE, TABLE OF CONTENTS FOR
TWILIGHT LAND

MBPI2391
HEADPIECE WITH ILLUSTRATED INITIAL I,
INTRODUCTION FOR TWILIGHT LAND

MBPI2392
TITLE PAGE DECORATION FOR FIRST YEAR
BOOK OF THE BIBLIOPHILE SOCIETY

MBPI2393
THE BIBLIOPHILE

MBPI2394
COVER DESIGN FOR THE STORY OF KING
ARTHUR AND HIS KNIGHTS

MBPI2395
SPINE DESIGN FOR THE STORY OF KING
ARTHUR AND HIS KNIGHTS

MBPI2396
TITLE PAGE DECORATION FOR THE STORY
OF KING ARTHUR AND HIS KNIGHTS

MBPI2397
TAILPIECE, FOREWORD FOR THE STORY OF
KING ARTHUR AND HIS KNIGHTS

MBPI2398
TAILPIECE, CONTENTS FOR THE STORY OF
KING ARTHUR AND HIS KNIGHTS

MBPI2399
TAILPIECE, LIST OF ILLUSTRATIONS FOR
THE STORY OF KING ARTHUR AND HIS
KNIGHTS

MBPI2400
SUBTITLE PAGE DECORATION FOR THE
STORY OF KING ARTHUR AND HIS
KNIGHTS

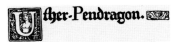

MBPI2401
Illustrated initial U with heading for The Story of King Arthur and His Knights

MBPI2402
Uther-Pendragon

MBPI2403
Tailpiece, Prologue for The Story of King Arthur and His Knights

MBPI2404
Tailpiece for The Story of King Arthur and His Knights

MBPI2405
Tailpiece for The Story of King Arthur and His Knights

MBPI2406
Tailpiece for The Story of King Arthur and His Knights

MBPI2407
Tailpiece for The Story of King Arthur and His Knights

MBPI2408
Illustrated initial T with heading for The Story of King Arthur and His Knights

MBPI2409
The Lady of Ye Lake

MBPI2410
Tailpiece for The Story of King Arthur and His Knights

MBPI2411
Illustrated initial T with heading for The Story of King Arthur and His Knights

MBPI2412
The Enchantress Vivien

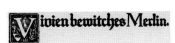

MBPI2413
Illustrated initial V with heading for The Story of King Arthur and His Knights

MBPI2414
Vivien bewitches Merlin

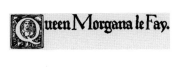

MBPI2415
Illustrated initial Q with heading for The Story of King Arthur and His Knights

MBPI2416
Queen Morgana le Fay

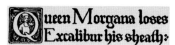

MBPI2417
ILLUSTRATED INITIAL Q WITH HEADING FOR THE STORY OF KING ARTHUR AND HIS KNIGHTS

MBPI2418
QUEEN MORGANA LOSES EXCALIBUR HIS SHEATH

MBPI2419
TAILPIECE FOR THE STORY OF KING ARTHUR AND HIS KNIGHTS

MBPI2420
TAILPIECE FOR THE STORY OF KING ARTHUR AND HIS KNIGHTS

MBPI2421
ILLUSTRATED INITIAL S WITH HEADING FOR THE STORY OF KING ARTHUR AND HIS KNIGHTS

MBPI2422
SIR GAWAINE THE SON OF LOT, KING OF ORKNEY

MBPI2423
HEADPIECE FOR THE STORY OF KING ARTHUR AND HIS KNIGHTS

MBPI2424
ILLUSTRATED INITIAL K WITH HEADING FOR THE STORY OF KING ARTHUR AND HIS KNIGHTS

MBPI2425
KING ARTHUR FINDETH YE OLD WOMAN IN YE HUT

MBPI2426
ILLUSTRATED INITIAL S WITH HEADING FOR THE STORY OF KING ARTHUR AND HIS KNIGHTS

MBPI2427
SIR GAWAINE FINDS THE BEAUTIFUL LADY

MBPI2428
TAILPIECE FOR THE STORY OF KING ARTHUR AND HIS KNIGHTS

MBPI2429
COVER DESIGN FOR THE STORY OF CHAMPIONS OF THE ROUND TABLE

MBPI2430
SPINE DESIGN FOR THE STORY OF THE CHAMPIONS OF THE ROUND TABLE

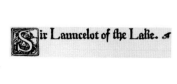

MBPI2431
ILLUSTRATED INITIAL S WITH HEADING FOR THE STORY OF THE CHAMPIONS OF THE ROUND TABLE

MBPI2432
SIR LAUNCELOT OF THE LAKE

MBPI2433
Headpiece, Foreword for The Story of the Champions of the Round Table

MBPI2434
Tailpiece, Foreword for The Story of the Champions of the Round Table

MBPI2435
Headpiece, Contents for The Story of the Champions of the Round Table

MBPI2436
Tailpiece, Contents for The Story of the Champions of the Round Table

MBPI2437
Headpiece, List of Illustrations for The Story of the Champions of the Round Table

MBPI2438
Tailpiece, List of Illustrations for The Story of the Champions of the Round Table

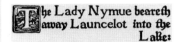

MBPI2439
Illustrated initial T with heading for The Story of the Champions of the Round Table

MBPI2440
The Lady Nymue beareth away Launcelot into the Lake

MBPI2441
Headpiece for The Story of the Champions of the Round Table

MBPI2442
Tailpiece for The Story of the Champions of the Round Table

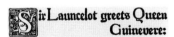

MBPI2443
Illustrated initial S with heading for The Story of the Champions of the Round Table

MBPI2444
Sir Launcelot greets Queen Guinevere

MBPI2445
Headpiece for The Story of the Champions of the Round Table

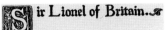

MBPI2446
Illustrated initial S with heading for The Story of the Champions of the Round Table

MBPI2447
Sir Lionel of Britain

MBPI2448
Illustrated initial Q with heading for The Story of the Champions of the Round Table

MBPI2449
QUEEN MORGANA APPEARS UNTO SIR LAUNCELOT

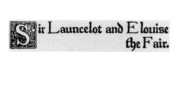

MBPI2450
ILLUSTRATED INITIAL S WITH HEADING FOR THE STORY OF THE CHAMPIONS OF THE ROUND TABLE

MBPI2451
SIR LAUNCELOT DOETH BATTLE WITH SIR TURQUINE

MBPI2452
ILLUSTRATED INITIAL S WITH HEADING FOR THE STORY OF THE CHAMPIONS OF THE ROUND TABLE

MBPI2453
SIR LAUNCELOT SITS WITH SIR HILAIRE AND CROISETTE

MBPI2454
ILLUSTRATED INITIAL S WITH HEADING FOR THE STORY OF THE CHAMPIONS OF THE ROUND TABLE

MBPI2455
SIR LAUNCELOT AND ELOUISE THE FAIR

MBPI2456
ILLUSTRATED INITIAL S WITH HEADING FOR THE STORY OF THE CHAMPIONS OF THE ROUND TABLE

MBPI2457
SIR LAUNCELOT CLIMBS TO CATCH THE LADY'S FALCON

MBPI2458
ILLUSTRATED INITIAL S WITH HEADING FOR THE STORY OF THE CHAMPIONS OF THE ROUND TABLE

MBPI2459
SIR LAUNCELOT TAKES THE ARMOR OF SIR KAY

MBPI2460
TAILPIECE FOR THE STORY OF THE CHAMPIONS OF THE ROUND TABLE

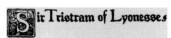

MBPI2461
ILLUSTRATED INITIAL S WITH HEADING FOR THE STORY OF THE CHAMPIONS OF THE ROUND TABLE

MBPI2462
SIR TRISTRAM OF LYONESSE

MBPI2463
HEADPIECE FOR THE STORY OF THE CHAMPIONS OF THE ROUND TABLE

MBPI2464
TAILPIECE FOR THE STORY OF THE CHAMPIONS OF THE ROUND TABLE

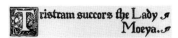

MBPI2465
ILLUSTRATED INITIAL T WITH HEADING
FOR THE STORY OF THE CHAMPIONS OF
THE ROUND TABLE

MBPI2466
TRISTRAM SUCCORS THE LADY MOEYA

MBPI2467
HEADPIECE FOR THE STORY OF THE
CHAMPIONS OF THE ROUND TABLE

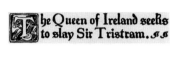

MBPI2468
ILLUSTRATED INITIAL K WITH HEADING
FOR THE STORY OF THE CHAMPIONS OF
THE ROUND TABLE

MBPI2469
KING MARK OF CORNWALL

MBPI2470
ILLUSTRATED INITIAL T WITH HEADING
FOR THE STORY OF THE CHAMPIONS OF
THE ROUND TABLE

MBPI2471
THE LADY BELLE ISOULT

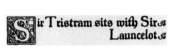

MBPI2472
ILLUSTRATED INITIAL T WITH HEADING
FOR THE STORY OF THE CHAMPIONS OF
THE ROUND TABLE

MBPI2473
THE QUEEN OF IRELAND SEEKS TO SLAY
SIR TRISTRAM

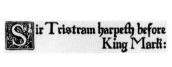

MBPI2474
ILLUSTRATED INITIAL S WITH HEADING
FOR THE STORY OF THE CHAMPIONS OF
THE ROUND TABLE

MBPI2475
SIR TRISTRAM HARPETH BEFORE KING
MARK

MBPI2476
ILLUSTRATED INITIAL S WITH HEADING
FOR THE STORY OF THE CHAMPIONS OF
THE ROUND TABLE

MBPI2477
SIR TRISTRAM SITS WITH SIR LAUNCELOT

MBPI2478
TAILPIECE FOR THE STORY OF THE
CHAMPIONS OF THE ROUND TABLE

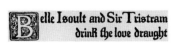

MBPI2479
ILLUSTRATED INITIAL B WITH HEADING
FOR THE STORY OF THE CHAMPIONS OF
THE ROUND TABLE

MBPI2480
BELLE ISOULT AND SIR TRISTRAM DRINK
THE LOVE DRAUGHT

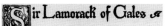

MBPI2481

TAILPIECE FOR THE STORY OF THE CHAMPIONS OF THE ROUND TABLE

MBPI2482

ILLUSTRATED INITIAL S WITH HEADING FOR THE STORY OF THE CHAMPIONS OF THE ROUND TABLE

MBPI2483

SIR LAMORACK OF GALES

MBPI2484

HEADPIECE FOR THE STORY OF THE CHAMPIONS OF THE ROUND TABLE

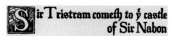

MBPI2485

ILLUSTRATED INITIAL S WITH HEADING FOR THE STORY OF THE CHAMPIONS OF THE ROUND TABLE

MBPI2486

SIR TRISTRAM COMETH TO YE CASTLE OF SIR NABON

MBPI2487

ILLUSTRATED INITIAL S WITH HEADING FOR THE STORY OF THE CHAMPIONS OF THE ROUND TABLE

MBPI2488

SIR LAMORACK HERDS THE SWINE OF SIR NABON

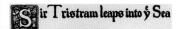

MBPI2489

TAILPIECE FOR THE STORY OF THE CHAMPIONS OF THE ROUND TABLE

MBPI2490

ILLUSTRATED INITIAL S WITH HEADING FOR THE STORY OF THE CHAMPIONS OF THE ROUND TABLE

MBPI2491

SIR TRISTRAM ASSAULTS KING MARK

MBPI2492

HEADPIECE FOR THE STORY OF THE CHAMPIONS OF THE ROUND TABLE

MBPI2493

ILLUSTRATED INITIAL S WITH HEADING FOR THE STORY OF THE CHAMPIONS OF THE ROUND TABLE

MBPI2494

SIR KAY AND THE FOREST MADMAN

MBPI2495

ILLUSTRATED INITIAL S WITH HEADING FOR THE STORY OF THE CHAMPIONS OF THE ROUND TABLE

MBPI2496

SIR TRISTRAM LEAPS INTO YE SEA

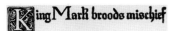

MBPI2497
ILLUSTRATED INITIAL K WITH HEADING
FOR THE STORY OF THE CHAMPIONS OF
THE ROUND TABLE

MBPI2498
KING MARK BROODS MISCHIEF

MBPI2499
TAILPIECE FOR THE STORY OF THE
CHAMPIONS OF THE ROUND TABLE

MBPI2500
HENDRYK HUDSON AND THE HALF-MOON

MBPI2501
PETER STUYVESANT AND THE ENGLISH
FLEET

MBPI2502
LIFE IN AN OLD DUTCH TOWN

MBPI2503
DUTCH SOLDIER

MBPI2504
ENGLISH SOLDIER

MBPI2505
SPRING

MBPI2506
THE GARDEN OF YOUTH

MBPI2507
THE MIDSUMMER MOON

MBPI2508
THE ENCHANTED SEAS

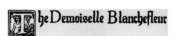

MBPI2509
ILLUSTRATED INITIAL T WITH HEADING
FOR THE STORY OF THE CHAMPIONS OF
THE ROUND TABLE

MBPI2510
THE DEMOISELLE BLANCHEFLEUR

MBPI2511
MAROONED

MBPI2512
THE MERMAID

MBPI2513

TAILPIECE FOR THE STORY OF THE CHAMPIONS OF THE ROUND TABLE

MBPI2514

COVER DESIGN FOR THE STORY OF SIR LAUNCELOT AND HIS COMPANIONS

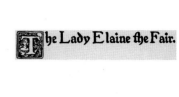

MBPI2515

SPINE DESIGN FOR THE STORY OF SIR LAUNCELOT AND HIS COMPANIONS

MBPI2516

ILLUSTRATED INITIAL T WITH HEADING FOR THE STORY OF SIR LAUNCELOT AND HIS COMPANIONS

MBPI2517

THE LADY ELAINE THE FAIR

MBPI2518

HEADPIECE, FOREWORD FOR THE STORY OF SIR LAUNCELOT AND HIS COMPANIONS

MBPI2519

TAILPIECE, FOREWORD FOR THE STORY OF SIR LAUNCELOT AND HIS COMPANIONS

MBPI2520

HEADPIECE, CONTENTS FOR THE STORY OF SIR LAUNCELOT AND HIS COMPANIONS

MBPI2521

TAILPIECE, CONTENTS FOR THE STORY OF SIR LAUNCELOT AND HIS COMPANIONS

MBPI2522

HEADPIECE, LIST OF ILLUSTRATIONS FOR THE STORY OF SIR LAUNCELOT AND HIS COMPANIONS

MBPI2523

TAILPIECE, LIST OF ILLUSTRATIONS FOR THE STORY OF SIR LAUNCELOT AND HIS COMPANIONS

MBPI2524

ILLUSTRATED INITIAL S WITH HEADING FOR THE STORY OF SIR LAUNCELOT AND HIS COMPANIONS

MBPI2525

SIR MELLEGRANS INTERRUPTS THE SPORT OF THE QUEEN

MBPI2526

HEADPIECE FOR THE STORY OF SIR LAUNCELOT AND HIS COMPANIONS

MBPI2527

TAILPIECE FOR THE STORY OF SIR LAUNCELOT AND HIS COMPANIONS

MBPI2528

ILLUSTRATED INITIAL D WITH HEADING FOR THE STORY OF SIR LAUNCELOT AND HIS COMPANIONS

MBPI2529
Denneys and the Hermit help Sir
Launcelot to his armor

MBPI2530
Headpiece for The Story of Sir
Launcelot and his Companions

MBPI2531
Illustrated initial H with heading
for The Story of Sir Launcelot and
his Companions

MBPI2532
How Sir Launcelot rode errant in a
cart

MBPI2533
Illustrated initial T with heading
for The Story of Sir Launcelot and
his Companions

MBPI2534
The Damsel Elose the Fair rescues Sir
Launcelot

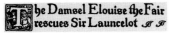

MBPI2535
Illustrated initial S with heading
for The Story of Sir Launcelot and
his Companions

MBPI2536
Sir Gareth of Orkney

MBPI2537
Headpiece for The Story of Sir
Launcelot and his Companions

MBPI2538
Illustrated initial T with heading
for The Story of Sir Launcelot and
his Companions

MBPI2539
The Damsel Lynette

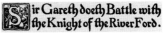

MBPI2540
Illustrated initial S with heading
for The Story of Sir Launcelot and
his Companions

MBPI2541
Sir Gareth doeth Battle with the
Knight of the River Ford

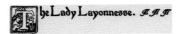

MBPI2542
Illustrated initial T with heading
for The Story of Sir Launcelot and
his Companions

MBPI2543
The Lady Layonnesse

MBPI2544
Illustrated initial T with heading
for The Story of Sir Launcelot and
his Companions

MBPI2545

THE LADY LAYONNESSE COMETH TO THE PAVILION OF SIR GARETH

MBPI2546

TAILPIECE FOR THE STORY OF SIR LAUNCELOT AND HIS COMPANIONS

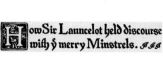

MBPI2547

ILLUSTRATED INITIAL H WITH HEADING FOR THE STORY OF SIR LAUNCELOT AND HIS COMPANIONS

MBPI2548

HOW SIR LAUNCELOT HELD DISCOURSE WITH YE MERRY MINSTRELS

MBPI2549

HEADPIECE FOR THE STORY OF SIR LAUNCELOT AND HIS COMPANIONS

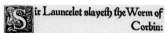

MBPI2550

ILLUSTRATED INITIAL S WITH HEADING FOR THE STORY OF SIR LAUNCELOT AND HIS COMPANIONS

MBPI2551

SIR LAUNCELOT SLAYETH THE WORM OF CORBIN

MBPI2552

ILLUSTRATED INITIAL S WITH HEADING FOR THE STORY OF SIR LAUNCELOT AND HIS COMPANIONS

MBPI2553

SIR LAUNCELOT CONFIDETH HIS SHIELD TO ELAINE THE FAIR

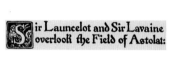

MBPI2554

ILLUSTRATED INITIAL S WITH HEADING FOR THE STORY OF SIR LAUNCELOT AND HIS COMPANIONS

MBPI2555

SIR LAUNCELOT AND SIR LAVAINE OVERLOOK THE FIELD OF ASTOLAT

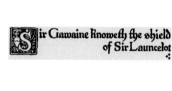

MBPI2556

ILLUSTRATED INITIAL S WITH HEADING FOR THE STORY OF SIR LAUNCELOT AND HIS COMPANIONS

MBPI2557

SIR GAWAINE KNOWETH THE SHIELD OF SIR LAUNCELOT

MBPI2558

ILLUSTRATED INITIAL S WITH HEADING FOR THE STORY OF SIR LAUNCELOT AND HIS COMPANIONS

MBPI2559

SIR LAUNCELOT LEAPETH FROM THE WINDOW

MBPI2560

TAILPIECE FOR THE STORY OF SIR LAUNCELOT AND HIS COMPANIONS

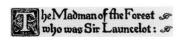

MBPI2561

ILLUSTRATED INITIAL T WITH HEADING for THE STORY OF SIR LAUNCELOT AND HIS COMPANIONS

MBPI2562

THE MADMAN OF THE FOREST WHO WAS SIR LAUNCELOT

MBPI2563

HEADPIECE FOR THE STORY OF SIR LAUNCELOT AND HIS COMPANIONS

MBPI2564

ILLUSTRATED INITIAL T WITH HEADING for THE STORY OF SIR LAUNCELOT AND HIS COMPANIONS

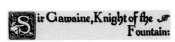

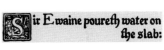

MBPI2565

THE FOREST MADMAN SAVETH YE LIFE OF KING ARTHUR

MBPI2566

ILLUSTRATED INITIAL T WITH HEADING for THE STORY OF SIR LAUNCELOT AND HIS COMPANIONS

MBPI2567

THE LADY ELAINE THE FAIR KNOWETH SIR LAUNCELOT

MBPI2568

TAILPIECE FOR THE STORY OF SIR LAUNCELOT AND HIS COMPANIONS

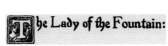

MBPI2569

ILLUSTRATED INITIAL S WITH HEADING for THE STORY OF SIR LAUNCELOT AND HIS COMPANIONS

MBPI2570

SIR GAWAINE, KNIGHT OF THE FOUNTAIN

MBPI2571

HEADPIECE FOR THE STORY OF SIR LAUNCELOT AND HIS COMPANIONS

MBPI2572

ILLUSTRATED INITIAL S WITH HEADING for THE STORY OF SIR LAUNCELOT AND HIS COMPANIONS

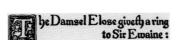

MBPI2573

SIR EWAINE POURETH WATER ON THE SLAB

MBPI2574

ILLUSTRATED INITIAL T WITH HEADING for THE STORY OF SIR LAUNCELOT AND HIS COMPANIONS

MBPI2575

THE DAMSEL ELOSE GIVETH A RING TO SIR EWAINE

MBPI2576

ILLUSTRATED INITIAL T WITH HEADING for THE STORY OF SIR LAUNCELOT AND HIS COMPANIONS

MBPI2577
The Lady of the Fountain

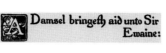

MBPI2578
Illustrated initial A with heading for The Story of Sir Launcelot and his Companions

MBPI2579
A Damsel bringeth aid unto Sir Ewaine

MBPI2580
Tailpiece for The Story of Sir Launcelot and his Companions

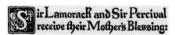

MBPI2581
Illustrated initial S with heading for The Story of Sir Launcelot and his Companions

MBPI2582
Sir Lamorack and Sir Percival receive their Mother's Blessing

MBPI2583
Headpiece for The Story of Sir Launcelot and his Companions

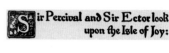

MBPI2584
Illustrated initial S with heading for The Story of Sir Launcelot and his Companions

MBPI2585
Sir Percival and Sir Ector look upon the Isle of Joy

MBPI2586
Illustrated initial S with heading for The Story of Sir Launcelot and his Companions

MBPI2587
Sir Lavaine the Son of Pelles

MBPI2588
Illustrated initial M with heading for The Story of Sir Launcelot and his Companions

MBPI2589
Merlin Prophesieth from a Cloud of Mist

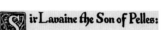

MBPI2590
Headpiece for The Story of Sir Launcelot and his Companions

MBPI2591
Illustrated initial S with heading for The Story of Sir Launcelot and his Companions

MBPI2592
Sir Bors de Ganis, the good

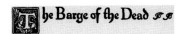   

MBPI2593
ILLUSTRATED INITIAL T WITH HEADING FOR THE STORY OF SIR LAUNCELOT AND HIS COMPANIONS

MBPI2594
THE BARGE OF THE DEAD

MBPI2595
COVER DESIGN FOR THE STORY OF THE GRAIL AND THE PASSING OF ARTHUR

MBPI2596
SPINE DESIGN FOR THE STORY OF THE GRAIL AND THE PASSING OF ARTHUR

MBPI2597
ILLUSTRATED INITIAL S WITH HEADING FOR THE STORY OF THE GRAIL AND THE PASSING OF ARTHUR

MBPI2598
SIR GALAHAD OF THE GRAIL

MBPI2599
HEADPIECE, FOREWORD FOR THE STORY OF THE GRAIL AND THE PASSING OF ARTHUR

MBPI2600
TAILPIECE FOR THE STORY OF THE GRAIL AND THE PASSING OF ARTHUR

MBPI2601
HEADPIECE, CONTENTS FOR THE STORY OF THE GRAIL AND THE PASSING OF ARTHUR

MBPI2602
TAILPIECE, CONTENTS FOR THE STORY OF THE GRAIL AND THE PASSING OF ARTHUR

MBPI2603
HEADPIECE, LIST OF ILLUSTRATIONS FOR THE STORY OF THE GRAIL AND THE PASSING OF ARTHUR

MBPI2604
TAILPIECE, LIST OF ILLUSTRATIONS FOR THE STORY OF THE GRAIL AND THE PASSING OF ARTHUR

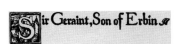   

MBPI2605
ILLUSTRATED INITIAL S WITH HEADING FOR THE STORY OF THE GRAIL AND THE PASSING OF ARTHUR

MBPI2606
SIR GERAINT, SON OF ERBIN

MBPI2607
HEADPIECE FOR THE STORY OF THE GRAIL AND THE PASSING OF ARTHUR

MBPI2608
TAILPIECE FOR THE STORY OF THE GRAIL AND THE PASSING OF ARTHUR

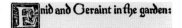

MBPI2609
Illustrated initial E with heading for The Story of the Grail and the Passing of Arthur

MBPI2610
Enid and Geraint in the garden

MBPI2611
Headpiece for The Story of the Grail and the Passing of Arthur

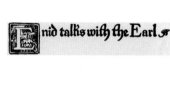

MBPI2612
Illustrated initial S with heading for The Story of the Grail and the Passing of Arthur

MBPI2613
Sir Geraint and the Knight of the Sparrowhawk

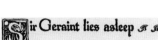

MBPI2614
Illustrated initial S with heading for The Story of the Grail and the Passing of Arthur

MBPI2615
Sir Geraint lies asleep

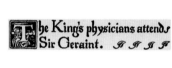

MBPI2616
Illustrated initial E with heading for The Story of the Grail and the Passing of Arthur

MBPI2617
Enid talks with the Earl

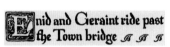

MBPI2618
Illustrated initial E with heading for The Story of the Grail and the Passing of Arthur

MBPI2619
Enid and Geraint ride past the Town bridge

MBPI2620
Illustrated initial T with heading for The Story of the Grail and the Passing of Arthur

MBPI2621
The King's Physicians attend Sir Geraint

MBPI2622
Spine design for Stops of Various Quills

MBPI2623
Illustrated initial S with heading for The Story of the Grail and the Passing of Arthur

MBPI2624
Sir Galahad cometh with the Hermit of the Forest

MBPI2625
Headpiece for The Story of the Grail and the Passing of Arthur

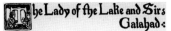

MBPI2626
Illustrated initial T with heading for The Story of the Grail and the Passing of Arthur

MBPI2627
The Lady of the Lake and Sir Galahad

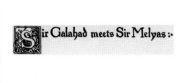

MBPI2628
Illustrated initial S with heading for The Story of the Grail and the Passing of Arthur

MBPI2629
Sir Galahad meets Sir Melyas

MBPI2630
Illustrated initial T with heading for The Story of the Grail and the Passing of Arthur

MBPI2631
The Grail is manifested, and Sir Launcelot sleepeth

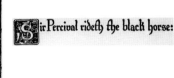

MBPI2632
Illustrated initial S with heading for The Story of the Grail and the Passing of Arthur

MBPI2633
Sir Percival rideth the black horse

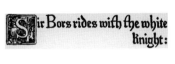

MBPI2634
Illustrated initial S with heading for The Story of the Grail and the Passing of Arthur

MBPI2635
Sir Bors rides with the white knight

MBPI2636
Illustrated initial S with heading for The Story of the Grail and the Passing of Arthur

MBPI2637
Sir Galahad rides with the Lady

MBPI2638
Illustrated initial T with heading for The Story of the Grail and the Passing of Arthur

MBPI2639
The Queen's pages clothe Sir Launcelot

MBPI2640
Headpiece for The Story of the Grail and the Passing of Arthur

MBPI2641
Illustrated initial S with heading for The Story of the Grail and the Passing of Arthur

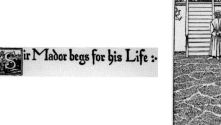

MBPI2642
Sir Mador de la Porte

MBPI2643
Illustrated initial S with heading for The Story of the Grail and the Passing of Arthur

MBPI2644
Sir Mador begs for his Life

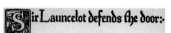

MBPI2645
Illustrated initial S with heading for The Story of the Grail and the Passing of Arthur

MBPI2646
Sir Launcelot defends the door

MBPI2647
Illustrated initial T with heading for The Story of the Grail and the Passing of Arthur

MBPI2648
The Bishop of Rochester and the King

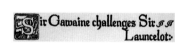

MBPI2649
Illustrated initial S with heading for The Story of the Grail and the Passing of Arthur

MBPI2650
Sir Gawaine challenges Sir Launcelot

MBPI2651
Illustrated initial T with heading for The Story of the Grail and the Passing of Arthur

MBPI2652
The Passing of Sir Gawaine

MBPI2653
Illustrated initial S with heading for The Story of the Grail and the Passing of Arthur

MBPI2654
Sir Mordred the traitor

MBPI2655
Illustrated initial T with heading for The Story of the Grail and the Passing of Arthur

MBPI2656
The Passing of Arthur

MBPI2657

ILLUSTRATED INITIAL T WITH HEADING
FOR THE STORY OF THE GRAIL AND THE
PASSING OF ARTHUR

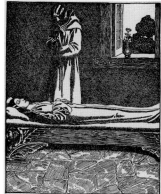

MBPI2658

THE PASSING OF GUINEVERE

MBPI2659

TAILPIECE FOR THE STORY OF THE GRAIL
AND THE PASSING OF ARTHUR

MBPI2660

ILLUSTRATION FOR MCGUFFEY'S FIFTH
ECLECTIC READER

MBPI2661

ILLUSTRATION FOR MCGUFFEY'S FIFTH
ECLECTIC READER

MBPI2662

THE QUACK

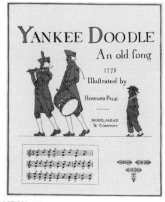

MBPI2663

FRONT COVER DESIGN FOR YANKEE
DOODLE

MBPI2664

FRONTISPIECE FOR YANKEE DOODLE

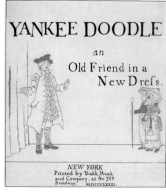

MBPI2665

TITLE PAGE ILLUSTRATION FOR YANKEE
DOODLE

MBPI2666

FATHER AND I WENT DOWN TO CAMP…

MBPI2667

THERE WAS CAPTAIN WASHINGTON…

MBPI2668

AND THEN THE FEATHERS IN HIS HAT…

MBPI2669

ILLUSTRATION FOR YANKEE DOODLE

MBPI2670

MY JEMIMA.

MBPI2671

AND THEN THEY HAD A SWAMPIN GUN…

MBPI2672

AND EVERY TIME THEY FIRED IT OFF…

MBPI2673
ILLUSTRATION FOR YANKEE DOODLE

MBPI2674
IT MADE A NOISE LIKE FATHER'S GUN…

MBPI2675
I WENT AS NEAR TO IT MYSELF…

MBPI2676
ILLUSTRATION FOR YANKEE DOODLE

MBPI2677
COUSIN SIMON GREW SO BOLD…

MBPI2678
IT SCARED ME SO I SHRINKED OFF…

MBPI2679
AND THERE I SEE A PUMPKIN SHELL…

MBPI2680
ILLUSTRATION FOR YANKEE DOODLE

MBPI2681
AND EVERY TIME THEY TOUCHED IT OFF…

MBPI2682
AND THERE I SEE A LITTLE KEG…

MBPI2683
AND THEN THEY'D FIFE AWAY LIKE FUN…

MBPI2684
AND SOME HAD RIBBONS RED AS BLOOD…

MBPI2685
ILLUSTRATION FOR YANKEE DOODLE

MBPI2686
THE TROOPERS, TOO, WOULD GALLOP UP…

MBPI2687
OLD UNCLE SAM COME THEN TO
CHANGE…

MBPI2688
ILLUSTRATION FOR YANKEE DOODLE

MBPI2689

FOR 'LASSES CAKE, TO CARRY HOME…

MBPI2690

I SEE ANOTHER SNARL OF MEN…

MBPI2691

IT SCARED ME SO, I HOOKED IT OFF…

MBPI2692

NOR TURNED ABOUT TILL I GOT HOME…

MBPI2693

ILLUSTRATION FOR YANKEE DOODLE

MBPI2694

BACK COVER DESIGN FOR YANKEE DOODLE

MBPI2695

DECORATIVE ILLUSTRATIONS FOR THE LADY OF SHALOTT

MBPI2696

DECORATIVE ILLUSTRATIONS FOR THE LADY OF SHALOTT

MBPI2697

TITLE PAGE DECORATION FOR THE LADY OF SHALOTT

MBPI2698

DECORATIVE ILLUSTRATION FOR THE LADY OF SHALOTT

MBPI2699

PART I FOR THE LADY OF SHALOTT

MBPI2700

A DESCRIPTION OF THE CASTLE

MBPI2701

THE PEOPLE PASSING THE ISLAND

MBPI2702

THE FAIRY LADY OF SHALOTT IN THE SPACE OF FLOWERS

MBPI2703

A DESCRIPTION OF THE SAME

MBPI2704

THE BOATS PASSING ALONG THE RIVER

MBPI2705

Illustration for The Lady of Shalott

MBPI2706

Decorative illustrations for The Lady of Shalott

MBPI2707

How the Reapers Hear Her Singing

MBPI2708

The Weary Reapers Beneath the Moon Hear Her Singing

MBPI2709

Part II for The Lady of Shalott

MBPI2710

How the Lady Weaveth Day by Day

MBPI2711

What She Sees in the Mirror

MBPI2712

Still the Poem Speaketh of the Sights Within the Mirror

MBPI2713

All These Things She Weaveth Into the Web

MBPI2714

Illustration for The Lady of Shalott

MBPI2715

Part III for The Lady of Shalott

MBPI2716

In This Verse is Spoken of the Coming of Sir Lancelot the Bold

MBPI2717

This Verse Speaketh Also of Lancelot the Bold

MBPI2718

The Third Verse Describeth Also the Coming of the Bold Knight

MBPI2719

The Fourth Verse Describing the Gallant Knight Sir Lancelot the Bold

MBPI2720

Illustration for The Lady of Shalott

MBPI2721

DECORATIVE ILLUSTRATION FOR THE LADY OF SHALOTT

MBPI2722

THE LADY BRINGS THE CURSE UPON HER

MBPI2723

ILLUSTRATION FOR THE LADY OF SHALOTT

MBPI2724

PART IV FOR THE LADY OF SHALOTT

MBPI2725

IN WHICH THE FAIRY LADY SEEKS THE RIVER

MBPI2726

ILLUSTRATION FOR THE LADY OF SHALOTT

MBPI2727

DECORATIVE ILLUSTRATION FOR THE LADY OF SHALOTT

MBPI2728

ILLUSTRATION AND TEXT FOR THE LADY OF SHALOTT

MBPI2729

ILLUSTRATION AND TEXT FOR THE LADY OF SHALOTT

MBPI2730

THE LADY DIETH FLOATING ADOWN THE STREAM

MBPI2731

THE DEAD LADY FLOATETH DOWN YE STREAM TOWARD CAMELOT

MBPI2732

DECORATIVE ILLUSTRATION FOR THE LADY OF SHALOTT

MBPI2733

ILLUSTRATION AND TEXT FOR THE LADY OF SHALOTT

MBPI2734

ILLUSTRATION FOR THE LADY OF SHALOTT

MBPI2735

DECORATIVE ILLUSTRATION FOR THE LADY OF SHALOTT

MBPI2736

ILLUSTRATION AND TEXT FOR THE LADY OF SHALOTT

MBPI2737
ILLUSTRATION FOR THE LADY OF SHALOTT

MBPI2738
THE END FOR THE LADY OF SHALOTT

MBPI2739
DECORATION FOR THE LADY OF SHALOTT

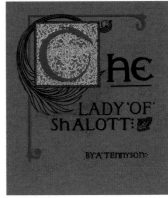

MBPI2740
FRONT COVER DESIGN FOR LADY OF SHALOTT

MBPI2741
SPINE DESIGN FOR LADY OF SHALOTT

MBPI2742
THE FORGING OF BALMUNG

MBPI2743
THE DEATH OF FAFNIR

MBPI2744
THE AWAKENING OF BRUNHILD

MBPI2745
THE TRIAL OF STRENGTH

MBPI2746
THE QUARREL OF THE QUEENS

MBPI2747
THE DEATH OF SIEGFRIED

MBPI2748
"HO, DRUMMER! QUICK, SILENCE YON CAPET"

MBPI2749
"AWFUL, AND PROUD, AND ERECT"

MBPI2750
"SHE LOOKED FROM THE BARS OF HER PRISON"

MBPI2751
"AUNT MARY EXPRESSING HER MIND"

MBPI2752
"THE MOURNING CLAM-MAN"

MBPI2753
GRANDFATHER AND LITTLE BENNY

MBPI2754
THE BELOVED PASTOR

MBPI2755
ILLUSTRATION FOR SWINTON'S FIFTH
READER AND SPEAKER

MBPI2756
ILLUSTRATION FOR SWINTON'S FIFTH
READER AND SPEAKER

MBPI2757
INAUGURAL PROCESSION

MBPI2758
A KENTUCKY WEDDING

MBPI2759
SCENE IN THE THEATRE IN PHILADELPHIA
1794

MBPI2760
DUTCH AND INDIANS TRADING

MBPI2761
ROGER WILLIAMS IN EXILE

MBPI2762
THE INDIAN AND THE PIONEER

MBPI2763
WHITMAN STARTING FOR WASHINGTON

MBPI2764
NOTES: DESCRIPTIVE AND BIOGRAPHIC

MBPI2765
HEADPIECE, LEXINGTON

MBPI2766
THE EMBARKATION

MBPI2767
"BLAZING AND CLANGING FROM THICKET
AND WALL"

MBPI2768
"FOR THEY ALL THOUGHT HE WAS DYING,
AS THEY GATHERED ROUND HIM CRYING"

MBPI2769

ILLUSTRATION FOR SWINTON'S ADVANCED THIRD READER

MBPI2770

"HER NATIVE SONGS FOR HIM SHE SUNG"

MBPI2771

HEADBAND FOR A HISTORY OF NEW YORK

MBPI2772

ILLUSTRATED INITIAL A FOR A HISTORY OF NEW YORK

MBPI2773

TAILPIECE FOR A HISTORY OF NEW YORK

MBPI2774

SAT, LIKE A FATE, AND WATCHED THE FLYING THREAD

MBPI2775

SHE HEARD THE STIR OF HIS BLACK MANTLE TRAILING IN THE DUST

MBPI2776

WHILE YET HER CHEEK WAS BRIGHT WITH SUMMER BLOOM

MBPI2777

BREATHED THROUGH HER LIPS A SAD AND TREMULOUS TUNE

MBPI2778

DEATH AND WINTER CLOSED THE AUTUMN SCENE

MBPI2779

PYRRHUS FINDS PHILOCTETES IN A CAVE

MBPI2780

ODYSSEUS AND HIS MOTHER

MBPI2781

APOLLO SLAYING THE PYTHON

MBPI2782

MELEAGER REFUSES TO HELP IN THE DEFENCE OF THE CITY

MBPI2783

THE SILVER-FOOTED THETIS RISING FROM THE WAVES

MBPI2784

THE SWINEHERD TELLING HIS STORY TO ODYSSEUS

MBPI2785
ALPHEUS AND ARETHUSA

MBPI2786
ODYSSEUS ADVISES KING TYNDAREUS
CONCERNING HELEN'S SUITORS

MBPI2787
DEIANEIRA AND THE DYING CENTAUR
NESSUS

MBPI2788
PROMETHEUS

MBPI2789
PALAMEDES TESTS THE MADNESS OF
ODYSSEUS

MBPI2790
ODYSSEUS AND MENELAUS PERSUADING
AGAMEMNON TO SACRIFICE IPHIGENIA

MBPI2791
THE BOYS PRESENT THE SALMAGUNDI TO
HEER GOVERNOR STUYVESANT

MBPI2792
WASHINGTON, THE YOUNG SURVEYOR

MBPI2793
"THE SACHEM'S DAUGHTER"

MBPI2794
"THE VISION OF ECHARD"

MBPI2795
THE DEACON

MBPI2796
HEADPIECE, PREFACE FOR THE ONE HOSS
SHAY

MBPI2797
TAILPIECE, PREFACE FOR THE ONE HOSS
SHAY

MBPI2798
HEADPIECE, LIST OF ILLUSTRATIONS FOR
THE ONE HOSS SHAY

MBPI2799
TAILPIECE, LIST OF ILLUSTRATIONS FOR
THE ONE HOSS SHAY

MBPI2800
HALF-TITLE FOR THE DEACON'S
MASTERPIECE

MBPI2801
THE MASTERPIECE

MBPI2802
"A CHAISE BREAKS DOWN"

MBPI2803
"THE DEACON INQUIRED OF THE VILLAGE FOLK"

MBPI2804
"NAOW SHE'LL DEW"

MBPI2805
"SHE WAS A WONDER, AND NOTHING LESS"

MBPI2806
"DEACON AND DEACONESS DROPPED AWAY"

MBPI2807
"EIGHTEEN HUNDRED"

MBPI2808
"FIFTY-FIVE"

MBPI2809
"ITS HUNDREDTH YEAR"

MBPI2810
"A GENERAL FLAVOR OF MILD DECAY"

MBPI2811
"IN ANOTHER HOUR IT WILL BE WORN OUT"

MBPI2812
"THE PARSON TAKES A DRIVE"

MBPI2813
"ALL AT ONCE THE HORSES STOOD STILL"

MBPI2814
"THEN SOMETHING DECIDEDLY LIKE A SPILL"

MBPI2815
"JUST AS BUBBLES DO WHEN THEY BURST"

MBPI2816
"END OF THE WONDERFUL ONE-HOSS-SHAY"

MBPI2817
HALF-TITLE FOR HOW THE OLD HORSE
WON THE BET

MBPI2818
"THE FAMOUS TROTTING GROUND"

MBPI2819
"MANY A NOTED STEED"

MBPI2820
"THE SUNDAY SWELL"

MBPI2821
"THE JOINTED TANDEM"

MBPI2822
"SO SHY WITH US, SO FREE WITH THESE"

MBPI2823
"THE LOVELY BONNETS BEAMED THEIR
SMILES"

MBPI2824
"I'LL BET YOU TWO TO ONE"

MBPI2825
"HARNESSED IN HIS ONE-HOSS-SHAY"

MBPI2826
"THE SEXTON...LED FORTH THE HORSE"

MBPI2827
"A SIGHT TO SEE"

MBPI2828
"THEY LEAD HIM, LIMPING, TO THE
TRACK"

MBPI2829
"TO LIMBER OUT EACH STIFFENED JOINT"

MBPI2830
"SOMETHING LIKE A STRIDE"

MBPI2831
"A MIGHTY STRIDE HE SWUNG"

MBPI2832
"OFF WENT A SHOE"

MBPI2833
"And now the stand he rushes by"

MBPI2834
"And off they spring"

MBPI2835
"They follow at his heels"

MBPI2836
"They're losing ground"

MBPI2837
"He's distanced all the lot"

MBPI2838
"Some took his time"

MBPI2839
"Back in the one-hoss-shay he went"

MBPI2840
"A horse can trot, for all he's old"

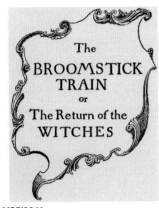

MBPI2841
Half-title for The Broomstick Train

MBPI2842
"Clear the track"

MBPI2843
"An Essex Deacon dropped in to call"

MBPI2844
"The old dwellings"

MBPI2845
"The small square windows"

MBPI2846
"Dark, dim, Dante-like solitudes"

MBPI2847
"Norman's Woe"

MBPI2848
"The Screeching Woman of Marblehead"

MBPI2849
"It is n't fair"

MBPI2850
"You're a good old–fellow–come, let us go"

MBPI2851
"See how tall they 've grown"

MBPI2852
"They called the cats"

MBPI2853
"The Essex people had dreadful times"

MBPI2854
"The withered hags were free"

MBPI2855
"A strange sea-monster stole their bait"

MBPI2856
"They could hear him twenty miles"

MBPI2857
"They came…at their master's call"

MBPI2858
"You can hear the black cat's purr"

MBPI2859
"Catch a gleam from her wicked eye"

MBPI2860
Tailpiece for The Broomstick Train

MBPI2861
The Last Leaf

MBPI2862
The One Hoss Shay

MBPI2863
Dorothy Q

MBPI2864
The Boston Tea Party

MBPI2865
GRANDMOTHER'S STORY OF BUNKER HILL
BATTLE

MBPI2866
DOROTHY Q

MBPI2867
HALF-TITLE FOR DOROTHY Q

MBPI2868
PAINTING THE PICTURE

MBPI2869
"GIRLISH BUST, BUT WOMANLY AIR"

MBPI2870
"HINT AND PROMISE OF STATELY MIEN"

MBPI2871
"THE YOUTHFUL SIRE"

MBPI2872
"SOFT IS THE BREATH OF A MAIDEN'S YES"

MBPI2873
"LADY AND LOVER"

MBPI2874
"THE BOSTON TEAPOT BUBBLED"

MBPI2875
HALF-TITLE FOR A BALLAD OF THE
BOSTON TEA-PARTY

MBPI2876
A CUP OF TEA

MBPI2877
"MANY A SIX FOOT GRENADIER—THE FLAT-
TENED GRASS HAD MEASURED"

MBPI2878
"HER TEARFUL MEMORIES TREASURED"

MBPI2879
"BEHOLD THE GUESTS ADVANCING"

MBPI2880
"THE LIVELY BARBER"

MBPI2881
"The truant tapster"

MBPI2882
"The cooper's boys"

MBPI2883
"The lusty young Fort-Hillers"

MBPI2884
"The Tories seize the omen"

MBPI2885
"The Mohawk band is swarming"

MBPI2886
"So gracious, sweet, and purring"

MBPI2887
"The quiet dame"

MBPI2888
An Old North-Ender

MBPI2889
Tailpiece for A Ballad of the Boston Tea-Party

MBPI2890
Watching the Battle from the Steeple

MBPI2891
Title for Grandmother's Story of Bunker Hill Battle

MBPI2892
The Grandmother

MBPI2893
Half-title for Grandmother's Story of Bunker-Hill Battle

MBPI2894
"Lord Percy's hunted soldiers"

MBPI2895
"Says grandma, 'What's the matter?'"

MBPI2896
"The Mohawks killed her father"

MBPI2897

"'Don't you fret and worry any'"

MBPI2898

"Down my hair went as I hurried"

MBPI2899

"The Corporal marched before"

MBPI2900

"We climbed the creaking stair"

MBPI2901

"The earthwork hid them from us"

MBPI2902

"The cannons' deafening thrill"

MBPI2903

"Like a gentleman of leisure"

MBPI2904

"The belted grenadiers"

MBPI2905

"The barges gliding onward"

MBPI2906

"Again they formed in order"

MBPI2907

"They wait and answer not"

MBPI2908

"The Corporal, our old cripple"

MBPI2909

Dan'l Malcolm's Grave

MBPI2910

"In the hush of expectation"

MBPI2911

"Like a thunder-cloud it breaks"

MBPI2912

"A headlong crowd is flying"

MBPI2913
"Are they beaten?"

MBPI2914
"They are baffled, not defeated"

MBPI2915
"The roofs of Charlestown blazing"

MBPI2916
"We can see each massive column"

MBPI2917
"The ominous calm is broken"

MBPI2918
"The frightened braves of Howe"

MBPI2919
"We looked, poor timid creatures"

MBPI2920
"'Have a drop of old Jamaiky'"

MBPI2921
"They were creeping round to four"

MBPI2922
"In close array they come"

MBPI2923
"They surged above the breast-work"

MBPI2924
"They say I fainted"

MBPI2925
"'Here's a soldier bleeding'"

MBPI2926
"Brought him from the battle"

MBPI2927
"I saw his eyes were blue"

MBPI2928
"We came to know each other"

MBPI2929
"His picture Copley painted"

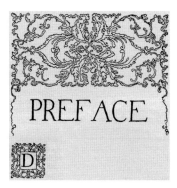

MBPI2930
Headpiece with illustrated initial D, Preface for Dorothy Q

MBPI2931
Tailpiece, Preface for Dorothy Q

MBPI2932
Headpiece, List of Illustrations for Dorothy Q

MBPI2933
Tailpiece, List of Illustrations for Dorothy Q

MBPI2934
Decorative heading for Dorothy Q

MBPI2935
Decorative border for Dorothy Q

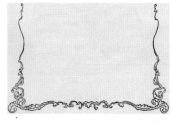

MBPI2936
Decorative heading for Dorothy Q

MBPI2937
Decorative border for Dorothy Q

MBPI2938
Decorative heading for Dorothy Q

MBPI2939
Decorative border for Dorothy Q

MBPI2940
Decorative heading for Dorothy Q

MBPI2941
Decorative border for Dorothy Q

MBPI2942
Decorative heading for Dorothy Q

MBPI2943
Decorative border for Dorothy Q

MBPI2944
Decorative border with title for A Ballad of the Boston-Tea Party

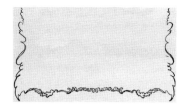

MBPI2945
DECORATIVE BORDER FOR A BALLAD OF THE BOSTON-TEA PARTY

MBPI2946
DECORATIVE HEADING FOR A BALLAD OF THE BOSTON-TEA PARTY

MBPI2947
TAILPIECE FOR A BALLAD OF THE BOSTON-TEA PARTY

MBPI2948
DECORATIVE HEADING FOR A BALLAD OF THE BOSTON-TEA PARTY

MBPI2949
TAILPIECE FOR A BALLAD OF THE BOSTON-TEA PARTY

MBPI2950
DECORATIVE HEADING FOR A BALLAD OF THE BOSTON-TEA PARTY

MBPI2951
DECORATIVE HEADING FOR A BALLAD OF THE BOSTON-TEA PARTY

MBPI2952
TAILPIECE FOR A BALLAD OF THE BOSTON-TEA PARTY

MBPI2953
DECORATIVE HEADING FOR A BALLAD OF THE BOSTON-TEA PARTY

MBPI2954
TAILPIECE FOR A BALLAD OF THE BOSTON-TEA PARTY

MBPI2955
DECORATIVE HEADING FOR A BALLAD OF THE BOSTON-TEA PARTY

MBPI2956
TAILPIECE FOR A BALLAD OF THE BOSTON-TEA PARTY

MBPI2957
DECORATIVE HEADING FOR A BALLAD OF THE BOSTON-TEA PARTY

MBPI2958
TAILPIECE FOR A BALLAD OF THE BOSTON-TEA PARTY

MBPI2959
DECORATIVE HEADING FOR A BALLAD OF THE BOSTON-TEA PARTY

MBPI2960
TAILPIECE FOR A BALLAD OF THE BOSTON-TEA PARTY

MBPI2961
Balboa's Discovery of the Pacific

MBPI2962
"The Meeting of Cortes and Montezuma"

MBPI2963
Oliver Wendell Holmes at age of 41

MBPI2964
Headpiece, List of llustrations for The Autocrat of the Breakfast-Table

MBPI2965
Headpiece with initial T, Preface for The Autocrat of the Breakfast-Table

MBPI2966
Headpiece with initial T for Autocrat's Autobiography

MBPI2967
Tailpiece for Autocrat's Autobiography

MBPI2968
Headpiece with initial I, Part I for The Autocrat of the Breakfast-Table

MBPI2969
The Mutual Admiration Society

MBPI2970
Album Verses with initial W

MBPI2971
The Man of Family

MBPI2972
Latter-Day Warnings with initial W

MBPI2973
Tailpiece, Part I for The Autocrat of the Breakfast-Table

MBPI2974
Headpiece with initial I, Part II for The Autocrat of the Breakfast-Table

MBPI2975
The Trotting Match

MBPI2976
Sun and Shadow with initial A

MBPI2977
THIS IS IT with initial A

MBPI2978
HEADPIECE with initial T, Part III for
THE AUTOCRAT OF THE BREAKFAST-TABLE

MBPI2979
AT THE CLUB

MBPI2980
THE OLD MAN DREAMS with initial O

MBPI2981
TAILPIECE FOR THE OLD MAN DREAMS

MBPI2982
HEADPIECE with initial I, Part IV for
THE AUTOCRAT OF THE BREAKFAST-TABLE

MBPI2983
A REMINISCENCE OF THE MARIGOLD

MBPI2984
THE CHAMBERED NAUTILUS with initial
T

MBPI2985
TAILPIECE FOR THE CHAMBERED
NAUTILUS

MBPI2986
HEADPIECE with initial A, Part V for
THE AUTOCRAT OF THE BREAKFAST-TABLE

MBPI2987
THE OLD VIOLIN

MBPI2988
MARE RUBRUM with initial F

MBPI2989
TAILPIECE FOR MARE RUBRUM

MBPI2990
HEADPIECE with initial S, Part VI for
THE AUTOCRAT OF THE BREAKFAST-TABLE

MBPI2991
THE CLOSED DOOR

MBPI2992
WHAT WE ALL THINK with initial T

MBPI2993
Tailpiece for What We All Think

MBPI2994
Oliver Wendell Holmes at the age of 76

MBPI2995
Headpiece with initial T, Part VII for The Autocrat of the Breakfast-Table

MBPI2996
The Last Blossom with initial T

MBPI2997
The Professor in his Boat

MBPI2998
The Living Temple

MBPI2999
Headpiece with initial S, Part VIII for The Autocrat of the Breakfast-Table

MBPI3000
Into the River

MBPI3001
Spring Has Come with initial T

MBPI3002
Headpiece with initial I, Part IX for The Autocrat of the Breakfast-Table

MBPI3003
First Love

MBPI3004
A Good Time Going

MBPI3005
The Two Armies with initial A

MBPI3006
Tailpiece for The Two Armies

MBPI3007
Headpiece with initial T, Part X for The Autocrat of the Breakfast-Table

MBPI3008
The First Walk

MBPI3009
Musa with initial O

MBPI3010
Tailpiece for Musa

MBPI3011
Headpiece with initial T, Part XI for
The Autocrat of the Breakfast-Table

MBPI3012
Headpiece for The Deacon's
Masterpiece

MBPI3013
Æstivation with initial I

MBPI3014
The Mountain Home

MBPI3015
Contentment with initial L

MBPI3016
Tailpiece for The Autocrat of the
Breakfast-Table

MBPI3017
Headpiece with initial I, Part XII for
The Autocrat of the Breakfast-Table

MBPI3018
Headpiece with title for Parson
Turell's Legacy

MBPI3019
Parson Turell's legacy

MBPI3020
The Voiceless with initial W

MBPI3021
Tailpiece for The Autocrat of the
Breakfast-Table

MBPI3022
Title page decoration for Stops of
Various Quills

MBPI3023
Title page decoration for Stops of
Various Quills

MBPI3024
Headpiece, Table of Contents for
Stops of Various Quills

MBPI3025
TAILPIECE FOR MIDWAY

MBPI3026
TAILPIECE FOR THE BEWILDERED GUEST

MBPI3027
COMPANY

MBPI3028
TAILPIECE FOR COMPANY

MBPI3029
TWELVE P. M.

MBPI3030
TAILPIECE FOR IN THE DARK

MBPI3031
TAILPIECE FOR SOLITUDE

MBPI3032
CONSCIENCE

MBPI3033
ILLUSTRATED INITIAL J FOR CONSCIENCE

MBPI3034
TAILPIECE FOR CONSCIENCE

MBPI3035
TAILPIECE FOR REWARD AND PUNISHMENT

MBPI3036
ILLUSTRATION FOR PARABLE

MBPI3037
TAILPIECE FOR PARABLE

MBPI3038
VISION

MBPI3039
DECORATION FOR SOCIETY

MBPI3040
FRIENDS AND FOES

MBPI3041
SPHINX

MBPI3042
MATERIALS OF A STORY

MBPI3043
THE KING DINES

MBPI3044
ILLUSTRATED INITIAL T FOR THE KING DINES

MBPI3045
LABOR AND CAPITAL

MBPI3046
TAILPIECE FOR LABOR AND CAPITAL

MBPI3047
EQUALITY

MBPI3048
JUDGMENT DAY

MBPI3049
MORTALITY

MBPI3050
ANOTHER DAY

MBPI3051
TAILPIECE FOR ANOTHER DAY

MBPI3052
SOME ONE ELSE

MBPI3053
ILLUSTRATED INITIAL L FOR STOPS OF VARIOUS QUILLS

MBPI3054
LIFE

MBPI3055
TAILPIECE FOR LIFE

MBPI3056
WEATHER-BREEDER

MBPI3057
PEONAGE

MBPI3058
RACE

MBPI3059
TAILPIECE FOR RACE

MBPI3060
TEMPERAMENT

MBPI3061
WHAT SHALL IT PROFIT?

MBPI3062
TAILPIECE FOR WHAT SHALL IT PROFIT?

MBPI3063
ILLUSTRATED INITIAL B FOR STOPS OF VARIOUS QUILLS

MBPI3064
HEADBAND FOR STOPS OF VARIOUS QUILLS

MBPI3065
VIGNETTE FOR A MAID'S CHOICE

MBPI3066
VIGNETTE FOR A MAID'S CHOICE

MBPI3067
VIGNETTE FOR A MAID'S CHOICE

MBPI3068
VIGNETTE FOR A MAID'S CHOICE

MBPI3069
VIGNETTE FOR A MAID'S CHOICE

MBPI3070
VIGNETTE FOR A MAID'S CHOICE

MBPI3071
VIGNETTE FOR A MAID'S CHOICE

MBPI3072
VIGNETTE FOR A MAID'S CHOICE

MBPI3073
VIGNETTE FOR A MAID'S CHOICE

MBPI3074
VIGNETTE FOR A MAID'S CHOICE

MBPI3075
VIGNETTE FOR A MAID'S CHOICE

MBPI3076
VIGNETTE FOR A MAID'S CHOICE

MBPI3077
VIGNETTE FOR A MAID'S CHOICE

MBPI3078
VIGNETTE FOR A MAID'S CHOICE

MBPI3079
VIGNETTE FOR A MAID'S CHOICE

MBPI3080
VIGNETTE FOR A MAID'S CHOICE

MBPI3081
VIGNETTE FOR A MAID'S CHOICE

MBPI3082
VIGNETTE FOR A MAID'S CHOICE

MBPI3083
VIGNETTE FOR A MAID'S CHOICE

MBPI3084
VIGNETTE FOR A MAID'S CHOICE

MBPI3085
VIGNETTE FOR A MAID'S CHOICE

MBPI3086
VIGNETTE FOR A MAID'S CHOICE

MBPI3087
VIGNETTE FOR A MAID'S CHOICE

MBPI3088
VIGNETTE FOR A MAID'S CHOICE

MBPI3089
Vignette for A Maid's Choice

MBPI3090
Vignette for A Maid's Choice

MBPI3091
Vignette for A Maid's Choice

MBPI3092
Vignette for A Maid's Choice

MBPI3093
Vignette for A Maid's Choice

MBPI3094
Vignette for A Maid's Choice

MBPI3095
Vignette for A Maid's Choice

MBPI3096
Vignette for A Maid's Choice

MBPI3097
Vignette for A Maid's Choice

MBPI3098
Vignette for A Maid's Choice

MBPI3099
Vignette for A Maid's Choice

MBPI3100
Vignette for A Maid's Choice

MBPI3101
Father Hennepin Celebrating Mass

MBPI3102
Assassination of LaSalle

MBPI3103
The Return from Deerfield

MBPI3104
Lygia and Vinicius in the Garden of Aulus

MBPI3105
The Punishment of Chilo by Vinicius

MBPI3106
Nero holding a Golden Lute, with Rome in Flames

MBPI3107
"Peractum est!"

MBPI3108
The Conversion of Chilo

MBPI3109
"Quo Vadis, Domine!"

MBPI3110
The Fall of Montcalm

MBPI3111
"They scrambled up the parapet and went surging over the crest, pell mell, upon The British"

MBPI3112
"Why don't you end it?"

MBPI3113
Half-title decoration for The Man with the Hoe and Other Poems

MBPI3114
Frontispiece for The Man with the Hoe and Other Poems

MBPI3115
Headpiece, Dedication for The Man with the Hoe and Other Poems

MBPI3116
Headpiece, Prefatory Note for The Man with the Hoe and Other Poems

MBPI3117
Headpiece, The Contents for The Man with the Hoe and Other Poems

MBPI3118
The Man With the Hoe

MBPI3119
A Look Into the Gulf

MBPI3120
Brotherhood

MBPI3121
Song of the Followers of Pan

MBPI3122
Little Brothers of the Ground

MBPI3123
Wail of the Wandering Dead

MBPI3124
A Prayer

MBPI3125
The Poet

MBPI3126
The Whirlwind Road

MBPI3127
The Desire of Nations

MBPI3128
Headband I for The Man with the Hoe and Other Poems

MBPI3129
The Goblin Laugh

MBPI3130
Poetry

MBPI3131
A Meeting

MBPI3132
Infinite Depths

MBPI3133
A Leaf From the Devil's Jest-Book

MBPI3134
The Paymaster

MBPI3135
The Last Furrow

MBPI3136
In the Storm

MBPI3137
After Reading Shakespeare

MBPI3138
Headband II for The Man with the Hoe and Other Poems

MBPI3139
The Poets

MBPI3140
Love's Vigil

MBPI3141
Two at a Fireside

MBPI3142
Headband III for The Man with the Hoe and Other Poems

MBPI3143
To William Watson

MBPI3144
Man

MBPI3145
In High Sierras

MBPI3146
The Wharf of Dreams

MBPI3147
To Louise Michel

MBPI3148
Shepherd Boy and Nereid

MBPI3149
A Song at the Start

MBPI3150
My Comrade

MBPI3151
Joy of the Morning

MBPI3152
A Cry in the Night

MBPI3153
FAYS

MBPI3154
IN DEATH VALLEY

MBPI3155
AT DAWN

MBPI3156
"FOLLOW ME"

MBPI3157
IN POPPY FIELDS

MBPI3158
THE JOY OF THE HILLS

MBPI3159
THE INVISIBLE BRIDE

MBPI3160
THE VALLEY

MBPI3161
THE CLIMB OF LIFE

MBPI3162
MIDSUMMER NOON

MBPI3163
GRIEFS

MBPI3164
AN OLD ROAD

MBPI3165
MUSIC

MBPI3166
FAY SONG

MBPI3167
THE OLD EARTH

MBPI3168
DIVINE ADVENTURE

MBPI3169
To High-born Poets

MBPI3170
The Toilers

MBPI3171
On the Gulf of Night

MBPI3172
A Harvest Song

MBPI3173
The Man Under the Stone

MBPI3174
Song to the Divine Mother

MBPI3175
From the Hand of a Child

MBPI3176
The Rock-Breaker

MBPI3177
These Songs Will Perish

MBPI3178
Assassination of William of Orange

MBPI3179
A Thousand Miles a Day

MBPI3180
Vignette for A Wonder Book

MBPI3181
"Behold it then!" cried Perseus

MBPI3182
Theseus caught the monster off his guard

MBPI3183
"Who are you?" thundered the giant

MBPI3184
"Let me hasten onward"

MBPI3185
"'Let me go to him!' she shrieked, in her anguish of soul"

MBPI3186
Title page decoration for The Odes & Epodes of Horace

MBPI3187
The Poet at Twilight

MBPI3188
Subtitle page decoration for The Odes & Epodes of Horace

MBPI3189
"Euterpe"

MBPI3190
Horace Reading to Maecenas

MBPI3191
"There was exchange of thrust and parry"

MBPI3192
Lorna Doone

MBPI3193
Inauguration of Washington in New York

MBPI3194
Then the old man's lips began to move

MBPI3195
Illustration for A Report of the truth concerning the last sea-fight of the Revenge

MBPI3196
Caxton at his Press

MBPI3197
"Friar" Bacon in his Study

MBPI3198
Erasmus reading to Colet And More

MBPI3199
"Izaak" Walton

MBPI3200
Richard DeBury and the Young Edward III

MBPI3201
ILLUSTRATION FOR THE ECLOGUES OF
VERGIL

MBPI3202
SUBTITLE PAGE DECORATION FOR BREVIARY
TREASURES

MBPI3203
HOSEA AND THE "CRUETIN SARJUNT"

MBPI3204
HOSEA AND THE PARSON

MBPI3205
ZEKLE AND HULDY

MBPI3206
"SUNTHIN IN THE PASTORAL LINE"

MBPI3207
HEADPIECE, PUBLISHER'S NOTE FOR THE
ONE HOSS SHAY

MBPI3208
TAILPIECE FOR THE ONE HOSS SHAY

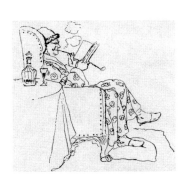

MBPI3209
DOFOBIUS

MBPI3210
COVER DESIGN FOR THE TUESDAY CLUB

MBPI3211
HEADPIECE FOR THE TUESDAY CLUB

MBPI3212
DECORATION FOR THE TUESDAY CLUB

MBPI3213
THE MESSIAH COVER DESIGN FOR THE
TUESDAY CLUB

MBPI3214
COVER DESIGN FOR THE CECILIA SOCIETY

MBPI3215
HEADPIECE FOR BI-CENTENNIAL
COMMEMORATION, HOLY TRINITY, OLD
SWEDES CHURCH

MBPI3216
COVER DESIGN FOR TWELFTH NIGHT AT
EAGLEROOST

MBPI3217
TITLE PAGE DECORATION FOR TWELFTH NIGHT AT EAGLEROOST

MBPI3218
HEADPIECE FOR TWELFTH NIGHT AT EAGLEROOST

MBPI3219
COVER DESIGN FOR CENTURIA'S GREETINGS

MBPI3220
HEADPIECE FOR CENTURIA'S GREETINGS

MBPI3221
ILLUSTRATED INITIAL G FOR CENTURIA'S GREETINGS

MBPI3222
POOR RICHARD

MBPI3223
DESIGN FOR THE PLAYERS BOOKPLATE

MBPI3224
DESIGN FOR THE PLAYERS BOOKPLATE

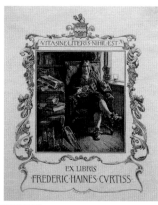

MBPI3225
DESIGN FOR FREDERICK HAINES CURTISS BOOKPLATE

MBPI3226
DESIGN FOR HOWARD PYLE BOOKPLATE

MBPI3227
DESIGN FOR EDITH KERMIT ROOSEVELT BOOKPLATE

MBPI3228
DESIGN FOR THE YALE CLUB OF NEW YORK CITY BOOKPLATE

MBPI3229
DESIGN FOR KEATS-SHELLEY MEMORIAL BOOKPLATE

MBPI3230
THE DUPONT POWDER WAGON

MBPI3231
TO HAVE AND TO HOLD

MBPI3232
THE GENUS OF LITERATURE

MBPI3233
SHEPHERD AND GIRL

MBPI3234
THE GENUS OF ART

MBPI3235
THE GENUS OF MUSIC

MBPI3236
YOUNG FLOWERING TREES

MBPI3237
FLOWERING TREE II

MBPI3238
THE GENUS OF DRAMA

MBPI3239
THE BATTLE OF NASHVILLE

MBPI3240
THE LANDING OF CARTERET

MBPI3241
ILLUSTRATION FOR A TRANSFERRED
ROMANCE

MBPI3242
THE HOME-MADE PRESS

PDPI0001
THE TIGER

PDPI0002
PRELIMINARY STUDY FOR PROPOSED
MURAL FOR SOLDIERS AND SAILORS
MEMORIAL HALL OF ALLEGHENY COUNTY,
PENNSYLVANIA

PDPI0003
BIRTHDAY TRIBUTE TO THEODORE
ROOSEVELT

PDPI0004
HOWARD PYLE SELF PORTRAIT PAINTING

PDPI0005
HOWARD PYLE SCRIPT BOOK LABEL

PDPI0006
THE PORTRAIT OF A YOUNG GENTLEMAN
WHO ALWAYS SAYS "THANK YOU!"

PDPI0007
THE ESCAPE

PDPI0008
PRELIMINARY STUDY FOR MBPI2501 PETER
STUYVESANT AND THE ENGLISH FLEET

PDPI0009
PRELIMINARY STUDY FOR MBPI2500
HENDRYK HUDSON AND THE HALF-MOON

PDPI0010
PRELIMINARY STUDY FOR MBPI2502 LIFE
IN AN OLD DUTCH TOWN

PDPI0011
STRIP OF GREEN FOR MURAL PANEL

PDPI0012
FLOWERING TREE I

PDPI0013
GENERAL PRESCOTT

PDPI0014
YE QUEEN OF HEARTS

PDPI0015
A MATTER OF FATE

PDPI0016
A VIEW IN JAMAICA

PDPI0017
SUSPICIOUS STRANGERS

PDPI0018
YE PIRATE BOLD, AS IMAGINED BY A
QUAKER GENTLEMAN

PDPI0019
ILLUSTRATED INITIAL F WITH DECORATION
FOR THE CAPTAIN'S WELL

PDPI0020
VIGNETTE FOR NEWSPAPER HEAD

PDPI0021
CAVALIER WITH SWORD

PDPI0022
THE INQUISITIVE PEASANT

PDPI0023
DESIGN FOR DRINKING MUG

PDPI0024
TAILPIECE DESIGN AND VERSE FOR DRINK-
ING MUG

PDPI0025
DECORATION AND ILLUSTRATED INITIAL T
FOR QUILL AND GRILL CLUB INVITATION

PDPI0026
SEAL DECORATION FOR QUILL AND GRILL
CLUB INVITATION

PDPI0027
DESIGN FOR UNUSED HOWARD PYLE BOOK-
PLATE

PDPI0028
UNUSED COLOR DESIGN FOR HOWARD PYLE
BOOKPLATE

PDPI0029
ANGEL OF DEATH

PDPI0030
SPINE DESIGN FOR TWILIGHT LAND

PDPI0031
THE INDIANS AIMING AT THE LOOP-HOLES

PDPI0032
BUGLER AT FORT MACON

PDPI0033
VIGNETTE, WOMAN ON A HOUSEBOAT

PDPI0034
YOUNG WOMAN STANDING UNDER TREE

PDPI0035
PENNSYLVANIA AVENUE

PDPI0036
ILLUSTRATION FOR ODES OF ANACREON
ANACREONTICS

PDPI0037
"THE SERENADE"

PDPI0038
SOMETHING FRESH

PDPI0039

A Very Merry Christmas In The "Good Old Times"

PDPI0040

Illustrated initial A for A Very Merry Christmas in The "Good Old Times"

PDPI0041

"A Study"

PDPI0042

Design for The Grolier Club bookplate

PDPI0043

Theatrical costumes designed by Howard Pyle

PDPI0044

Renaissance Couple

PDPI0045

Portrait of Joshua Clayton

PDPI0046

Design for punch bowl

PDPI0047

Design for centerpiece

PDPI0048

Design for candelabra–candlestick–electrolier

PDPI0049

Medieval Scene

PDPI0050

Soldier with spear

PDPI0051

The Sly Fox

PDPI0052

The Flute Player

PDPI0053

Illustrated initial T for The Star Bearer

PDPI0054

Tailpiece for The Star Bearer

PDPI0055
"All eyes were turned to Abraham Davenport. He rose, slow cleaving with his steady voice the intolerable hush."

PDPI0056
The Garfield Ambulance Train on its way to Elberon, N.J.

PDPI0057
Cover design for Report of the Board of Park Commissioners, Wilmington, Delaware

PDPI0058
Woman at a Spinning Wheel

PDPI0059
The Deacon's Masterpiece: or the Wonderful "One-Hoss-Shay" with initial H

PDPI0060
Peter Rugg Ye Bostonian

PDPI0061
Young Woman in Elizabethan Dress

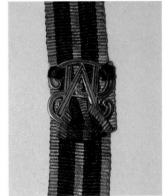

PDPI0062
Design for Howard Pyle School of Art lapel pin

PDPI0063
Woman carrying urn

PDPI0064
Design for 1908 Christmas Seal

PDPI0065
Design for 1908 Christmas Seal–Rounded corners

PDPI0066
Cover design without border for Tuesday Club

PDPI0067
Headpiece with title, A Relay Tavern

PDPI0068
A Race for Life

PDPI0069
Front cover decorative border for McClure's Magazine

PDPI0070
The Burning of the Guillotine Before the Statue of Voltaire

PDPI0071
THE FRIGHTFUL ACCIDENT

PDPI0072
AND WE KEPT THOSE FELLOWS ALEE, ASTERN

PDPI0073
FOR MANY A MILE WE SAILED

PDPI0074
HER DECKS ARE RED WITH HER GALLANT DEAD

PDPI0075
RIVER ROCKS

PDPI0076
THE SEA FIGHT

PDPI0077
SPINE DESIGN FOR PEPPER & SALT

PDPI0078
HEADBAND FOR THE GODS OF THE COPYBOOK MAXIMS

PDPI0079
TAILPIECE FOR THE PAINTED PITCHER

PDPI0080
BEACH SCENE

PDPI0081
ILLUSTRATED INITIAL M FOR INVITATION

PDPI0082
TAILPIECE FOR INVITATION

PDPI0083
OCEAN VIEW

PDPI0084
"MAY I HAVE THE PLEASURE FOR THE NEXT"

PDPI0085
BUST PROFILE WITH CHALICE

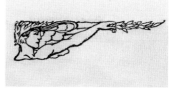

PDPI0086
BUST PROFILE ARM EXTENDED

PDPI0087
Head I

PDPI0088
Head II

PDPI0089
Head III

PDPI0090
Head I with wings

PDPI0091
Head II with wings

PDPI0092
Head III with wings

PDPI0093
Head IV with wings

PDPI0094
Wings

PDPI0095
Subtitle decoration I

PDPI0096
Subtitle decoration II

PDPI0097
Old Fire-Place, Aunt Saber's Kitchen

PDPI0098
Marooned

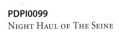

PDPI0099
Night Haul of The Seine

PDPI0100
Cover border design for The Ladies'
Home Journal

PDPI0101
Sea Battle between Two Frigates

PDPI0102
Cor Cordia: A Christmas Greeting
from Thy Husband

PDPI0103
ILLUSTRATION FOR THE ADVENTURE OF A MOUSE

PDPI0104
"BUT THE PROUDEST AND GRANDEST OF ALL THE FLOCK WAS GOBBLE, OUR GORGEOUS TURKEY-COCK."

PDPI0105
THEATRICAL COSTUMES DESIGNED BY HOWARD PYLE

MBOP0001
HOWARD PYLE PHOTO PORTRAIT

MBOP0002
HOWARD PYLE PHOTO PORTRAIT

MBOP0003
HOWARD PYLE PHOTO PORTRAIT

MBOP0004
HOWARD PYLE PHOTO PORTRAIT

PDOP0001
HOWARD PYLE PHOTO PORTRAIT

PDOP0002
HOWARD PYLE PHOTO PORTRAIT

PDOP0003
HOWARD PYLE PHOTO PORTRAIT

PDOP0004
HOWARD PYLE PHOTO PORTRAIT

PDOP0005
HOWARD PYLE PHOTO PORTRAIT

PDOP0006
HOWARD PYLE PHOTO PORTRAIT

PDOP0007
HOWARD PYLE PHOTO PORTRAIT

PDOP0008
HOWARD PYLE PHOTO PORTRAIT

PDOP0009
HOWARD PYLE PHOTO PORTRAIT

PDOP0010
HOWARD PYLE PHOTO PORTRAIT

PDOP0011
HOWARD PYLE PHOTO PORTRAIT

PDOP0012
HOWARD PYLE PHOTO PORTRAIT

PDOP0013
HOWARD PYLE PHOTO PORTRAIT

PDOP0014
HOWARD PYLE SILHOUETTE PHOTO POR-
TRAIT

PDOP0015
HOWARD PYLE PHOTO PORTRAIT

PDOP0016
HOWARD PYLE PHOTO PORTRAIT

PDOP0017
HOWARD PYLE PHOTO PORTRAIT

PDOP0018
HOWARD PYLE PHOTO PORTRAIT

PDOP0019
HOWARD PYLE PHOTO PORTRAIT

PDOP0020
HOWARD PYLE PHOTO PORTRAIT

PDOP0021
HOWARD PYLE PORTRAIT LIKENESS

MBOI0001
ARRIVALS AT THE CREAMERY

MBOI0002
RECEIVING MILK

MBOI0003
MAKING CHEESE

MBOI0004
EARLY MORNING ON THE FERRIES

MBOI0005
Assorting the Peaches

MBOI0006
Headpiece with title for The Sea Man

MBOI0007
The storm of 1821

MBOI0008
The Tile House, New Castle, Delaware

MBOI0009
Wayne Homestead

MBOI0010
Tailpiece for Gretelein and Her
Queer Stove

Photograph Credits Illustration/Art

With few exceptions, Howard Pyle's illustration/art was published during his lifetime. All illustrations pictured in this book except those listed below are from published mediums.

MBPI1303	Preliminary study for The Landing...	Delaware Art Museum
MBPI2505	Spring	Brandywine River Museum
MBPI2506	The Garden of Youth	Delaware Art Museum
MBPI2508	The Enchanted Seas	Private Collection
MBPI2511	Marooned	Delaware Art Museum
MBPI2512	The Mermaid	Delaware Art Museum
PDPI0002	Preliminary study for proposed mural for...	Rehoboth Art League
PDPI0003	Birthday Tribute to Theodore Roosevelt	Houghton Library/Harvard
PDPI0004	Howard Pyle self portrait painting	National Academy of Design
PDPI0006	The portrait of a young gentleman...	Brokaw Family Collection
PDPI0007	The Escape	Brokaw Family Collection
PDPI0013	General Prescott	Delaware Art Museum
PDPI0014	Ye Queen of Hearts	Brokaw Family Collection
PDPI0015	A Matter of Fate	Delaware Art Museum
PDPI0016	A view in Jamaica	Brokaw Family Collection
PDPI0017	Suspicious Strangers	Brokaw Family Collection
PDPI0022	The Inquisitive Peasant	Anne D. Williams
PDPI0023	Design for drinking mug	Delaware Art Museum
PDPI0024	Tailpiece design and verse for drinking ...	Delaware Art Museum
PDPI0027	Design for unused Howard Pyle bookplate	Delaware Art Museum
PDPI0028	Unused color design for Howard Pyle bookplate	Brokaw Family Collection
PDPI0033	Vignette, woman on a houseboat	Brokaw Family Collection
PDPI0042	Design for The Grolier Club bookplate	Brokaw Family Collection
PDPI0043	Theatrical costumes designed by Howard Pyle	New York Public Library
PDPI0044	Renaissance Couple	Kelly Collection of American Illustration
PDPI0045	Portrait of Joshua Clayton	State of Delaware
PDPI0046	Design for punch bowl	Delaware Public Archives
PDPI0047	Design for centerpiece	Delaware Public Archives
PDPI0048	Design for candelabra...	Delaware Public Archives
PDPI0049	Medieval Scene	Delaware Art Museum
PDPI0052	The Flute Player	Mrs. William H. Brewer
PDPI0058	Woman at a Spinning Wheel	Brokaw Family Collection
PDPI0059	The Deacon's Masterpiece...	Brokaw Family Collection
PDPI0060	Peter Rugg Ye Bostonian	Brokaw Family Collection
PDPI0062	Design for Howard Pyle School of Art lapel pin	Historical Society of Delaware
PDPI0075	River Rocks	Dr. and Mrs. William A. Morton, Jr.
PDPI0076	The Sea Fight	Brown County Library,Green Bay
PDPI0083	Ocean View	Delaware Art Museum
PDPI0098	Marooned	Private Collection
PDPI0101	Sea Battle between Two Frigates	Brokaw Family Collection
PDPI0102	Cor Cordia: A Christmas Greeting from...	Brokaw Family Collection
MBPI3232	Mural panels from Pyle's home:	Delaware Art Museum
	MBPI3233, MBPI3234, MBPI3235, MBPI3236,	
	MBPI3237, MBPI3238, PDPI0011, PDPI0012	

Photograph Credits Portraits

All Photo/Portraits in this book, except those listed below were published during Pyle's lifetime or are in the collection of the compiler.

PDOP0003	Howard Pyle	Brokaw Family Collection
PDOP0005	Howard Pyle	Library of Congress
PDOP0006	Howard Pyle	Brokaw Family Collection
PDOP0007	Howard Pyle	Brokaw Family Collection
PDOP0008	Howard Pyle	Delaware Art Museum
PDOP0009	Howard Pyle	Delaware Art Museum
PDOP0010	Howard Pyle	Delaware Art Museum
PDOP0011	Howard Pyle	Delaware Art Museum
PDOP0012	Howard Pyle	Delaware Art Museum
PDOP0014	Howard Pyle	Historical Society of Delaware
PDOP0015	Howard Pyle	Brokaw Family Collection
PDOP0016	Howard Pyle	Brokaw Family Collection
PDOP0017	Howard Pyle	Brokaw Family Collection
PDOP0019	Howard Pyle	Library of Congress
PDOP0020	Howard Pyle	Library of Congress

Index–Titles and Alternate Titles of Pyle's Art

List includes all known published and unpublished completed works of art. Titles are listed alphabetically with alternate titles in italics.

Aaron Burr's Wooing . . . . MBPI0354 . . 423

"The abbot and the town major personating   MBPI0389 . . 425
    conquered Spain"

Abbot Otto of St. Michaelsburg was a . . . . MBPI2297 . . 544
    gentle, patient, pale-faced old man

Abraham Davenport . . . . PDPI0055 . . . 607

Abraham Lincoln . . . . MBPI0988 . . 462

Abraham Lincoln During the Civil War . . . . MBPI0988 . . 462

An Accident in the Circus . . . . MBPI1191 . . 475

The Accident of Birth, with title, ... MBPI1344 . . 484
    illustrations and verse

Address to "Old Hickory" . . . . MBPI0208 . . 413

Adhelmar Climbed The Stairs Slowly, For . . . . . MBPI0903 . . 457
    He Was Growing Very Feeble Now"

"The Admiral came in his gig of state" . . . . MBPI0025 . . 402

"The Admiral lost all control of himself, ... MBPI0282 . . 418
    and in a rage ordered his son to quit the house"

Æstivation with initial I . . . . MBPI3013 . . 589

After Dinner . . . . MBPI0251 . . 416

After Reading Shakespeare . . . . MBPI3137 . . 597

After the Massacre; Samuel Adams . . . . MBPI0846 . . 453
    demanding of Governor Hutchinson the instant withdrawal
    of British Troops

"Again Sebastian served a feast" . . . . MBPI1735 . . 509

"Again they formed in order" . . . . MBPI2906 . . 582

The Aged Palmer gives Young David of . . . . . . MBPI2102 . . 532
    Doncaster news of Will Stutely

"'Ah me!' said the Parson, 'I wish I were . . . . MBPI2019 . . 527
    young'"

"Alas! he had turned to a terrible boy" . . . . MBPI2020 . . 527

"'Alas, my poor friend!' said he" . . . . MBPI1737 . . 509

Album Verses with initial W . . . . MBPI2970 . . 586

"All at once the horses stood still" . . . . MBPI2813 . . 576

"All eyes were turned to Abraham . . . . PDPI0055 . . . 607
    Davenport. He rose, slow cleaving with his steady voice the
    intolerable hush."

All These Things She Weaveth Into the Web . . . MBPI2713 . . 570

"All was a red blaze behind them" . . . . MBPI1668 . . 505

Allan a Dale lieth beside the Fountain . . . . MBPI2115 . . 533

Allan a Dale Singeth Before Our Good . . . . MBPI2131 . . 534
    Queen Eleanor

Allan a Dale tells his Story . . . . MBPI2116 . . 533

Along the Canal in Old Manhattan . . . . MBPI0570 . . 436

Along the Chester Valley . . . . MBPI0240 . . 415

"Along the Horizon a Few White Clouds . . . . . . MBPI0762 . . 448
    Were Heaped in Shining Domes"

Along the Water Front, New York, About . . . . . . MBPI0572 . . 436
    1780

Along the Waterfront, New York, About . . . . MBPI0572 . . 436
    1780

Along the Waterfront, Old New York . . . . MBPI0572 . . 436

Alpheus and Arethusa . . . . MBPI2785 . . 575

Always it was one picture that little . . . . MBPI2303 . . 544
    Otto sought

The Ambuscade . . . . MBPI1959 . . 523

"The American captain with his mate . . . . MBPI1032 . . 465
    boarded us"

Among the Daffodillies . . . . MBPI0315 . . 420

"An ancient sibyl-like figure" . . . . MBPI0403 . . 426

"And again my Captain took the biggest" . . . . . MBPI0636 . . 440

"And blew as he'd not blown since he was . . . MBPI1317 . . 483
    born"

And every time they fired it off. . . . . MBPI2672 . . 567

And every time they touched it off. . . . . MBPI2681 . . 568

"And now the stand he rushes by" . . . . MBPI2833 . . 578

"And off they spring" . . . . MBPI2834 . . 578

"And see that you watch well," he snarled . . . . . MBPI1097 . . 469

And some had ribbons red as blood. . . . . MBPI2684 . . 568

"And stripped the false body off of him . . . . . . MBPI0148 . . 410
    as you would strip off a man's coat"

And that was the end of the Dwarf . . . . MBPI1548 . . 497

And then the feathers in his hat. . . . . MBPI2668 . . 567

And then they had a swampin gun. . . . . MBPI2671 . . 567

And then they'd fife away like fun. . . . . MBPI2683 . . 568

And there I see a little keg. . . . . MBPI2682 . . 568

And there I see a pumpkin shell. . . . . MBPI2679 . . 568

"And thither children brought donkeys . . . . . . MBPI0411 . . 426
    every morning"

"And twenty one and twenty two" . . . . MBPI1163 . . 473

And we kept those fellows alee, astern . . . . PDPI0072 . . . 608

"'And who's going to support 'em?' . . . . MBPI0764 . . 448
    demanded Mrs. Barkley"

"And you shall not hinder me" . . . . MBPI0777 . . 449

"'And you would not give me a chance to . . . . MBPI0372 . . 424
    tell you,'–she repeated, pleadingly,–touching his arm"

The Angel and the Youngest Brother said . . . . MBPI1571 . . 499
    "Good-bye" and trudged away

Angel of Death . . . . PDPI0029 . . . 605

Ann Hutchinson . . . . MBPI0835 . . 453

Anne Hutchinson . . . . MBPI0835 . . 453

Anne Hutchinson preaching in her house in . . MBPI0835 . . 453
    Boston

Another Day . . . . MBPI3050 . . 591

Another rush of breakers pitching the . . . . MBPI2004 . . 526
    boat, cork-like, into the air

"The Ant and the Grasshopper" . . . . MBPI1242 . . 478

Anthony Von Corlear, The Trumpeter of New . . MBPI2067 . . 530
    Amsterdam

Apollo Slaying the Python . . . . MBPI2781 . . 574

"Are they beaten?" . . . . MBPI2913 . . 583

Index–Titles and Alternate Titles of Pyle's Art

"Are you ever lonely here?" he inquired . . . . MBPI0932 . . 459

Arethusa, Nymph of the Spring Near Korax . . . . MBPI2785 . . 575

The arms of his captor held him as in a . . . . . . MBPI0984 . . 462
     vise

Arnold . . . . MBPI2000 . . 525

Arnold and his wife . . . . MBPI0040 . . 403

Arnold Tells his Wife of the Discovery of . . . . . MBPI2000 . . 525
     his Treason

"Around and around they spun and whirled" . . MBPI1644 . . 503

"Around the archways and the square stone . . MBPI0392 . . 425
     pillars, buzzing like angry hornets"

The Arrest . . . . MBPI1239 . . 478

Arresting a Witch . . . . MBPI0299 . . 419

Arresting a Witch in Old New England . . . . MBPI0299 . . 419

The Arrival at the Blue Boar Inn . . . . MBPI1216 . . 476

Arrival of Stuyvesant at New Amsterdam . . . . . MBPI0836 . . 453

Arrival of Stuyvesant in New Amsterdam . . . . . MBPI0836 . . 453

Arrival of the Coach at an Old Stage . . . . MBPI0209 . . 414
     Station

Arrival of the Young Women at Jamestown . . . . MBPI0294 . . 419

Arrivals at the Creamery . . . . MBOI0001 . . 611

The Artist . . . . MBPI0899 . . 457

"As for the King, he could not believe . . . . MBPI1726 . . 508
     his eyes when he saw it"

"As good as new" . . . . MBPI1799 . . 513

"As it sang it sang so sweetly and so . . . . MBPI1581 . . 499
     sadly"

"As she spoke, she took his hand, and . . . . . . MBPI0199 . . 413
     then paused one moment"

Assassination of LaSalle . . . . MBPI3102 . . 594

Assassination of William of Orange . . . . MBPI3178 . . 599

The Assembly Ball . . . . MBPI0746 . . 447

Assorting the Peaches . . . . MBOI0005 . . 612

At Baltimore, Maryland . . . . MBPI0513 . . 433

At Boston, Massachusetts . . . . MBPI0507 . . 432

At Charleston, South Carolina . . . . MBPI0514 . . 433

At Daddy Bayne's . . . . MBPI0169 . . 411

At David's bedside . . . . MBPI0488 . . 431

At Dawn . . . . MBPI3155 . . 598

At Dover, Delaware . . . . MBPI0505 . . 432

At Evening . . . . MBPI0259 . . 417

At Halifax, North Carolina . . . . MBPI0512 . . 432

"At her appearing the multitude was . . . . MBPI1762 . . 511
     hushed, awed by that air she wore"

"At last they dashed against one another" . . . . MBPI1607 . . 501

"At last they had the poor boy down" . . . . MBPI1673 . . 505

At Mrs. Washington's Reception . . . . MBPI0313 . . 420

At Newport, Rhode Island . . . . MBPI0509 . . 432

At Philadelphia, Pennsylvania . . . . MBPI0503 . . 432

At Portsmouth, New Hampshire . . . . MBPI0508 . . 432

At Princeton, New Jersey . . . . MBPI0504 . . 432

At Savannah, Georgia . . . . MBPI0515 . . 433

"At sight of me the good soul gave a . . . . MBPI1919 . . 520
     guttural exclamation, and stared at me open-mouthed"

"At that moment she looked up" . . . . MBPI0135 . . 409

At the Camp . . . . MBPI0738 . . 447

At the Club . . . . MBPI2979 . . 587

At the gate of the Castle . . . . MBPI0895 . . 456

At the Gates of Life . . . . MBPI0057 . . 404

"At the open doorway stood Gaspard and . . . MBPI0139 . . 409
     his master"

At the Precipice Edge . . . . MBPI2016 . . 526

"At the same time he extended toward King . . MBPI1746 . . 510
     Louis the precious Memorial"

At the Turn of the Glass . . . . MBPI1750 . . 510

At the Vauxhall . . . . MBPI0437 . . 428

At Valley Forge . . . . MBPI0717 . . 445

At Williamsburg, Virginia . . . . MBPI0511 . . 432

Atlas and Hercules . . . . MBPI3183 . . 599

An attack on a galleon . . . . MBPI0953 . . 460

The Attack On The Chew House, Germantown . MBPI1996 . . 525

The Attack on the Gaspee . . . . MBPI0847 . . 453

The Attack Upon the Chew House . . . . MBPI1996 . . 525

Aunt Gainor . . . . MBPI0035 . . 403

"Aunt Mary Expressing Her Mind" . . . . MBPI2751 . . 572

Aunt Saber . . . . MBPI0178 . . 412

Aunt Sally . . . . MBPI0184 . . 412

"'Austin,' she said, 'I have come to tell . . . . MBPI1267 . . 480
     you our engagement is at an end'"

"*Autumn*" . . . . MBPI0814 . . 451

Autumn . . . . MBPI0814 . . 451

An Autumn Evening . . . . MBPI0271 . . 417

An autumn field of which she had dreamed . . . MBPI0879 . . 455

"Autumn Leaves" . . . . MBPI1231 . . 477

Avary sells his jewels . . . . MBPI0350 . . 422

The Awakening of Brunhild . . . . MBPI2744 . . 572

"Away flew the carpet swifter than the . . . . . . MBPI1641 . . 503
     wind"

"Away flew the stool" . . . . MBPI1659 . . 504

"Away the boat went, swifter than the . . . . MBPI1604 . . 501
     wind"

Away they rode with clashing hoofs and . . . . . MBPI2289 . . 544
     ringing armor

"Away with you, and never let me see your . . . MBPI1601 . . 501
     face again"

"Awful, and proud, and erect" . . . . MBPI2749 . . 572

The baby drifts in the basket down the . . . . MBPI1529 . . 496
     river to the reeds beside the bank where the she-bear finds it

Back cover design for Pepper & Salt . . . . MBPI2148 . . 535

Back cover design for The Price of Blood . . . . . MBPI1807 . . 513

Back cover design for Yankee Doodle . . . . MBPI2694 . . 569

"Back in the one-hoss-shay he went" . . . . MBPI2839 . . 578

Balboa's Discovery of the Pacific . . . . MBPI2961 . . 586

"The ball began with French dances" . . . . MBPI0430 . . 427

A Banquet to Genet . . . . MBPI0753 . . 448

"Barbarously murdered the first, and . . . . MBPI0638 . . 440
     grievously wounded the latter"

The Barge of the Dead . . . . MBPI2594 . . 563

Index–Titles and Alternate Titles of Pyle's Art

"The barges gliding onward" .... MBPI2905 .. 582

"A basin filled with jewels" .... MBPI1707 .. 507

The basket with the baby in it drifted .... MBPI1529 .. 496
    down the river

"The Bastille is not a very healthy .... MBPI0969 .. 461
    place"

"Battered and Bruised, Forever Abused, He .... MBPI1212 .. 476
    Lay by the Morning Sea"

Battle between the "Bon Homme Richard" ... MBPI1312 .. 482
    and the "Serapis"

"Battle of Brandywine" .... MBPI1992 .. 525

The Battle of Bunker Hill .... MBPI1992 .. 525

The Battle of Bunker Hill .... MBPI0849 .. 454

The Battle of Fort Moultrie .... MBPI0306 .. 420

Battle of Germantown .... MBPI1996 .. 525

Battle of Germantown – The Attack Upon ..... MBPI1996 .. 525
    the Chew House

Battle of Great Meadows .... MBPI0677 .. 443

Battle of Lexington .... MBPI0305 .. 420

Battle of Lexington .... MBPI1991 .. 525

"Battle of Lexington" .... MBPI1991 .. 525

The Battle of Lexington .... MBPI1991 .. 525

Battle of Nashville .... MBPI3239 .. 603

The Battle of Nashville .... MBPI3239 .. 603

The Battle of the Stairs .... MBPI0907 .. 457

Battle of Yorktown .... MBPI3111 .. 595

The Battle on Lexington Common, April ...... MBPI1991 .. 525
    19th, 1775

The Battle with the Sable Knight .... MBPI1864 .. 517

Beach Scene .... PDPI0080 ... 608

The Bear & the Fox go to farmer John's .... MBPI1527 .. 496
    again

The bear would stand upon his hind legs .... MBPI1140 .. 472
    and dance

Bearskin and the Princess .... MBPI1530 .. 496

Bearskin and the Swineherd had a fine ...... MBPI1532 .. 496
    feast together

Bearskin and ye Swineherd have a grand ...... MBPI1532 .. 496
    feast

Bearskin slayeth ye Dragon but will not .... MBPI1530 .. 496
    go with ye Princess to ye castle

"Beat the statue with her steel-tipped .... MBPI1605 .. 501
    whip"

Beatrix and Esmond .... MBPI0963 .. 461

"The beautiful sweeping curve of harbor" ..... MBPI0387 .. 425

The beaux distinguished themselves by .... MBPI2755 .. 573
    their adroitness in replenishing this pot from a huge copper tea-
    kettle

Becky Sharp and Lord Steyne .... MBPI0964 .. 461

Before the picture .... MBPI0485 .. 431

"The beggar crawled out" .... MBPI1650 .. 504

"Behind trees and in gullies" .... MBPI1309 .. 482

"Behold it then!" cried Perseus .... MBPI3181 .. 599

"Behold the guests advancing" .... MBPI2879 .. 580

"'Belike thou sought to take this lad's .... MBPI1678 .. 505
    life,' said Sir James"

Belle Isoult and Sir Tristram drink the .... MBPI2480 .. 555
    love draught

The Beloved Pastor .... MBPI2754 .. 573

"The belted grenadiers" .... MBPI2904 .. 582

Benjamin Franklin and Richard Oswald ...... MBPI2002 .. 526
    Discussing the Treaty of Peace at Paris

"Beppo offers the King milk" .... MBPI1736 .. 509

Beppo sat in the Notary's house talking ..... MBPI1130 .. 471
    about the will

Bertha, the much beloved .... MBPI0909 .. 457

The Bewildered Guest .... MBPI0561 .. 436

The Bibliophile .... MBPI2393 .. 550

"Bidding his companions to await his .... MBPI0080 .. 405
    return...he followed his interlocutor"

Billy Patterson .... MBPI2052 .. 529

The Birth of Literature .... MBPI3232 .. 602

Birthday Tribute to Theodore Roosevelt .... PDPI0003 ... 603

"The Bishop of Montors had returned" .... MBPI0897 .. 457

The Bishop of Rochester and the King .... MBPI2648 .. 566

A bit of sentiment .... MBPI0196 .. 413

Black Night .... MBPI1013 .. 464

Blackbeard .... MBPI1828 .. 515

Blackbeard buries his treasure .... MBPI0352 .. 422

Blackbeard's last fight .... MBPI1838 .. 515

The Blacksmith brings ye wonderful little ..... MBPI1547 .. 497
    bird and tree to ye Queen

The Blacksmith carries the Golden Tree to .... MBPI1547 .. 497
    the Queen

The blacksmith chooses ye raven and runs ..... MBPI1546 .. 497
    away with it

The blacksmith takes ye dwarf's .... MBPI1545 .. 497
    pine-cones

Blair and Andros .... MBPI0841 .. 453

"Blazing and clanging from thicket and ...... MBPI2767 .. 573
    wall"

"Blazing with diamonds and rubies and ..... MBPI1629 .. 502
    emeralds"

Bliss .... MBPI2044 .. 528

"The blow–the whole crushing series of ..... MBPI1921 .. 521
    blows–had fallen!"

Blow ye horn for ye ferry man .... MBPI1355 .. 485

Blue–Skin The Pirate .... MBPI1768 .. 511

Bluetree declines Lord Diddledaddle's .... MBPI1803 .. 513
    offer

"'Boat ahoy!' I cried out, and then .... MBPI1254 .. 479
    levelled my pistol and fired"

The boat and I went by him with a rush .... MBPI2011 .. 526

The Boats Passing Along the River .... MBPI2704 .. 569

The Body and the Soul .... MBPI0788 .. 450

The Body Piping To the Soul .... MBPI0788 .. 450

The Boggart Rejoices .... MBPI1409 .. 489

Bonhomme Richard and Serapis .... MBPI0850 .. 454

Index–Titles and Alternate Titles of Pyle's Art

BONHOMME RICHARD AND THE SERAPIS

Bonhomme Richard and the Serapis . . . . MBPI0850 . . 454

The Bonhomme Richard and Ye Serapis . . . . . . MBPI0021 . . 402

Boots tricks the Princess into showing . . . . MBPI1461 . . 492
herself

The Boston Massacre, March 5, 1770 . . . . MBPI0301 . . 419

The "Boston Massacre" . . . . MBPI0301 . . 419

The Boston Tea Party . . . . MBPI0848 . . 453

The Boston Tea Party . . . . MBPI2864 . . 579

"The Boston teapot bubbled" . . . . MBPI2874 . . 580

The Botanist . . . . MBPI0232 . . 415

A Bowl of Milk for Robin Goodfellow . . . . MBPI1804 . . 513

"A box of adamant" . . . . MBPI1633 . . 503

The Boys consult Jack-in-the-Box . . . . MBPI1810 . . 514

The Boys present the Salmagundi to Heer . . . MBPI2791 . . 575
Governor Stuyvesant

Braddock's Defeat, Battle of Monongahela . . . . . MBPI0677 . . 443

Branwen . . . . MBPI1010 . . 464

The Brave Soldier bringeth his Trouble to . . . . . MBPI1452 . . 491
ye town along with him

"Bread as white as snow, and a piece of . . . . . . MBPI1628 . . 502
cheese"

"Breaking from her companions with an . . . . . MBPI1211 . . 476
excited exclamation, Mlle. Bland grasped the old woman by
the wrists"

"Breaking the News" . . . . MBPI1185 . . 475

Breathed through her lips a sad and . . . . MBPI2777 . . 574
tremulous tune

Breton Peasants at a Wayside Cross . . . . MBPI1932 . . 521

"Bringing fire and terror to roof tree . . . . MBPI1980 . . 524
and bed"

"Bringing in the May" . . . . MBPI0317 . . 420

Bringing in the Yule-Log . . . . MBPI1220 . . 477

Bringing the powder to Bunker Hill . . . . MBPI0335 . . 421

The British in Wilmington . . . . MBPI0263 . . 417

The Broken Flute . . . . MBPI0793 . . 450

The Brooks Forces evacuating the State . . . . . MBPI1973 . . 524
House at Little Rock

Brother Fox comes near tramping on the . . . . MBPI1537 . . 497
Mole's House

Brotherhood . . . . MBPI3120 . . 595

"Brought him from the battle" . . . . MBPI2926 . . 583

Brownejohn's Wharf . . . . MBPI0425 . . 427

The Buccaneer . . . . MBPI0952 . . 460

The buccaneer was a picturesque fellow . . . . . . MBPI0952 . . 460

Buccaneers Extorting Tribute from . . . . MBPI0955 . . 460
Citizens of Carthagens

The Buccaneers . . . . MBPI0952 . . 460

The Buccaneers . . . . MBPI1266 . . 480

The bugle call . . . . MBPI0417 . . 427

Bugler at Fort Macon . . . . PDPI0032 . . . 605

Building a Floating Town . . . . MBPI0689 . . 444

A Bumboat trading upon the Hudson River . . . . MBPI0694 . . 444

Burburlangs . . . . MBPI2010 . . 526

The Burburlangs . . . . MBPI2010 . . 526

CAPTAIN KIDD

The Burden . . . . MBPI0644 . . 441

A burial at sea on board the "Welcome" . . . . MBPI0285 . . 418

The Burial of Braddock . . . . MBPI0678 . . 443

The Burial of General Fraser . . . . MBPI1995 . . 525

The Burial of Jim Shields . . . . MBPI0775 . . 449

"The Burial of Jim Shields" . . . . MBPI0775 . . 449

"Buried his head on her bosom" . . . . MBPI0487 . . 431

Buried Treasure . . . . MBPI0887 . . 456

The Burning Galleon . . . . MBPI0100 . . 407

The Burning of Jamestown . . . . MBPI0837 . . 453

Burning of the Gaspé . . . . MBPI0847 . . 453

Burning of the "Gaspee" . . . . MBPI0847 . . 453

The Burning of the Guillotine Before the . . . . . PDPI0070 . . . 607
Statue of Voltaire

The Burning Ship . . . . MBPI0100 . . 407

The Burning Ship . . . . MBPI0886 . . 456

Burning the Ship . . . . MBPI0886 . . 456

Bust profile arm extended . . . . PDPI0086 . . . 608

Bust profile with chalice . . . . PDPI0085 . . . 608

"But tell me, Robin Ingoldsby, dost know . . . . MBPI1677 . . 505
aught more of this matter?"

"But the Proudest and Grandest of All the . . . . PDPI0104 . . . 610
Flock Was Gobble, Our Gorgeous Turkey-Cock."

"By Land and Sea" . . . . MBPI0655 . . 441

"By Land and Sea" . . . . MBPI0656 . . 441

"By Land and Sea" . . . . MBPI0659 . . 442

"By Land and Sea" . . . . MBPI0660 . . 442

"By Land and Sea" . . . . MBPI0663 . . 442

"By Land and Sea" . . . . MBPI0664 . . 442

"By Land and Sea" . . . . MBPI0667 . . 442

"By Land and Sea" . . . . MBPI0668 . . 442

By Land and Sea . . . . MBPI0655 . . 441

By Land and Sea . . . . MBPI0659 . . 442

By Land and Sea . . . . MBPI0663 . . 442

By Land and Sea . . . . MBPI0667 . . 442

The cabin of the Adventurers . . . . MBPI0120 . . 408

The Cabin of the Treasure Seekers . . . . MBPI0120 . . 408

Calvary . . . . MBPI0631 . . 440

A Calvary Charge During the Civil War . . . . MBPI0917 . . 458

Camping Out . . . . MBPI2051 . . 529

A Canadian Sketch . . . . MBPI1179 . . 474

The Canal Locks at Waterford . . . . MBPI0700 . . 444

Canal Locks in the Mountains . . . . MBPI0706 . . 445

The Canal Street of New Amsterdam . . . . MBPI0570 . . 436

"The cannons' deafening thrill" . . . . MBPI2902 . . 582

Cap'n Goldsack . . . . MBPI0670 . . 442

The Capitol at Williamsburg . . . . MBPI0682 . . 443

The Capitulation of Louisbourg . . . . MBPI0845 . . 453

The Capitulation of Louisburg . . . . MBPI0845 . . 453

Capt. Kidd . . . . MBPI0885 . . 456

Capt. Kidd at Sandy Hook . . . . MBPI0610 . . 439

Captain Keitt . . . . MBPI0987 . . 462

Captain Kidd . . . . MBPI0885 . . 456

Captain Kidd and Buried Treasure . . . . MBPI0887 . . 456

"Captain Kidd on the deck of the . . . . MBPI0885 . . 456
'Adventure Galley' an example of Howard Pyle's later conception of the pirate"

Captain Kidd's gift to Mercy Redmond . . . . MBPI0229 . . 415

Captain Kidd's Treasure . . . . MBPI0887 . . 456

"'Captain Mackra,' said he, coldly, 'you . . . . MBPI1255 . . 479
were pleased to put upon me last night
a gross and uncalled for insult.'"

"Captain Malyoe shot Captain Brand . . . . MBPI1282 . . 481
through the head"

The Captain of the Yacht "Delaware" . . . . MBPI0195 . . 413

Capture of a Galleon . . . . MBPI0953 . . 460

Capture of Elizabeth and Frances Callaway . . . MBPI0344 . . 422
and Jemima Boone

Capture of the Galleon . . . . MBPI0347 . . 422

"Captured by Indians" . . . . MBPI0344 . . 422

"Cards and gaming were features" . . . . MBPI0432 . . 427

"Cargoes of favorite vintages" . . . . MBPI0434 . . 428

Carlotta–tall, white, queenly–a cluster . . . . MBPI0938 . . 459
of flowers in her arms

Carnival, Philadelphia, 1778 . . . . MBPI0167 . . 411

Carpenter's Hall, Philadelphia . . . . MBPI0720 . . 445

Caspar and the cunning Landlord . . . . MBPI1508 . . 495

Caspar and the Three rascals go to see . . . . . . MBPI1511 . . 495
the King

Caspar findeth money in the willow-tree . . . . . . MBPI1509 . . 495

Caspar finds the Gold in the Willow-Tree . . . . . MBPI1509 . . 495

Cassacinci and the runaway horse . . . . MBPI1143 . . 472

"Catch a gleam from her wicked eye" . . . . MBPI2859 . . 579

Catching a pony . . . . MBPI2033 . . 528

Catching Muskallonge . . . . MBPI2050 . . 529

Catherine . . . . MBPI1382 . . 487

Catherine de Vaucelles, in her garden . . . . MBPI0914 . . 458

Catherine Duke quickened her steps . . . . MBPI0925 . . 458

The Cavalier . . . . MBPI0904 . . 457

Cavalier with sword . . . . PDPI0021 . . . 604

Caxton at his Press . . . . MBPI3196 . . 600

Celebration in New York on the Night of . . . . . MBPI0361 . . 423
Washington's Inauguration

Celebration on the Night of the . . . . MBPI0361 . . 423
Inauguration

"'Celeste!' breathed Oliver through the . . . . . . MBPI0163 . . 411
crack in the door"

"The chair was carried by hand and the . . . . . MBPI0431 . . 427
harness was worn by the bearers"

"A chaise breaks down" . . . . MBPI2802 . . 576

The Challenge . . . . MBPI1688 . . 506

The Chambered Nautilus with initial T . . . . MBPI2984 . . 587

Change . . . . MBPI0626 . . 440

"'Change it? My name?' she said" . . . . MBPI0761 . . 448

The Chantey-Man . . . . MBPI0888 . . 456

The Chapman . . . . MBPI0444 . . 428

Chapter heading with illustrated initial A . . . . MBPI0805 . . 451
for A Puppet of Fate

Chapter heading with illustrated initial . . . . . . MBPI0802 . . 451
F for A Puppet of Fate

Chapter heading with illustrated initial . . . . . . MBPI0797 . . 450
N for A Puppet of Fate

The Charge at Yorktown . . . . MBPI3111 . . 595

The charge . . . . MBPI0917 . . 458

The Chase of the Slaver . . . . MBPI0989 . . 462

"The Cherokees Are Coming" . . . . MBPI0326 . . 421

"The chief treasurer emptied a bag of . . . . MBPI1620 . . 502
money into the fur cap"

"A child, sunburned, and with many . . . . MBPI1770 . . 511
fluttering shreds of raiment"

The Children are sent to the Asylum . . . . MBPI1447 . . 491

"The choicest pieces of her cargo were . . . . . . MBPI0634 . . 440
sold at auction"

The Chorus of the Six Jolly Feeders . . . . MBPI1337 . . 484

The Christ Thorn . . . . MBPI0236 . . 415

Christine and the Apple . . . . MBPI1428 . . 490

Christine gives the Apple to the King . . . . MBPI1432 . . 490

Christine's Mother and Sisters wish for . . . . . . MBPI1427 . . 490
the Apple

Christmas 1896, Cover Design . . . . MBPI0731 . . 446

A Christmas Carol, with title, ... MBPI1314 . . 483
illustrations, and verse

Christmas Morn . . . . MBPI0070 . . 405

Christmas Morning in Old New York . . . . MBPI1193 . . 475

A Christmas Party In Our Grand Parents' . . . . . PDPI0084 . . 608
Time

Christmas presents for the Squire . . . . MBPI1215 . . 476

Christmas Pudding . . . . MBPI1223 . . 477

The Christmas Tree, title inserted . . . . MBPI1202 . . 476

The Circus . . . . MBPI1191 . . 475

Citizen Genet formally presented to . . . . MBPI0756 . . 448
Washington

The civil procession, headed by General . . . . . MBPI0308 . . 420
Washington and Governor Clinton

"The Clang of the Yankee Reaper, on . . . . MBPI0239 . . 415
Salisbury Plain!"

"The Clang of the Yankee Reaper" . . . . MBPI0239 . . 415

Clark on his way to Kaskaskia . . . . MBPI1997 . . 525

Clark On The Way To Kaskaskia . . . . MBPI1997 . . 525

Clark on the Way to Kaskaskia . . . . MBPI1997 . . 525

Claude DuVal proposes a Dance on the . . . . . . MBPI0445 . . 428
Heath

Claus and the Manikin . . . . MBPI1423 . . 489

Claus and the Master of Black-Arts . . . . MBPI1420 . . 489

Claus and the White Snake . . . . MBPI1419 . . 489

Claus listens to the talk of the two . . . . MBPI1422 . . 489
ravens

"Clear the track" . . . . MBPI2842 . . 578

Clever Peter and the Unlucky Bottle . . . . MBPI1400 . . 488

Clever Peter opens the Unlucky Bottle for . . . . MBPI1401 . . 488
the King and Princess

Clever Peter rides to the King's Palace . . . . MBPI1398 . . 488
upon his fine Horse

Index–Titles and Alternate Titles of Pyle's Art

CLEVER PETER & THE LITTLE GENTLEMAN IN BLACK

A CREAMERY

Clever Peter & the Little Gentleman in .... MBPI1397 .. 488
Black

The Clever Scholar remains a Ruby Ring no ... MBPI1474 .. 493
longer, having regained his own true shape

The Climb of Life .... MBPI3161 .. 598

Clive And Ethel Newcome .... MBPI1011 .. 464

Clive and Ethel Newcome .... MBPI1011 .. 464

"Close your doors! close your doors! her ..... MBPI1722 .. 508
Highness the Princess comes to ride"

The Closed Door .... MBPI2991 .. 587

"The clown counted the money" .... MBPI1813 .. 514

"Coffee mill, surrounded by flat stone .... MBPI0413 .. 426
terraces"

"Colonel Parker reached out and laid his ..... MBPI1837 .. 515
hand upon Jack's shoulder; 'Ay,' said he, 'tis a good, honest
face'"

Colonel Rhett and Pirate Stede Bonnet .... MBPI0844 .. 453

Colonel Rhett and the Pirates .... MBPI0844 .. 453

Colonel Rhett and the pirates .... MBPI0844 .. 453

Columbia Speaks .... MBPI0091 .. 406

"The combatants cut and slashed with .... MBPI1838 .. 515
savage fury"

"Come, come, your Future Majesty! Cheer .... MBPI0933 .. 459
up!"

"Come hither, lads," she said .... MBPI1116 .. 470

"'Come with me,' said the little old man" ..... MBPI1697 .. 507

The coming of Lancaster .... MBPI1009 .. 464

Coming of the English .... PDPI0008 ... 604

The Coming of the English .... PDPI0009 ... 604

The Coming of the English .... PDPI0010 ... 604

The Coming Tide .... MBPI1071 .. 467

Company .... MBPI3027 .. 590

A complimentary Address to Old .... MBPI0208 .. 413
Hickory–Interior of Ben Bean's ("Barton") House

A Conference with the Colonists .... MBPI1230 .. 477

The Conflagration in 1776 .... MBPI0574 .. 436

The Conflagration of 1776 .... MBPI0574 .. 436

The Connecticut Settlers entering the .... MBPI2009 .. 526
Western Reserve

Conscience .... MBPI3032 .. 590

The Constitution's Last Fight .... MBPI0027 .. 402

The "Constitution's" Last Fight .... MBPI0027 .. 402

Consulting the Wise Woman .... MBPI1182 .. 474

Contentment with initial L .... MBPI3015 .. 589

The Contra-Dance .... MBPI1224 .. 477

The Convalescent .... MBPI0742 .. 447

The Conversion of Chilo .... MBPI3108 .. 595

Cooking a Camp Dinner .... MBPI2055 .. 529

Cooking shanty .... MBPI0183 .. 412

"The cooper's boys" .... MBPI2882 .. 581

Cor Cordia: A Christmas Greeting from Thy ... PDPI0102 ... 609
Husband

The Corn Fields on the Hill-Side .... MBPI0273 .. 418

"The Corporal marched before" .... MBPI2899 .. 582

"The Corporal, our old cripple" .... MBPI2908 .. 582

The Councilor finds one in the Sack who ...... MBPI1460 .. 492
teaches him wisdom

The Councilor finds the Wisdom Sack .... MBPI1460 .. 492

"The Count de St. Germaine, without .... MBPI0157 .. 410
removing his eyes from his victim, took another deep, luxurious pinch of snuff"

The Country Clerk, Eastville .... MBPI0176 .. 411

Coureur De Bois .... MBPI0357 .. 423

Coureurs de Bois .... MBPI0357 .. 423

Courtship .... MBPI1742 .. 509

Cousin Greylegs and the Great Red Fox go ..... MBPI1535 .. 496
together to ye fair

Cousin Greylegs steals away from the inn, ... MBPI1536 .. 496
carrying off a bag full of this & that with him

Cousin Greylegs steals away with the bag .... MBPI1536 .. 496
of nails

Cousin Simon grew so bold... .... MBPI2677 .. 568

Cover border design for The Ladies' Home ... PDPI0100 ... 609
Journal

Cover design for Centuria's Greetings .... MBPI3219 .. 602

Cover design for McClure's Magazine .... MBPI1748 .. 510

Cover design for Men of Iron .... MBPI2351 .. 547

Cover design for Otto of the Silver Hand ...... MBPI2273 .. 543

Cover design for Report of the Board of ..... PDPI0057 ... 607
Park Commissioners, Wilmington, Delaware

Cover design for Stops of Various Quills .... MBPI2383 .. 549

Cover design for The Cecilia Society .... MBPI3214 .. 601

Cover design for The Garden Behind the ..... MBPI2353 .. 548
Moon

Cover design for The Merry Adventures of ... MBPI2145 .. 535
Robin Hood

Cover design for The Story of Champions .... MBPI2429 .. 552
of the Round Table

Cover design for The Story of King Arthur .... MBPI2394 .. 550
and His Knights

Cover design for The Story of Sir .... MBPI2514 .. 558
Launceot and his Companions

Cover design for The Story of the Grail ...... MBPI2595 .. 563
and the Passing of Arthur

Cover design for The Tuesday Club .... MBPI3210 .. 601

Cover design for The Wonder Clock .... MBPI2163 .. 536

Cover design for Twelfth Night at .... MBPI3216 .. 601
Eagleroost

Cover design for Twilight Land .... MBPI2387 .. 550

Cover Design in Colors .... PDPI0100 ... 609

Cover design without border for Tuesday ... PDPI0066 ... 607
Club

Cover illustration for Around Old Chester ...... MBPI0762 .. 448

Cover illustration for The Buccaneers .... MBPI0887 .. 456

"Crack! Crack! went the guns of the .... MBPI1309 .. 482
Indians"

A Creamery .... MBOI0001 .. 611

A Creamery .... MBOI0002 .. 611

A Creamery .... MBOI0003 .. 611

Index–Titles and Alternate Titles of Pyle's Art

A Creamery

A Creamery . . . . MBOI0004 . . 611
"Creeping cautiously forward, Oliver came . . . MBPI0140 . . 409
    to the chimney-place"
"The crooked winding road that leads into . . MBPI0409 . . 426
    the village"
Crossing to Assateague . . . . MBPI2039 . . 528
"A crowd gathered around" . . . . MBPI0404 . . 426
The crowd scattered . . . . MBPI1170 . . 474
The Crown-Prince Karl, dead by his own . . . . . MBPI0937 . . 459
    hand
The cruiser piled on all sail . . . . MBPI0991 . . 462
A Cry in the Night . . . . MBPI3152 . . 597
The cunning landlord telleth Caspar where . . . . MBPI1508 . . 495
    to take his hen to sell it for a good price
The Cup of Fate . . . . MBPI0003 . . 401
A cup of Tea . . . . MBPI2876 . . 580
"A curious group traveling along a hot . . . . . . MBPI0383 . . 424
    dusty road"
Curlett and his Ambrotype . . . . MBPI0734 . . 446
Cutting off a queue to bind a wound . . . . MBPI1310 . . 482
Cutting the Cross Out of the English Flag . . . . . MBPI0295 . . 419
"D'ye see what the wretches have left?" . . . . . . MBPI1042 . . 466
Daisies . . . . MBPI0128 . . 408
Dame Bridget's Prophecy . . . . MBPI1522 . . 496
Dame Charity Greene meeteth Ye Strange . . . MBPI1237 . . 478
    Little Man
Dame Mally Griggs . . . . MBPI1405 . . 488
Dame Margery Twist goeth to see the merry   MBPI1392 . . 487
    doings at the Fair
Dame Twist drinketh tea . . . . MBPI1389 . . 487
Dame Twist drives away the Little Folks . . . . . . MBPI1393 . . 488
Dame Twist sees the Little Man in Green . . . . . MBPI1394 . . 488
    for the last time
Dame Twist visits a Strange Patient . . . . MBPI1391 . . 487
A Damsel bringeth aid unto Sir Ewaine . . . . . . MBPI2579 . . 562
The Damsel Elose giveth a ring to Sir . . . . MBPI2575 . . 561
    Ewaine
The Damsel Elose the Fair rescues Sir . . . . MBPI2534 . . 559
    Launcelot
The Damsel Lynette . . . . MBPI2539 . . 559
Dan'l Malcolm's Grave . . . . MBPI2909 . . 582
The Dance of the Veterans . . . . MBPI1184 . . 474
"The Dancer" . . . . MBPI1054 . . 466
The Dancer . . . . MBPI0804 . . 451
"The dark and shadowy outline of a man" . . . . MBPI2074 . . 530
"Dark, dim, Dante-like solitudes" . . . . MBPI2846 . . 578
The dark folk trooped to meet them on the . . MBPI0908 . . 457
    shore
The dark, smiling Salim, with his magic . . . . . MBPI1012 . . 464
    pack, was welcome
David . . . . MBPI0477 . . 430
David looked up into Hans Krout's face . . . . . . MBPI2363 . . 548
David sat down on the wooden bench and . . MBPI2367 . . 548
    took up a big blue star

Decorative border for A Ballad of the Boston-Tea ...

de Gourgues Avenging the Massacre of the . . . . . MBPI0290 . . 419
    Huguenots
de Gourgues Avenging the Massacre of the . . . . . MBPI0290 . . 419
    Huguenots by Menendez
De Lesken entertaining . . . . MBPI2063 . . 529
"De profundis clamavi ad te, Domine" . . . . MBPI3109 . . 595
"Deacon and deaconess dropped away" . . . . . . MBPI2806 . . 576
"The Deacon inquired of the village folk" . . . . . MBPI2803 . . 576
The Deacon . . . . MBPI2795 . . 575
The Deacon's Masterpiece: or the . . . . PDPI0059 . . . 607
    Wonderful "One-Hoss-Shay" with initial H
The Deacon's One–Hoss Shay . . . . MBPI2862 . . 579
The Dead Lady Floateth Down Ye Stream . . . . MBPI2731 . . 571
    Toward Camelot
Dead Men Tell No Tales . . . . MBPI0089 . . 406
The Dead Stowaway . . . . MBPI1212 . . 476
Death and Winter closed the autumn scene . . . MBPI2778 . . 574
The Death of Braddock . . . . MBPI1960 . . 523
The Death of Cazaio . . . . MBPI0970 . . 461
The Death of Colonel John Laurens . . . . MBPI1747 . . 510
The Death of Fafnir . . . . MBPI2743 . . 572
Death of King Philip . . . . MBPI0296 . . 419
The Death of Siegfried . . . . MBPI2747 . . 572
Death of the Indian Chief Alexander . . . . MBPI0327 . . 421
"Death of the Medicine-Man" . . . . MBPI1308 . . 482
The Death of Washington . . . . MBPI0729 . . 446
Decatur and his men boarding the gun-boat . . MBPI1313 . . 483
Decoration and illustrated initial T for . . . . PDPI0025 . . . 605
    Quill and Grill Club Invitation
Decoration for Pepper & Salt . . . . MBPI2159 . . 535
Decoration for Pepper & Salt . . . . MBPI2160 . . 535
Decoration for Pepper & Salt . . . . MBPI2161 . . 536
Decoration for Pepper & Salt . . . . MBPI2162 . . 536
Decoration for Society . . . . MBPI3039 . . 590
Decoration for The Body to the Soul . . . . MBPI0791 . . 450
Decoration for The Lady of Shalott . . . . MBPI2739 . . 572
Decoration for The Tuesday Club . . . . MBPI3212 . . 601
Decoration for The Wonder Clock . . . . MBPI2191 . . 537
Decoration for The Wonder Clock . . . . MBPI2214 . . 539
Decoration for The Wonder Clock . . . . MBPI2220 . . 539
Decoration for The Wonder Clock . . . . MBPI2242 . . 541
Decoration for The Wonder Clock . . . . MBPI2253 . . 541
Decoration with title for A Sahib's War . . . . MBPI0093 . . 406
Decoration with title for North Folk . . . . MBPI0863 . . 454
    Legends of the Sea
Decoration with title for North Folk . . . . MBPI0865 . . 455
    Legends of the Sea
Decoration with title for Old Chester . . . . MBPI0758 . . 448
    Tales
Decoration with title for Poisoned Ice . . . . MBPI0071 . . 405
Decoration with title for The Man with . . . . . . MBPI1173 . . 474
    the Hoe
Decorative border for A Ballad of the . . . . MBPI2945 . . 585
    Boston-Tea Party

Index–Titles and Alternate Titles of Pyle's Art

Decorative border for Dorothy Q ....MBPI2935 .. 584
Decorative border for Dorothy Q ....MBPI2937 .. 584
Decorative border for Dorothy Q ....MBPI2939 .. 584
Decorative border for Dorothy Q ....MBPI2941 .. 584
Decorative border for Dorothy Q ....MBPI2943 .. 584
Decorative border with title for A Ballad .....MBPI2944 .. 584
of the Boston-Tea Party
Decorative border with title for January .....MBPI1963 .. 523
and May
Decorative heading for A Ballad of the ......MBPI2946 .. 585
Boston-Tea Party
Decorative heading for A Ballad of the ......MBPI2948 .. 585
Boston-Tea Party
Decorative heading for A Ballad of the ......MBPI2950 .. 585
Boston-Tea Party
Decorative heading for A Ballad of the ......MBPI2951 .. 585
Boston-Tea Party
Decorative heading for A Ballad of the ......MBPI2953 .. 585
Boston-Tea Party
Decorative heading for A Ballad of the ......MBPI2955 .. 585
Boston-Tea Party
Decorative heading for A Ballad of the ......MBPI2957 .. 585
Boston-Tea Party
Decorative heading for A Ballad of the ......MBPI2959 .. 585
Boston-Tea Party
Decorative heading for Dorothy Q ....MBPI2934 .. 584
Decorative heading for Dorothy Q ....MBPI2936 .. 584
Decorative heading for Dorothy Q ....MBPI2938 .. 584
Decorative heading for Dorothy Q ....MBPI2940 .. 584
Decorative heading for Dorothy Q ....MBPI2942 .. 584
Decorative heading for "The Book of Three ....MBPI2400 .. 550
Worthies"
Decorative heading for "The Story of ....MBPI2467 .. 555
Percival"
Decorative illustration for The Lady of ....MBPI2698 .. 569
Shalott
Decorative illustration for The Lady of ....MBPI2721 .. 571
Shalott
Decorative illustration for The Lady of ....MBPI2727 .. 571
Shalott
Decorative illustration for The Lady of ....MBPI2732 .. 571
Shalott
Decorative illustration for The Lady of ....MBPI2735 .. 571
Shalott
Decorative illustrations for The Lady of .....MBPI2695 .. 569
Shalott
Decorative illustrations for The Lady of .....MBPI2696 .. 569
Shalott
Decorative illustrations for The Lady of .....MBPI2706 .. 570
Shalott
Decorative tailpiece for "The Story of ....MBPI2489 .. 556
Sir Tristram"
Decorative title for A Pastoral Without ....MBPI1933 .. 521
Words
Decorative title for The Dead Finger ....MBPI1127 .. 471

Decorative title for The Evil Eye ....MBPI1144 .. 472
Decorative title for The Painted Pitcher ....MBPI1137 .. 472
Decorative title, L'Envoy for A Pastoral ....MBPI1943 .. 522
Without Words
Decorative title, Verse I for A Pastoral ....MBPI1935 .. 521
Without Words
Decorative title, Verse II for A Pastoral ....MBPI1937 .. 522
Without Words
Decorative title, Verse III for A ....MBPI1939 .. 522
Pastoral Without Words
Decorative title, Verse IV for A Pastoral ....MBPI1941 .. 522
Without Words
Decorative title with illustrated initial ....MBPI2012 .. 526
S for Sindbad on Burrator
Decorative title with illustrated initial ....MBPI1075 .. 468
T for The Salem Wolf
Decorative title with illustrated initial ....MBPI1102 .. 469
T for Ysobel de Corveaux
Decorative title with illustrated initial ....MBPI1037 .. 465
U for The Mysterious Chest
Dedication for Twilight Land ....MBPI2389 .. 550
Defence of the Station ....MBPI0345 .. 422
"Defending The Fort" ....MBPI0345 .. 422
Defense of the Station at Boonesborough ....MBPI0345 .. 422
Deianeira and the Dying Centaur Nessus ......MBPI2787 .. 575
A Delegation From "The Club" ....MBPI2969 .. 586
"Demetrious sent little boats" ....MBPI0953 .. 460
"Demetrious stood among them giving ....MBPI0908 .. 457
orders"
"Demetrious wrenched the sword from its .....MBPI0910 .. 457
scabbard"
The Demoiselle Blanche–Fleur ....MBPI2510 .. 557
The Demoiselle Blanchefleur ....MBPI2510 .. 557
"The Demon leaped from the earth" ....MBPI1706 .. 507
Denneys and the Hermit help Sir Launcelot ..MBPI2529 .. 559
to his armor
Dennis Kearney being drawn through the ...MBPI1975 .. 524
streets of San Francisco after his release from the House of
Correction
"A dense cloud of blue smoke rose in the ....MBPI1716 .. 508
air"
Departure for New York ....MBPI0238 .. 415
The Departure of the "Welcome" ....MBPI0284 .. 418
The Departure ....MBPI1407 .. 488
A Description of the Castle ....MBPI2700 .. 569
A Description of the Same ....MBPI2703 .. 569
Design for 1908 Christmas Seal ....PDPI0064 ... 607
Design for 1908 Christmas Seal–Rounded ....PDPI0065 ... 607
corners
Design for ....PDPI0048 ... 606
candelabra–candlestick–electrolier
Design for centerpiece ....PDPI0047 ... 606
Design for drinking mug ....PDPI0023 ... 605
Design for Eben C. Hill bookplate ....MBPI2297 .. 544
Design for Edith Kermit Roosevelt ....MBPI3227 .. 602
bookplate

Index–Titles and Alternate Titles of Pyle's Art

DESIGN FOR FREDERICK HAINES CURTISS BOOKPLATE

Design for Frederick Haines Curtiss .... MBPI3225 .. 602
bookplate
Design for Howard Pyle bookplate .... MBPI3226 .. 602
Design for Howard Pyle School of Art .... PDPI0062 ... 607
lapel pin
Design for Keats-Shelley Memorial .... MBPI3229 .. 602
bookplate
Design for punch bowl .... PDPI0046 ... 606
Design For Stained Glass Window .... PDPI0029 ... 605
Design for The Grolier Club bookplate .... PDPI0042 ... 606
Design for The Players bookplate .... MBPI3223 .. 602
Design for The Players bookplate .... MBPI3224 .. 602
Design for The Yale Club of New York City .... MBPI3228 .. 602
bookplate
Design for unused Howard Pyle bookplate .... PDPI0027 ... 605
Design for Willard S. Morse bookplate .... MBPI2393 .. 550
Design on front cover with title for .... MBPI3216 .. 601
Twelfth Night at The Century
The Desire of Nations .... MBPI3127 .. 596
The Destruction of the Sign .... MBPI0262 .. 417
Diana Sherley .... MBPI1034 .. 465
"Didst thou tell them I taught thee?" .... MBPI0031 .. 402
Dietrich examines the disaster from a .... MBPI2059 .. 529
distance
"The dignified sober figure of Abraham ..... MBPI1923 .. 521
Ten Broeck appeared in our wrathful circle"
"The dignified sober figure of Abraham .... MBPI1923 .. 521
Ten Broeck appeared in our watchful circle"
Dim and faded pictures at times came ...... MBPI1062 .. 467
before them
"The dim, shadowy forms of vessels riding ... MBPI0375 .. 424
at anchor in the night"
Dinner at Cornelius Dubois's .... MBPI0251 .. 416
Dinner-bell at an Eastville Tavern .... MBPI0175 .. 411
Diplomats .... MBPI0967 .. 461
The Diplomats .... MBPI0967 .. 461
A Disappointment, with title, ... MBPI1343 .. 484
illustrations and verse
Dividing the Treasure .... MBPI0954 .. 460
Divine Adventure .... MBPI3168 .. 598
"Do you find the hole?" asked the Little ..... MBPI1499 .. 494
Pig
"'Do you know,' said the Marquis, 'what a .... MBPI0153 .. 410
thing it is that you ask?'"
"Do you live with Santa Claus in his own ..... MBPI1321 .. 483
house?"
"'Do you not know me?' said she; 'I am .... MBPI1739 .. 509
the Queen'"
"Do you see this knife?" .... MBPI2024 .. 527
Dofobius .... MBPI3209 .. 601
"'The Dog's Head in the Pot' (of great .... MBPI0423 .. 427
antiquity)"
The doge sat alone in a great carven .... MBPI0948 .. 460
chair
"The Doge" .... MBPI0948 .. 460

DUPONT POWDER WAGON CARRYING POWDER TO LAKE ...

Dominique de Gourgues avenging the .... MBPI0290 .. 419
Murder of the Huguenot Colony
Don Quixote's Encounter with the Windmill ... MBPI0047 .. 403
"'Don't you fret and worry any'" .... MBPI2897 .. 582
The door was opened by a poor man .... MBPI1560 .. 498
Dora–Dorothy .... MBPI1334 .. 484
A Dormitory in the Sisters' House, ... MBPI0363 .. 423
Ephrata
Dorothy Q .... MBPI2863 .. 579
Dorothy Q .... MBPI2866 .. 580
"Down fell the fisherman" .... MBPI1621 .. 502
"Down my hair went as I hurried" .... MBPI2898 .. 582
"Down she came from the pedestal where ... MBPI1699 .. 507
she stood"
Dr. Franklin on His Way To France .... MBPI1311 .. 482
Dr. Lavendar .... MBPI0759 .. 448
Dragging the Duke out of the Coach .... MBPI0597 .. 438
"The dragon leaped into the air" .... MBPI1614 .. 501
Drake's Attack on San Domingo .... MBPI0288 .. 418
"Drake's Attack Upon St. Domingo" .... MBPI0288 .. 418
Drama .... MBPI3238 .. 603
The drawing of the sword .... MBPI0910 .. 457
Drawing Room of General Wayne's House ...... MBPI0246 .. 416
Drawing-Room, Wayne Homestead .... MBPI0246 .. 416
A dreadful spectacle .... MBPI1045 .. 466
A Dream of Young Summer .... MBPI0854 .. 454
Dredging for oysters .... MBPI0181 .. 412
"Drew a circle upon the ground with his ..... MBPI1712 .. 507
finger-tip"
Drilling Recruits For the Continental .... MBPI1814 .. 514
Army
"The drum beat in the streets of the .... MBPI0435 .. 428
city"
The Drummer captures the one-eyed Raven ... MBPI1516 .. 495
The Drummer carries the Old Body across ..... MBPI1513 .. 495
the River
The Drummer carries the Old Man across .... MBPI1513 .. 495
the River
The Drummer catches ye one-eyed raven .... MBPI1516 .. 495
The Drummer helps himself to the good .... MBPI1515 .. 495
things, though no one can see him
The Drummer with his Cap of Darkness in ... MBPI1515 .. 495
the Witch's House
The duel between John Blumer and Cazaio ... MBPI0968 .. 461
The Duel .... MBPI0041 .. 403
The Duel .... MBPI1225 .. 477
The Duel .... MBPI0016 .. 401
The Duke of Gloucester sent for Edward ..... MBPI1060 .. 467
Maudelain
"DuMoreau was leaning part way across the MBPI0109 .. 407
table"
DuPont Powder Wagon Carrying Powder to ... MBPI3230 .. 602
Lake Erie for Commodore Perry

Index–Titles and Alternate Titles of Pyle's Art

The DuPont Powder Wagon . . . . MBPI3230 . . 602

Dutch and Indians trading . . . . MBPI2760 . . 573

Dutch Courting . . . . MBPI0250 . . 416

Dutch Soldier . . . . MBPI2503 . . 557

"Each to be honored with bumpers . . . . MBPI0426 . . 427
  innumerable of rich wine and punch"

The Earl of Mackworth receives King Henry . . MBPI1682 . . 506
  IV

"An early illustration from the . . . . MBPI1922 . . 521
  historical novel by Harold Frederic, 'In The Valley' reproduced
  by wood-cut"

"An early magazine illustration by Howard . . . . MBPI0372 . . 424
  Pyle originally reproduced in woodcut"

Early Morning on the Ferries . . . . MBOI0004 . . 611

Early Settlers Crossing The Plains . . . . MBPI2009 . . 526

Early settlers going to meeting . . . . MBPI1305 . . 482

Early Settlers in New England . . . . MBPI1305 . . 482

An Earth Child . . . . MBPI0793 . . 450

"The earthwork hid them from us" . . . . MBPI2901 . . 582

Easter & Saturday . . . . MBPI1339 . . 484

"Edmund Burton, you are a genius!" . . . . MBPI1809 . . 514

Edric the singer . . . . MBPI1013 . . 464

"Eighteen Hundred" . . . . MBPI2807 . . 576

An Eighteenth-Century Pirate . . . . MBPI0952 . . 460

Eileen slipped the ring into the nest . . . . MBPI0906 . . 457

"Elizabeth Jourdain, who lodged Her . . . . MBPI0421 . . 427
  Majesty's soldiers"

The Elopement . . . . MBPI1226 . . 477

The Embarkation . . . . MBPI2766 . . 573

"The embrasures are blind and empty" . . . . . . MBPI0398 . . 425

"An 'Eminent Person from Whitehall' . . . . MBPI0121 . . 408
  visited him in his chambers"

The Emperor Commodus . . . . MBPI2073 . . 530

The Enchanted Seas . . . . MBPI2508 . . 557

The Enchanter Merlin . . . . MBPI1841 . . 516

The Enchantress Vivien . . . . MBPI2412 . . 551

The end for The Lady of Shalott . . . . MBPI2738 . . 572

"End of the wonderful one-hoss-shay" . . . . MBPI2816 . . 576

The End . . . . MBPI2032 . . 527

Endicott cutting the cross out of the . . . . MBPI0295 . . 419
  English flag

The Enemy at the Door . . . . MBPI1977 . . 524

English in India . . . . MBPI2014 . . 526

English Soldier . . . . MBPI2504 . . 557

Enid and Geraint in the garden . . . . MBPI2610 . . 564

Enid and Geraint ride past the Town . . . . MBPI2619 . . 564
  bridge

Enid talks with the Earl . . . . MBPI2617 . . 564

Entangled . . . . MBPI1177 . . 474

Enter Fourth of July bowing and followed . . . . MBPI1336 . . 484
  by Washington's Birthday

Enter New Years Day saluting . . . . MBPI1341 . . 484

"Enter Oliver and Mademoiselle Celeste" . . . . . MBPI2352 . . 547

The Entertaining Story-Teller . . . . MBPI1680 . . 505

Equality . . . . MBPI3047 . . 591

Erasmus, Colet And More . . . . MBPI3198 . . 600

Erasmus reading to Colet And More . . . . MBPI3198 . . 600

"Erie" October 26, 1825 . . . . MBPI0576 . . 436

The Escape of Arnold . . . . MBPI0719 . . 445

Escape of Arnold to the Sloop of War . . . . MBPI0719 . . 445
  "Vulture"

The escape of Hannah Dustin . . . . MBPI1307 . . 482

The Escape . . . . PDPI0007 . . 604

Esmond and the Prince . . . . MBPI1978 . . 524

"An Essex Deacon dropped in to call" . . . . MBPI2843 . . 578

"The Essex people had dreadful times" . . . . MBPI2853 . . 579

Estercel . . . . MBPI0904 . . 457

"Euterpe" . . . . MBPI3189 . . 600

The evacuation 1783 . . . . MBPI1232 . . 477

Evacuation Day . . . . MBPI1232 . . 477

Evacuation Day One Hundred Years Ago–The . . MBPI1232 . . 477
  Continental Army Marching Down the Old Bowery, New York,
  November 25, 1783

The Evacuation of Charleston by the . . . . MBPI1999 . . 525
  British December 14, 1782

Evacuation of Charlestown . . . . MBPI1999 . . 525

The Evacuation of Charlestown . . . . MBPI1999 . . 525

"Even Sir William Berkeley Saw He Must . . . . . MBPI0673 . . 443
  Yield"

"Even Sir William Berkeley, the . . . . MBPI0673 . . 443
  redoubtable Cavalier Governor, saw he must yield"

Evening in Old Manhattan . . . . MBPI0570 . . 436

"Every day there was feasting and dancing . . . MBPI1642 . . 503
  and singing"

"Everything you wish for shall be yours" . . . . . . MBPI1126 . . 471

"The Evil Eye," he said . . . . MBPI1150 . . 472

Excalibur the Sword . . . . MBPI1867 . . 517

"Exchanged thrusts with the merciless . . . . . . MBPI0438 . . 428
  Junius"

"Executing an intricate passage" . . . . MBPI0480 . . 430

The Execution of Mary Dyer . . . . MBPI1762 . . 511

Extorting tribute from the citizens . . . . MBPI0955 . . 460

Extravaganza . . . . MBPI2013 . . 526

An Extravaganza . . . . MBPI2013 . . 526

Fact and Fancy . . . . MBPI1402 . . 488

"A fair brick house in the Green Lane of . . . . . . MBPI0115 . . 408
  North Boston"

Fair Suppliant . . . . MBPI0971 . . 461

The Fair Suppliant . . . . MBPI0971 . . 461

The Fairy Lady of Shalott in the Space of . . . . . MBPI2702 . . 569
  Flowers

The Fairy Morgana . . . . MBPI0869 . . 455

The Faithful Servant gives ye young King . . . . . MBPI1553 . . 498
  ye golden bracelet from his wrist as the other desires

The Faithful Servant is borne on the . . . . MBPI1551 . . 497
  wings of the North Wind

The Fakir . . . . MBPI2012 . . 526

The Fall of Montcalm . . . . MBPI3110 . . 595

Index–Titles and Alternate Titles of Pyle's Art

THE FALLING LEAF IS AT THE DOOR …

The falling leaf is at the door; The . . . . MBPI0814 . . 451
     Autumn Wind is on the Hill
Fame With Burning Torch and Olive Wreath . . . MBPI0730 . . 446
Fame With Burning Torch and Olive Wreath . . . MBPI0727 . . 446
Family Cares . . . . MBPI2043 . . 528
"The famous trotting ground" . . . . MBPI2818 . . 577
Fancy and Fact, with title, illustrations . . . . . . MBPI1402 . . 488
     and verse
A farm "Pluck" . . . . MBPI0189 . . 412
Farmer Georgie Griggs . . . . MBPI1404 . . 488
Farmer Griggs and the Boggart . . . . MBPI1406 . . 488
Farmer Griggs and the Wise Man . . . . MBPI1408 . . 488
Fast flew the black winged horse . . . . MBPI2380 . . 549
Father and I went down to camp... . . . . MBPI2666 . . 567
Father and Son . . . . MBPI0737 . . 447
"Father, Father!" . . . . MBPI0548 . . 435
Father Hennepin Celebrating Mass . . . . MBPI3101 . . 594
Father Longlegs, the Stork, puts the . . . . MBPI1565 . . 498
     Fisher Lad in ye way of catching a strange fish in his nets
Fay Song . . . . MBPI3166 . . 598
Fays . . . . MBPI3153 . . 598
"Feasting and drinking and junketing and . . . MBPI1730 . . 509
     merry-making"
Fermina opens the casket . . . . MBPI0172 . . 411
The ferry . . . . MBPI0433 . . 428
"*A few strokes of the paddle bring them* . . . . . . MBPI1307 . . 482
     back to the island"
The Fiddler and the little, black . . . . MBPI1506 . . 495
     mannikin
The Fiddler finds ye Princess in the . . . . MBPI1505 . . 495
     cavern of the Dwarf
The Fiddler gives the old Woman all that . . . . . MBPI1503 . . 494
     he has in his purse
The Fiddler gives the word & the staff . . . . MBPI1504 . . 494
     falls to drubbing the Dwarf as he deserves
"*The field o' Lexin'ton where England* . . . . MBPI2767 . . 573
     tried."
The fields around lay bare to the moon . . . . . . MBPI0499 . . 432
The Fifth Sketch . . . . MBPI0016 . . 401
"Fifty-five" . . . . MBPI2808 . . 576
"*A fight between a privateer and a* . . . . MBPI0780 . . 449
     merchantman"
Fight between "Bonhomme Richard" and . . . . MBPI0850 . . 454
     "Serapis"
The Fight Between Bonhomme Richard and . . . MBPI0850 . . 454
     Serapis
The Fight for the Crown . . . . MBPI0602 . . 438
The Fight for the Lady . . . . MBPI0972 . . 461
Fight in Forest . . . . MBPI0968 . . 461
The fight in the fog . . . . MBPI1775 . . 511
The Fight in the Forest . . . . MBPI0968 . . 461
The fight is done and the day is won . . . . MBPI1277 . . 480
The Fight on Lexington Common, April 19, . . . MBPI1991 . . 525
     1775

FOR 'LASSES CAKE, TO CARRY HOME…

The Fight on the Common Lexington . . . . MBPI1991 . . 525
"The Fight on the Sands" . . . . MBPI1114 . . 470
Fighting a 'longe . . . . MBPI2050 . . 529
"The figure of war our hero asked to step . . . . . MBPI1169 . . 474
     aside with him"
A figure to provoke tears . . . . MBPI0965 . . 461
Finding the body of Joseph Hay in the . . . . . . MBPI0356 . . 423
     Trail
"The fingers of the hand were clutched . . . . . . MBPI1252 . . 479
     like a claw"
Finis for The Merry Adventures of Robin . . . . . MBPI2144 . . 534
     Hood
The First Christmas Tree . . . . MBPI1945 . . 522
First Love . . . . MBPI3003 . . 588
The First Public Reading of the . . . . MBPI1190 . . 475
     Declaration of Independence
The First Sketch . . . . MBPI0008 . . 401
"The first violin would be played by a . . . . MBPI0436 . . 428
     'gentleman lately arrived'"
The First Visit of William Penn to . . . . MBPI1230 . . 477
     America
The First Walk . . . . MBPI3008 . . 588
The Fisher Lad catches a strange fish . . . . MBPI1565 . . 498
The Fisher Lad comes to the Gray Master's . . . MBPI1566 . . 498
     house
The Fisher Lad cometh to the Grey . . . . MBPI1566 . . 498
     Master's house
The Fishing of Thor and Hymir . . . . MBPI0866 . . 455
The Fishing of Thor . . . . MBPI0866 . . 455
Fishing shanty . . . . MBPI0185 . . 412
Fitting a long arrow to his bow he sent . . . . . . MBPI1359 . . 485
     it directly through the foremost horseman
"Five red-coated soldiers on horse-back, ... MBPI1913 . . 520
     with another cloaked to the eyes… Clustering about these, a
     motley score of poor people, young and old"
Flaggingly the reed pen went up and down . . MBPI1093 . . 469
     the vellum
"*Fleur–de–lis*" . . . . MBPI0999 . . 463
Fleur-de-lis . . . . MBPI0999 . . 463
"Flew away swifter than the wind" . . . . MBPI1718 . . 508
The Flight from Falworth Castle . . . . MBPI1670 . . 505
The Flight of the Swallow . . . . MBPI0130 . . 409
A Floating Town . . . . MBPI0687 . . 443
Flowering Tree . . . . PDPI0012 . . . 604
Flowering Tree . . . . MBPI3237 . . 603
Flowering Tree I . . . . PDPI0012 . . . 604
Flowering Tree II . . . . MBPI3237 . . 603
The Flute Player . . . . PDPI0052 . . . 606
The Flying Dutchman . . . . MBPI0090 . . 406
"Follow Me" . . . . MBPI3156 . . 598
For a moment they stood swaying backward . . MBPI2342 . . 547
     and forward
"For a while no one said a word" . . . . MBPI1961 . . 523
For 'lasses cake, to carry home... . . . . MBPI2689 . . 569

For many a mile we sailed . . . . PDPI0073 . . . 608

"For they all thought he was dying, as . . . . MBPI2768 . . 573
  they gathered round him crying"

The Force of Need, with title, ... MBPI1376 . . 486
  illustrations and verse

The Forest Madman saveth ye Life of King . . . MBPI2565 . . 561
  Arthur

The Forging of Balmung . . . . MBPI2742 . . 572

Fortuna . . . . MBPI1592 . . 500

Four Knights serve the Gardener Lad . . . . MBPI1876 . . 518

Four Pages armed with spears attendant . . . . . . MBPI1340 . . 484

The Four Yeomen have Merry Sport with a . . . MBPI2113 . . 533
  Stout Miller

The Fourth Sketch . . . . MBPI0014 . . 401

The Fourth Verse Describing the Gallant . . . . . MBPI2719 . . 570
  Knight Sir Lancelot the Bold

Fox and Chickens . . . . PDPI0051 . . . 606

The Fox and the Tablet . . . . MBPI1778 . . 512

The Fox calls on the Cock . . . . MBPI1464 . . 492

The Fox calls on the Sausage . . . . MBPI1465 . . 492

The Fox tells Father Goat a strange story . . . . MBPI1525 . . 496

The Fox, the Monkey, and the Pig . . . . MBPI1798 . . 513

The Fox's Wife makes his bed . . . . MBPI1466 . . 492

Franklin on his way to France . . . . MBPI1311 . . 482

Fred . . . . MBPI1333 . . 484

French Canadian . . . . MBPI2048 . . 528

The French Officers at Newport . . . . MBPI0311 . . 420

"Friar" Bacon in his Studio . . . . MBPI3197 . . 600

"Friar" Bacon in his Study . . . . MBPI3197 . . 600

A Friendly Difference . . . . MBPI2015 . . 526

Friends and Foes . . . . MBPI3040 . . 590

"The frightened braves of Howe" . . . . MBPI2918 . . 583

The Frightful Accident . . . . PDPI0071 . . . 608

Fritz guides the Baron . . . . MBPI1783 . . 512

Fritz, the swineherd, sat eating his late . . . . MBPI2322 . . 546
  supper of porridge

From Generation to Generation . . . . MBPI0558 . . 435

From the Hand of a Child . . . . MBPI3175 . . 599

Front cover decorative border for . . . . PDPI0069 . . . 607
  McClure's Magazine

Front cover design for Lady of Shalott . . . . MBPI2740 . . 572

Front cover design for Pepper & Salt . . . . MBPI2147 . . 535

Front cover design for Stolen Treasure . . . . MBPI0887 . . 456

Front cover design for The Price of Blood . . . . . MBPI1802 . . 513

Front cover design for Yankee Doodle . . . . MBPI2663 . . 567

A Frontier Tragedy . . . . MBPI0839 . . 453

A frontier tragedy . . . . MBPI0839 . . 453

Frontispiece for North Folk Legends of . . . . . . MBPI0862 . . 454
  the Sea

Frontispiece for Pebbles . . . . MBPI0643 . . 441

Frontispiece for The Body to the Soul . . . . MBPI0788 . . 450

Frontispiece for The Man with the Hoe and . . . MBPI3114 . . 595
  Other Poems

Frontispiece for The Wonder Clock . . . . MBPI2165 . . 536

Frontispiece for Yankee Doodle . . . . MBPI2664 . . 567

"Gallantry" . . . . MBPI0968 . . 461

The Galleon . . . . MBPI0953 . . 460

Gallows Point . . . . MBPI0386 . . 425

Gambetta Proclaiming the Republic of . . . . . . MBPI1909 . . 520
  France

Game of Bowls . . . . MBPI0422 . . 427

The Garden of Youth . . . . MBPI2506 . . 557

A Garden Party . . . . MBPI0222 . . 414

A Garden Party given to General . . . . MBPI0222 . . 414
  Washington

The Garden Path . . . . MBPI0237 . . 415

The Gardener Lad takes off his Cap . . . . MBPI1879 . . 518

The Garfield Ambulance Train on its way . . . . . PDPI0056 . . . 607
  to Elberon, N.J.

Garrison–House at Oyster River . . . . PDPI0031 . . 605
  Successfully Defended

Gazed down upon the dreadful object . . . . MBPI1043 . . 466

The Gems of Art . . . . MBPI3234 . . 603

The Gems of Drama . . . . MBPI3238 . . 603

The Gems of Literature . . . . MBPI3232 . . 602

The Gems of Music . . . . MBPI3235 . . 603

General Andrew Jackson receiving the . . . . MBPI2007 . . 526
  plaudits of his motley army after the victory of New Orleans

General Braddock's Troops In An Indian . . . . . . MBPI1959 . . 523
  Ambuscade

"A general flavor of mild decay" . . . . MBPI2810 . . 576

General Greene Relieves General Gates of . . . . . MBPI1998 . . 525
  Command at Charlotte

General Jackson, President-elect, on his . . . . MBPI1196 . . 475
  way to Washington

General Lee on his famous charger . . . . MBPI1117 . . 470
  "Traveler"

General Prescott . . . . PDPI0013 . . . 604

General Sheridan in Camp . . . . MBPI1064 . . 467

General Washington as he appeared in . . . . MBPI0716 . . 445
  Battle with Troops pressing forward to the Attack

General Washington's Sword embellished . . . . . . MBPI0725 . . 446
  with a Wreath of Laurel

General Wayne endeavoring to quell the . . . . MBPI2006 . . 526
  mutiny of the Pennsylvania Regiments at Morristown, N.J.

General Wayne's Grave . . . . MBPI0244 . . 416

"The Genie had flown with her through the . . MBPI1723 . . 508
  air"

"The Genie snatched the Minister up and . . . . MBPI1728 . . 508
  flew away with him"

Genius of Art . . . . MBPI3234 . . 603

The Genius of Art . . . . MBPI3234 . . 603

"The Genius of Art" . . . . MBPI3234 . . 603

The Genius of Drama . . . . MBPI3238 . . 603

The Genius of Literature . . . . MBPI3232 . . 602

The Genius of Music . . . . MBPI3235 . . 603

The Genus of Art . . . . MBPI3234 . . 603

The Genus of Drama . . . . MBPI3238 . . 603

Index–Titles and Alternate Titles of Pyle's Art

THE GENUS OF LITERATURE

The Genus of Literature . . . . MBPI3232 . . 602
The Genus of Music . . . . MBPI3235 . . 603
George and Martha Washington entertaining   MBPI1743 . . 509
    their friends on the lawn at Mount Vernon
George Campbell . . . . MBPI2056 . . 529
George, the cook . . . . MBPI0186 . . 412
George Washington . . . . MBPI0681 . . 443
George Washington as a surveyor . . . . MBPI2792 . . 575
The giant fell crashing upon the stones . . . . MBPI2382 . . 549
"The gigantic monster dragged the hacked . . MBPI0005 . . 401
    and headless corpse of his victim up the staircase"
"Girl number twenty," said Mr. Gradgrind . . . . . MBPI2756 . . 573
    squarely pointing with his square forefinger
Girl With Silver Veil . . . . MBPI0973 . . 461
"The Girl with the Silver Veil" . . . . MBPI0973 . . 461
"Girlish bust, but womanly air" . . . . MBPI2869 . . 580
"Give the poor old Woman a penny or two" . . . MBPI1503 . . 494
"Glancing at the white-robed girlish . . . . MBPI1206 . . 476
    figure before him, with evident admiration, he made a
    becoming obeisance"
The Glee Singers . . . . MBPI1221 . . 477
"Go, Madam, and leave the Prodigal among . . MBPI1035 . . 465
    his husks"
The Goblin Laugh . . . . MBPI3129 . . 596
Going to Church . . . . MBPI0258 . . 417
Going to Meeting . . . . MBPI0365 . . 423
"A golden swan leaped into the air" . . . . MBPI1580 . . 499
"The good, aged Doctor, the appearance of . . MBPI1745 . . 510
    whose rotund figure on the streets was the signal for the
    Parisians to doff their hats"
"'Good day, Monsieur,' said a familiar . . . . MBPI0141 . . 409
    voice"
Good For The Soul . . . . MBPI0761 . . 448
Good Society . . . . MBPI0618 . . 439
A Good Time Going . . . . MBPI3004 . . 588
"Good-by, big brother," she said softly . . . . MBPI1917 . . 520
The Gooseherd & her Daughter meet the . . . . MBPI1438 . . 490
    Princess at the Roadside
The Gooseherd plays with a Golden Ball . . . . . MBPI1518 . . 495
The Gorgon's Head . . . . MBPI3181 . . 599
The Gorgon's head . . . . MBPI3181 . . 599
The Gosling is punished . . . . MBPI1777 . . 512
The Gosling states his opinion of the . . . . MBPI1776 . . 511
    Cock
Gottenlieb's music works a charm . . . . MBPI1780 . . 512
The Gourd and the Oak . . . . MBPI1801 . . 513
"Government Toll-Gate on the Cumberland . . . MBPI0210 . . 414
    Rd"
Government Toll-Gate on the Cumberland . . . . MBPI0210 . . 414
    Road
Governor Andros and the Boston People . . . . . MBPI0297 . . 419
Governor Andros in Boston . . . . MBPI0297 . . 419
Governor Huntington attacked by wolves . . . . . MBPI0331 . . 421
Governor Sloughter Signing The Death . . . . . . MBPI0843 . . 453
    Warrant of Leisler

THE GREY MASTER IS CAUGHT IN THE STREAM...

Governor Spottiswood visits Colonel . . . . MBPI1834 . . 515
    Parker
"The Governor was among the very first to . . . MBPI0397 . . 425
    set foot upon the deck"
The Grail is manifested, and Sir . . . . MBPI2631 . . 565
    Launcelot sleepeth
The Grain Ship . . . . MBPI1058 . . 467
The Grain Ship . . . . MBPI1059 . . 467
The grand duke gave him a golden chain . . . . . MBPI1132 . . 471
Grandfather and Little Benny . . . . MBPI2753 . . 573
"Grandfather came in with a back-load of . . . . MBPI1323 . . 483
    sleds"
The Grandmother . . . . MBPI2892 . . 581
Grandmother's Story of Bunker Hill Battle . . . . MBPI2865 . . 580
Granny Greene Falleth Into Ill Repute . . . . MBPI1238 . . 478
Granny Greene seeketh the Life of ye Hen . . . . MBPI1236 . . 478
Grasshopper and Ant . . . . MBPI0895 . . 456
The Grasshopper and the Ant . . . . MBPI0895 . . 456
The Gray Goose meets the Sausage . . . . MBPI1463 . . 492
The Gray Master is caught in the stream . . . . . MBPI1567 . . 498
    and is swept away
A Great Black Bear came out of the Woods . . . . MBPI1805 . . 513
"A great crowd of horses laden with balls . . . . MBPI1625 . . 502
    and bundles of rich stuffs"
"A great day this, my young friend," said . . . . . MBPI2075 . . 530
    Mr. John Adams of Massachusetts
"The Great Red Fox and Cousin Greylegs . . . . . MBPI1535 . . 496
    were great cronies"
The Great Red Fox at the Store-house . . . . MBPI1524 . . 496
The Great Red Fox beareth all that he can . . . . . MBPI1538 . . 497
The Great Red Fox calls upon the Sausage . . . . . MBPI1465 . . 492
The Great Red Fox goes to call on . . . . MBPI1464 . . 492
    neighbor Cock at his house because he will crow in the morn
The Great Red Fox goeth to the . . . . MBPI1524 . . 496
    store-house and helps himself to the good things
The Great Red Fox meets ye old, blind . . . . MBPI1537 . . 497
    Mole
The Great Red Fox rests softly at home . . . . MBPI1466 . . 492
The Great Red Fox shut his teeth and . . . . MBPI1538 . . 497
    grinned
"A great section of bamboo trunk balanced . . MBPI0414 . . 426
    upon her head"
"A great tall Demon" . . . . MBPI1704 . . 507
A great, ugly, poisonous snake crept out . . . . . MBPI1572 . . 499
    of a hole in the wall
The Great Ugly Troll finds the Prince by . . . . . . MBPI1437 . . 490
    the Fire
" 'The Greater You Are,' Said the . . . . MBPI0772 . . 449
    Acrobat, 'The More Folks Envy You' "
Gretelein and the Elf King . . . . MBPI1806 . . 513
The 'Grey' Goose goes out into the wide . . . . . . MBPI1463 . . 492
    world, where she and a discontented Sausage meet the Cock and
    the Fox
The Grey Master is caught in the stream . . . . . . MBPI1567 . . 498
    and is swept away, but ye Fisher Lad crosses it dry-shod

Index–Titles and Alternate Titles of Pyle's Art

GRIEF AND INDIGNATION

Grief and indignation . . . . MBPI2022 . . 527
Griefs . . . . MBPI3163 . . 598
The grim Baron sat silent with his chin . . . . . . MBPI2312 . . 545
    resting upon his clenched fist
Group of nomadic "Plucks" . . . . MBPI0190 . . 412
Guarded by rough English soldiers . . . . MBPI0922 . . 458
"Guarding their wives and children" . . . . MBPI1305 . . 482
Guarding their wives and children . . . . MBPI1305 . . 482
"Hail Ye That Are My Kinsmen!" . . . . MBPI1060 . . 467
Hale receiving instructions from . . . . MBPI0254 . . 416
    Washington
Hale's Execution . . . . MBPI0255 . . 416
Half-title decoration for Otto of the . . . . MBPI2274 . . 543
    Silver Hand
Half-title decoration for Pepper & Salt . . . . MBPI2149 . . 535
Half-title decoration for The Man with . . . . MBPI3113 . . 595
    the Hoe and Other Poems
Half-title decoration for The Merry . . . . MBPI2086 . . 531
    Adventures of Robin Hood
Half-title decoration for The Wonder . . . . MBPI2164 . . 536
    Clock
Half-title for A Ballad of the Boston . . . . MBPI2875 . . 580
    Tea-Party
Half-title for Dorothy Q . . . . MBPI2867 . . 580
Half-title for Grandmother's Story of . . . . MBPI2893 . . 581
    Bunker-Hill Battle
Half-title for How the Old Horse Won the . . . . MBPI2817 . . 577
    Bet
Half-title for The Broomstick Train . . . . MBPI2841 . . 578
Half-title for The Deacon's Masterpiece . . . . MBPI2800 . . 575
Hamilton addressing the mob . . . . MBPI0319 . . 420
Hanging the violin . . . . MBPI0476 . . 430
Hannah Dustin Escaping From the Indians . . . . . MBPI1307 . . 482
Hannah Dustin's Escaping From The Indians . . . MBPI1307 . . 482
Hans discovers Claus's Luck . . . . MBPI1424 . . 489
Hans finds his Luck . . . . MBPI1385 . . 487
Hans Hecklemann . . . . MBPI1381 . . 487
Hans Hecklemann and the Old Wise-Woman . . MBPI1384 . . 487
Hans Hecklemann goes to the cottage of . . . . MBPI1383 . . 487
    the Old Wise-Woman in search of his Luck
Hans Hecklemann ploughs for Gold . . . . MBPI1386 . . 487
Hans held up a necklace of blue and white . . . MBPI2323 . . 546
    beads
"Harnessed in his one-hoss-shay" . . . . MBPI2825 . . 577
Harry Warrington And The Baroness De . . . . . . MBPI1125 . . 471
    Bernstein
Harvest Song . . . . MBPI3172 . . 599
A Harvest Song . . . . MBPI3172 . . 599
"A Harvest Song" . . . . MBPI3172 . . 599
The Haunted House . . . . MBPI0925 . . 458
"'Have a drop of old Jamaiky'" . . . . MBPI2920 . . 583
"Have you a roasted apple to put in my . . . . . . MBPI1498 . . 494
    mouth?"
Having been thrice adjudged in the wrong, ... MBPI1540 . . 497
    the poor man is left by the rich man blind upon the highway

"HE LAY AWHILE CONSCIOUS OF GREAT COMFORT"

He asked this figure of war to step aside . . . . . MBPI1169 . . 474
    for him
"He balanced the earthen jar on his head" . . . . MBPI1643 . . 503
"He began to play" . . . . MBPI0475 . . 430
"He brought both Catholic Priests and . . . . . . MBPI0291 . . 419
    Huguenot Ministers, who disputed heartily on the Way"
"He called on Franklin and received the . . . . . MBPI1744 . . 509
    necessary recognition"
"He called the wisest men of the island . . . . . . MBPI1698 . . 507
    to him"
He came to her–in his helmet a fox brush . . . . MBPI0944 . . 459
    spangled with jewels
"He came to the cross-roads and the stone . . . MBPI1665 . . 505
    cross"
"He caught something that weighed heavily . . . MBPI1618 . . 502
    as lead"
He climbed the stairs slowly, for he was . . . . . . MBPI0903 . . 457
    growing feeble
"He crawled forward, and looked down . . . . . . MBPI1324 . . 483
    through the scuttle hole"
"He drew out his pipe, and began to play" . . . . MBPI1666 . . 505
"He examined with astonishment and . . . . MBPI1791 . . 512
    delight"
"He fell in love" . . . . MBPI0114 . . 408
"He fell on his face and kissed the . . . . MBPI1705 . . 507
    ground"
"He found in his clinched hand a lace . . . . MBPI0162 . . 411
    cravat"
He found Melite alone . . . . MBPI0901 . . 457
"He gazed and gazed until his heart . . . . MBPI1613 . . 501
    melted within him"
"He glared at the girl in the dim light" . . . . MBPI0110 . . 407
"He had a noble feast set for them" . . . . MBPI1609 . . 501
"He had beautiful manners" . . . . MBPI0470 . . 430
"He had found the Captain agreeable and . . . MBPI0607 . . 438
    companionable"
He had lost the soul of M. Fournier . . . . MBPI0124 . . 408
"He had seen great guns in the bottom of . . . MBPI0117 . . 408
    the sea"
"He held his hammer poised for a moment" . . . MBPI1251 . . 479
"He held tightly to the fallen man's . . . . MBPI1690 . . 506
    horse"
"He held tightly to the saddle-bow of the . . . . MBPI1690 . . 506
    fallen man's horse"
"He is clad in a loose dressing-robe of . . . . MBPI0152 . . 410
    figured cloth and lies in bed reading his book"
"He kissed the little hand" . . . . MBPI2060 . . 529
He knew not what ailed her or what to do . . . . MBPI1154 . . 473
"He knocked upon the brazen gate" . . . . MBPI1649 . . 504
"He laid his hand heavily on the boy's . . . . MBPI2315 . . 545
    shoulder"
He laid the mantle over the girl's . . . . MBPI0949 . . 460
    shoulders
"He lay awhile conscious of great . . . . MBPI0950 . . 460
    comfort"

Index–Titles and Alternate Titles of Pyle's Art

"He lay silent and still, with his face half buried..."

"He lay silent and still, with his face half buried in the sand" .... MBPI1768 .. 511

"He lay there sighing and groaning" .... MBPI1645 .. 503

"He leaned over and looked into her face" .... MBPI0146 .. 410

He leaped to the wheel .... MBPI1171 .. 474

"He led Jack up to a man who sat on a barrel" ...... MBPI1831 .. 515

"He lighted a match and dropped it into the vase" ..... MBPI0137 .. 409

He looked down and sang out, "Lower away!" .... MBPI2005 .. 526

"He lost his hold and fell, taking me with him" .... MBPI1059 .. 467

"He met a poor woman coming home from market" .. MBPI1655 .. 504

He perused the inscription with great particularity .... MBPI1049 .. 466

"He picked up the bird and held it out at arm's length" .... MBPI1830 .. 515

"He prayed with unusual fervor" .... MBPI0478 .. 430

"He put the glass to his lips and drank at one gulp" .... MBPI0003 .. 401

"He raised the dagger to strike" .... MBPI1615 .. 501

"He rested his Musket" .... MBPI0292 .. 419

He sang for her as they sat in the gardens .... MBPI0902 .. 457

"He sank upon his knees beside her" .... MBPI0154 .. 410

"He sat down beside her on the bench" .... MBPI0568 .. 436

"He sat down by the garden gate" .... MBPI0410 .. 426

"He saw a dull heavy yellow smoke arise to the ceiling" ..... MBPI0159 .. 410

He saw a great coach approaching .... MBPI1131 .. 471

"He saw within an oval mirror, set in a heavy frame of copper" .... MBPI0147 .. 410

"He seized and held the treasure near the light" .... MBPI1243 .. 478

He snatched it and ran .... MBPI1546 .. 497

"He spread the money out on the table" ..... MBPI1653 .. 504

"He staggers with him through the woods" ..... MBPI1306 .. 482

"He stopped when he had come close to Carl" .... MBPI1247 .. 478

"He stops at the Sign of the Weathervane" .... MBPI0267 .. 417

He stretched out his hand to the curtains ..... MBPI0900 .. 457

He strode forward into the room and laid his hand heavily on the boy's shoulder .... MBPI2315 .. 545

"He struck once and again at the bald, narrow forehead beneath him" .... MBPI1769 .. 511

"He suddenly began an uncouth grotesque dance" .. MBPI0134 .. 409

He thought of his love .... MBPI0892 .. 456

He thrust the cobbler back against the door .... MBPI1133 .. 471

"He told them, when we chanced to sit around the fires of an evening, most remarkable stories of field and forest" ...... MBPI1918 .. 520

Headband, Chapter X for The Garden Behind the ...

He took her hand and set it to his lips .... MBPI2348 .. 547

He touched the lock with the little black stone ..... MBPI1541 .. 497

"He turned the slab-like leaves rapidly" .... MBPI0106 .. 407

"He was a tall dark gentleman dressed in black from head to foot" .... MBPI0133 .. 409

He was an old man no longer, but a Blessed Angel .... MBPI1570 .. 499

"He was doubtless a tramp" .... MBPI1199 .. 475

He was engaged to Caterina .... MBPI1145 .. 472

He was gazing straight before him with a set and stony face .... MBPI2337 .. 547

He was greatly addicted to little supper parties of his own sex ..... MBPI1044 .. 466

"He was like one bereft of wits" .... MBPI1623 .. 502

He was lying on the library floor in the morning ...... MBPI1155 .. 473

He was poor as ever .... MBPI1134 .. 471

"He was seated upon a throne" .... MBPI1651 .. 504

He was standing at an open window .... MBPI2369 .. 549

"He watched me as a cat watches a mouse" ... MBPI1058 .. 467

"He would not take an unfair advantage" ..... MBPI2080 .. 530

"He would shout opprobrious words after the other in the streets" ..... MBPI1291 .. 481

"'He'll come to by and by; he's only stunned a trifle,' said the Captain" .... MBPI1825 .. 515

"He's distanced all the lot" .... MBPI2837 .. 578

Head and sidepiece with illustrated initial T for Through Inland Waters .... MBPI0684 .. 443

Head I .... PDPI0087 ... 609

Head I with wings .... PDPI0090 ... 609

Head II .... PDPI0088 ... 609

Head II with wings .... PDPI0091 ... 609

Head III .... PDPI0089 ... 609

Head III with wings .... PDPI0092 ... 609

Head IV with wings .... PDPI0093 ... 609

Headband, Chapter II for The Garden Behind the Moon .... MBPI2360 .. 548

Headband, Chapter III for The Garden Behind the Moon .... MBPI2361 .. 548

Headband, Chapter IV for The Garden Behind the Moon .... MBPI2362 .. 548

Headband, Chapter IX for The Garden Behind the Moon .... MBPI2372 .. 549

Headband, Chapter V for The Garden Behind the Moon   MBPI2364 .. 548

Headband, Chapter VI for The Garden Behind the Moon .... MBPI2366 .. 548

Headband, Chapter VII for The Garden Behind the Moon .... MBPI2368 .. 548

Headband, Chapter VIII for The Garden Behind the Moon ...... MBPI2371 .. 549

Headband, Chapter X for The Garden Behind the Moon . MBPI2373 .. 549

Index–Titles and Alternate Titles of Pyle's Art

Headband, Chapter XI for The Garden Behind the ...

Headband, Chapter XI for The Garden Behind the Moon . . . . MBPI2374 . . 549

Headband, Chapter XII for The Garden Behind the Moon . . . . MBPI2375 . . 549

Headband, Chapter XIII for The Garden Behind the Moon . . . . . . MBPI2377 . . 549

Headband, Chapter XIV for The Garden Behind the Moon . . . . . . MBPI2378 . . 549

Headband, Chapter XIX for The Garden Behind the Moon . . . . . . MBPI2385 . . 550

Headband, Chapter XV for The Garden Behind the Moon . . . . . . MBPI2379 . . 549

Headband, Chapter XVI for The Garden Behind the Moon . . . . . . MBPI2381 . . 549

Headband, Chapter XVIII for The Garden Behind the Moon . . . . . MBPI2384 . . 549

Headband for A History of New York . . . . MBPI2771 . . 574

Headband for At the Turn of the Glass . . . . MBPI1749 . . 510

Headband for Chapter I for The Ghost of Captain Brand . . . . . . MBPI1285 . . 481

Headband for Chapter II for The Ghost of Captain Brand . . . . . MBPI1287 . . 481

Headband for Chapter III for The Ghost of Captain Brand . . . . MBPI1286 . . 481

Headband for Chapter IV for The Ghost of Captain Brand . . . . MBPI1283 . . 481

Headband for Chapter V for The Ghost of Captain Brand . . . . . MBPI1289 . . 481

Headband for Land and Sea . . . . MBPI0656 . . 441

Headband for Land and Sea . . . . MBPI0660 . 442

Headband for Land and Sea . . . . MBPI0664 . . 442

Headband for Land and Sea . . . . MBPI0668 . . 442

Headband for Stops of Various Quills . . . . MBPI3064 . . 592

Headband for The Fate of a Treasure Town . . . . MBPI0956 . . 460

Headband for The Fox Brush . . . . MBPI0945 . . 460

Headband for The Garden Behind the Moon . . MBPI2355 . . 548

Headband for The Gods of the Copybook Maxims . . . . PDPI0078 . . . 608

Headband For The Initial Paper . . . . MBPI0671 . . 442

Headband for The Pilgrimage of Truth . . . . MBPI0828 . . 452

Headband for The Pilgrimage of Truth . . . . MBPI0829 . . 452

Headband for The Second-Class Passenger . . . . MBPI1759 . . 510

Headband for The Story of King Arthur and His Knights . . . MBPI1857 . . 517

Headband for The Story of King Arthur and His Knights . . . MBPI1872 . . 517

Headband for The Story of King Arthur and His Knights . . . MBPI1882 . . 518

Headband for The Story of King Arthur and His Knights . . . MBPI1885 . . 518

Headband for The Story of King Arthur and His Knights . . . MBPI1892 . . 519

Headband for The Story of King Arthur and His Knights . . . MBPI1842 . . 516

Headpiece, Chapter XII for Otto of the Silver Hand

Headband for The Story of King Arthur and His Knights . . . MBPI1850 . . 516

Headband for The Story of King Arthur and His Knights . . . MBPI1877 . . 518

Headband for The Story of King Arthur and His Knights . . . MBPI1887 . . 518

Headband I for The Man with the Hoe and Other Poems . . . MBPI3128 . . 596

Headband II for The Man with the Hoe and Other Poems . . . MBPI3138 . . 597

Headband III for The Man with the Hoe and Other Poems . . MBPI3142 . . 597

Headband, Illustrations for The Garden Behind the Moon . . . . . . MBPI2356 . . 548

Headband with title for Tom Chist and the Treasure Box . . . MBPI1161 . . 473

"A headlong crowd is flying" . . . . MBPI2912 . . 582

Headpiece, Afterword for Otto of the Silver Hand . . . . MBPI2349 . . 547

Headpiece and title for Which is Best? . . . . MBPI1539 . . 497

Headpiece, Arrival of Genet at Gray's Ferry . . . . MBPI0754 . . 448

Headpiece, Chapter I for Otto of the Silver Hand . . . . MBPI2283 . . 543

Headpiece, Chapter I for The Garden Behind the Moon . . . . MBPI2359 . . 548

Headpiece, Chapter II for Otto of the Silver Hand . . . . MBPI2287 . . 543

Headpiece, Chapter II for The Price of Blood . . . . MBPI0081 . . 406

Headpiece, Chapter III for Otto of the Silver Hand . . . . MBPI2291 . . 544

Headpiece, Chapter III for The Price of Blood . . . . . . MBPI0083 . . 406

Headpiece, Chapter IV for Otto of the Silver Hand . . . . MBPI2295 . . 544

Headpiece, Chapter IV for The Price of Blood . . . . . . MBPI0085 . . 406

Headpiece, Chapter IX for Otto of the Silver Hand . . . . . . MBPI2320 . . 545

Headpiece, Chapter V for Otto of the Silver Hand . . . . . . MBPI2300 . . 544

Headpiece, Chapter V for The Price of Blood . . . . . . MBPI0087 . . 406

Headpiece, Chapter VI for Otto of the Silver Hand . . . . . . MBPI2305 . . 545

Headpiece, Chapter VII for Otto of the Silver Hand . . . . . . MBPI2310 . . 545

Headpiece, Chapter VIII for Otto of the Silver Hand . . . . . MBPI2317 . . 545

Headpiece, Chapter X for Otto of the Silver Hand . . . . . . MBPI2325 . . 546

Headpiece, Chapter XI for Otto of the Silver Hand . . . . . . MBPI2331 . . 546

Headpiece, Chapter XII for Otto of the Silver Hand . . . . . . MBPI2335 . . 546

Index–Titles and Alternate Titles of Pyle's Art

HEADPIECE, CHAPTER XIII FOR OTTO OF THE SILVER HAND

Headpiece, Chapter XIII for Otto of the Silver Hand . . . . . . MBPI2339 . . 547

Headpiece, Chapter XIV for Otto of the Silver Hand . . . . . . MBPI2344 . . 547

Headpiece, Contents for Otto of the Silver Hand . . . . MBPI2276 . . 543

Headpiece–Contents for The Story of King Arthur and His Knights . . . . . MBPI1887 . . 518

Headpiece, Contents for The Story of Sir Launcelot and his Companions . . . . . MBPI2520 . . 558

Headpiece, Contents for The Story of the Champions of the Round Table . . . . MBPI2435 . . 553

Headpiece, Contents for The Story of the Grail and the Passing of Arthur . . . . MBPI2601 . . 563

Headpiece, Dedication for The Man with the Hoe and Other Poems . . . . . MBPI3115 . . 595

Headpiece for A Sahib's War . . . . MBPI0092 . . 406

Headpiece For a Short Story . . . . MBPI1283 . . 481

Headpiece For a Short Story . . . . MBPI1287 . . 481

Headpiece for A Thread Without a Knot . . . . MBPI1263 . . 479

Headpiece for Among the Sand Hills . . . . MBPI0517 . . 433

Headpiece for Bi-Centennial Commemoration, Holy Trinity, Old Swedes Church . . . . MBPI3215 . . 601

Headpiece for Centuria's Greetings . . . . MBPI3220 . . 602

Headpiece for Colonel Washington . . . . MBPI0677 . . 443

Headpiece for "Good For the Soul" . . . . MBPI0762 . . 448

Headpiece for Hope and Memory . . . . MBPI0050 . . 404

Headpiece for Jamaica, New and Old . . . . MBPI0395 . . 425

Headpiece for "Justice and the Judge" . . . . MBPI0769 . . 449

Headpiece for King Custom . . . . MBPI0855 . . 454

Headpiece for Love and Death . . . . MBPI0751 . . 447

Headpiece for Margaret of Cortona . . . . MBPI0860 . . 454

Headpiece for McAndrew's Hymn . . . . MBPI1966 . . 523

Headpiece for McAndrew's Hymn . . . . MBPI1969 . . 524

Headpiece for "Miss Maria" . . . . MBPI0763 . . 448

Headpiece for North Folk Legends of the Sea . . . . MBPI0867 . . 455

Headpiece for North Folk Legends of the Sea . . . . MBPI0870 . . 455

Headpiece for North Folk Legends of the Sea . . . . MBPI0873 . . 455

Headpiece for North Folk Legends of the Sea . . . . MBPI0876 . . 455

Headpiece for Old Captain . . . . MBPI0778 . . 449

Headpiece for Poisoned Ice . . . . MBPI0072 . . 405

Headpiece for "Sally" . . . . MBPI0773 . . 449

Headpiece for The Battle of Copenhagen . . . . . MBPI0043 . . 403

Headpiece for "The Child's Mother" . . . . MBPI0767 . . 448

Headpiece for The Deacon's Masterpiece . . . . . . MBPI3012 . . 589

Headpiece for The Fate of a Treasure Town . . . . MBPI0957 . . 460

Headpiece for The Ghost of Captain Brand . . . . MBPI1285 . . 481

Headpiece for The Ghost of Captain Brand . . . . MBPI1286 . . 481

Headpiece for The Ghost of Captain Brand . . . . MBPI1287 . . 481

Headpiece for The Ghost of Captain Brand . . . . MBPI1289 . . 481

Headpiece for The Grolier Club . . . . MBPI2771 . . 574

HEADPIECE FOR THE STORY OF THE CHAMPIONS …

Headpiece for The Little Maid at the Door . . . . . MBPI2076 . . 530

Headpiece for The Price of Blood . . . . MBPI0080 . . 405

Headpiece for "The Promises of Dorthea" . . . . . MBPI0759 . . 448

Headpiece for The Re-Christening of Phoebe . . . . MBPI0024 . . 402

Headpiece for The Real Right Thing . . . . MBPI0074 . . 405

Headpiece for The Salem Wolf . . . . MBPI1084 . . 468

Headpiece for The Story of King Arthur and His Knights . . . . . MBPI1842 . . 516

Headpiece for The Story of King Arthur and His Knights . . . . . MBPI1850 . . 516

Headpiece for The Story of King Arthur and His Knights . . . . . MBPI1857 . . 517

Headpiece for The Story of King Arthur and His Knights . . . . . MBPI1872 . . 517

Headpiece for The Story of King Arthur and His Knights . . . . . MBPI1877 . . 518

Headpiece for The Story of King Arthur and His Knights . . . . . MBPI1882 . . 518

Headpiece for The Story of King Arthur and His Knights . . . . . MBPI1887 . . 518

Headpiece for The Story of King Arthur and His Knights . . . . . MBPI1892 . . 519

Headpiece for The Story of King Arthur and His Knights . . . . . MBPI1897 . . 519

Headpiece for The Story of King Arthur and His Knights . . . . . MBPI2423 . . 552

Headpiece for The Story of King Arthur and His Knights . . . . MBPI1846 . . 516

Headpiece for The Story of King Arthur and His Knights . . . . MBPI1865 . . 517

Headpiece for The Story of Sir Launcelot and his Companions . . . . . MBPI2526 . . 558

Headpiece for The Story of Sir Launcelot and his Companions . . . . . MBPI2530 . . 559

Headpiece for The Story of Sir Launcelot and his Companions . . . . . MBPI2537 . . 559

Headpiece for The Story of Sir Launcelot and his Companions . . . . . MBPI2549 . . 560

Headpiece for The Story of Sir Launcelot and his Companions . . . . . MBPI2563 . . 561

Headpiece for The Story of Sir Launcelot and his Companions . . . . . MBPI2571 . . 561

Headpiece for The Story of Sir Launcelot and his Companions . . . . . MBPI2583 . . 562

Headpiece for The Story of Sir Launcelot and his Companions . . . . . MBPI2590 . . 562

Headpiece for The Story of the Champions of the Round Table . . . MBPI2441 . . 553

Headpiece for The Story of the Champions of the Round Table . . . MBPI2445 . . 553

Headpiece for The Story of the Champions of the Round Table . . . MBPI2463 . . 554

Headpiece for The Story of the Champions of the Round Table . . . MBPI2467 . . 555

Index–Titles and Alternate Titles of Pyle's Art

HEADPIECE FOR THE STORY OF THE CHAMPIONS ...

Headpiece for The Story of the Champions ... MBPI2484 .. 556
of the Round Table

Headpiece for The Story of the Champions ... MBPI2492 .. 556
of the Round Table

Headpiece for The Story of the Grail and ..... MBPI2607 .. 563
the Passing of Arthur

Headpiece for The Story of the Grail and ..... MBPI2611 .. 564
the Passing of Arthur

Headpiece for The Story of the Grail and ..... MBPI2625 .. 565
the Passing of Arthur

Headpiece for The Story of the Grail and ..... MBPI2640 .. 565
the Passing of Arthur

Headpiece for "The Thief" .... MBPI0766 .. 448

Headpiece for The True Captain Kidd .... MBPI0882 .. 456

Headpiece for The Tuesday Club .... MBPI3211 .. 601

Headpiece for The Two Cornets of Monmouth MBPI1261 .. 479

Headpiece for "The Unexpectedness of Mr. ... MBPI0775 .. 449
Horace Shields"

Headpiece for The Voice .... MBPI0878 .. 455

Headpiece for The Yellow of the Leaf .... MBPI0811 .. 451

Headpiece for Twelfth Night at Eagleroost .... MBPI3218 .. 602

Headpiece for Twelfth Night at The .... MBPI3218 .. 602
Century

Headpiece for "Where the Laborers Are ...... MBPI0771 .. 449
Few"

Headpiece for Witchcraft .... MBPI0321 .. 421

Headpiece for Ysobel de Coreaux .... MBPI1113 .. 470

Headpiece, Foreword for Otto of the .... MBPI2280 .. 543
Silver Hand

Headpiece, Foreword for The Garden Behind MBPI2357 .. 548
the Moon

Headpiece–Foreword for The Story of King .... MBPI1842 .. 516
Arthur and His Knights

Headpiece, Foreword for The Story of Sir ..... MBPI2518 .. 558
Launcelot and his Companions

Headpiece, Foreword for The Story of the .... MBPI2433 .. 553
Champions of the Round Table

Headpiece, Foreword for The Story of the .... MBPI2599 .. 563
Grail and the Passing of Arthur

Headpiece, In 1776, The Conflagration .... MBPI0574 .. 436

Headpiece, Lexington .... MBPI2765 .. 573

Headpiece, List of Illustrations for .... MBPI2932 .. 584
Dorothy Q

Headpiece, List of Illustrations for Otto ...... MBPI2278 .. 543
of the Silver Hand

Headpiece, List of Illustrations for .... MBPI2156 .. 535
Pepper & Salt

Headpiece, List of Illustrations for The .... MBPI2092 .. 531
Merry Adventures of Robin Hood

Headpiece, List of Illustrations for The .... MBPI2798 .. 575
One Hoss Shay

Headpiece–List of Illustrations for The .... MBPI1877 .. 518
Story of King Arthur and His Knights

Headpiece, List of Illustrations for The .... MBPI2522 .. 558
Story of Sir Launcelot and his Companions

HEADPIECE WITH INITIAL I, PART II FOR THE ...

Headpiece, List of Illustrations for The .... MBPI2437 .. 553
Story of the Champions of the Round Table

Headpiece, List of Illustrations for The .... MBPI2603 .. 563
Story of the Grail and the Passing of Arthur

Headpiece, List of Illustrations for The .... MBPI2171 .. 536
Wonder Clock

Headpiece, List of Ilustrations for The .... MBPI2964 .. 586
Autocrat of the Breakfast-Table

Headpiece, Preface for Pepper & Salt .... MBPI2152 .. 535

Headpiece, Preface for The Merry .... MBPI2089 .. 531
Adventures of Robin Hood

Headpiece, Preface for The One Hoss Shay .... MBPI2796 .. 575

Headpiece, Preface for The Wonder Clock ..... MBPI2167 .. 536

Headpiece, Prefatory Note for The Man ...... MBPI3116 .. 595
with the Hoe and Other Poems

Headpiece–Prologue for The Story of King ..... MBPI1850 .. 516
Arthur and His Knights

Headpiece, Publisher's Note for The One ..... MBPI3207 .. 601
Hoss Shay

Headpiece, Sketch Four for By Land and ..... MBPI0668 .. 442
Sea

Headpiece, Sketch Three for By Land and .... MBPI0664 .. 442
Sea

Headpiece, Sketch Two for By Land and Sea ... MBPI0660 .. 442

Headpiece, Table of Contents for Pepper & ... MBPI2154 .. 535
Salt

Headpiece, Table of Contents for Stops of .... MBPI3024 .. 589
Various Quills

Headpiece, Table of Contents for The .... MBPI2091 .. 531
Merry Adventures of Robin Hood

Headpiece, Table of Contents for The .... MBPI2169 .. 536
Wonder Clock

Headpiece, Table of Contents for Twilight .... MBPI2390 .. 550
Land

Headpiece, The Contents for The Man with ... MBPI3117 .. 595
the Hoe and Other Poems

Headpiece, Vivien for The Story of King ...... MBPI1902 .. 519
Arthur and His Knights

Headpiece with decoration and title for ..... MBPI0833 .. 453
Colonies and Nation

Headpiece with illustrated initial D, ... MBPI2930 .. 584
Preface for Dorothy Q

Headpiece with illustrated initial I, ... MBPI2391 .. 550
Introduction for Twilight Land

Headpiece with illustrated initial K for .... MBPI1446 .. 491
The Book of Balbo

Headpiece with illustrated initial T for .... MBPI1574 .. 499
The Princess on the Glass Hill

Headpiece with initial A, Part V for The ...... MBPI2986 .. 587
Autocrat of the Breakfast-Table

Headpiece with initial D for Christmas .... MBPI1214 .. 476
Time Two Hundred Years Ago

Headpiece with initial I, Part I for The .... MBPI2968 .. 586
Autocrat of the Breakfast-Table

Headpiece with initial I, Part II for The .... MBPI2974 .. 586
Autocrat of the Breakfast-Table

Index–Titles and Alternate Titles of Pyle's Art

Headpiece with initial I, Part IV for The ...

Headpiece with initial I, Part IV for The . . . . MBPI2982 . . 587
Autocrat of the Breakfast-Table
Headpiece with initial I, Part IX for The . . . . MBPI3002 . . 588
Autocrat of the Breakfast-Table
Headpiece with initial I, Part XII for . . . . MBPI3017 . . 589
The Autocrat of the Breakfast-Table
Headpiece with initial O for A Soldier of . . . . . MBPI0591 . . 437
Fortune
Headpiece with initial S, Part VI for The . . . . . . MBPI2990 . . 587
Autocrat of the Breakfast-Table
Headpiece with initial S, Part VIII for . . . . MBPI2999 . . 588
The Autocrat of the Breakfast-Table
Headpiece with initial T for Autocrat's . . . . MBPI2966 . . 586
Autobiography
Headpiece with initial T for The Sword of . . . . MBPI1370 . . 486
Hildebrand
Headpiece with initial T, Part III for . . . . MBPI2978 . . 587
The Autocrat of the Breakfast-Table
Headpiece with initial T, Part VII for . . . . MBPI2995 . . 588
The Autocrat of the Breakfast-Table
Headpiece with initial T, Part X for The . . . . . . MBPI3007 . . 588
Autocrat of the Breakfast-Table
Headpiece with initial T, Part XI for The . . . . . MBPI3011 . . 589
Autocrat of the Breakfast-Table
Headpiece with initial T, Preface for The . . . . . MBPI2965 . . 586
Autocrat of the Breakfast-Table
Headpiece with subtitle for Through . . . . MBPI0688 . . 443
Inland Waters
Headpiece with title, A Relay Tavern . . . . PDPI0067 . . . 607
Headpiece with title and decorated border . . . MBPI0048 . . 403
for Hope and Memory
Headpiece with title and decorative . . . . MBPI0516 . . 433
border for Two Moods
Headpiece with title and illustrated . . . . MBPI0671 . . 442
initial G for In Washington's Day
Headpiece with title and illustrated . . . . MBPI0637 . . 440
initial O for New York Colonial Privateers
Headpiece with title and illustrated . . . . MBPI1410 . . 489
initial O–The Skillful Huntsman
Headpiece with title and illustrated . . . . MBPI1579 . . 499
initial T for That Which is Done Never Dies
Headpiece with title and illustrated . . . . MBPI1981 . . 524
initial T for The Birds of Cirencester
Headpiece with title and illustrated . . . . MBPI0578 . . 437
initial T for The Cocklane Ghost
Headpiece with title and illustrated . . . . MBPI0571 . . 436
initial T for The Evolution of New York
Headpiece with title and illustrated . . . . MBPI0608 . . 438
initial T for The Sea Robbers of New York
Headpiece with title and initial F for . . . . MBPI1403 . . 488
Farmer Griggs's Boggart
Headpiece with title and initial for The . . . . . . MBPI1701 . . 507
Talisman of Solomon
Headpiece with title and initial T for . . . . MBPI0022 . . 402
Paul Jones
Headpiece with title and initial T for . . . . MBPI1425 . . 490
The Apple of Contentment

Headpiece with title for One Good Turn ...

Headpiece with title and initial T for . . . . MBPI1753 . . 510
The Chase of the Tide
Headpiece with title and initial T for . . . . MBPI0700 . . 444
Through Inland Waters
Headpiece with title and initial W for . . . . MBPI1815 . . 514
The Soldiering of Beniah Stidham
Headpiece with title At the Gates of Life . . . . . . MBPI0067 . . 405
Headpiece with title for A Piece of Good . . . . . MBPI1719 . . 508
Luck
Headpiece with title for A Prelude . . . . MBPI0807 . . 451
Headpiece with title for All Things Are . . . . MBPI1646 . . 503
as Fate Wills
Headpiece with title for Bearskin . . . . MBPI1528 . . 496
Headpiece with title for By Land and Sea . . . . . MBPI0656 . . 441
Headpiece with title for Claus & His . . . . MBPI1418 . . 489
Wonderful Staff
Headpiece with title for Clever Peter & . . . . . . MBPI1396 . . 488
the Two Bottles
Headpiece with title for Cousin Greylegs, ... MBPI1534 . . 496
Ye Great Red Fox and Grandfather Mole
Headpiece with title for Empty Bottles . . . . MBPI1610 . . 501
Headpiece with title for First in Peace . . . . MBPI0722 . . 446
Headpiece with title for General . . . . MBPI0716 . . 445
Washington
Headpiece with title for Good Gifts and a . . . . MBPI1639 . . 503
Fool's Folly
Headpiece with title for How Boots . . . . MBPI1456 . . 491
Befooled the King
Headpiece with title for How One Turned . . . . MBPI1451 . . 491
His Trouble to Some Account
Headpiece with title for How the . . . . MBPI0502 . . 432
Declaration was Received in the Old Thirteen
Headpiece with title for How the Good . . . . . . MBPI1482 . . 493
Gifts were Used by Two
Headpiece with title for How the . . . . MBPI1517 . . 495
Princess's Pride was Broken
Headpiece with title for How Three Little . . . . MBPI1497 . . 494
Pigs Had the Best of the Great Wicked Ogre
Headpiece with title for How Three Went . . . . MBPI1462 . . 492
Out into the Wide World
Headpiece with title for How Two Went . . . . . . MBPI1523 . . 496
into Partnership
Headpiece with title for Ill-Luck and the . . . . . MBPI1585 . . 500
Fiddler
Headpiece with title for King Stork . . . . MBPI1512 . . 495
Headpiece with title for Master Jacob . . . . MBPI1492 . . 494
Headpiece with title for Monochromes . . . . MBPI0550 . . 435
Headpiece with title for Mother . . . . MBPI1487 . . 493
Hildegarde
Headpiece with title for Much Shall Have . . . . MBPI1652 . . 504
More and Little Shall Have Less
Headpiece with title for Not a Pin to . . . . MBPI1622 . . 502
Choose
Headpiece with title for One Good Turn . . . . . MBPI1564 . . 498
Deserves Another

Index–Titles and Alternate Titles of Pyle's Art

Headpiece with title for Parson Turell's ...... MBPI3018 .. 589
    Legacy
Headpiece with title for Pebbles .... MBPI0644 .. 441
Headpiece with title for Peter Rugg Ye .... MBPI1947 .. 522
    Bostonian
Headpiece with title for Peterkin and the .... MBPI1477 .. 493
    Little Gray Hare
Headpiece with title for Sailors and .... MBPI1271 .. 480
    Landsmen, A Story of 1812
Headpiece with title for Society .... MBPI0640 .. 440
Headpiece with title for Stops of Various ..... MBPI0613 .. 439
    Quills
Headpiece with title for The Assembly .... MBPI0747 .. 447
    Ball
Headpiece with title for The Best that .... MBPI1544 .. 497
    Life Has to Give
Headpiece with title for The Bird in the ...... MBPI1433 .. 490
    Linden Tree
Headpiece with title for The Body to the ..... MBPI0789 .. 450
    Soul
Headpiece with title for The Buccaneers ...... MBPI1168 .. 473
Headpiece with title for The Captain's .... MBPI1763 .. 511
    Well
Headpiece with title for The Clever .... MBPI1472 .. 492
    Student and the Master of Black Arts
Headpiece with title for The .... MBPI0026 .. 402
    Constitution's Last Fight
Headpiece with title for The Enchanted ...... MBPI1691 .. 506
    Island
Headpiece with title for The First .... MBPI0727 .. 446
    President of the United States
Headpiece with title for The First .... MBPI0165 .. 411
    Thanksgiving
Headpiece with title for The Fox Brush .... MBPI0942 .. 459
Headpiece with title for The Fruit of .... MBPI1664 .. 504
    Happiness
Headpiece with title for The Ghost of .... MBPI1283 .. 481
    Captain Brand
Headpiece with title for The Good of a ...... MBPI1729 .. 509
    Few Words
Headpiece with title for The Pilgrimage ...... MBPI0822 .. 452
    of Truth
Headpiece with title for The Price of .... MBPI0076 .. 405
    Blood
Headpiece with title for The Princess .... MBPI1467 .. 492
    Golden-Hair and the Great Black Raven
Headpiece with title for The Quaker Lady ..... MBPI0452 .. 429
Headpiece with title for The Revolt of .... MBPI1332 .. 484
    the Holidays
Headpiece with title for The Romance of ..... MBPI0732 .. 446
    an Ambrotype
Headpiece with title for The Salt of Life ...... MBPI1600 .. 500
Headpiece with title for The Sea Man .... MBOI0006 .. 612
Headpiece with title for The Simpleton ...... MBPI1507 .. 495
    and his Little Black Hen
Headpiece with title for The Staff and .... MBPI1502 .. 494
    the Fiddle

Headpiece with title for The Step-mother ..... MBPI1554 .. 498
Headpiece with title for The Stool of .... MBPI1657 .. 504
    Fortune
Headpiece with title for The Swan Maiden .... MBPI1441 .. 491
Headpiece with title for The Three .... MBPI1569 .. 499
    Fortunes
Headpiece with title for The Water of .... MBPI1549 .. 497
    Life
Headpiece with title for The White Bird .... MBPI1559 .. 498
Headpiece with title for Where to Lay the .... MBPI1616 .. 501
    Blame
Headpiece with title for Wisdom's Wages .... MBPI1592 .. 500
    and Folly's Pay
Headpiece with title for Woman's Wit .... MBPI1632 .. 502
Headpiece with title for Ye True Story of ..... MBPI1233 .. 478
    Granny Greene of Salem Town
Headpiece with title In the Meadows of ..... MBPI0061 .. 404
    Youth
Headpiece with title In the Valley of the ..... MBPI0064 .. 404
    Shadows
Headpiece with title The Travels of the ...... MBPI0059 .. 404
    Soul
Headpiece with title with illustrated .... MBPI0795 .. 450
    initial T for A Puppet of Fate
"Heart of gold! kindest of men!" .... MBPI1204 .. 476
Hendryk Hudson and the Half-Moon .... MBPI2500 .. 557
Henry Morgan Recruiting for the Attack .... MBPI0348 .. 422
Henry V. and Katherine of France .... MBPI0941 .. 459
Her captain was a Cuban .... MBPI0990 .. 462
Her decks are red with her gallant dead .... PDPI0074 ... 608
"Her glance fell, under his steady gaze" .... MBPI0329 .. 421
Her head and shoulders hung over the ...... MBPI0912 .. 457
    space without
"Her native songs for him she sung" .... MBPI2770 .. 574
Her outstretched arms seemed to close ..... MBPI0939 .. 459
    upon something
"Her tearful memories treasured" .... MBPI2878 .. 580
Her whisper was so soft he only guessed .... MBPI0898 .. 457
    the words
Herald .... MBPI1332 .. 484
Hercules and Atlas .... MBPI3183 .. 599
"Here and there one comes upon an old ..... MBPI0399 .. 425
    house"
"Here, André! A Spy!" .... MBPI0038 .. 403
"Here comes the farmer and his men to see .. MBPI1501 .. 494
    what all the stir is about"
"Here is all I have to give thee–It is .... MBPI1299 .. 482
    the King's Jewel"
"Here it turned, and said 'Knowest thou ...... MBPI0206 .. 413
    who I am?'"
Here Once The Embattled Farmers Stood ...... MBPI0103 .. 407
Here the Brave Soldier brings his Trouble ...... MBPI1453 .. 491
    before the King to find if it shall follow him wherever he goes
"'Here's a soldier bleeding'" .... MBPI2925 .. 583
Heredity .... MBPI0621 .. 439

Index–Titles and Alternate Titles of Pyle's Art

Hero and Heroine seated each at a Dish ...

Hero and Heroine seated each at a Dish of . . . . . MBPI0034 . . 403
    Tea, Upon the Lawn
Herr Vollmer quietly stepped out into the . . . . MBPI1158 . . 473
    street
"Hey, black cat! hey, my pretty black . . . . MBPI0546 . . 435
    cat"
"Hilda, airily mounting a high pair of . . . . MBPI1205 . . 476
    steps, proceeded to catalogue the various articles that she
    now dropped one by one into Grettel's wide-spread apron"
"Hint and promise of stately mien" . . . . MBPI2870 . . 580
His army broke up and followed him, ... MBPI1118 . . 470
    weeping and sobbing
His eyes fell on the dancer in her . . . . MBPI1055 . . 466
    shimmering scarlet
"His Gold's on the capstan, His Blood's . . . . MBPI0089 . . 406
    on His Gown"
"His head bowed on his folded arms" . . . . MBPI0489 . . 431
"His long nightly labors" . . . . MBPI0471 . . 430
"His Majesty would furnish no more money . . MBPI0112 . . 407
    for treasure hunting"
His niece had found him lying dead . . . . MBPI2003 . . 526
"His picture Copley painted" . . . . MBPI2929 . . 584
"His strength with his life blood was . . . . MBPI2085 . . 531
    flowing fast."
"Ho, Drummer! quick, silence yon Capet" . . . . . . MBPI2748 . . 572
"Holding forth the missive, he stood by, ... MBPI1203 . . 476
    breathless and speechless"
The Home-made Press . . . . MBPI3242 . . 603
Hope . . . . MBPI0563 . . 436
Hope . . . . MBPI0646 . . 441
Hope and Memory . . . . MBPI0049 . . 404
Horace Reading to Maecenas . . . . MBPI3190 . . 600
"Horror! Devastation! Agony!" . . . . MBPI2030 . . 527
Horse and man plunged heavily after her . . . . . MBPI1008 . . 463
"A horse can trot, for all he's old" . . . . MBPI2840 . . 578
Hosea and the "cruetin Sarjunt" . . . . MBPI3203 . . 601
Hosea and the Parson . . . . MBPI3204 . . 601
"A hot, broad, all-pervading glare of . . . . MBPI0376 . . 424
    sunlight"
Household Scene in New Amsterdam . . . . MBPI2755 . . 573
How Arthur drew forth Ye Sword . . . . MBPI1856 . . 516
How Hans was caught . . . . MBPI2158 . . 535
How one clad all in black did a wonder . . . . . . MBPI1845 . . 516
    before King Leodegrance of Camilard
How Sir Launcelot held discourse with ye . . . . MBPI2548 . . 560
    merry Minstrels
How Sir Launcelot rode errant in a cart . . . . . . MBPI2532 . . 559
How the Buccaneers Kept Christmas . . . . MBPI1298 . . 482
How the Connecticut Pioneers came into . . . . . . MBPI2009 . . 526
    the Western Reserve
How the Devil Haunted the Meeting-House, . . MBPI1291 . . 481
    Part I.
How the Devil Stole the Collector's Snuff . . . . MBPI1292 . . 481
    Box, Part II.

"I don't want to be anybody's servant, ..."

How the Devil Was Cast Out of the . . . . MBPI1295 . . 481
    Meeting-House, Part V.
How the Lady Weaveth Day by Day . . . . MBPI2710 . . 570
How the Reapers Hear Her Singing . . . . MBPI2707 . . 570
Howard Pyle book cover . . . . MBPI2147 . . 535
Howard Pyle photo portrait . . . . MBOP0001 . 610
Howard Pyle photo portrait . . . . MBOP0002 . 610
Howard Pyle photo portrait . . . . MBOP0003 . 610
Howard Pyle photo portrait . . . . MBOP0004 . 610
Howard Pyle photo portrait . . . . PDOP0001 . . 610
Howard Pyle photo portrait . . . . PDOP0002 . . 610
Howard Pyle photo portrait . . . . PDOP0003 . . 610
Howard Pyle photo portrait . . . . PDOP0004 . . 610
Howard Pyle photo portrait . . . . PDOP0005 . . 610
Howard Pyle photo portrait . . . . PDOP0006 . . 610
Howard Pyle photo portrait . . . . PDOP0007 . . 610
Howard Pyle photo portrait . . . . PDOP0008 . . 610
Howard Pyle photo portrait . . . . PDOP0009 . . 610
Howard Pyle photo portrait . . . . PDOP0010 . . 611
Howard Pyle photo portrait . . . . PDOP0011 . . 611
Howard Pyle photo portrait . . . . PDOP0012 . . 611
Howard Pyle photo portrait . . . . PDOP0013 . . 611
Howard Pyle photo portrait . . . . PDOP0015 . . 611
Howard Pyle photo portrait . . . . PDOP0016 . . 611
Howard Pyle photo portrait . . . . PDOP0017 . . 611
Howard Pyle photo portrait . . . . PDOP0018 . . 611
Howard Pyle photo portrait . . . . PDOP0019 . . 611
Howard Pyle photo portrait . . . . PDOP0020 . . 611
Howard Pyle portrait likeness . . . . PDOP0021 . . 611
Howard Pyle script book label . . . . PDPI0005 . . . 603
Howard Pyle self portrait painting . . . . PDPI0004 . . . 603
Howard Pyle silhouette photo portrait . . . . PDOP0014 . . 611
Howard Pyle's Conception of the gift of . . . . MBPI1867 . . 517
    the magic jeweled sword Ex-Calibur, to Arthur the King
Hugh and Darthea . . . . MBPI0042 . . 403
"Hugh Wynne striking down his Cousin" . . . . . . MBPI0033 . . 403
"Humbility is the fountain of all wirtue" . . . . . . MBPI2018 . . 527
A Hundred Years Ago . . . . MBPI1176 . . 474
The Huntsman . . . . MBPI0944 . . 459
"I am a ruined man" . . . . MBPI1152 . . 472
"'I am Captain John Mackra,' said I, and . . . . . . MBPI1257 . . 479
    I sat down upon the gunwale of the boat"
"I am going to run away with you" . . . . MBPI1248 . . 478
"'I am ready,' said the young man . . . . MBPI1717 . . 508
    steadily"
"I am the daughter of that unfortunate . . . . . . MBPI0973 . . 461
    Captain Keitt!"
"I am the Grand Duke" . . . . MBPI1346 . . 485
"'I am thy Uncle,' said the strange . . . . MBPI0136 . . 409
    gentleman"
I began to play . . . . MBPI2013 . . 526
I clutched at his ankle . . . . MBPI2016 . . 526
"I don't want to be anybody's servant, ... MBPI1829 . . 515
    lady, and wouldn't if I could help it"

Index–Titles and Alternate Titles of Pyle's Art

"I FOUND HIM AND HE WASN'T ALONE"

"I found him and he wasn't alone" . . . . MBPI1090 . . 469

"I grow old, having no son but Randver" . . . . . MBPI1088 . . 468

"I had enemies in my line" . . . . MBPI0772 . . 449

"I have been reserved for this–to free . . . . MBPI1760 . . 510
the land from spiritual tyranny"

"I have broken it," she wailed . . . . MBPI1096 . . 469

"I have brought you the Baron's head" . . . . MBPI1784 . . 512

"I have loved you for a great while, fair . . . . . MBPI1122 . . 471
Mervisaunt"

"I heard a land-breeze ca'" . . . . MBPI1968 . . 523

I knelt by the whispering, muttering old . . . . . MBPI0934 . . 459
man

"I knew it, I knew it," exclaimed the . . . . MBPI1167 . . 473
great man

"I know thy heart, that thou dost love me . . . . MBPI1300 . . 482
well"

"I loved the husk of a man" . . . . MBPI0941 . . 459

"I never had wood that I liked half so . . . . MBPI0264 . . 417
well–do see who has nice crooked fuel to sell"

"I often took my Bible and sat in hollow . . . . . MBPI0278 . . 418
trees"

"I only regret that I have but one life . . . . MBPI0255 . . 416
to lose for my country"

"I rose slowly from my chair, and stood . . . . . MBPI1258 . . 479
with my hand leaning upon the table"

I sat at her feet while she drilled the . . . . MBPI2014 . . 526
island language into me

"I sat gazing upon her as she leaned . . . . MBPI0340 . . 422
forward"

"I sat in a hay-stack, and said nothing . . . . . . MBPI0280 . . 418
for some hours"

"I saw her face white even in all that . . . . MBPI0256 . . 416
immense ruddy glare"

"I saw him pass his sword through the . . . . . . MBPI0002 . . 401
mate's body"

"I saw his eyes were blue" . . . . MBPI2927 . . 583

I see another snarl of men... . . . . MBPI2690 . . 569

"I see naught but a little maid at the . . . . MBPI2078 . . 530
door"

"I Sing of Death" . . . . MBPI1000 . . 463

"I stopped, for the woman's head had . . . . MBPI1269 . . 480
fallen back–she had fainted"

"'I think everybody has gone mad,' said . . . . . . MBPI1709 . . 507
the young man"

"I thought of you, when I was falling," . . . . . . MBPI0919 . . 458
he said vaguely

"I turned the sheet over and over in my . . . . . MBPI1928 . . 521
hands, re-reading lines here and there"

"I was conscious only of her eyes" . . . . MBPI1268 . . 480

"I was conscious only of her own eyes . . . . . . MBPI1268 . . 480
looking down at me, gray, deep, inscrutable"

I went as near to it myself... . . . . MBPI2675 . . 568

"I will have him between these hands" . . . . . . MBPI1030 . . 465

"I will teach thee to answer thy elders" . . . . . MBPI0032 . . 402

"'I wish to God we were well out of this . . . . . MBPI1929 . . 521
all,' he said, almost gloomily"

ILLUSTRATED INITIAL A WITH HEADING FOR ...

"I'll bet you two to one" . . . . MBPI2824 . . 577

"I'll do it!" . . . . MBPI2023 . . 527

"I'm an owl; you're another" . . . . MBPI0198 . . 413

"I'm Bijah" . . . . MBPI1320 . . 483

"I've kept my ears open to all your . . . . MBPI1290 . . 481
doings"

"The idea was abroad that she had a . . . . MBPI0220 . . 414
'malignant touch' "

Idleness . . . . MBPI0893 . . 456

If . . . . MBPI0563 . . 436

"If I catch you here again you'll need . . . . MBPI2015 . . 526
someone to sew you up"

"If the shot had cracked the sky he could . . . . MBPI1658 . . 504
not have been more frightened"

"If this dreadful thing is not taken away . . . . . MBPI1050 . . 466
I shall go mad"

Illuminated Title for the Romance of an . . . . . . MBPI0732 . . 446
Ambrotype

"The Illumination In New York on the . . . . MBPI0361 . . 423
Occasion of the Inauguration of President Washington"

Illustrated initial A for A History of . . . . MBPI2772 . . 574
New York

Illustrated initial A for A Very Merry . . . . PDPI0040 . . . 606
Christmas in The "Good Old Times"

Illustrated initial A for At the Gates of . . . . . . MBPI0068 . . 405
Life

Illustrated initial A for Old New York . . . . MBPI0418 . . 427
Taverns

Illustrated initial A for Otto of the . . . . MBPI2318 . . 545
Silver Hand

Illustrated initial A for Otto of the . . . . MBPI2340 . . 547
Silver Hand

Illustrated initial A for Solitude . . . . MBPI0625 . . 440

Illustrated initial A for The Birds of . . . . MBPI1983 . . 524
Cirencester

Illustrated initial A for The Birds of . . . . MBPI1984 . . 524
Cirencester

Illustrated initial A for The Fate of a . . . . MBPI0958 . . 460
Treasure Town

Illustrated initial A for The Fifth . . . . MBPI0017 . . 402
Sketch

Illustrated initial A for The First . . . . MBPI0009 . . 401
Sketch

Illustrated initial A for The Merry . . . . MBPI2138 . . 534
Adventures of Robin Hood

Illustrated initial A for The Merry . . . . MBPI2143 . . 534
Adventures of Robin Hood

Illustrated initial A for The Price of . . . . MBPI0082 . . 406
Blood

Illustrated initial A for The Second . . . . MBPI0011 . . 401
Sketch

Illustrated initial A for The Story of . . . . MBPI1843 . . 516
King Arthur and His Knights

Illustrated initial A with heading for . . . . MBPI2187 . . 537
The Clever Student and the Master of Black Arts

Index–Titles and Alternate Titles of Pyle's Art

Illustrated initial A with heading for . . . . MBPI2578 . . 562
The Story of Sir Launcelot and his Companions
Illustrated initial B for Among the Sand . . . . . . MBPI0527 . . 433
Hills
Illustrated initial B for Among the Sand . . . . . . MBPI0535 . . 434
Hills
Illustrated initial B for Otto of the . . . . MBPI2288 . . 543
Silver Hand
Illustrated initial B for Otto of the . . . . MBPI2292 . . 544
Silver Hand
Illustrated initial B for Otto of the . . . . MBPI2336 . . 546
Silver Hand
Illustrated initial B for Stops of . . . . MBPI3063 . . 592
Various Quills
Illustrated initial B for The Ghost of . . . . MBPI1284 . . 481
Captain Brand
Illustrated initial B for The Pilgrimage . . . . MBPI0830 . . 452
of Truth
Illustrated initial B for The Song of The . . . . . . MBPI1189 . . 475
Whip-poor-Will
Illustrated initial B, Foreword for Otto . . . . MBPI2281 . . 543
of the Silver Hand
Illustrated initial B with heading for . . . . MBPI2175 . . 536
Bearskin
Illustrated initial B with heading for . . . . MBPI2479 . . 555
The Story of the Champions of the Round Table
Illustrated initial C for Among the Sand . . . . . . MBPI0533 . . 434
Hills
Illustrated initial C for The Merry . . . . MBPI2128 . . 533
Adventures of Robin Hood
Illustrated initial C with heading for . . . . MBPI2198 . . 538
Cousin Greylegs, Ye Great Red Fox and Grandfather Mole
Illustrated initial C with heading for . . . . MBPI2199 . . 538
Cousin Greylegs, Ye Great Red Fox and Grandfather Mole
Illustrated initial D for Respite . . . . MBPI0566 . . 436
Illustrated initial D for The Birds of . . . . MBPI1982 . . 524
Cirencester
Illustrated initial D for Time . . . . MBPI0617 . . 439
Illustrated initial D with heading for . . . . MBPI2528 . . 558
The Story of Sir Launcelot and his Companions
Illustrated initial E for The Price of . . . . MBPI0086 . . 406
Blood
Illustrated initial E for The Song of The . . . . . . MBPI1188 . . 475
Whip-poor-Will
Illustrated initial E, Sketch Four for By . . . . MBPI0669 . . 442
Land and Sea
Illustrated initial E with heading for . . . . MBPI2609 . . 564
The Story of the Grail and the Passing of Arthur
Illustrated initial E with heading for . . . . MBPI2616 . . 564
The Story of the Grail and the Passing of Arthur
Illustrated initial E with heading for . . . . MBPI2618 . . 564
The Story of the Grail and the Passing of Arthur
Illustrated initial F for Among the Sand . . . . . . MBPI0525 . . 433
Hills
Illustrated initial F for Otto of the . . . . MBPI2321 . . 546
Silver Hand

Illustrated initial F for Sympathy . . . . MBPI0648 . . 441
Illustrated initial F for The Birds of . . . . MBPI1985 . . 525
Cirencester
Illustrated initial F for The Birds of . . . . MBPI1989 . . 525
Cirencester
Illustrated initial F for The Pilgrimage . . . . MBPI0823 . . 452
of Truth
Illustrated initial F with decoration for . . . . PDPI0019 . . . 604
The Captain's Well
Illustrated initial F with heading for . . . . MBPI2201 . . 538
One Good Turn Deserves Another
Illustrated initial G for Centuria's . . . . MBPI3221 . . 602
Greetings
Illustrated initial H for Living . . . . MBPI0554 . . 435
Illustrated initial H for Otto of the . . . . MBPI2326 . . 546
Silver Hand
Illustrated initial H for The Birds of . . . . MBPI1987 . . 525
Cirencester
Illustrated initial H for The Pilgrimage . . . . MBPI0832 . . 452
of Truth
Illustrated initial H with heading for . . . . MBPI2182 . . 537
How One Turned His Trouble to Some Account
Illustrated initial H with heading for . . . . MBPI2531 . . 559
The Story of Sir Launcelot and his Companions
Illustrated initial H with heading for . . . . MBPI2547 . . 560
The Story of Sir Launcelot and his Companions
Illustrated initial H with heading for . . . . MBPI2239 . . 540
Which is Best?
Illustrated initial I for Calvary . . . . MBPI0632 . . 440
Illustrated initial I for Cousin . . . . MBPI2197 . . 538
Greylegs, Ye Great Red Fox and Grandfather Mole
Illustrated initial I for From Generation . . . . . . MBPI0559 . . 435
to Generation
Illustrated initial I for Jamaica, New . . . . MBPI0373 . . 424
and Old
Illustrated initial I for The Assembly . . . . MBPI0748 . . 447
Ball
Illustrated initial I for The Bewildered . . . . MBPI0562 . . 436
Guest
Illustrated initial I for The Burden . . . . MBPI0645 . . 441
Illustrated initial I for The Merry . . . . MBPI2096 . . 531
Adventures of Robin Hood
Illustrated initial I for The Merry . . . . MBPI2111 . . 532
Adventures of Robin Hood
Illustrated initial I for The Merry . . . . MBPI2117 . . 533
Adventures of Robin Hood
Illustrated initial I for The Price of . . . . MBPI0077 . . 405
Blood
Illustrated initial I for The Story of . . . . MBPI1847 . . 516
King Arthur and His Knights
Illustrated initial I, Preface for The . . . . MBPI2168 . . 536
Wonder Clock
Illustrated initial I, Sketch Two for By . . . . MBPI0661 . . 442
Land and Sea
Illustrated initial J for Conscience . . . . MBPI3033 . . 590

Index–Titles and Alternate Titles of Pyle's Art

ILLUSTRATED INITIAL J FOR THE LITTLE MAID AT THE DOOR

Illustrated initial J for The Little Maid .... MBPI2077 . . 530
    at the Door
Illustrated initial K with heading for .... MBPI2424 . . 552
    The Story of King Arthur and His Knights
Illustrated initial K with heading for .... MBPI2468 . . 555
    The Story of the Champions of the Round Table
Illustrated initial K with heading for .... MBPI2497 . . 557
    The Story of the Champions of the Round Table
Illustrated initial L for McAndrew's Hymn ...... MBPI1967 . . 523
Illustrated initial L for Otto of the .... MBPI2332 . . 546
    Silver Hand
Illustrated initial L for Stops of .... MBPI3053 . . 591
    Various Quills
Illustrated initial M for Invitation .... PDPI0081 . . . 608
Illustrated initial M for King Custom .... MBPI0856 . . 454
Illustrated initial M with heading for .... MBPI2226 . . 540
    Master Jacob
Illustrated initial M with heading for .... MBPI2228 . . 540
    Master Jacob
Illustrated initial M with heading for .... MBPI2237 . . 540
    Mother Hildegarde
Illustrated initial M with heading for .... MBPI2588 . . 562
    The Story of Sir Launcelot and his Companions
Illustrated initial N for Among the Sand ...... MBPI0542 . . 434
    Hills
Illustrated initial N for In the Valley .... MBPI0065 . . 405
    of the Shadows
Illustrated initial N for The Merry .... MBPI2100 . . 532
    Adventures of Robin Hood
Illustrated initial N for The Merry .... MBPI2106 . . 532
    Adventures of Robin Hood
Illustrated initial O for How Boots .... MBPI2215 . . 539
    Befooled the King
Illustrated initial O for In the Meadows ...... MBPI0062 . . 404
    of Youth
Illustrated initial O for Master Jacob .... MBPI2225 . . 540
Illustrated initial O for Mother .... MBPI2233 . . 540
    Hildegarde
Illustrated initial O for One Good Turn .... MBPI2200 . . 538
    Deserves Another
Illustrated initial O for The First .... MBPI0166 . . 411
    Thanksgiving
Illustrated initial O for The Pilgrimage .... MBPI0831 . . 452
    of Truth
Illustrated initial O for The Price of .... MBPI0084 . . 406
    Blood
Illustrated initial O for The Princess .... MBPI2192 . . 537
    Golden-Hair and the Great Black Raven
Illustrated initial O for The Step-mother ...... MBPI2221 . . 539
Illustrated initial O for The Swan Maiden ...... MBPI2246 . . 541
Illustrated initial O for The Water of .... MBPI2176 . . 536
    Life
Illustrated initial O for The White Bird .... MBPI2205 . . 538
Illustrated initial O for To-Morrow .... MBPI0556 . . 435
Illustrated initial P for A Sahib's War .... MBPI0094 . . 406
Illustrated initial P for Jamaica, New .... MBPI0396 . . 425
    and Old

ILLUSTRATED INITIAL S WITH HEADING FOR THE STORY ...

Illustrated initial P with heading for .... MBPI2216 . . 539
    How Boots Befooled the King
Illustrated initial P with heading for .... MBPI2217 . . 539
    How Boots Befooled the King
Illustrated initial P with heading for .... MBPI2230 . . 540
    Peterkin and the Little Grey Hare
Illustrated initial P with heading for .... MBPI2231 . . 540
    Peterkin and the Little Grey Hare
Illustrated initial P with heading for .... MBPI2232 . . 540
    Peterkin and the Little Grey Hare
Illustrated initial P with heading for .... MBPI2194 . . 538
    The Princess Golden-Hair and the Great Black Raven
Illustrated initial P with heading for .... MBPI2195 . . 538
    The Princess Golden-Hair and the Great Black Raven
Illustrated initial Q with heading for .... MBPI2415 . . 551
    The Story of King Arthur and His Knights
Illustrated initial Q with heading for .... MBPI2417 . . 552
    The Story of King Arthur and His Knights
Illustrated initial Q with heading for .... MBPI2448 . . 553
    The Story of the Champions of the Round Table
Illustrated initial S for Among the Sand ...... MBPI0520 . . 433
    Hills
Illustrated initial S for Among the Sand ...... MBPI0530 . . 434
    Hills
Illustrated initial S for Change .... MBPI0627 . . 440
Illustrated initial S for Midway .... MBPI0630 . . 440
Illustrated initial S for Otto of the .... MBPI2301 . . 544
    Silver Hand
Illustrated initial S for Question .... MBPI0551 . . 435
Illustrated initial S for Statistics .... MBPI0653 . . 441
Illustrated initial S for The Birds of .... MBPI1986 . . 525
    Cirencester
Illustrated initial S for The Birds of .... MBPI1988 . . 525
    Cirencester
Illustrated initial S for The Merry .... MBPI2123 . . 533
    Adventures of Robin Hood
Illustrated initial S for The Story of .... MBPI1860 . . 517
    King Arthur and His Knights
Illustrated initial S for Ye True Story .... MBPI1234 . . 478
    of Granny Greene of Salem Town
Illustrated initial S with heading for .... MBPI2211 . . 539
    How the Good Gifts were Used by Two
Illustrated initial S with heading for .... MBPI2212 . . 539
    How the Good Gifts were Used by Two
Illustrated initial S with heading for .... MBPI2421 . . 552
    The Story of King Arthur and His Knights
Illustrated initial S with heading for .... MBPI2426 . . 552
    The Story of King Arthur and His Knights
Illustrated initial S with heading for .... MBPI2524 . . 558
    The Story of Sir Launcelot and his Companions
Illustrated initial S with heading for .... MBPI2535 . . 559
    The Story of Sir Launcelot and his Companions
Illustrated initial S with heading for .... MBPI2540 . . 559
    The Story of Sir Launcelot and his Companions
Illustrated initial S with heading for .... MBPI2550 . . 560
    The Story of Sir Launcelot and his Companions

Index–Titles and Alternate Titles of Pyle's Art

ILLUSTRATED INITIAL S WITH HEADING FOR THE STORY ...

Illustrated initial S with heading for . . . . MBPI2552 . . 560
The Story of Sir Launcelot and his Companions
Illustrated initial S with heading for . . . . MBPI2554 . . 560
The Story of Sir Launcelot and his Companions
Illustrated initial S with heading for . . . . MBPI2556 . . 560
The Story of Sir Launcelot and his Companions
Illustrated initial S with heading for . . . . MBPI2558 . . 560
The Story of Sir Launcelot and his Companions
Illustrated initial S with heading for . . . . MBPI2569 . . 561
The Story of Sir Launcelot and his Companions
Illustrated initial S with heading for . . . . MBPI2572 . . 561
The Story of Sir Launcelot and his Companions
Illustrated initial S with heading for . . . . MBPI2581 . . 562
The Story of Sir Launcelot and his Companions
Illustrated initial S with heading for . . . . MBPI2584 . . 562
The Story of Sir Launcelot and his Companions
Illustrated initial S with heading for . . . . MBPI2586 . . 562
The Story of Sir Launcelot and his Companions
Illustrated initial S with heading for . . . . MBPI2591 . . 562
The Story of Sir Launcelot and his Companions
Illustrated initial S with heading for . . . . MBPI2431 . . 552
The Story of the Champions of the Round Table
Illustrated initial S with heading for . . . . MBPI2443 . . 553
The Story of the Champions of the Round Table
Illustrated initial S with heading for . . . . MBPI2446 . . 553
The Story of the Champions of the Round Table
Illustrated initial S with heading for . . . . MBPI2450 . . 554
The Story of the Champions of the Round Table
Illustrated initial S with heading for . . . . MBPI2452 . . 554
The Story of the Champions of the Round Table
Illustrated initial S with heading for . . . . MBPI2454 . . 554
The Story of the Champions of the Round Table
Illustrated initial S with heading for . . . . MBPI2456 . . 554
The Story of the Champions of the Round Table
Illustrated initial S with heading for . . . . MBPI2458 . . 554
The Story of the Champions of the Round Table
Illustrated initial S with heading for . . . . MBPI2461 . . 554
The Story of the Champions of the Round Table
Illustrated initial S with heading for . . . . MBPI2474 . . 555
The Story of the Champions of the Round Table
Illustrated initial S with heading for . . . . MBPI2476 . . 555
The Story of the Champions of the Round Table
Illustrated initial S with heading for . . . . MBPI2482 . . 556
The Story of the Champions of the Round Table
Illustrated initial S with heading for . . . . MBPI2485 . . 556
The Story of the Champions of the Round Table
Illustrated initial S with heading for . . . . MBPI2487 . . 556
The Story of the Champions of the Round Table
Illustrated initial S with heading for . . . . MBPI2490 . . 556
The Story of the Champions of the Round Table
Illustrated initial S with heading for . . . . MBPI2493 . . 556
The Story of the Champions of the Round Table
Illustrated initial S with heading for . . . . MBPI2495 . . 556
The Story of the Champions of the Round Table
Illustrated initial S with heading for . . . . MBPI1898 . . 519
The Story of the Champions of the Round Table

ILLUSTRATED INITIAL T FOR NORTH FOLK LEGENDS OF ...

Illustrated initial S with heading for . . . . MBPI1900 . . 519
The Story of the Champions of the Round Table
Illustrated initial S with heading for . . . . MBPI1903 . . 519
The Story of the Champions of the Round Table
Illustrated initial S with heading for . . . . MBPI1905 . . 520
The Story of the Champions of the Round Table
Illustrated initial S with heading for . . . . MBPI2597 . . 563
The Story of the Grail and the Passing of Arthur
Illustrated initial S with heading for . . . . MBPI2605 . . 563
The Story of the Grail and the Passing of Arthur
Illustrated initial S with heading for . . . . MBPI2612 . . 564
The Story of the Grail and the Passing of Arthur
Illustrated initial S with heading for . . . . MBPI2614 . . 564
The Story of the Grail and the Passing of Arthur
Illustrated initial S with heading for . . . . MBPI2623 . . 564
The Story of the Grail and the Passing of Arthur
Illustrated initial S with heading for . . . . MBPI2628 . . 565
The Story of the Grail and the Passing of Arthur
Illustrated initial S with heading for . . . . MBPI2632 . . 565
The Story of the Grail and the Passing of Arthur
Illustrated initial S with heading for . . . . MBPI2634 . . 565
The Story of the Grail and the Passing of Arthur
Illustrated initial S with heading for . . . . MBPI2636 . . 565
The Story of the Grail and the Passing of Arthur
Illustrated initial S with heading for . . . . MBPI2641 . . 566
The Story of the Grail and the Passing of Arthur
Illustrated initial S with heading for . . . . MBPI2643 . . 566
The Story of the Grail and the Passing of Arthur
Illustrated initial S with heading for . . . . MBPI2645 . . 566
The Story of the Grail and the Passing of Arthur
Illustrated initial S with heading for . . . . MBPI2649 . . 566
The Story of the Grail and the Passing of Arthur
Illustrated initial S with heading for . . . . MBPI2653 . . 566
The Story of the Grail and the Passing of Arthur
Illustrated initial T for A Prelude . . . . MBPI0808 . . 451
Illustrated initial T for Among the Sand . . . . . . MBPI0518 . . 433
Hills
Illustrated initial T for Among the Sand . . . . . . MBPI0522 . . 433
Hills
Illustrated initial T for Among the Sand . . . . . . MBPI0539 . . 434
Hills
Illustrated initial T for Bearskin . . . . MBPI2173 . . 536
Illustrated initial T for Heredity . . . . MBPI0622 . . 439
Illustrated initial T for How One Turned . . . . . . MBPI2180 . . 537
His Trouble to Some Account
Illustrated initial T for How the Good . . . . MBPI2210 . . 539
Gifts were Used by Two
Illustrated initial T for How the . . . . MBPI2258 . . 542
Princess's Pride was broken
Illustrated initial T for How Three Went . . . . . . MBPI2183 . . 537
Out into the Wide World
Illustrated initial T for How Two went . . . . MBPI2261 . . 542
into Partnership
Illustrated initial T for King Stork . . . . MBPI2264 . . 542
Illustrated initial T for North Folk . . . . MBPI0864 . . 454
Legends of the Sea

Index–Titles and Alternate Titles of Pyle's Art

ILLUSTRATED INITIAL T FOR OTTO OF THE SILVER HAND

Illustrated initial T for Otto of the .... MBPI2306 .. 545
Silver Hand
Illustrated initial T for Otto of the .... MBPI2311 .. 545
Silver Hand
Illustrated initial T for Otto of the .... MBPI2345 .. 547
Silver Hand
Illustrated initial T for Otto of the .... MBPI2350 .. 547
Silver Hand
Illustrated initial T for Parable .... MBPI0651 .. 441
Illustrated initial T for Peterkin and .... MBPI2229 .. 540
the Little Grey Hare
Illustrated initial T for The Best that .... MBPI2268 .. 542
Life has to give
Illustrated initial T for The Clever .... MBPI2186 .. 537
Student and the Master of Black Arts
Illustrated initial T for The Flight of .... MBPI0131 .. 409
the Swallow
Illustrated initial T for The Fourth .... MBPI0015 .. 401
Sketch
Illustrated initial T for The King Dines .... MBPI3044 .. 591
Illustrated initial T for The Merry .... MBPI2133 .. 534
Adventures of Robin Hood
Illustrated initial T for The Pilgrimage .... MBPI0825 .. 452
of Truth
Illustrated initial T for The Pilgrimage .... MBPI0827 .. 452
of Truth
Illustrated initial T for The Price of .... MBPI0079 .. 405
Blood
Illustrated initial T for The Price of .... MBPI0088 .. 406
Blood
Illustrated initial T for The Romance of .... MBPI0733 .. 446
an Ambrotype
Illustrated initial T for The Ruby of .... MBPI0975 .. 461
Kishmoor
Illustrated initial T for The Simpleton .... MBPI2243 .. 541
and his Little Black Hen
Illustrated initial T for The Sixth .... MBPI0019 .. 402
Sketch
Illustrated initial T for The Staff and .... MBPI2254 .. 541
the Fiddle
Illustrated initial T for The Star Bearer .... PDPI0053 ... 606
Illustrated initial T for The Third .... MBPI0013 .. 401
Sketch
Illustrated initial T for The Three .... MBPI2250 .. 541
Little Pigs and the Ogre
Illustrated initial T for The Travels of .... MBPI0060 .. 404
the Soul
Illustrated initial T for The Yellow of .... MBPI0813 .. 451
the Leaf
Illustrated initial T for Twelve P. M. .... MBPI0651 .. 441
Illustrated initial T for Which is Best? .... MBPI2238 .. 540
Illustrated initial T, Sketch One for By .... MBPI0665 .. 442
Land and Sea
Illustrated initial T with heading for .... MBPI2174 .. 536
Bearskin

ILLUSTRATED INITIAL T WITH HEADING FOR THE ...

Illustrated initial T with heading for .... MBPI2218 .. 539
How Boots Befooled the King
Illustrated initial T with heading for .... MBPI2219 .. 539
How Boots Befooled the King
Illustrated initial T with heading for .... MBPI2181 .. 537
How One Turned His Trouble to Some Account
Illustrated initial T with heading for .... MBPI2213 .. 539
How the Good Gifts were Used by Two
Illustrated initial T with heading for .... MBPI2259 .. 542
How the Princess's Pride was broken
Illustrated initial T with heading for .... MBPI2260 .. 542
How the Princess's Pride was broken
Illustrated initial T with heading for .... MBPI2184 .. 537
How Three Went Out into the Wide World
Illustrated initial T with heading for .... MBPI2185 .. 537
How Three Went Out into the Wide World
Illustrated initial T with heading for .... MBPI2262 .. 542
How Two went into Partnership
Illustrated initial T with heading for .... MBPI2265 .. 542
King Stork
Illustrated initial T with heading for .... MBPI2266 .. 542
King Stork
Illustrated initial T with heading for .... MBPI2267 .. 542
King Stork
Illustrated initial T with heading for .... MBPI2227 .. 540
Master Jacob
Illustrated initial T with heading for .... MBPI2234 .. 540
Mother Hildegarde
Illustrated initial T with heading for .... MBPI2235 .. 540
Mother Hildegarde
Illustrated initial T with heading for .... MBPI2236 .. 540
Mother Hildegarde
Illustrated initial T with heading for .... MBPI2202 .. 538
One Good Turn Deserves Another
Illustrated initial T with heading for .... MBPI2203 .. 538
One Good Turn Deserves Another
Illustrated initial T with heading for .... MBPI2204 .. 538
One Good Turn Deserves Another
Illustrated initial T with heading for .... MBPI2269 .. 542
The Best that Life has to give
Illustrated initial T with heading for .... MBPI2270 .. 542
The Best that Life has to give
Illustrated initial T with heading for .... MBPI2271 .. 542
The Best that Life has to give
Illustrated initial T with heading for .... MBPI2188 .. 537
The Clever Student and the Master of Black Arts
Illustrated initial T with heading for .... MBPI2189 .. 537
The Clever Student and the Master of Black Arts
Illustrated initial T with heading for .... MBPI2193 .. 538
The Princess Golden-Hair and the Great Black Raven
Illustrated initial T with heading for .... MBPI2196 .. 538
The Princess Golden-Hair and the Great Black Raven
Illustrated initial T with heading for .... MBPI2244 .. 541
The Simpleton and his Little Black Hen
Illustrated initial T with heading for .... MBPI2245 .. 541
The Simpleton and his Little Black Hen

Index–Titles and Alternate Titles of Pyle's Art

ILLUSTRATED INITIAL T WITH HEADING FOR The ...

Illustrated initial T with heading for ....MBPI2255 ..541
The Staff and the Fiddle
Illustrated initial T with heading for ....MBPI2256 ..541
The Staff and the Fiddle
Illustrated initial T with heading for ....MBPI2257 ..542
The Staff and the Fiddle
Illustrated initial T with heading for ....MBPI2222 ..539
The Step-mother
Illustrated initial T with heading for ....MBPI2223 ..539
The Step-mother
Illustrated initial T with heading for ....MBPI2224 ..539
The Step-mother
Illustrated initial T with heading for ....MBPI2408 ..551
The Story of King Arthur and His Knights
Illustrated initial T with heading for ....MBPI2411 ..551
The Story of King Arthur and His Knights
Illustrated initial T with heading for ....MBPI2516 ..558
The Story of Sir Launcelot and his Companions
Illustrated initial T with heading for ....MBPI2533 ..559
The Story of Sir Launcelot and his Companions
Illustrated initial T with heading for ....MBPI2538 ..559
The Story of Sir Launcelot and his Companions
Illustrated initial T with heading for ....MBPI2542 ..559
The Story of Sir Launcelot and his Companions
Illustrated initial T with heading for ....MBPI2544 ..559
The Story of Sir Launcelot and his Companions
Illustrated initial T with heading for ....MBPI2561 ..561
The Story of Sir Launcelot and his Companions
Illustrated initial T with heading for ....MBPI2564 ..561
The Story of Sir Launcelot and his Companions
Illustrated initial T with heading for ....MBPI2566 ..561
The Story of Sir Launcelot and his Companions
Illustrated initial T with heading for ....MBPI2574 ..561
The Story of Sir Launcelot and his Companions
Illustrated initial T with heading for ....MBPI2576 ..561
The Story of Sir Launcelot and his Companions
Illustrated initial T with heading for ....MBPI2593 ..563
The Story of Sir Launcelot and his Companions
Illustrated initial T with heading for ....MBPI2439 ..553
The Story of the Champions of the Round Table
Illustrated initial T with heading for ....MBPI2465 ..555
The Story of the Champions of the Round Table
Illustrated initial T with heading for ....MBPI2470 ..555
The Story of the Champions of the Round Table
Illustrated initial T with heading for ....MBPI2472 ..555
The Story of the Champions of the Round Table
Illustrated initial T with heading for ....MBPI2509 ..557
The Story of the Champions of the Round Table
Illustrated initial T with heading for ....MBPI1907 ..520
The Story of the Champions of the Round Table
Illustrated initial T with heading for ....MBPI2620 ..564
The Story of the Grail and the Passing of Arthur
Illustrated initial T with heading for ....MBPI2626 ..565
The Story of the Grail and the Passing of Arthur
Illustrated initial T with heading for ....MBPI2630 ..565
The Story of the Grail and the Passing of Arthur

ILLUSTRATED INITIAL Y FOR SOCIETY

Illustrated initial T with heading for ....MBPI2638 ..565
The Story of the Grail and the Passing of Arthur
Illustrated initial T with heading for ....MBPI2647 ..566
The Story of the Grail and the Passing of Arthur
Illustrated initial T with heading for ....MBPI2651 ..566
The Story of the Grail and the Passing of Arthur
Illustrated initial T with heading for ....MBPI2655 ..566
The Story of the Grail and the Passing of Arthur
Illustrated initial T with heading for ....MBPI2657 ..567
The Story of the Grail and the Passing of Arthur
Illustrated initial T with heading for ....MBPI2247 ..541
The Swan Maiden
Illustrated initial T with heading for ....MBPI2248 ..541
The Swan Maiden
Illustrated initial T with heading for ....MBPI2249 ..541
The Swan Maiden
Illustrated initial T with heading for ....MBPI2251 ..541
The Three Little Pigs and the Ogre
Illustrated initial T with heading for ....MBPI2252 ..541
The Three Little Pigs and the Ogre
Illustrated initial T with heading for ....MBPI2177 ..537
The Water of Life
Illustrated initial T with heading for ....MBPI2178 ..537
The Water of Life
Illustrated initial T with heading for ....MBPI2179 ..537
The Water of Life
Illustrated initial T with heading for ....MBPI2206 ..538
The White Bird
Illustrated initial T with heading for ....MBPI2207 ..538
The White Bird
Illustrated initial T with heading for ....MBPI2208 ..538
The White Bird
Illustrated initial T with heading for ....MBPI2209 ..539
The White Bird
Illustrated initial T with heading for ....MBPI2240 ..540
Which is Best?
Illustrated initial T with heading for ....MBPI2241 ..541
Which is Best?
Illustrated initial U for Otto of the ....MBPI2284 ..543
Silver Hand
Illustrated initial U with heading for ....MBPI2263 ..542
for How Two went into Partnership
Illustrated initial U with heading for ....MBPI2401 ..551
The Story of King Arthur and His Knights
Illustrated initial V with heading for ....MBPI2413 ..551
The Story of King Arthur and His Knights
Illustrated initial W for Otto of the ....MBPI2296 ..544
Silver Hand
Illustrated initial W for Sphinx ....MBPI0614 ..439
Illustrated initial W for The True ....MBPI0884 ..456
Captain Kidd
Illustrated initial W with heading for ....MBPI2190 ..537
The Wonder Clock
Illustrated initial Y for Hope ....MBPI0564 ..436
Illustrated initial Y for If ....MBPI0564 ..436
Illustrated initial Y for Society ....MBPI0619 ..439

Index–Titles and Alternate Titles of Pyle's Art

Illustrated initial Y for The Birds of .... MBPI1990 .. 525
Cirencester
Illustration and text for The Lady of .... MBPI2728 .. 571
Shalott
Illustration and text for The Lady of .... MBPI2729 .. 571
Shalott
Illustration and text for The Lady of .... MBPI2733 .. 571
Shalott
Illustration and text for The Lady of .... MBPI2736 .. 571
Shalott
Illustration for A Forgotten Tale .... MBPI1971 .. 524
Illustration for A Forgotten Tale .... MBPI1972 .. 524
Illustration for A Puppet of Fate .... MBPI0804 .. 451
Illustration for A Report of the truth .... MBPI3195 .. 600
concerning the last sea-fight of the Revenge
Illustration for A Transferred Romance .... MBPI3241 .. 603
Illustration for Dr. Lavendar's People .... MBPI0759 .. 448
Illustration for How Willy-Wolly Went .... MBPI1795 .. 513
A-Fishing
Illustration for How Willy-Wolly Went .... MBPI1796 .. 513
A-Fishing
Illustration for How Willy-Wolly Went .... MBPI1797 .. 513
A-Fishing
Illustration for Hugo Grotius and His .... MBPI1533 .. 496
Book Chest
Illustration for John Greenleaf .... PDPI0055 .. 607
Whittier's, Abraham Davenport
Illustration for McAndrew's Hymn .... MBPI1965 .. 523
Illustration for McGuffey's Fifth .... MBPI2660 .. 567
Eclectic Reader
Illustration for McGuffey's Fifth .... MBPI2661 .. 567
Eclectic Reader
Illustration for Men of Iron .... MBPI1672 .. 505
Illustration for Men of Iron .... MBPI1685 .. 506
Illustration for Men of Iron .... MBPI1686 .. 506
Illustration for Men of Iron .... MBPI1689 .. 506
Illustration for Odes of Anacreon .... PDPI0036 ... 605
Anacreontics
Illustration for Old Captain .... MBPI0779 .. 449
Illustration for Old Captain .... MBPI0780 .. 449
Illustration for Old Captain .... MBPI0781 .. 449
Illustration for Old Captain .... MBPI0782 .. 449
Illustration for Old Captain .... MBPI0783 .. 449
Illustration for Old Captain .... MBPI0784 .. 449
Illustration for Old Captain .... MBPI0785 .. 450
Illustration for Old Captain .... MBPI0786 .. 450
Illustration for Parable .... MBPI3036 .. 590
Illustration for Poisoned Ice, by "Q" .... MBPI0073 .. 405
Illustration for Stamford's Soprano .... MBPI1265 .. 480
Illustration for Stops of Various Quills .... MBPI0612 .. 439
Illustration for Swinton's Advanced Third ..... MBPI2769 .. 574
Reader
Illustration for Swinton's Fifth Reader .... MBPI2755 .. 573
and Speaker
Illustration for Swinton's Fifth Reader .... MBPI2756 .. 573
and Speaker

Illustration for The Adventure of a Mouse ..... PDPI0103 ... 610
Illustration for The Captain's Well .... MBPI1764 .. 511
Illustration for The Captain's Well .... MBPI1765 .. 511
Illustration for The Captain's Well .... MBPI1766 .. 511
Illustration for The Captain's Well .... MBPI1767 .. 511
Illustration for The Chase of the Tide .... MBPI1756 .. 510
Illustration for The Eclogues of Vergil .... MBPI3201 .. 601
Illustration for The Lady of Shalott .... MBPI2705 .. 570
Illustration for The Lady of Shalott .... MBPI2714 .. 570
Illustration for The Lady of Shalott .... MBPI2720 .. 570
Illustration for The Lady of Shalott .... MBPI2723 .. 571
Illustration for The Lady of Shalott .... MBPI2726 .. 571
Illustration for The Lady of Shalott .... MBPI2734 .. 571
Illustration for The Lady of Shalott .... MBPI2737 .. 572
"Illustration for The Last Furrow" .... MBPI3135 .. 596
"Illustration for The Man With the Hoe" .... MBPI3113 .. 595
Illustration for The Mysterious Chest .... MBPI1047 .. 466
Illustration for The Parasite .... MBPI1270 .. 480
Illustration for Through Inland Waters .... MBPI0706 .. 445
Illustration for Through Inland Waters .... MBPI0712 .. 445
Illustration for Yankee Doodle .... MBPI2669 .. 567
Illustration for Yankee Doodle .... MBPI2673 .. 568
Illustration for Yankee Doodle .... MBPI2676 .. 568
Illustration for Yankee Doodle .... MBPI2680 .. 568
Illustration for Yankee Doodle .... MBPI2685 .. 568
Illustration for Yankee Doodle .... MBPI2688 .. 568
Illustration for Yankee Doodle .... MBPI2693 .. 569
Illustration to "The Man With the Hoe" .... MBPI3125 .. 596
Illustration with illustrated initial M .... MBPI1964 .. 523
for McAndrew's Hymn
The Illustrious Hero Walking in .... MBPI0722 .. 446
Conversation With the Marquis Lafayette
Impressment of American Seamen .... MBPI0314 .. 420
Impressment of American Seamen One of the .. PDPI0314 .. 420
Causes of the War of 1812
Impressment of Seamen .... MBPI0314 .. 420
"In all houses one finds the filter and .... MBPI0412 .. 426
the water jar"
In an instant he was flung back and down .... MBPI2329 .. 546
In an instant those long fingers closed ...... MBPI1031 .. 465
on the Governor
"In another hour it will be worn out" .... MBPI2811 .. 576
In Aunt Gainor's Garden .... MBPI0034 .. 403
"In came the gang of thieves" .... MBPI1667 .. 505
"In close array they come" .... MBPI2922 .. 583
In Colonial Days A Fight with Carolina .... MBPI1838 .. 515
Pirates
In Connecticut .... MBPI0510 .. 432
In Death Valley .... MBPI3154 .. 598
In High Sierras .... MBPI3145 .. 597
"In mid-harbor the tainted crafts were .... MBPI0385 .. 425
burned in sight of all"
In New York (At Headquarters) .... MBPI0506 .. 432

Index–Titles and Alternate Titles of Pyle's Art

In place of the apple hung a little .... MBPI1056 .. 466
   gilded skull
In Poppy Fields .... MBPI3157 .. 598
In Pursuit of Revenge .... MBPI2016 .. 526
In Springtime .... MBPI0809 .. 451
In the Belfry .... MBPI2275 .. 543
In the Bookseller's Shop .... MBPI0126 .. 408
In the Dark .... MBPI0623 .. 439
In the "Eyry" .... MBPI1675 .. 505
"In the Garden" .... MBPI0104 .. 407
In The Garden at Mount Vernon .... MBPI0721 .. 446
In the garden behind the moon .... MBPI2354 .. 548
In the Hospital .... MBPI0741 .. 447
"In the hush of expectation" .... MBPI2910 .. 582
"In The Likeness of a Fair Woman" .... MBPI1061 .. 467
In the market place .... MBPI0384 .. 424
In the Meadows of Youth .... MBPI0055 .. 404
In the middle of the narrow way stood the ... MBPI2341 .. 547
   motionless, steel-clad figure
In the night .... MBPI0893 .. 456
In the Northern Market–"Peaches, one ...... MBPI0188 .. 412
   cent"
In the Old Raleigh Tavern .... MBPI0683 .. 443
In The Orchestra .... MBPI2066 .. 530
In the Park .... MBPI2045 .. 528
In the presence of Washington .... MBPI0036 .. 403
In the Prison .... MBPI0037 .. 403
In the reading-room .... MBPI0427 .. 427
In the Storm .... MBPI3136 .. 596
In the train of King Alfonzo .... MBPI0897 .. 457
In the Twilight .... MBPI0696 .. 444
In the Valley of Delight .... MBPI1862 .. 517
In the Valley of the Shadows .... MBPI0056 .. 404
In the Wood-Carver's Shop .... MBPI0655 .. 441
In This Verse is Spoken of the Coming of ..... MBPI2716 .. 570
   Sir Lancelot the Bold
In Which the Fairy Lady Seeks the River .... MBPI2725 .. 571
In Yellow and Black .... MBPI0999 .. 463
Inaugural Procession .... MBPI2757 .. 573
"Inauguration of President Washington" .... MBPI0360 .. 423
Inauguration of Washington .... MBPI3193 .. 600
Inauguration of Washington in New York ...... MBPI3193 .. 600
The Inauguration of Washington .... MBPI0360 .. 423
The Inauguration .... MBPI0360 .. 423
The Indian and the Pioneer .... MBPI2762 .. 573
Indian Woman Saving The Life Of John .... MBPI0338 .. 422
   Brown
The Indians Aiming at the Loop-Holes .... PDPI0031 ... 605
Indians Ambuscading a Puritan Farmer .... MBPI0839 .. 453
Indians on the Warpath .... MBPI0839 .. 453
Infinite Depths .... MBPI3132 .. 596
"An initial by Howard Pyle drawn for .... MBPI0373 .. 424
   'Harpers Magazine' in 1890"
"The innkeeper served him in person" .... MBPI0149 .. 410

The Inquisitive Peasant .... PDPI0022 ... 604
Instantly there appeared before her a .... MBPI1354 .. 485
   strange being
Instantly there stood by her side a .... MBPI1358 .. 485
   School Trustee
Interior of Chapel .... MBPI0370 .. 424
Interior of fishing station .... MBPI0187 .. 412
The Interior of the Boat .... MBPI0715 .. 445
An Interrupted Performance .... MBPI1191 .. 475
Interview Between General Washington and ... MBPI0756 .. 448
   "Citizen" Genet
An interview between Sir Edmund Andros ... MBPI0841 .. 453
   and James Blair
Into Strange Lands .... MBPI2011 .. 526
Into the River .... MBPI3000 .. 588
The Intruder .... MBPI2015 .. 526
The Invisible Bride .... MBPI3159 .. 598
"Is it Yes or No, Darthea?" .... MBPI0042 .. 403
"Is your hanging-party ready?" he said .... MBPI1927 .. 521
Isaac Bradley carrying Joseph into the .... MBPI1306 .. 482
   settlement
Isaac Sears addressing the Mob .... MBPI0274 .. 418
"It crossed the river to the Long Island ...... MBPI0424 .. 427
   side of the Brooklyn Ferry"
"It is all a mistake, my friend, a .... MBPI0253 .. 416
   grievous mistake"
"It is n't fair" .... MBPI2849 .. 579
"It is the Cathedral of St. Katherine" .... MBPI0393 .. 425
"It is the leader, and all the others .... MBPI0406 .. 426
   follow it"
"It is the Lord's Great Day! Let us .... PDPI0055 .. 607
   adjourn," some said; and then, as if with one accord, all eyes
   turned to Abraham Davenport. He rose, slow cleaving with his
   steady voice the intolerable hush.
It made a noise like father's gun................ MBPI2674 .. 568
"It poised for an instant above the .... MBPI1946 .. 522
   child's fair head–death cruel and imminent"
It scared me so, I hooked it off... .... MBPI2691 .. 569
It scared me so I shrinked off... .... MBPI2678 .. 568
"It seemed to lie sound asleep, with a .... MBPI1319 .. 483
   snow blanket all over its roof"
It was a comrade from his own regiment ...... MBPI1072 .. 467
"It was a very gay dinner" .... MBPI0483 .. 431
"It was along this wall that the wounded .... MBPI0369 .. 424
   soldiers sat"
"It was at this juncture...that an .... MBPI0085 .. 406
   apologetic knock fell upon the door"
It was his belief that the chest was .... MBPI1039 .. 465
   certainly haunted
It was the great Emperor Rudolph .... MBPI2346 .. 547
"It was the King's daughter passing by" .... MBPI1635 .. 503
"It was to represent the Narrow Way" .... MBPI0368 .. 423
Ita Primo Ita Semper .... MBPI2388 .. 550
"Its hundredth year" .... MBPI2809 .. 576
"Izaak" Walton .... MBPI3199 .. 600

Index–Titles and Alternate Titles of Pyle's Art

J. A. M. Whealton . . . . MBPI2042 . . 528

Jack and Dred rescue Eleanor–The Start . . . . . . MBPI1835 . . 515

"Jack followed the Captain and the young . . . MBPI1832 . . 515
    lady up the crooked path to the house"

Jacob and Gretchen get the best of the . . . . . . MBPI1417 . . 489
    Red One and go home together happily

"Jacob and the King left in the desert by . . . . . MBPI1727 . . 508
    the Genie"

Jacob and the Magic Plough . . . . MBPI1415 . . 489

Jacob and The Red One . . . . MBPI1412 . . 489

Jacob and the Red One go hunting together . . MBPI1416 . . 489

Jacob shoots at– . . . . MBPI1413 . . 489

"Jacob's magnificent court suit" . . . . MBPI1725 . . 508

Jacob's Mother & the Herr Mayor . . . . MBPI1411 . . 489

Jacques Cartier Erects a Cross . . . . MBPI0289 . . 419

"Jacques Cartier setting up a Cross at . . . . MBPI0289 . . 419
    Gaspé"

Jacques Cartier Setting Up a Cross at . . . . MBPI0289 . . 419
    Gaspé

Jan returns . . . . MBPI2065 . . 530

Jan's courtship . . . . MBPI2062 . . 529

January and May . . . . MBPI1962 . . 523

"Jefferson Writing the Declaration of . . . . MBPI1993 . . 525
    Independence"

The Jester . . . . MBPI0889 . . 456

"Joan of Arc" . . . . MBPI0921 . . 458

Jocelin, with many encomiums, displayed . . . . MBPI1121 . . 471
    his emeralds

John Adams Prophesying "The Glorious . . . . . . MBPI2075 . . 530
    Fourth"

"John Cape takes down the quaint old . . . . . . MBPI0441 . . 428
    sign"

John Dubois's drive to Newburgh . . . . MBPI0249 . . 416

"John Still, 'an honest barber and . . . . MBPI0429 . . 427
    peruke-maker from London'"

"Johnson with Goldsmith and Boswell" . . . . . . MBPI2969 . . 586

"The jointed tandem" . . . . MBPI2821 . . 577

The jolly red-faced Man comes to Town . . . . . . MBPI1448 . . 491

Jonathan and a Client–The Lady with the . . . . MBPI0450 . . 429
    Green Pocket-book

Jonathan as an Enemy arresting a Thief . . . . . . MBPI0449 . . 429

Jonathan in the Wood Street Compter . . . . MBPI0448 . . 428
    Prison

Jonathan Quidd . . . . MBPI0204 . . 413

Jonathan Rugg . . . . MBPI0976 . . 461

Jonathan Rugg was married to Martha Dobbs MBPI0986 . . 462
    the following year

"Jonathan threw himself upon the stranger . . . . MBPI0982 . . 462
    with the fury of a madman"

Joseph Brown leading his company to . . . . MBPI0339 . . 422
    Nicojack

Joseph Gladd . . . . MBPI2053 . . 529

The Joy of the Hills . . . . MBPI3158 . . 598

Joy of the Morning . . . . MBPI3151 . . 597

"Judge Morrison read these harmless . . . . MBPI0765 . . 448
    jingles, chuckling and sneering"

Judgment Day . . . . MBPI3048 . . 591

Jupiter and the Philosopher . . . . MBPI1811 . . 514

"Just as bubbles do when they burst" . . . . MBPI2815 . . 576

"'Keep the bag of money for yourself,' . . . . MBPI1656 . . 504
    said the King"

A Kentucky Wedding . . . . MBPI2758 . . 573

Kidd at Gardiner's Island . . . . MBPI0610 . . 439

Kidd on the Deck of the "Adventure . . . . MBPI0885 . . 456
    Galley"

The King and his Prime Minister . . . . MBPI1782 . . 512

"The King and the beggar feasted" . . . . MBPI1648 . . 503

The King and the Fair Petitioner . . . . MBPI0971 . . 461

King Arthur findeth ye old woman in ye . . . . . MBPI2425 . . 552
    hut

King Arthur meets the Lady Guinevere . . . . MBPI1881 . . 518

King Arthur of Britain . . . . MBPI1859 . . 517

The King being lost in ye Forest meets . . . . MBPI1468 . . 492
    with the Great Black Raven

The King caresses the White Dove . . . . MBPI1558 . . 498

The King Dines . . . . MBPI3043 . . 591

The King finds his children . . . . MBPI1450 . . 491

King Florimel greets the Princess . . . . MBPI1521 . . 496

The King gives the Water of Life to the . . . . . . MBPI1552 . . 497
    beautiful Princess

The king glared down at her . . . . MBPI0971 . . 461

The King goes to cut off the Faithful . . . . MBPI1553 . . 498
    Servant's arm

"The King himself hauled me out of gaol" . . . . MBPI0916 . . 458

"The King Himself Hauled Me Out of Meung . . MBPI0916 . . 458
    Goal"

"The King laid his hands on Beppo's . . . . MBPI1738 . . 509
    shoulders"

King Leodegrance cometh to the assay of . . . . MBPI1854 . . 516
    the Sword

King Mark broods mischief . . . . MBPI2498 . . 557

King Mark of Cornwall . . . . MBPI2469 . . 555

The King meets the Great Black Raven in . . . . MBPI1468 . . 492
    the Forest

"The King opened the closet door and . . . . . . MBPI1583 . . 499
    brought forth the true bride"

The King peeps over the hedge and sees . . . . . . MBPI1519 . . 495
    what is going on upon the other side

The King peeps over the hedge . . . . MBPI1519 . . 495

The King reaches for the Apple . . . . MBPI1430 . . 490

The King rescues the Maiden from a deep . . . MBPI1556 . . 498
    pit

"The king sat upon a chair of state, with . . . . . MBPI1793 . . 513
    a learned judge at each side"

The King talks with the Wise Man . . . . MBPI1429 . . 490

The King . . . . MBPI1088 . . 468

"The King's Head, kept by one Roger . . . . MBPI0420 . . 427
    Baker"

The King's Physicians attend Sir Geraint . . . . . . MBPI2621 . . 564

The King's Steward and Christine . . . . MBPI1431 . . 490

Index–Titles and Alternate Titles of Pyle's Art

THE KISS OF PEACE

The Kiss of Peace . . . . MBPI0366 . . 423
Kitty and Turkish Merchant . . . . MBPI1789 . . 512
The Kloster . . . . MBPI0364 . . 423
Kobus and his pupil . . . . MBPI2061 . . 529
Kobus brings news of Mynheer Jan . . . . MBPI2064 . . 529
L'Envoy, A Pastoral Without Words . . . . MBPI1944 . . 522
La Salle Before Louis XIV . . . . MBPI0930 . . 459
La Salle christening the country . . . . MBPI0929 . . 459
   "Louisiana"
La Salle on The Mississippi . . . . MBPI0929 . . 459
La Salle petitions the King for . . . . MBPI0930 . . 459
   permission to explore the Mississippi
"Labor an' He Did Disagree" . . . . MBPI2054 . . 529
Labor And Capital . . . . MBPI3045 . . 591
"Lady Adeliza Came Upon The Balcony" . . . . . . MBPI0891 . . 456
Lady Adeliza came wondering to the . . . . MBPI0891 . . 456
   balcony
"Lady and lover" . . . . MBPI2873 . . 580
The Lady Belle Isoult . . . . MBPI2471 . . 555
The Lady Brings the Curse Upon Her . . . . MBPI2722 . . 571
The Lady Dieth Floating Adown the Stream . . . MBPI2730 . . 571
The Lady Elaine the Fair Knoweth Sir . . . . MBPI2567 . . 561
   Launcelot
The Lady Elaine the Fair . . . . MBPI2517 . . 558
The Lady Guinevere . . . . MBPI1869 . . 517
"Lady, I have a favor to ask of thee" . . . . MBPI1685 . . 506
The Lady Layonnesse cometh to the . . . . MBPI2545 . . 560
   Pavilion of Sir Gareth
The Lady Layonnesse . . . . MBPI2543 . . 559
The Lady Nymue beareth away Launcelot . . . . MBPI2440 . . 553
   into the Lake
The Lady of the Fountain . . . . MBPI2577 . . 562
The lady of the house . . . . MBPI2035 . . 528
The Lady of the Lake and Sir Galahad . . . . MBPI2627 . . 565
The Lady of the Lake finds Sir Pellias . . . . MBPI1896 . . 519
   wounded
The Lady of the Lake sits by the Fountain . . . . . MBPI1891 . . 519
   in Arroy
The Lady of Ye Lake . . . . MBPI2409 . . 551
Lady Washington's Arrival at . . . . MBPI0718 . . 445
   Headquarters, Cambridge
The lady with the silver veil . . . . MBPI0985 . . 462
The Lady Yvette the Fair . . . . MBPI1908 . . 520
Landing Negro Slaves at Jamestown . . . . MBPI0834 . . 453
Landing negroes at Jamestown from Dutch . . MBPI0834 . . 453
   man-of-war, 1619
Landing of Cadillac . . . . MBPI0336 . . 421
The Landing of Cadillac . . . . MBPI0336 . . 421
The Landing of Carteret . . . . MBPI3240 . . 603
Landing of Governor Philip Carteret at . . . . . . MBPI3240 . . 603
   Elizabethtowne, N.J. 1665
The Landing of the Pilgrims . . . . MBPI0293 . . 419
Landing Slaves From a Dutch Man-of-War at . . MBPI0834 . . 453
   Jamestown, Virginia

THE LITTLE MAN AND THE GREAT HORSE

The Last Blossom with initial T . . . . MBPI2996 . . 588
The last boat-load of the British leaving . . . . . MBPI0307 . . 420
   New York
The Last Evening Caller . . . . MBPI1194 . . 475
The Last Furrow . . . . MBPI3135 . . 596
The Last Haul Before Dawn . . . . MBPI1197 . . 475
The Last Leaf . . . . MBPI2861 . . 579
The last of the "Naronic" . . . . MBPI1135 . . 471
Latter-Day Warnings with initial W . . . . MBPI2972 . . 586
"Laying the old violin tenderly beneath . . . . . . MBPI0200 . . 413
   his chin"
A Leaf From the Devil's Jest-Book . . . . MBPI3133 . . 596
Leander . . . . MBPI0214 . . 414
Leaving Mount Vernon for Continental . . . . . . MBPI0681 . . 443
   Congress
Leaving Mount Vernon for the Congress of . . . MBPI0681 . . 443
   the Colonies
Legal Intervention . . . . MBPI1180 . . 474
"Lesson: The Tiger" . . . . PDPI0001 . . . 603
" 'Let me go to him!' she shrieked" . . . . MBPI3185 . . 600
"'Let me go to him!' she shrieked, in her . . . . . MBPI3185 . . 600
   anguish of soul"
"Let me hasten onward" . . . . MBPI3184 . . 599
Lexington . . . . MBPI1991 . . 525
Lexington Green–"If they want a War, let . . . . . MBPI0305 . . 420
   it begin here"
"Lieutenant Wyman, creeping up, put a . . . . . . MBPI1308 . . 482
   bullet through him"
Life . . . . MBPI3054 . . 591
Life in an Old Dutch Town . . . . MBPI2502 . . 557
The lighters were soon alongside . . . . MBPI0997 . . 463
"Like a gentleman of leisure" . . . . MBPI2903 . . 582
"Like a thunder-cloud it breaks" . . . . MBPI2911 . . 582
Likeness of Lawrence Washington, Esq., ... MBPI0680 . . 443
   and a picture of Mount Vernon in the Distance
The Lily Lake . . . . MBPI0544 . . 434
Lincoln . . . . MBPI0988 . . 462
Lincoln Memorial . . . . PDPI0002 . . . 603
A lithe, young, slender figure . . . . MBPI0923 . . 458
"The little boys cheered vigorously as he . . . . . MBPI0205 . . 413
   pushed off"
Little Brother of the Ground . . . . MBPI3122 . . 596
Little Brothers of the Ground . . . . MBPI3122 . . 596
The little gentleman in black emitted a . . . . . . MBPI0980 . . 462
   piercing scream
The little gentleman with one eye . . . . MBPI0978 . . 462
Little John in ye guise of a Friar stops . . . . MBPI2126 . . 533
   three Lasses
Little John journeys in Holy Company . . . . MBPI2127 . . 533
Little John knoweth not which road to . . . . . . MBPI2110 . . 532
   take
Little John overcomes Eric o' Lincoln . . . . MBPI2107 . . 532
Little Lord Geraldine . . . . MBPI2071 . . 530
The Little Man and the Great Horse . . . . MBPI1390 . . 487

The little man asks for his cap . . . . MBPI1426 . . 490

The little man raced down the stairs and . . . . . MBPI1160 . . 473
    out into the street

"The little man set him to work on the . . . . . . MBPI1634 . . 503
    bench"

"The little pink finger and the huge . . . . MBPI0168 . . 411
    black index came to a full stop under this commandment"

The little tin horn has no effect . . . . MBPI1495 . . 494

"The lively barber" . . . . MBPI2880 . . 580

Living . . . . MBPI0553 . . 435

The Living Temple . . . . MBPI2998 . . 588

Loading Ships in Albemarle Sound . . . . MBPI0838 . . 453

Loading vessels in Albermarle Sound . . . . MBPI0838 . . 453

A Lock Keeper . . . . MBPI0709 . . 445

"A lodging-house very well known to all . . . . . MBPI0377 . . 424
    Jamaica travellers"

A lonely duel in the middle of a great, ... MBPI1065 . . 467
    sunny field

"The long straggling aqueduct" . . . . MBPI0407 . . 426

"'Look at yonder poor man,' said she to . . . . . . MBPI1731 . . 509
    her nurse"

A Look Into the Gulf . . . . MBPI3119 . . 595

Looking into the Prussian Lines from the . . . . MBPI1910 . . 520
    Chateau de la Muette

"Loot" . . . . MBPI0073 . . 405

Loot . . . . MBPI0073 . . 405

"Lord George led him to where the King . . . . . MBPI1683 . . 506
    stood"

"The Lord hath sent me here to die like . . . . . . MBPI1761 . . 511
    Stephen at the feet of Saul"

"The Lord Knows I Haven't Hurt Them" . . . . MBPI1760 . . 510

Lord of the Earth . . . . MBPI1009 . . 464

A Lord of the Earth . . . . MBPI1009 . . 464

"Lord Percy's hunted soldiers" . . . . MBPI2894 . . 581

Lorna Doone . . . . MBPI3192 . . 600

Lost in the Snow . . . . MBPI1179 . . 474

A Love Affair of the Olden . . . . MBPI1182 . . 474
    Time–Consulting the Wise Woman

Love and Death . . . . MBPI0750 . . 447

Love at Valley Forge . . . . MBPI1741 . . 509

A Love Feast Among the Dunkers . . . . MBPI1228 . . 477

Love's Vigil . . . . MBPI3140 . . 597

"The lovely bonnets beam their smiles" . . . . MBPI2823 . . 577

"The lovely bonnets beamed their smiles" . . . . . MBPI2823 . . 577

The Lovers . . . . MBPI0949 . . 460

Lowland Brook . . . . MBPI0270 . . 417

The Lowland Brook . . . . MBPI0270 . . 417

Lugged the mysterious chest to the . . . . MBPI1051 . . 466
    lawyer's house

"The lusty young Fort-Hillers" . . . . MBPI2883 . . 581

Lygia and Vinicius in the Garden of Aulus . . . . . MBPI3104 . . 594

"'Mad!' said Oliver, 'why am I mad?'" . . . . MBPI0150 . . 410

The Madman of the Forest who was Sir . . . . . . MBPI2562 . . 561
    Launcelot

The Magic Flute . . . . MBPI0469 . . 430

Magic Harper . . . . MBPI1013 . . 464

The Magic Harper . . . . MBPI1013 . . 464

The Magic Sword . . . . MBPI0910 . . 457

–the Magpie . . . . MBPI1414 . . 489

Maid Marian's Song . . . . MBPI0030 . . 402

Maid Marian's Song with title . . . . MBPI0029 . . 402

A Maid's Choice . . . . MBPI0490 . . 431

The majesty of the law . . . . MBPI2038 . . 528

Making Cheese . . . . MBOI0003 . . 611

Making shingles . . . . MBPI0193 . . 413

"Making strange figures upon the table" . . . . . . MBPI1611 . . 501

Malvern Hill . . . . MBPI0740 . . 447

Man . . . . MBPI3144 . . 597

Man and staff sank into the peat mud . . . . MBPI1120 . . 470

"A man in it, standing upright, and . . . . MBPI0006 . . 401
    something lying in a lump at the bow"

The Man Is Grander Than The King . . . . MBPI0303 . . 419

A man lay prone there, half turned upon . . . . . MBPI0927 . . 458
    his face

The Man of Family . . . . MBPI2971 . . 586

The Man Under the Stone . . . . MBPI3173 . . 599

The man was Long Jacob, the bowman . . . . MBPI2328 . . 546

The man with the broken nose . . . . MBPI0983 . . 462

The Man With the Hoe . . . . MBPI3118 . . 595

"The Man With The Hoe" . . . . MBPI3118 . . 595

The man with the silver earrings . . . . MBPI0981 . . 462

The Mangrove . . . . MBPI0390 . . 425

"Many a noted steed" . . . . MBPI2819 . . 577

"Many a six foot grenadier–The flattened . . . . MBPI2877 . . 580
    grass had measured"

"Many Were The Physical Encounters . . . . MBPI1871 . . 517
    Between The Knights"

Marched From Jail For The Last Time . . . . MBPI1762 . . 511

Mare Rubrum with initial F . . . . MBPI2988 . . 587

Marginal decoration, female with . . . . MBPI0946 . . 460
    outstretched arm

Marginal decoration, female with ship . . . . MBPI0959 . . 460

Marginal decoration for At the Turn of . . . . MBPI1751 . . 510
    the Glass

Marginal decoration for Edric and . . . . MBPI1015 . . 464
    Sylvaine

Marginal decoration for Edric and . . . . MBPI1016 . . 464
    Sylvaine

Marginal decoration for Edric and . . . . MBPI1017 . . 464
    Sylvaine

Marginal decoration for Edric and . . . . MBPI1018 . . 464
    Sylvaine

Marginal decoration for Edric and . . . . MBPI1019 . . 464
    Sylvaine

Marginal decoration for Edric and . . . . MBPI1020 . . 464
    Sylvaine

Marginal decoration for Edric and . . . . MBPI1021 . . 464
    Sylvaine

Marginal decoration for Edric and . . . . MBPI1022 . . 464
    Sylvaine

Marginal decoration for Edric and .... MBPI1023 .. 464
Sylvaine
Marginal decoration for Edric and .... MBPI1024 .. 464
Sylvaine
Marginal decoration for Edric and .... MBPI1025 .. 465
Sylvaine
Marginal decoration for Edric and .... MBPI1026 .. 465
Sylvaine
Marginal decoration for Edric and .... MBPI1027 .. 465
Sylvaine
Marginal decoration for Edric and .... MBPI1028 .. 465
Sylvaine
Marginal decoration for Hope and Memory ... MBPI0052 .. 404
Marginal decoration for Hope and Memory ... MBPI0053 .. 404
Marginal decoration for King Custom .... MBPI0857 .. 454
Marginal decoration for Society .... MBPI0641 .. 441
Marginal decoration for The Body to the ..... MBPI0790 .. 450
Soul
Marginal decoration for The Body to the ..... MBPI0792 .. 450
Soul
Marginal decoration for The Body to the ..... MBPI0793 .. 450
Soul
Marginal decoration for The Star Bearer .... MBPI2083 .. 531
Marginal decoration for The Star Bearer .... MBPI2084 .. 531
Marginal decoration, male with sword and ... MBPI0947 .. 460
shield
Marginal decoration, male with tree .... MBPI0960 .. 460
Marginal decoration with title for Edric ...... MBPI1014 .. 464
and Sylvaine
Marginal decoration with title for The .... MBPI2082 .. 531
Star Bearer
Marginal illustration for The Chase of .... MBPI1754 .. 510
the Tide
Marginal illustration for The Salem Wolf .... MBPI1077 .. 468
Marginal illustration for The Salem Wolf ...... MBPI1080 .. 468
Marginal illustration for The Salem Wolf .... MBPI1081 .. 468
Marginal illustration for Ysobel de .... MBPI1103 .. 469
Corveaux
Marginal illustration for Ysobel de .... MBPI1104 .. 469
Corveaux
Marginal illustration for Ysobel de .... MBPI1105 .. 470
Corveaux
Marginal illustration for Ysobel de .... MBPI1106 .. 470
Corveaux
Marginal illustration for Ysobel de .... MBPI1107 .. 470
Corveaux
Marginal illustration for Ysobel de .... MBPI1108 .. 470
Corveaux
Marginal illustration for Ysobel de .... MBPI1109 .. 470
Corveaux
Marginal illustration for Ysobel de .... MBPI1110 .. 470
Corveaux
Marginal illustration for Ysobel de .... MBPI1111 .. 470
Corveaux
Marginal illustration for Ysobel de .... MBPI1112 .. 470
Corveaux

Marooned .... MBPI0351 .. 422
Marooned .... MBPI2511 .. 557
Marooned .... PDPI0098 ... 609
"Mary turned white, then s`he dropped down MBPI0768 .. 448
at his feet"
"Master and Pupil" .... MBPI1772 .. 511
"The Master caused vs to haue some Beere" ... MBPI0309 .. 420
The Master is Angry .... MBPI1421 .. 489
Master Jacob and the three Cronies meet .... MBPI1496 .. 494
in the Woods
Master Jacob brings his Pig to Market .... MBPI1493 .. 494
Master Jacob comes to ye town with his .... MBPI1493 .. 494
fine, fat pig and there falls in with the Priest and the Provost
Master Jacob goes to Town with his Goat ..... MBPI1494 .. 494
Master Jacob takes his black goat to town ...... MBPI1494 .. 494
Master Jacob with his two pots meets the ...... MBPI1496 .. 494
three cronies in the woods
The Master of Black Arts bringeth a .... MBPI1475 .. 493
curious little Black Hen to the King
The Master of Black Arts with a Hen .... MBPI1475 .. 493
Master of the World at Nineteen .... MBPI2073 .. 530
The Masterpiece .... MBPI2801 .. 576
The mate elevated and sighted the gun .... MBPI0996 .. 463
Materials of a Story .... MBPI3042 .. 591
Mather Byles preaching to Quakers .... MBPI0228 .. 415
A Matrimonial Difficulty–Legal .... MBPI1180 .. 474
Intervention
A Matter of Fate .... PDPI0015 ... 604
"May I have the pleasure for the next" .... PDPI0084 ... 608
"Maybe the snow deadened his footsteps, ... MBPI1245 .. 478
maybe it was the Devil"
McCue .... MBPI2054 .. 529
Medieval lady and gentleman .... PDPI0044 ... 606
Medieval Scene .... PDPI0049 ... 606
A Meeting .... MBPI3131 .. 596
Meeting of Captain Tollemache and Captain .. MBPI0440 .. 428
Pennington at the New York Arms
"The Meeting of Cortes and Montezuma" ..... MBPI2962 .. 586
The Meeting of General Greene and General ... MBPI1998 .. 525
Gates
Meeting of Greene and Gates .... MBPI1998 .. 525
The Meeting of Greene and Gates at .... MBPI1998 .. 525
Charlotte, N.C.
The Meeting of Greene and Gates at .... MBPI1998 .. 525
Charlotte, N.C., Upon the Former's Assuming Command
The Meeting of Greene and Gates Upon .... MBPI1998 .. 525
Greene's Assuming Command
Melancholia .... MBPI0613 .. 439
Meleager Refuses to Help in the Defence .... MBPI2782 .. 574
of the City
Melicent stood motionless like a wild .... MBPI0926 .. 458
thing at gaze
Melissy .... MBPI0248 .. 416

Index–Titles and Alternate Titles of Pyle's Art

The Members of Congress Leaving .... MBPI1190 .. 475
   Independence Hall
"The men brought Selim up in front of the ... MBPI1695 .. 506
   statue"
"The men who met at Hampden Hall" .... MBPI0442 .. 428
Menendey's Expedition on it's way to The ..... MBPI0291 .. 419
   New World
Menendez's Expedition on its Way to the ...... MBPI0291 .. 419
   New World
Meregrett, daughter of Philippe the Bold ...... MBPI0999 .. 463
Merlin Prophesieth from a Cloud of Mist ...... MBPI2589 .. 562
Merlin the Enchanter .... MBPI1841 .. 516
The Mermaid .... MBPI2512 .. 557
The Merry Friar carries Robin across the ...... MBPI2087 .. 531
   Water
The Merry Friar carrieth Robin across the .... MBPI2087 .. 531
   Water
The Merry Friar sings a goodly song .... MBPI2118 .. 533
Merry Robin clad as a Beggar stops the ...... MBPI2129 .. 534
   Corn Engrosser by the Cross nigh Ollerton
Merry Robin hath the worst of a Bargain ...... MBPI2139 .. 534
Merry Robin stops a Sorrowful Knight .... MBPI2121 .. 533
Merry Robin stops a Stranger in Scarlet ...... MBPI2112 .. 532
The Messiah cover design for The Tuesday ... MBPI3213 .. 601
   Club
A Midnight Court–Martial .... MBPI1067 .. 467
The Midnight Court Martial .... MBPI1067 .. 467
The Midsummer Moon .... MBPI2507 .. 557
Midsummer Noon .... MBPI3162 .. 598
Midway .... MBPI0629 .. 440
The Mighty Fight betwixt Little John and .... MBPI2108 .. 532
   the Cook
"A mighty stride he swung" .... MBPI2831 .. 577
The Military Ballet dance .... MBPI1338 .. 484
The Milkmaid's Song, with title and poem .... MBPI1183 .. 474
   inserted
The Minute Man .... MBPI0102 .. 407
Mirth and Sorrow .... MBPI0892 .. 456
"The Mischianza" .... MBPI0167 .. 411
Miss Nancy takes leave of the officers .... MBPI1304 .. 482
Miss Smith .... MBPI0743 .. 447
Miss Van Lew Bringing Food To The Union .... MBPI1124 .. 471
   Soldier In The Secret Room
Mistress Betty .... MBPI2058 .. 529
The Mizzen Top of the "Redoubtable" .... MBPI0046 .. 403
Modern American Heading .... MBPI0833 .. 453
Modern Sindbad .... MBPI2010 .. 526
Modern Sindbad .... MBPI2011 .. 526
Modern Sindbad .... MBPI2013 .. 526
Modern Sindbad .... MBPI2014 .. 526
Modern Sindbad .... MBPI2015 .. 526
Modern Sindbad .... MBPI2016 .. 526
"The Mohawk band is swarming" .... MBPI2885 .. 581
"The Mohawks killed her father" .... MBPI2896 .. 581

"A moment later there was a great .... MBPI1912 .. 520
   hammering at the door"
"A moment later there was a great .... MBPI1912 .. 520
   hammering on the oak door"
"Monsieur the Count de St. Germaine" .... MBPI0156 .. 410
Montofacini, the Magician .... MBPI1138 .. 472
Montofacini, the Magician .... MBPI1151 .. 472
Moral Blindness, with title, ... MBPI1349 .. 485
   illustrations and verse
Morgan at Porto Bello .... MBPI0358 .. 423
Morgan found himself, by virtue of his .... MBPI0348 .. 422
   strength and ferocity, the leader of a wild band
"Morgan Recruiting for the Attack On .... MBPI0348 .. 422
   Porto Bello"
Morgan Recruiting for the Attack on .... MBPI0348 .. 422
   Puerto Bello
The Morning Dram .... MBPI0266 .. 417
Mortality .... MBPI3049 .. 591
A Mother and Child .... MBPI0699 .. 444
Mother Carey .... MBPI0875 .. 455
Mother Hildegarde and the Princess .... MBPI1488 .. 493
Mother Hildegarde carries away the Baby ..... MBPI1491 .. 494
Mother Hildegarde carries ye baby away ...... MBPI1491 .. 494
   from the castle of the King
A Mountain Farm-House .... MBPI0269 .. 417
The Mountain Home .... MBPI3014 .. 589
The Mountain Orchard .... MBPI0272 .. 417
A Mountaineer .... MBPI0707 .. 445
"The Mourning Clam-Man" .... MBPI2752 .. 572
Mr. Fox Singing "Hail, Columbia!" .... MBPI2759 .. 573
"Mr. Horace looked at her with instant .... MBPI0776 .. 449
   sympathy"
Mr. Leuba .... MBPI0479 .. 430
"Mr. Longways looked up under his brows ... MBPI1253 .. 479
   at me with a very curious leer"
"Mr. Parker stood looking at his visitor .... MBPI1828 .. 515
   with his usual calm reserve"
"Mr. Parker stood looking steadily at his ...... MBPI1828 .. 515
   visitor"
Mrs. Washington's Arrival at .... MBPI0718 .. 445
   Headquarters, Cambridge
Mrs. Washington's Reception .... MBPI0313 .. 420
Muhlenberg in His Pulpit .... MBPI2017 .. 527
The Mummers .... MBPI1218 .. 477
Musa with initial O .... MBPI3009 .. 589
Music .... MBPI3165 .. 598
Music .... MBPI3235 .. 603
Mustered Out—A Rest by the Wayside .... MBPI0724 .. 446
Mustered out–A rest on the way home .... MBPI0724 .. 446
The Mutual Admiration Society .... MBPI2969 .. 586
"My boy wanted to do the divin', but .... MBPI1091 .. 469
   'twas me that went down"
My Cicerone .... MBPI0367 .. 423
My Comrade .... MBPI3150 .. 597

Index–Titles and Alternate Titles of Pyle's Art

"My dear," said General Washington, ... MBPI1741 . . 509
   "Captain Prescott's behavior was inexcusable"

"My hatred of him seemed suddenly to have . MBPI1931 . . 521
   taken to itself wings"

My Jemima. . . . . MBPI2670 . . 567

My Lady Betty . . . . MBPI3185 . . 600

My Lady of Brede . . . . MBPI0859 . . 454

"My Lord," said he, "the favor was given . . . . . . MBPI1686 . . 506
   to me by the Lady Alice"

" 'My Prisoner!' She Said" . . . . MBPI1006 . . 463

"Myles as in a dream kneeled, and . . . . MBPI1671 . . 505
   presented the letter"

Myles entertains the Lady Anne and the . . . . . MBPI1680 . . 505
   Lady Alice with his adventures

"Myles found himself standing beside the . . . MBPI1681 . . 506
   bed"

"Myles kneeled upon the stone step while . . . . . . MBPI1689 . . 506
   the good priest blessed him"

"Myles pushed the door further open" . . . . MBPI1674 . . 505

Mynheer's Morning Horn . . . . MBPI0266 . . 417

The Mysterious Guest . . . . MBPI1229 . . 477

"Naow she'll dew" . . . . MBPI2804 . . 576

Nathaniel Bacon And His Followers Burning . . . MBPI0837 . . 453
   Jamestown

The nation is at war and must have men . . . . . . MBPI1086 . . 468

The Nation Makers . . . . MBPI0103 . . 407

The Natural-Born Preacher . . . . MBPI2018 . . 527

A neat and shrivelled gentleman sat at a . . . . . MBPI0961 . . 461
   desk

The negress beckoned him to draw nearer . . . . MBPI0977 . . 462

"The Negro advanced to the . . . . MBPI0087 . . 406
   portmanteau...and displayed the contents to his master"

"The negro boy, arms whirling wide in . . . . MBPI1920 . . 520
   air, shot over the side of the cliff"

Nelson at Copenhagen . . . . MBPI0044 . . 403

Nelson sealing his letter to the Crown . . . . MBPI0044 . . 403
   Prince of Denmark

Nero Harping While Rome Burns . . . . MBPI3106 . . 595

Nero holding a Golden Lute, with Rome in . . . MBPI3106 . . 595
   Flames

New Year's Day Seventy Years Ago–The Last . . MBPI1194 . . 475
   Evening Caller

New York in 1665 . . . . MBPI0571 . . 436

New-Year's Hymn to St. Nicholas . . . . MBPI0265 . . 417

The Newcomes . . . . MBPI1011 . . 464

The News of the Execution of Louis XVI . . . . . . MBPI0755 . . 448

A Newspaper Puff, with title, ... MBPI1395 . . 488
   illustrations and verse

The next moment they were hanging in . . . . . MBPI2333 . . 546
   mid-air

"Next morning the Prime Minister looked . . . . MBPI1724 . . 508
   like a shorn sheep"

"Nicolas: A Son Livret" . . . . MBPI0961 . . 461

Nicolo and the Robber . . . . MBPI1157 . . 473

Nicolo, the tallow chandler . . . . MBPI1141 . . 472

Night Haul of The Seine . . . . PDPI0099 . . . 609

A Night in the Village Street . . . . MBPI0594 . . 438

No one was within but old Ursela, who sat . . . MBPI2293 . . 544
   crooning over a fire

Nor turned about till I got home... . . . . MBPI2692 . . 569

"Norman's Woe" . . . . MBPI2847 . . 578

The North Wind flies with ye Faithful . . . . MBPI1551 . . 497
   Servant

"Not for myself do I seek this vengeance" . . . . . MBPI1301 . . 482

The Notary beckons . . . . MBPI2025 . . 527

Notes: Descriptive and Biographic . . . . MBPI2764 . . 573

"Nothing harms me all the day" . . . . MBPI0894 . . 456

November . . . . MBPI0613 . . 439

November, 1776 . . . . MBPI1976 . . 524

"'Now,' said the King, 'now you are . . . . MBPI1733 . . 509
   married'"

"'Now,' said the Master, 'take me by the . . . . . . MBPI1612 . . 501
   belt'"

"'Now then, Gentlemen, how much do you . . . MBPI1826 . . 515
   bid for this boy?' said the auctioneer"

The Oak of Geismar . . . . MBPI1945 . . 522

Ocean View . . . . PDPI0083 . . . 608

Odysseus Advises King Tyndareus . . . . MBPI2786 . . 575
   Concerning Helen's Suitors

Odysseus and His Mother . . . . MBPI2780 . . 574

Odysseus and Menelaus Persuading . . . . MBPI2790 . . 575
   Agamemnon to Sacrifice Iphigenia

Odysseus as a Youth at Home with His . . . . MBPI2780 . . 574
   Mother

Odysseus Feigns Madness . . . . MBPI2789 . . 575

"Of the Olden Time" . . . . MBPI0266 . . 417

Off Hatteras . . . . MBPI0782 . . 449

"Off went a shoe" . . . . MBPI2832 . . 577

The officers would be waiting until she . . . . . . MBPI1003 . . 463
   should appear

The Ogre climbs the tree for the money . . . . MBPI1499 . . 494
   that he believes to be there

The Ogre meets the three little pigs in . . . . MBPI1498 . . 494
   the forest, whither they went to gather acorns

"The Ogre shut his eyes and began to . . . . MBPI1500 . . 494
   count"

The Ogre shuts his eyes and counts fifty . . . . MBPI1500 . . 494

The Ogre sticks fast in the window . . . . MBPI1501 . . 494

The Ojibway Maiden disclosing Pontiac's . . . . MBPI0337 . . 422
   Plot

Old Arsena . . . . MBPI0473 . . 430

The Old Bartram Homestead . . . . MBPI0233 . . 415

Old Bridge at Valley Forge . . . . MBPI0241 . . 416

The Old Capitol at Williamsburg . . . . MBPI0682 . . 443

Old Capitol at Williamsburg, Virginia . . . . MBPI0682 . . 443

The Old Captain . . . . MBPI0777 . . 449

The Old Chimney-Corner . . . . MBPI0231 . . 415

Old Corner Cupboard . . . . MBPI0234 . . 415

Old Dan Tucker . . . . MBPI2037 . . 528

Index–Titles and Alternate Titles of Pyle's Art

"THE OLD DWELLINGS"

"The old dwellings" .... MBPI2844 . . 578
The Old Earth .... MBPI3167 . . 598
Old Fire-Place, Aunt Saber's Kitchen .... PDPI0097 . . . 609
An Old Government Toll-Gate, with .... MBPI0210 . . 414
    Westward-Bound Express
Old Hempstead House .... MBPI0220 . . 414
Old Immortality .... MBPI0940 . . 459
Old Inscription .... MBPI0235 . . 415
Old Jacob Van Kleek had never favored our . . MBPI1036 . . 465
    hero's suit
Old Jacob Van Kleek the money-lender .... MBPI1046 . . 466
The Old King Rejoices at His New .... MBPI1440 . . 490
    Daughter-in-Law
An Old Lancaster House .... MBPI0362 . . 423
"The old man began to utter strange .... MBPI1617 . . 502
    spells"
The Old Man Dreams with initial O .... MBPI2980 . . 587
"An old man, lean and naked" .... MBPI0402 . . 426
"An old man looked down into the water" .... MBPI1602 . . 501
"The old man rapped on the door three ..... MBPI1693 . . 506
    times"
"An old man who had a curious necklace .... MBPI1702 . . 507
    for sale"
"An old man with a beard as white as .... MBPI1640 . . 503
    snow"
"The old man's face changed suddenly, and .. MBPI1210 . . 476
    he pressed his hand hard upon the arm of the hair-cloth
    sofa"
An Old Mile-Stone .... MBPI0219 . . 414
Old National Pike Bridge .... MBPI0213 . . 414
An Old North-Ender .... MBPI2888 . . 581
"Old Raleigh Tavern" .... MBPI0683 . . 443
Old records .... MBPI0177 . . 412
An Old Road .... MBPI3164 . . 598
An Old Smithy .... MBPI0217 . . 414
Old St. David's Church .... MBPI0245 . . 416
An Old Stager .... MBPI0211 . . 414
Old Swedes Church, Wilmington .... MBPI0257 . . 417
Old Swedes' Church, Wilmington, Delaware .... MBPI0257 . . 417
Old Swedish Church, Wilmington Delaware .... MBPI0257 . . 417
Old tiled Fire Place, Winthrop House .... MBPI0227 . . 415
An Old Time Cup of Coffee .... MBPI0224 . . 414
Old Uncle Sam come then to change... .... MBPI2687 . . 568
Old Valley Forge Bridge .... MBPI0241 . . 416
The Old Violin .... MBPI2987 . . 587
Old Way-Side Tavern .... MBPI0218 . . 414
An old woman & a young girl coming .... MBPI1353 . . 485
    towards the Castle
The Old Woman breaks things .... MBPI1459 . . 492
The Old Woman smashes pots and things at ... MBPI1459 . . 492
    Boots' bidding
The Old-time Landlord .... MBPI0419 . . 427
An Old-time May-Day in "Merrie England" ..... MBPI1794 . . 513
Old-Time School in Pennsylvania .... MBPI0261 . . 417

"OVER HIS SHOULDER HE CARRIED SOMETHING LIMP, ..."

The Oldest Inhabitant .... MBPI0940 . . 459
"Oliver fixed his gaze upon the smooth ...... MBPI0158 . . 410
    brilliant surface of the glass"
"Oliver gave a piping cry" .... MBPI0138 . . 409
"Oliver spread out the gems upon the .... MBPI0151 . . 410
    table with his hand"
Oliver Wendell Holmes at age of 41 .... MBPI2963 . . 586
Oliver Wendell Holmes at the age of 76 .... MBPI2994 . . 588
"The ominous calm is broken" .... MBPI2917 . . 583
On a Lumber Boat .... MBPI0697 . . 444
"On faultless ties and glossy tiles the .... MBPI2823 . . 577
    lovely bonnets beam their smiles"
"On sped the light chestnut, with the .... MBPI1262 . . 479
    little officer bending almost to the saddle-bow"
On the Edge of the Battle .... MBPI0739 . . 447
On the edge of the ring, guarded, stood ..... MBPI0073 . . 405
    Brother Bartholome and the Carmelite
On the great terrace of Donegal Castle .... MBPI2071 . . 530
On the Gulf of Night .... MBPI3171 . . 599
On the River Front .... MBPI0572 . . 436
On the Tortugas .... MBPI0346 . . 422
On the War-Path .... MBPI0839 . . 453
On the Way to Tyburn .... MBPI0451 . . 429
"On This Hot August Afternoon" .... MBPI0771 . . 449
Once it chased Dr. Wilkinson into the .... MBPI1076 . . 468
    very town itself
The One Hoss Shay .... MBPI2862 . . 579
One of the horses fell dead in the field .... MBPI1147 . . 472
"One of the policemen produced a .... MBPI1812 . . 514
    bull's-eye lantern"
"One of Those City Fellows"–A Hundred ..... MBPI1176 . . 474
    Years Ago
"One time it was alive with the great .... MBPI0391 . . 425
    lumbering coaches"
The One Who Wins Will Be Captain .... MBPI3112 . . 595
"The One Who Wins Will Be Captain" .... MBPI3112 . . 595
"The only picturesque object in the whole ... MBPI0416 . . 426
    horrid expanse"
Opening of the Erie Canal .... MBPI0576 . . 436
"Others have lived through greater woes .... MBPI1001 . . 463
    than ours"
Otto lay close to her feet upon a .... MBPI2308 . . 545
    bear-skin
"Our engagement is at an end " .... MBPI1267 . . 480
"Our hero leaping to the wheel, seized .... MBPI1171 . . 474
    the flying spokes"
Our Uncle, Innocent of Books .... MBPI3206 . . 601
Our young gentleman of the law .... MBPI1048 . . 466
"Out leaped a great hideous Genie" .... MBPI1627 . . 502
An out-of-door Tea Party in Colonial New .... MBPI0302 . . 419
    England
The Outcast's Return .... MBPI1186 . . 475
Over her gleaming shoulder her chalky ...... MBPI0125 . . 408
    face lowered at him, with a look of sullen hatred
"Over his shoulder he carried something .... MBPI0164 . . 411
    limp, like an empty skin, or a bundle of clothes tied together"

Over the next rise he ran, and so on over .... MBPI1165 .. 473
the sliding, shifting ground, panting and gasping

Overconfidence, with title, illustrations ...... MBPI1379 .. 487
and verse

Oyster shuckers .... MBPI0180 .. 412

"A page was appointed to escort it" .... MBPI1792 .. 512

Page was at the wheel, steering .... MBPI1100 .. 469

Painting the Picture .... MBPI2868 .. 580

A Pair of Canuck Girls .... MBPI0698 .. 444

"A palace of marble and gold" .... MBPI1708 .. 507

Palamedes Tests the Madness of Odysseus .... MBPI2789 .. 575

Paoli Monument .... MBPI0247 .. 416

Parable .... MBPI0650 .. 441

Parcenet covers Sir Pellias with a cloak .... MBPI1889 .. 519

The parson came down the street driving .... MBPI0484 .. 431
his flock of boys

Parson Rawson spoke to her with a .... MBPI0924 .. 458
pleasant chiding

"The parson takes a drive" .... MBPI2812 .. 576

Parson Turell's legacy .... MBPI3019 .. 589

Part I for The Lady of Shalott .... MBPI2699 .. 569

Part II for The Lady of Shalott .... MBPI2709 .. 570

Part III for The Lady of Shalott .... MBPI2715 .. 570

Part IV for The Lady of Shalott .... MBPI2724 .. 571

The Passing of Arthur .... MBPI2656 .. 566

The passing of Dona Victoria .... MBPI1004 .. 463

The Passing of Guinevere .... MBPI2658 .. 567

The Passing of Sir Gawaine .... MBPI2652 .. 566

A Pastoral Without Words .... MBPI1935 .. 521

A Pastoral Without Words .... MBPI1937 .. 522

A Pastoral Without Words .... MBPI1939 .. 522

A Pastoral Without Words .... MBPI1941 .. 522

A Pastoral Without Words .... MBPI1943 .. 522

A Pastoral Without Words .... MBPI1933 .. 521

A Pastoral Without Words .... MBPI1934 .. 521

A Pastoral Without Words .... MBPI1936 .. 521

A Pastoral Without Words .... MBPI1938 .. 522

A Pastoral Without Words .... MBPI1940 .. 522

A Pastoral Without Words .... MBPI1942 .. 522

"A Pastoral Without Words - I." .... MBPI1934 .. 521

"A Pastoral Without Words - II." .... MBPI1936 .. 521

"A Pastoral Without Words - III." .... MBPI1938 .. 522

"A Pastoral Without Words - IV." .... MBPI1940 .. 522

A Pastoral Without Words, No. 1 .... MBPI1934 .. 521

A Pastoral Without Words, No. 2 .... MBPI1936 .. 521

A Pastoral Without Words, No. 3 .... MBPI1938 .. 522

A Pastoral Without Words, No. 4 .... MBPI1940 .. 522

A Pastoral Without Words, No. 5 .... MBPI1942 .. 522

A Pastoral Without Words, No. 6 .... MBPI1944 .. 522

"A Pastoral Without Words - V." .... MBPI1942 .. 522

"A Pastoral Without Words - VI." .... MBPI1944 .. 522

Patty Hempstead in her Gran'ther's .... MBPI0225 .. 415
waistcoat

Paul comes home again from the king's .... MBPI1458 .. 492
castle with no luck

Paul goes Home again .... MBPI1458 .. 492

Paul Jones' fight in the "Bonhomme .... MBPI0021 .. 402
Richard" with the "Serapis"

Paul Jones raising the Rattlesnake Flag ...... MBPI0023 .. 402
on the "Alfred"

Paul Revere at Lexington .... MBPI1316 .. 483

Paul Revere bringing news to Sullivan .... MBPI0332 .. 421

The Paymaster .... MBPI3134 .. 596

Peace and War .... MBPI0179 .. 412

"The Peddler's Pack" .... MBPI2769 .. 574

The peeling-room .... MBPI0191 .. 412

A Peep over the Walls .... MBPI0943 .. 459

Peire at the castle .... MBPI0895 .. 456

Peire Vidal and Azalais .... MBPI0894 .. 456

Peire Vidal and the King .... MBPI0897 .. 457

"Pen" And The Major In St. James Street ...... MBPI0966 .. 461

"A pen drawing from 'Otto of The Silver ...... MBPI2297 .. 544
Hand', which shows the height of Howard Pyle's mastery of line"

"A pen drawing from 'The Wonder Clock', ... MBPI1555 .. 498
written and illustrated by Howard Pyle in 1888"

Pendennis .... MBPI0966 .. 461

Pennsylvania Avenue .... PDPI0035 ... 605

Pennsylvania Cave Dwellers .... MBPI0840 .. 453

Pennsylvania cave dwellers .... MBPI0840 .. 453

A Pennsylvania Cave-Dwelling in 1683 .... MBPI0840 .. 453

A Pennsylvania Cave-Dwelling XVIIth .... MBPI0840 .. 453
Century

Peonage .... MBPI3057 .. 592

The people passing the Island .... MBPI2701 .. 569

"Peractum est!" .... MBPI3107 .. 595

"Perhaps she sat there while she stoned ..... MBPI0252 .. 416
her raisins"

Persecuting a Quaker .... MBPI0281 .. 418

"A Person of Consequence, carefully fed ..... MBPI1808 .. 513
and attended to"

Peter asks the fatal question .... MBPI2021 .. 527

Peter Eats With the King and Princess .... MBPI1399 .. 488

Peter goes to befool the King .... MBPI1457 .. 492

Peter goes to the castle to befool the .... MBPI1457 .. 492
King, dressed in his finest clothes

Peter plays the fiddle for the Tavern .... MBPI0201 .. 413
Folk

Peter Rugg Ye Bostonian .... PDPI0060 ... 607

Peter Stuyvesant .... MBPI0836 .. 453

Peter Stuyvesant and the English Fleet .... MBPI2501 .. 557

Peter Stuyvesant tearing the Letter .... MBPI0300 .. 419
demanding the Surrender of New York

Peterkin as a girl combs the Giant's hair .... MBPI1481 .. 493

Peterkin bringeth ye little silver bell .... MBPI1480 .. 493
of the Giant to the King

Peterkin brings the Silver Bell to the .... MBPI1480 .. 493
King

Index–Titles and Alternate Titles of Pyle's Art

PETERKIN DRESSED AS A LASS, AND THE GIANT

Peterkin dressed as a lass, and the Giant ...... MBPI1481 .. 493

Peterkin makes off with the Giant's Goose ..... MBPI1479 .. 493

Peterkin, with ye help of the hare, ... MBPI1479 .. 493
   carries off the Giant's goose

Peterkin's brothers marvel at his fine ...... MBPI1478 .. 493
   trappings

Peterkin's brothers marvel at the fine .... MBPI1478 .. 493
   clothes that the hare gave him

The Phantom Horseman .... MBPI0194 .. 413

Phipps and the Sunken Treasure .... MBPI0842 .. 453

Phipps and the sunken treasure .... MBPI0842 .. 453

Phips recovering the sunken treasure .... MBPI0842 .. 453

Phoenician Traders .... MBPI0908 .. 457

Pictorial Puzzle .... MBPI1781 .. 512

A Picture Conveying the Title [for a .... MBPI1933 .. 521
   Pastoral Without Words]

Pierre Vidal chant a la Belle Azalais .... MBPI0894 .. 456

Pierre Vidal le Troubadour .... MBPI0896 .. 456

Pilgrimage of Truth .... MBPI0816 .. 451

Pilgrimage of Truth .... MBPI0817 .. 452

Pilgrimage of Truth .... MBPI0818 .. 452

Pilgrimage of Truth .... MBPI0819 .. 452

Pilgrimage of Truth .... MBPI0821 .. 452

Pilgrimage of Truth .... MBPI0820 .. 452

Pioneers Farming .... MBPI0355 .. 423

Piping a Roundelay .... MBPI0790 .. 450

The Piping Shepherd .... MBPI0790 .. 450

The Pirate and His Prey .... MBPI0882 .. 456

The Pirate and its Prey .... MBPI0882 .. 456

The pirate captain looked impassively on ..... MBPI1164 .. 473

Pirates Burning Merchantman .... MBPI0886 .. 456

The Pirates Christmas .... MBPI1266 .. 480

The pirates fire upon the fugitives .... MBPI1836 .. 515

Pirates Sometimes Serve Their Captains So ..... MBPI0609 .. 439

"Pirates used to do that to their .... MBPI0609 .. 439
   Captains now and then"

"Plantation houses standing back from the ... MBPI0405 .. 426
   roadside"

Planting In the Northwest Territory .... MBPI0355 .. 423

Play and Earnest .... MBPI1369 .. 486

Play & Earnest, with title, illustrations .... MBPI1369 .. 486
   and verse

The Players .... MBPI3223 .. 602

The Plow-Boy .... MBPI0809 .. 451

The Poet and the King .... MBPI0916 .. 458

The Poet at Twilight .... MBPI3187 .. 600

The Poet .... MBPI3125 .. 596

Poetry .... MBPI3130 .. 596

The Poets .... MBPI3139 .. 597

A Political Argument .... MBPI0853 .. 454

A Political argument .... MBPI0853 .. 454

A Political Discussion .... MBPI0853 .. 454

Politics in the Olden Times–General .... MBPI1196 .. 475
   Jackson, President-elect, on his way to Washington

THE PRINCE AND THE OLD WITCH WITH THREE EYES

The pony pen .... MBPI2041 .. 528

Poor Brother John came forward and took ... MBPI2307 .. 545
   the boy's hand

The Poor Brother opens the chest .... MBPI1542 .. 497

The Poor Man and St. Christopher .... MBPI1485 .. 493

The poor man finds that which is the best ..... MBPI1542 .. 497

The poor man touches the door with ye .... MBPI1541 .. 497
   stone

The Poor Man welcomes Saint Christopher .... MBPI1485 .. 493
   to his house

"Poor Piggy led the way" .... MBPI1786 .. 512

Poor Richard .... MBPI3222 .. 602

Poor Richard, design on title page .... MBPI3222 .. 602

The poor simple Brother sitting under the ... MBPI2302 .. 544
   pear tree close to the bee-hives, rocking the little baby in his
   arms

"Popping ineffectual round-shot after .... MBPI0374 .. 424
   her"

Portrait Gallery in Shaw Mansion .... MBPI0223 .. 414

The portrait of a young gentleman who ..... PDPI0006 ... 603
   always says "Thank you!"

Portrait of Joshua Clayton .... PDPI0045 ... 606

Portrait of Mistress Gainor Wynne .... MBPI0035 .. 403

Prayer .... MBPI3124 .. 596

A Prayer .... MBPI3124 .. 596

The precious minutes flew past, but she ..... MBPI1057 .. 467
   was silent

Preliminary study for MBPI2500 Hendryk .... PDPI0009 ... 604
   Hudson and the Half-Moon

Preliminary study for MBPI2501 Peter .... PDPI0008 ... 604
   Stuyvesant and the English Fleet

Preliminary study for MBPI2502 Life in an .... PDPI0010 ... 604
   Old Dutch Town

Preliminary study for MBPI3240 The .... MBPI1303 .. 482
   Landing of Carteret

Preliminary study for proposed Lincoln .... PDPI0002 .. 603
   Memorial

Preliminary study for proposed mural for .... PDPI0002 ... 603
   Soldiers and Sailors Memorial Hall of Allegheny County,
   Pennsylvania

Preparing for Highwaymen .... MBPI0216 .. 414

Prescott on the Rampart .... PDPI0013 ... 604

President Johnson teaching his first .... MBPI0318 .. 420
   class

President Washington and his Cabinet .... MBPI0727 .. 446

President Washington and his Cabinet .... MBPI0730 .. 446

The Press-Gang in New York .... MBPI0275 .. 418

"The prettiest princess the sun ever .... MBPI1660 .. 504
   shone upon"

Pride in Distress, with title, ... MBPI1348 .. 485
   illustrations and verse

The Priest, the Provost and the Master .... MBPI1495 .. 494
   Mayor blow and blow the little tin trumpet over ye black goat

The Prince aids the Old Woman .... MBPI1436 .. 490

The Prince and the Old Witch with three ..... MBPI1443 .. 491
   eyes

Index–Titles and Alternate Titles of Pyle's Art

THE PRINCE BATHES IN THE FOUNTAIN

The Prince bathes in the fountain . . . . MBPI1576 . . 499

Prince Charles sprang to his side: "If he . . . . . . MBPI2068 . . 530
goes, so do I!"

The Prince comes to the old, three eyed . . . . MBPI1443 . . 491
Witch's house

The Prince finds the Sword of brightness . . . . . . MBPI1562 . . 498
where sits an old man

The Prince finds ye three giants sleeping . . . . . . MBPI1561 . . 498
under the tree of life a snoring away like everything

Prince John . . . . MBPI1435 . . 490

The Prince kills the Dragon . . . . MBPI1577 . . 499

The Prince knocks at the door of the . . . . MBPI1560 . . 498
poor, mean, little house and not the great, rich one

The Prince looks through the Magic Key . . . . . . MBPI1439 . . 490

The Prince pours water into the barrel . . . . MBPI1575 . . 499

The Prince sits down beside ye garden . . . . MBPI1563 . . 498
gate and only one knoweth him

The Prince takes the Sword of Brightness . . . . . MBPI1562 . . 498

The Prince wins the Golden Apple and the . . . MBPI1578 . . 499
Silver Pear

The Princess and her Pigs . . . . MBPI1785 . . 512

The Princess and the Pigeons . . . . MBPI1490 . . 494

A Princess as pretty as a ripe Apple . . . . MBPI1505 . . 495

The Princess comes to Gruff's Door . . . . MBPI1470 . . 492

The Princess cometh into a wonderful . . . . MBPI1488 . . 493
country and to the house of a strange old woman

The Princess drinks from the Golden Cup . . . . . MBPI1469 . . 492

The Princess dwells in the oak tree where . . . . . MBPI1490 . . 494
ye wild pigeons come to feed her

The Princess finds her dear Prince again . . . . . . MBPI1471 . . 492

The Princess finds her Prince . . . . MBPI1471 . . 492

The Princess finds the Fisher Lad with . . . . MBPI1568 . . 498
he key of Luck's-House

The Princess finds the Fisher Lad with . . . . MBPI1568 . . 498
the key of Wish-House

The Princess goes to Market with her Eggs . . . . MBPI1520 . . 495

Princess Golden Hair, being a true . . . . MBPI1469 . . 492
princess, drinketh from the golden cup & touches neither ye silver nor ye clay

Princess Golden Hair cometh to Death's . . . . . . MBPI1470 . . 492
door where sits Death's aged Grandmother spinning flax within

The Princess knoweth the Young King . . . . MBPI1521 . . 496

"The Princess looked over the edge of the . . . MBPI1630 . . 502
balcony"

The Princess looks into that which she . . . . MBPI1489 . . 494
should not have done

The Princess peeped into the Jar . . . . MBPI1489 . . 494

"The Princess sits in the window and . . . . MBPI1582 . . 499
sings"

The Princess starts for the Witch's House . . . . . MBPI1514 . . 495

The Princess taketh her eggs to the . . . . MBPI1520 . . 495
market

The Princess walking beside the Sea . . . . MBPI1473 . . 493

"THE QUESTION WAS SO SUDDEN AND SO STARTLING..."

A Princess walks beside ye water, into . . . . MBPI1473 . . 493
whose basket leaps ye ring

The Princess wept and wept . . . . MBPI1531 . . 496

Prior Edward and Myles in the Priory . . . . MBPI1687 . . 506
Garden

The Privateer and its victim . . . . MBPI0778 . . 449

A Privateersman Ashore . . . . MBPI0575 . . 436

Profession & Practice, with title, ... MBPI1387 . . 487
illustrations and verse

"The professor and the child" . . . . MBPI1770 . . 511

The Professor in his Boat . . . . MBPI2997 . . 588

Prometheus . . . . MBPI2788 . . 575

The Punishment of Chilo by Vinicius . . . . MBPI3105 . . 595

The Puritan Governor interrupting the . . . . . . MBPI0310 . . 420
Christmas sports

Pyrrhus Finds Philoctetes in a Cave . . . . MBPI2779 . . 574

The Quack . . . . MBPI2662 . . 567

Quaker and King at Whitehall 1681 . . . . MBPI0283 . . 418

A Quaker at the Court of Charles II . . . . MBPI0283 . . 418

Quaker Exhorter in Colonial New England . . . . MBPI0298 . . 419

A Quaker Exhorter in New England . . . . MBPI0298 . . 419

A Quaker Preacher in Litchfield, England . . . . . MBPI0279 . . 418

A Quaker Preacher in Litchfield England . . . . . . MBPI0279 . . 418

A Quaker Wedding . . . . MBPI0129 . . 409

Quakers doing their duty . . . . MBPI0228 . . 415

Quakers on Their Way to Church in . . . . MBPI0258 . . 417
Colonial Times

The Quarrel of the Queens . . . . MBPI2746 . . 572

Queen Elizabeth and The Bacon Boys . . . . MBPI1116 . . 470

Queen Esther . . . . MBPI2008 . . 526

" 'Queen Esther' (Catharine Montour) . . . . MBPI2008 . . 526
inciting the Indians to attack Wyoming"

Queen Esther inciting the Indians to . . . . MBPI2008 . . 526
attack the settlers at Wyoming

Queen Esther Inciting The Indians To . . . . MBPI2008 . . 526
Revolt

"The Queen granted him an audience" . . . . MBPI0123 . . 408

Queen Guinevere . . . . MBPI1869 . . 517

Queen Morgana appears unto Sir Launcelot . . . MBPI2449 . . 554

Queen Morgana le Fay . . . . MBPI2416 . . 551

Queen Morgana loses Excalibur his sheath . . . . MBPI2418 . . 552

The Queen of Ireland seeks to slay Sir . . . . MBPI2473 . . 555
Tristram

Queen of the May–Unpropitious Skies . . . . MBPI1175 . . 474

"The Queen raised the veil and looked at . . . . MBPI1603 . . 501
the Prince"

The Queen read the Scriptures in the . . . . MBPI1061 . . 467
vulgar tongue

Queen Ysabeau in her carven chair . . . . MBPI1006 . . 463

The Queen's pages clothe Sir Launcelot . . . . MBPI2639 . . 565

Question . . . . MBPI0549 . . 435

Question . . . . MBPI0550 . . 435

The Question . . . . MBPI0744 . . 447

"The question was so sudden and so . . . . MBPI0142 . . 409
startling that Oliver sank back in his seat"

Index–Titles and Alternate Titles of Pyle's Art

Quick as a flash, David leaped out and .... MBPI2376 .. 549
   upon it
"The quiet dame" .... MBPI2887 .. 581
"Quo Vadis, Domine!" .... MBPI3109 .. 595
A Quotation from "King Lear" .... MBPI2046 .. 528
Race .... MBPI3058 .. 592
A Race for Life .... PDPI0068 ... 607
Raising cypress logs in the Dismal Swamp .... MBPI0192 .. 412
Rambustius reads the Book of Balbo .... MBPI1449 .. 491
"The raven spread his wings and flew" .... MBPI1606 .. 501
Reading the Declaration before .... MBPI0501 .. 432
   Washington's Army, New York, July 9, 1776
Receiving Milk .... MBOI0002 .. 611
The reconciliation .... MBPI2028 .. 527
The Recruiting Office .... MBPI0736 .. 446
"The Rejection" .... MBPI0127 .. 408
A Reminiscence of the Marigold .... MBPI2983 .. 587
Renaissance Couple .... PDPI0044 ... 606
Representing the manner of Peter's .... MBPI0203 .. 413
   Courtship
The rescue of Azilicz .... MBPI0911 .. 457
Rescue of Sevier .... MBPI0325 .. 421
Resisting the Indian Attack on .... MBPI0345 .. 422
   Boonesborough
Respite .... MBPI0567 .. 436
The rest were shot and thrown overboard ..... MBPI0995 .. 463
The Retreat Through the Jerseys .... MBPI1994 .. 525
The Return from Church, Christmas Morning .. MBPI1222 .. 477
The Return from Deerfield .... MBPI3103 .. 594
The Reverend Ebenezer Doolittle .... MBPI1041 .. 466
A Revolutionary Recruiting .... MBPI0221 .. 414
   Office–Privateersmen in New London
Reward and Punishment .... MBPI0649 .. 441
The Rich Brother takes the diamond from .... MBPI1543 .. 497
   the statue's hand
The Rich Man and the Two Saints .... MBPI1486 .. 493
The rich man findeth that which he .... MBPI1543 .. 497
   deserveth
The Rich Man finds Money and Trouble ...... MBPI1455 .. 491
The rich man spreads a feast for the .... MBPI1486 .. 493
   Saints
The rich man takes home money and trouble ... MBPI1455 .. 491
Richard DeBury and the Young Edward III ..... MBPI3200 .. 600
Richard deBury Tutoring Young Edward III .... MBPI3200 .. 600
"Riding in his gilded coach" .... MBPI1661 .. 504
"The rival editors" .... MBPI0428 .. 427
The Rivals .... MBPI0007 .. 401
River Rocks .... PDPI0075 ... 608
Robin and Little John go their ways in .... MBPI2137 .. 534
   search of Adventure
Robin and the Tinker at the Blue Boar Inn ..... MBPI2098 .. 532
Robin buys the Butcher's Meat .... MBPI2105 .. 532
Robin encounters John Little .... MBPI1328 .. 483

Robin Hood meeteth the tall Stranger on .... MBPI2094 .. 531
   the Bridge
Robin Hood meets the tall Stranger on the ..... MBPI2094 .. 531
   Bridge
Robin Hood slayeth Guy of Gisbourne .... MBPI2136 .. 534
Robin Hood steps betwixt Sir Stephen and ... MBPI2119 .. 533
   his Bride
Robin meets a fair lady .... MBPI1327 .. 483
Robin on his way to Nottingham .... MBPI1326 .. 483
Robin shooteth his Last Shaft .... MBPI2141 .. 534
Robin turns butcher and sells his meat in .... MBPI2104 .. 532
   Nottingham
The Robin's Vesper, with title and poem ...... MBPI1181 .. 474
   inserted
The Rock-Breaker .... MBPI3176 .. 599
Roger Bacon .... MBPI3197 .. 600
"Roger Feverel had kindled it for the .... MBPI0328 .. 421
   first time"
Roger Williams in exile .... MBPI2761 .. 573
A Romantic Episode in the Life of a Young ... MBPI1294 .. 481
   Lady, Part IV.
"The roofs of Charlestown blazing" .... MBPI2915 .. 583
Rosamund and Sir Gregory .... MBPI1005 .. 463
Rose Met Him at the Gate .... MBPI0766 .. 448
Rowand .... MBPI1064 .. 467
The Royal Bodyguard .... MBPI1787 .. 512
The Royal gooseherd playeth with the .... MBPI1518 .. 495
   golden ball
"'Rub-a-dub-dub!' says the Fiddler" .... MBPI1504 .. 494
The Ruby of Kishmoor .... MBPI0987 .. 462
Ruins of Old Fort, Carleton's Island .... MBPI2049 .. 529
Ruins of Old Post Tavern .... MBPI0212 .. 414
The rush from the New York Stock Exchange   MBPI1974 .. 524
   on September 18, 1873
"The Sachem's Daughter" .... MBPI2793 .. 575
Sack of Carthage .... MBPI0955 .. 460
Sack of Carthagena .... MBPI0955 .. 460
The Sack of Carthagena .... MBPI0955 .. 460
The Sack of Carthagenea .... MBPI0955 .. 460
The Sacking of Panama .... MBPI0349 .. 422
The Sacred Hammer of the God Thor .... MBPI1946 .. 522
The Sailor from Constantinople .... MBPI2029 .. 527
The Sailor is saved .... MBPI2031 .. 527
A Sailor's Sweetheart .... MBPI0659 .. 442
The Sailor's Sweetheart .... MBPI0659 .. 442
The Sailor's Wedding .... MBPI0663 .. 442
Saint Brendan .... MBPI0872 .. 455
Saint Nicholas at the Poor Man's House .... MBPI1484 .. 493
Saint Nicholas at the Rich Man's Door .... MBPI1483 .. 493
Saint Nicholas blesses the Poor Man's .... MBPI1484 .. 493
   crock and bowl with food and drink
Saint Nicholas knocks at the rich man's .... MBPI1483 .. 493
   door but finds only a chill welcome a cold faring
The Salem Wolf .... MBPI1074 .. 468

Index–Titles and Alternate Titles of Pyle's Art

"Sally Went Across the Road to the Greenhouse"

"Sally Went Across the Road to the . . . . MBPI0773 . . 449
    Greenhouse"
Sam Lawson telling stories . . . . MBPI0498 . . 432
The Sand Hills . . . . MBPI0523 . . 433
Santa Claus bursts into the room from the . . . MBPI1342 . . 484
    chimney followed by the Elves & Fairies. Tableau
"Sat down by the road-side to eat his . . . . MBPI1654 . . 504
    pie"
Sat, like a Fate, and watched the flying . . . . MBPI2774 . . 574
    thread
The Saving of King Ingé . . . . MBPI2085 . . 531
"Says grandma, 'What's the matter?'" . . . . MBPI2895 . . 581
"Scant Heed Had We of the Fleet, Sweet . . . . MBPI0889 . . 456
    Hours"
Scene in a Lifesaving Station . . . . MBPI1178 . . 474
Scene in a Tavern on the Old Albany Post . . . . MBPI1229 . . 477
    Road
Scene in an Old Quaker Town . . . . MBPI0259 . . 417
Scene in Old Colonial Court House . . . . MBPI0312 . . 420
Scene in the Theatre in Philadelphia 1794 . . . . . MBPI2759 . . 573
Scene in the Town Jail . . . . MBPI1266 . . 480
Scene on a Colonial Plantation . . . . MBPI0672 . . 442
Schwartz Carl, holding his arbelast in . . . . MBPI2314 . . 545
    his hand, stood silently watching
Scouts in Indian Country . . . . MBPI0339 . . 422
"The Screeching Woman of Marblehead" . . . . . . MBPI2848 . . 578
Sea Battle between Two Frigates . . . . PDPI0101 . . . 609
The sea boiled over the wreckage in . . . . MBPI1099 . . 469
    streaky white
The Sea Fight . . . . PDPI0076 . . . 608
"The Sea–He've cotched us!" . . . . MBPI1757 . . 510
The Sea Man . . . . MBPI0861 . . 454
The Sea-Gull's Song . . . . MBPI1213 . . 476
Seal decoration for Quill and Grill Club . . . . . . PDPI0026 . . . 605
    Invitation
The Search for Toinette . . . . MBPI0320 . . 420
Second Class Passenger . . . . MBPI1758 . . 510
The Second Class Passenger . . . . MBPI1758 . . 510
The Second Sketch . . . . MBPI0010 . . 401
The secret room . . . . MBPI1124 . . 471
"See how tall they 've grown" . . . . MBPI2851 . . 579
"Seeing no enemy, and themselves falling . . . MBPI1959 . . 523
    every moment from the fire"
"Selim the Baker lands on the desert . . . . MBPI1696 . . 506
    island"
"Selim the Fisherman finds a leaden box" . . . . . MBPI1692 . . 506
Serafina was leaning from the window . . . . MBPI1142 . . 472
"The Serenade" . . . . PDPI0037 . . . 605
Sergeant Jasper at Fort Moultrie . . . . MBPI0306 . . 420
Sergeant Jasper at the Battle of Fort . . . . MBPI0306 . . 420
    Moultrie
Serious Advice, with title, illustrations . . . . . . MBPI1350 . . 485
    and verse
The Sestina . . . . MBPI0961 . . 461

"She wasn't no kin when I marr'ed her, but we've..."

The settler . . . . MBPI0113 . . 408
"The sexton…led forth the horse" . . . . MBPI2826 . . 577
Shad-Fishing on the Lower Delaware at . . . . . MBPI1197 . . 475
    Night–The Last Haul Before Dawn
Shay's Mob in possession of a Court House . . . . MBPI0312 . . 420
"She and Master Henry would spend hours . . . . MBPI1172 . . 474
    together"
She arrayed herself in silence . . . . MBPI1007 . . 463
She became as famous for speed as her . . . . . MBPI0989 . . 462
    short career allowed
She began to talk to Huntford about . . . . MBPI1159 . . 473
    himself
She believed that she had daily speech . . . . . . MBPI0920 . . 458
    with angels
"She came close to him and laid her hand . . . MBPI1249 . . 479
    lovingly on his arm"
"She Could Not Take Her Eyes Away From . . . . . MBPI0767 . . 448
    the Child"
She cried out . . . . MBPI0880 . . 455
She drew bridle, listening–there was no . . . . . MBPI0931 . . 459
    sound
"She drew her down until the girl kneeled . . . MBPI0155 . . 410
    upon the floor beside the sofa"
She felt her blood tingling in every vein . . . . . . MBPI0881 . . 456
"She had fainted" . . . . MBPI1269 . . 480
"She Had Viewed the Great Conqueror" . . . . MBPI0999 . . 463
"She hadn't on anything but a little . . . . MBPI1771 . . 511
    nightgown, the same as if they'd snatched her out o' the
    berth, with no time to dress her"
She heard the stir of his black mantle . . . . MBPI2775 . . 574
    trailing in the dust
"She held the book to the flames whilest . . . . MBPI0145 . . 410
    talking, her eyes fixed intently upon it"
"She hung drooping in the great chair of . . . . MBPI0951 . . 460
    state"
"She looked from the bars of her prison" . . . . . . MBPI2750 . . 572
She placed her hands on his shoulders . . . . MBPI2386 . . 550
She pointed her finger at Caterina . . . . MBPI1146 . . 472
She put the silver coronet upon her head . . . . . MBPI1068 . . 467
She saw herself for what he had said, and . . . . MBPI1069 . . 467
    swooned
"She seemed 'a tall white lily,' he said" . . . . MBPI0760 . . 448
"She stood like a bronze. Gabriel was . . . . MBPI0371 . . 424
    beside her, his naked cutlass in his hand"
She Stood Up Serene But Heroic . . . . MBPI1761 . . 511
She told him her adventures in a breath . . . . . . MBPI1094 . . 469
"She tricked me, little maid" . . . . MBPI0913 . . 458
"She walked on after saying this, musing" . . . . . MBPI0170 . . 411
She was a solid mass of flame . . . . MBPI0998 . . 463
"She was a wonder, and nothing less" . . . . MBPI2805 . . 576
She Was a Wonder and Nothing Less . . . . MBPI2862 . . 579
She was continually beset by spies . . . . MBPI1123 . . 471
"She was silent for a moment, her eyes . . . . . . MBPI1922 . . 521
    seeking the floor"
"She wasn't no kin when I marr'ed her, ... MBPI1774 . . 511
    but we've lived together over thirty year"

Index–Titles and Alternate Titles of Pyle's Art

"She went by without looking at him" .... MBPI0171 .. 411

"She would sit quite still, permitting .... MBPI1288 .. 481
    Barnaby to gaze"

"She Would Sit Quite Still Permitting .... MBPI1288 .. 481
    Barnaby to Gaze at Her"

"She's yours" .... MBPI2026 .. 527

The Shell .... MBPI1053 .. 466

Shepherd and Girl .... MBPI3233 .. 603

Shepherd Boy and Nereid .... MBPI3148 .. 597

Shepherd Boy Nereid .... MBPI3148 .. 597

Sheridan's first interview with Rowand .... MBPI1064 .. 467

The Sheriff of Nottingham cometh before .... MBPI2101 .. 532
    the King at London

The Sheriff of Nottingham plotting .... MBPI2099 .. 532
    against Robin sends a messenger
    to Lincoln

Ships loading in Albemarle Sound .... MBPI0838 .. 453

"The ships rolled and wallowed in the .... MBPI0119 .. 408
    river"

Ships Were Rare .... MBPI0833 .. 453

"Ships Were Rare" .... MBPI0833 .. 453

The shopman .... MBPI1139 .. 472

"Sic transit gloria mundi" .... MBPI0394 .. 425

"A sight to see" .... MBPI2827 .. 577

The Silver-Footed Thetis Rising from the .... MBPI2783 .. 574
    Waves

Singing a Hymn to St. Nicholas .... MBPI0265 .. 417

Sir Bors de Ganis, the good .... MBPI2592 .. 562

Sir Bors rides with the white knight .... MBPI2635 .. 565

Sir Ewaine poureth water on the slab .... MBPI2573 .. 561

Sir Galahad cometh with the Hermit of the ... MBPI2624 .. 564
    Forest

Sir Galahad meets Sir Melyas .... MBPI2629 .. 565

Sir Galahad of the Grail .... MBPI2598 .. 563

Sir Galahad rides with the Lady .... MBPI2637 .. 565

Sir Gareth doeth Battle with the Knight ...... MBPI2541 .. 559
    of the River Ford

Sir Gareth of Orkney .... MBPI2536 .. 559

Sir Gawaine challenges Sir Launcelot .... MBPI2650 .. 566

Sir Gawaine finds the beautiful Lady .... MBPI2427 .. 552

Sir Gawaine, Knight of the Fountain .... MBPI2570 .. 561

Sir Gawaine knoweth the shield of Sir .... MBPI2557 .. 560
    Launcelot

Sir Gawaine sups with ye Lady Ettard .... MBPI1894 .. 519

Sir Gawaine the Son of Lot, King of .... MBPI2422 .. 552
    Orkney

Sir Geraint and the Knight of the .... MBPI2613 .. 564
    Sparrowhawk

Sir Geraint lies asleep .... MBPI2615 .. 564

Sir Geraint, Son of Erbin .... MBPI2606 .. 563

Sir James Thornhill painting Jack .... MBPI0446 .. 428
    Sheppard's portrait

Sir John shook his spear at the ladies .... MBPI0928 .. 458
    who sneered

Sir Kay and the Forest Madman .... MBPI2494 .. 556

Sir Kay breaketh his sword at ye .... MBPI1849 .. 516
    Tournament

Sir Kay interrupts ye meditations of Sir ...... MBPI1906 .. 520
    Percival

Sir Kay overthroweth his Enemies .... MBPI1846 .. 516

Sir Kay showeth the mystic Sword unto Sir ... MBPI1852 .. 516
    Ector

Sir Lamorack and Sir Percival receive .... MBPI2582 .. 562
    their Mother's Blessing

Sir Lamorack herds the swine of Sir Nabon .... MBPI2488 .. 556

Sir Lamorack of Gales .... MBPI2483 .. 556

Sir Lancelot Talks With The Minstrels .... MBPI2548 .. 560

Sir Launcelot and Elouise the Fair .... MBPI2455 .. 554

Sir Launcelot and Sir Lavaine overlook .... MBPI2555 .. 560
    the Field of Astolat

Sir Launcelot climbs to catch the lady's ...... MBPI2457 .. 554
    falcon

Sir Launcelot confideth his Shield to .... MBPI2553 .. 560
    Elaine the Fair

Sir Launcelot defends the door .... MBPI2646 .. 566

Sir Launcelot doeth battle with Sir .... MBPI2451 .. 554
    Turquine

Sir Launcelot greets Queen Guinevere .... MBPI2444 .. 553

Sir Launcelot leapeth from the window .... MBPI2559 .. 560

Sir Launcelot of the Lake .... MBPI2432 .. 552

Sir Launcelot sits with Sir Hilaire and .... MBPI2453 .. 554
    Croisette

Sir Launcelot slayeth the Worm of Corbin ..... MBPI2551 .. 560

Sir Launcelot takes the armor of Sir Kay ...... MBPI2459 .. 554

Sir Lavaine the Son of Pelles .... MBPI2587 .. 562

Sir Lionel of Britain .... MBPI2447 .. 553

Sir Mador begs for his Life .... MBPI2644 .. 566

Sir Mador de la Porte .... MBPI2642 .. 566

Sir Mellegrans interrupts the sport of .... MBPI2525 .. 558
    the Queen

Sir Mordred the traitor .... MBPI2654 .. 566

Sir Pellias encounters the Sorrowful Lady .... MBPI1884 .. 518
    in Arroy

Sir Pellias, the Gentle Knight .... MBPI1886 .. 518

Sir Percival and Sir Ector look upon the ...... MBPI2585 .. 562
    Isle of Joy

Sir Percival and Sir Lamorack ride .... MBPI1901 .. 519
    together

Sir Percival and Sir Pellinore ride .... MBPI1901 .. 519
    together

Sir Percival of Gales .... MBPI1899 .. 519

Sir Percival overcometh ye Enchantress ...... MBPI1904 .. 519
    Vivien

Sir Percival rideth the black horse .... MBPI2633 .. 565

Sir Richard pleadeth before the Prior of ...... MBPI2124 .. 533
    Emmet

Sir Tristram assaults King Mark .... MBPI2491 .. 556

Sir Tristram cometh to ye castle of Sir .... MBPI2486 .. 556
    Nabon

Sir Tristram harpeth before King Mark .... MBPI2475 .. 555

Sir Tristram leaps into ye Sea . . . . MBPI2496 . . 556
Sir Tristram of Lyonesse . . . . MBPI2462 . . 554
Sir Tristram sits with Sir Launcelot . . . . MBPI2477 . . 555
"'Sire,' said the Ambassador, 'I will . . . . MBPI1631 . . 502
    answer now for my master'"
"Sitting with piles of great pots and . . . . MBPI0382 . . 424
    bowls and queer jars of red earthenware"
The Sixth Sketch . . . . MBPI0018 . . 402
The skeletonlike stranger entered . . . . MBPI1038 . . 465
Sketch For Lincoln Memorial, Pittsburgh . . . . PDPI0002 . . . 603
A Sketch on Lower Lake Champlain . . . . MBPI0711 . . 445
Slaughter signing Leisler's death warrant
    warrant
Slaves at Jamestown . . . . MBPI0834 . . 453
Sloughter signing Leisler's death warrant
    warrant
Sloughter signing the death warrant of . . . . . . MBPI0843 . . 453
    Leisler
Slowly raising himself upon the narrow . . . . . . MBPI2313 . . 545
    foot-hold, he peeped cautiously within
The Sly Fox . . . . PDPI0051 . . . 606
"A small crowd had collected around the . . . . MBPI0481 . . 431
    entrance to the Museum"
Small Game Better Than None . . . . MBPI1297 . . 482
"Small heed had we of the fleet, sweet . . . . . . MBPI0889 . . 456
    hours"
"The small square windows" . . . . MBPI2845 . . 578
The Snapdragon . . . . MBPI1219 . . 477
So Beppo's first wish was fulfilled . . . . MBPI1128 . . 471
So for a heart-beat she saw him . . . . MBPI0943 . . 459
"So gracious, sweet, and purring" . . . . MBPI2886 . . 581
So long as Gann would follow, his Master . . . . MBPI1119 . . 470
    would lead
So may the future bring its wreath of . . . . MBPI1302 . . 482
    roses and of bay to you.
"So saying, she turned and left me" . . . . MBPI0316 . . 420
"So shy with us, so free with these" . . . . MBPI2822 . . 577
"So soon as they saw me they fell to . . . . MBPI1256 . . 479
    screaming and clung to one another"
So the Rich Man left him in his blindness . . . . . MBPI1540 . . 497
So the treasure was divided . . . . MBPI0954 . . 460
So they took the fir tree from its place . . . . MBPI1945 . . 522
So They Took The Little Fir From Its . . . . MBPI1945 . . 522
    Place
So Ye Great Reaper reapeth among the . . . . . . MBPI2142 . . 534
    Flowers
"'So you are stealing my pine cones,' . . . . MBPI1545 . . 497
    said he"
"So You're Hanging the Locusts?" . . . . MBPI0770 . . 449
"'So you're hanging the locusts?' . . . . MBPI0770 . . 449
    inquired the Judge, contemptuously"
"Soberly joined himself to the North . . . . MBPI0118 . . 408
    Church"
Society . . . . MBPI0618 . . 439
Society . . . . MBPI0640 . . 440

"Soft is the breath of a maiden's Yes" . . . . MBPI2872 . . 580
The Soldier and his Trouble . . . . MBPI1452 . . 491
The Soldier brings his Trouble before the . . . . MBPI1453 . . 491
    King
Soldier with spear . . . . PDPI0050 . . . 606
Solitude . . . . MBPI0624 . . 439
"Some of the by-standers said 'She is . . . . MBPI0633 . . 440
    drunk, it will soon pass away'"
Some One Else . . . . MBPI3052 . . 591
"Some took his time" . . . . MBPI2838 . . 578
Something Fresh . . . . PDPI0038 . . . 605
"Something like a stride" . . . . MBPI2830 . . 577
"The somewhat peculiar pastime of our . . . . . . MBPI0081 . . 406
    hero's second client"
A son of the soil . . . . MBPI2034 . . 528
A Song at the Start . . . . MBPI3149 . . 597
The Song of Captain Kidd . . . . MBPI0230 . . 415
Song of Peace . . . . MBPI0098 . . 407
Song of the Followers of Pan . . . . MBPI3121 . . 596
The Song of the Whip-poor-Will, with . . . . MBPI1187 . . 475
    title and poem inserted
Song to the Divine Mother . . . . MBPI3174 . . 599
"Sorcery" . . . . MBPI1902 . . 519
Spanish Dancer . . . . MBPI1054 . . 466
A Spanish Dancer . . . . MBPI1054 . . 466
The Spanish Dancer . . . . MBPI1054 . . 466
Spanish Galleon . . . . MBPI0378 . . 424
A Spanish Galleon in The Sixteenth . . . . MBPI0953 . . 460
    Century
The Spark of Life . . . . MBPI0792 . . 450
"'Speak up, boy,–speak up,' said the . . . . MBPI1827 . . 515
    gentleman"
Spearing Eels in Eel Bay . . . . MBPI2047 . . 528
Sphinx . . . . MBPI3041 . . 591
The Spies . . . . MBPI0075 . . 405
Spine design for Lady of Shalott . . . . MBPI2741 . . 572
Spine design for Men of Iron . . . . MBPI0277 . . 418
Spine design for Pepper & Salt . . . . PDPI0077 . . . 608
Spine design for Stops of Various Quills . . . . . . MBPI2622 . . 564
Spine design for The Merry Adventures of . . . MBPI2146 . . 535
    Robin Hood
Spine design for The Story of King Arthur . . . . MBPI2395 . . 550
    and His Knights
Spine design for The Story of Sir . . . . MBPI2515 . . 558
    Launcelot and his Companions
Spine design for The Story of the . . . . MBPI2430 . . 552
    Champions of the Round Table
Spine design for The Story of the Grail . . . . MBPI2596 . . 563
    and the Passing of Arthur
Spine design for Twilight Land . . . . PDPI0030 . . . 605
The Spirit and the Flesh . . . . MBPI0788 . . 450
Spirit of Spring . . . . MBPI1742 . . 509
Spring . . . . MBPI2505 . . 557
Spring Blossoms . . . . MBPI0324 . . 421

Spring Has Come with initial T . . . . MBPI3001 . . 588

Springtime . . . . MBPI1066 . . 467

"Squatted on a log, and talked in a sad, ... MBPI0388 . . 425
    melancholy manner"

"Squeer's Method" by Charles Dickens . . . . MBPI2661 . . 567

"The Squire went on as though he had not . . . MBPI1250 . . 479
    heard"

St. Valentine . . . . MBPI1174 . . 474

St. Valentine's Day in Merrie Old England . . . . . . MBPI1174 . . 474

St. Valentine's Day in the Morning . . . . MBPI1195 . . 475

The Stage . . . . MBPI0213 . . 414

"Stand off, ye wretches" . . . . MBPI0116 . . 408

The Star Bearer . . . . MBPI2081 . . 531

Stark Captured by Indians . . . . MBPI1309 . . 482

Statistics . . . . MBPI0652 . . 441

"The statue became flesh and blood" . . . . MBPI1608 . . 501

Stefano and Serafina at the well . . . . MBPI1136 . . 471

The Step-daughter follows the Golden Ball . . . MBPI1555 . . 498

The Step-daughter follows ye golden ball . . . . . . MBPI1555 . . 498
    in spite of herself

The Step-mother bringeth mischief upon . . . . . . MBPI1557 . . 498
    the Young Queen by sundry magic spells

The Step-mother changes the Queen into a . . MBPI1557 . . 498
    White Dove

"Still she looked upon me, though . . . . MBPI0342 . . 422
    silently and pale as death"

Still the Poem Speaketh of the Sights . . . . MBPI2712 . . 570
    Within the Mirror

The stirrup-cup . . . . MBPI1217 . . 477

Stopping the Christmas Stage . . . . MBPI1264 . . 479

"A store stood with open front toward the . . . MBPI0401 . . 426
    road"

"Stories and jests recited by some . . . . MBPI1679 . . 505
    strolling mummer or minstrel"

The storm of 1821 . . . . MBOI0007 . . 612

The stout bout between Little John and . . . . . MBPI2109 . . 532
    Arthur a Bland

Stout Robin hath a narrow escape . . . . MBPI2134 . . 534

The Strange Adventures of a Young . . . . MBPI1293 . . 481
    Gentleman of Quality, Part III.

"A strange sea-monster stole their bait" . . . . . . MBPI2855 . . 579

Strange Waters . . . . MBPI2011 . . 526

A Stranger shows the King the portrait of . . . MBPI1550 . . 497
    a beautiful Princess

The stranger threw himself upon Jonathan . . . MBPI0982 . . 462
    with the fury of a madman

Strawberry picking . . . . MBPI0182 . . 412

Strip of Green for mural panel . . . . PDPI0011 . . . 604

The Strolling Minstrel . . . . MBPI0895 . . 456

The Strolling Poet . . . . MBPI0895 . . 456

"Struck me with both fists" . . . . MBPI1270 . . 480

The Student and the Princess . . . . MBPI1474 . . 493

"A Study" . . . . PDPI0041 . . . 606

Stuyvesant Tearing Up the Letter . . . . MBPI0300 . . 419

Demanding the Surrender of New Amsterdam

Stuyvesant tearing up the letter . . . . MBPI0300 . . 419
    demanding the surrender of New Amsterdam

Subtitle, A Pastoral Without Words . . . . MBPI1934 . . 521

Subtitle decoration I . . . . PDPI0095 . . . 609

Subtitle decoration II . . . . PDPI0096 . . . 609

Subtitle page decoration for Breviary . . . . MBPI3202 . . 601
    Treasures

Subtitle page decoration for The Odes & . . . . . MBPI3188 . . 600
    Epodes of Horace

Subtitle page decoration for The Story of . . . MBPI2400 . . 550
    King Arthur and His Knights

Such a wreck was a Godsend to the poor . . . MBPI1162 . . 473
    and needy settlers

"Such was the workshop in which the two . . . MBPI0144 . . 409
    labored together"

Suddenly a half-door opened and there . . . . . MBPI2365 . . 548
    stood a little man

"Suddenly someone touched Oliver lightly . . . MBPI0161 . . 411
    upon the shoulder"

Suddenly their comedy turned tragic . . . . MBPI0972 . . 461

Suicide . . . . MBPI0937 . . 459

The Suicide . . . . MBPI0937 . . 459

Sun and Shadow with initial A . . . . MBPI2976 . . 586

Sunday in Old Catskill . . . . MBPI0250 . . 416

"The Sunday swell" . . . . MBPI2820 . . 577

"Sunthin' in the Pastoral Line" . . . . MBPI3206 . . 601

Superficial Culture, with title, ... MBPI1368 . . 486
    illustrations and verse

"Suppose you let me take care of this . . . . MBPI1200 . . 475
    young lady in future?"

Surprised by the Hero of Seventy . . . . MBPI2079 . . 530
    Fights–The Good Lord James of Douglas

The Surrender of Captain Pearson on the . . . . MBPI0020 . . 402
    Deck of the "Bonhomme Richard"

The Surrender of Captain Pearson . . . . MBPI0020 . . 402

The Surrender of Cornwallis at Yorktown . . . . . . MBPI1198 . . 475

The Surrender of Cornwallis . . . . MBPI1198 . . 475

Surrender of Fort Amsterdam . . . . MBPI0573 . . 436

The Surrender of Fort Amsterdam . . . . MBPI0573 . . 436

Surrender of Fort William and Mary . . . . MBPI0333 . . 421

Suspicious Strangers . . . . PDPI0017 . . . 604

The Swan carries the Prince away . . . . MBPI1442 . . 491

The Swan carries the Prince over the . . . . MBPI1442 . . 491
    hills and far away

The Swan Maiden helps ye young Prince . . . . . . MBPI1444 . . 491

"The Sweet, Love–Planted Christmas Tree" . . . . MBPI1202 . . 476

"The sweet love-planted Christmas Tree" . . . . . . MBPI1202 . . 476

"The Sweet, Love-Planted Christmas-Tree" . . . . . MBPI1202 . . 476

The Swineherd Telling His Story to . . . . MBPI2784 . . 574
    Odysseus

The Swineherd who knew curious things . . . . . MBPI1779 . . 512

Swinging his lanthorn and followed by his . . . MBPI1040 . . 465
    laboring assistants

Sylvia's troubles . . . . MBPI1773 . . 511

Index–Titles and Alternate Titles of Pyle's Art

Sympathy .... MBPI0647 .. 441

Tacy Kelp .... MBPI0202 .. 413

Tailpiece, Chapter I for Otto of the .... MBPI2286 .. 543
Silver Hand

Tailpiece, Chapter II for Otto of the .... MBPI2290 .. 544
Silver Hand

Tailpiece, Chapter III for Otto of the .... MBPI2294 .. 544
Silver Hand

Tailpiece, Chapter IV for Otto of the .... MBPI2299 .. 544
Silver Hand

Tailpiece, Chapter IX for Otto of the .... MBPI2324 .. 546
Silver Hand

Tailpiece, Chapter V for Otto of the .... MBPI2304 .. 544
Silver Hand

Tailpiece, Chapter VI for Otto of the .... MBPI2309 .. 545
Silver Hand

Tailpiece, Chapter VII for Otto of the .... MBPI2316 .. 545
Silver Hand

Tailpiece, Chapter X for Otto of the .... MBPI2330 .. 546
Silver Hand

Tailpiece, Chapter XI for Otto of the .... MBPI2334 .. 546
Silver Hand

Tailpiece, Chapter XII for Otto of the .... MBPI2338 .. 547
Silver Hand

Tailpiece, Chapter XIII for Otto of the .... MBPI2343 .. 547
Silver Hand

Tailpiece, Chapter XIV for Otto of the .... MBPI2347 .. 547
Silver Hand

Tailpiece, Contents for Otto of the .... MBPI2277 .. 543
Silver Hand

Tailpiece, Contents for The Story of King ..... MBPI2398 .. 550
Arthur and His Knights

Tailpiece, Contents for The Story of Sir .... MBPI2521 .. 558
Launcelot and his Companions

Tailpiece, Contents for The Story of the ...... MBPI2436 .. 553
Champions of the Round Table

Tailpiece, Contents for The Story of the ...... MBPI2602 .. 563
Grail and the Passing of Arthur

Tailpiece design and verse for drinking mug .. PDPI0024 ... 605

Tailpiece for A Ballad of the Boston .... MBPI2889 .. 581
Tea-Party

Tailpiece for A Ballad of the Boston-Tea ...... MBPI2947 .. 585
Party

Tailpiece for A Ballad of the Boston-Tea ...... MBPI2949 .. 585
Party

Tailpiece for A Ballad of the Boston-Tea ...... MBPI2952 .. 585
Party

Tailpiece for A Ballad of the Boston-Tea ...... MBPI2954 .. 585
Party

Tailpiece for A Ballad of the Boston-Tea ...... MBPI2956 .. 585
Party

Tailpiece for A Ballad of the Boston-Tea ...... MBPI2958 .. 585
Party

Tailpiece for A Ballad of the Boston-Tea ...... MBPI2960 .. 585
Party

Tailpiece for A History of New York .... MBPI2773 .. 574

Tailpiece for A Prelude .... MBPI0810 .. 451

Tailpiece for A Sahib's War .... MBPI0097 .. 407

Tailpiece for A True History of the Devil ...... MBPI1296 .. 481
at New Hope

Tailpiece for Another Day .... MBPI3051 .. 591

Tailpiece for At the Gates of Life .... MBPI0069 .. 405

Tailpiece for Autocrat's Autobiography .... MBPI2967 .. 586

Tailpiece for Calvary .... MBPI0557 .. 435

Tailpiece for Change .... MBPI0628 .. 440

Tailpiece for Colonel Washington .... MBPI0680 .. 443

Tailpiece for Company .... MBPI3028 .. 590

Tailpiece for Conscience .... MBPI3034 .. 590

Tailpiece for Drummer Fritz and His .... MBPI1788 .. 512
Exploits

Tailpiece for Edric and Sylvaine .... MBPI1029 .. 465

Tailpiece for First in Peace .... MBPI0725 .. 446

Tailpiece for Friends and Foes .... MBPI0557 .. 435

Tailpiece for Friends and Foes .... MBPI0641 .. 441

Tailpiece for From Generation to .... MBPI0560 .. 435
Generation

Tailpiece for George Washington .... MBPI0675 .. 443

Tailpiece for George Washington .... MBPI0716 .. 445

Tailpiece for George Washington .... MBPI0722 .. 446

Tailpiece for George Washington .... MBPI0727 .. 446

Tailpiece for Going To The Fair .... MBPI1780 .. 512

Tailpiece for Good Society .... MBPI0620 .. 439

Tailpiece for Gretelein and Her Queer .... MBOI0010 .. 612
Stove

Tailpiece for Hope .... MBPI0565 .. 436

Tailpiece for Hope and Memory .... MBPI0051 .. 404

Tailpiece for In The Dark .... MBPI3030 .. 590

Tailpiece for In the Meadows of Youth .... MBPI0063 .. 404

Tailpiece for In the Valley of the .... MBPI0066 .. 405
Shadows

Tailpiece for Invitation .... PDPI0082 ... 608

Tailpiece for Labor And Capital .... MBPI3046 .. 591

Tailpiece for Life .... MBPI3055 .. 591

Tailpiece for Living .... MBPI0552 .. 435

Tailpiece for Love and Death .... MBPI0752 .. 447

Tailpiece for Mare Rubrum .... MBPI2989 .. 587

Tailpiece for Materials of a Story .... MBPI0560 .. 435

Tailpiece for McAndrew's Hymn .... MBPI1970 .. 524

Tailpiece for Memorable Events in .... MBPI0757 .. 448
American History

Tailpiece for Memorable Events in .... MBPI0725 .. 446
American History

Tailpiece for Memorable Events in .... MBPI0716 .. 445
American History

Tailpiece for Memorable Events in .... MBPI0722 .. 446
American History

Tailpiece for Midway .... MBPI3025 .. 590

Tailpiece for Musa .... MBPI3010 .. 589

Tailpiece for New York Colonial .... MBPI0639 .. 440
Privateers

Index–Titles and Alternate Titles of Pyle's Art

Tailpiece for Old Captain .... MBPI0787 . . 450

Tailpiece for Old New York Taverns .... MBPI0443 . . 428

Tailpiece for Parable .... MBPI3037 . . 590

Tailpiece for Paul Jones .... MBPI0024 . . 402

Tailpiece for Poisoned Ice .... MBPI0074 . . 405

Tailpiece for Question .... MBPI0552 . . 435

Tailpiece for Race .... MBPI3059 . . 592

Tailpiece for Reward And Punishment .... MBPI3035 . . 590

Tailpiece for Society .... MBPI0620 . . 439

Tailpiece for Society .... MBPI0642 . . 441

Tailpiece for Solitude .... MBPI3031 . . 590

Tailpiece for Statistics .... MBPI0654 . . 441

Tailpiece for The Assembly Ball .... MBPI0749 . . 447

Tailpiece for The Autocrat of the .... MBPI3016 . . 589
Breakfast-Table

Tailpiece for The Autocrat of the .... MBPI3021 . . 589
Breakfast-Table

Tailpiece for The Battle of Copenhagen .... MBPI0045 . . 403

Tailpiece for The Bewildered Guest .... MBPI3026 . . 590

Tailpiece for The Birds of Cirencester .... MBPI0495 . . 431

Tailpiece for The Body to the Soul .... MBPI0794 . . 450

Tailpiece for The Broomstick Train .... MBPI2860 . . 579

Tailpiece for The Buccaneers .... MBPI0528 . . 433

Tailpiece for The Buccaneers .... MBPI0947 . . 460

Tailpiece for The Chambered Nautilus .... MBPI2985 . . 587

Tailpiece for The Cocklane Ghost .... MBPI0590 . . 437

Tailpiece for The Constitution's Last .... MBPI0028 . . 402
Fight

Tailpiece for The Enchanted Island .... MBPI1700 . . 507

Tailpiece for The Evolution of New York .... MBPI0573 . . 436

Tailpiece for The Evolution of New York .... MBPI0577 . . 437

Tailpiece for The First President of the .... MBPI0730 . . 446
United States

Tailpiece for The Flight of the Swallow .... MBPI0132 . . 409

Tailpiece for The Last Revel in Printz .... MBPI0207 . . 413
Hall

Tailpiece for The Mysterious Chest .... MBPI1052 . . 466

Tailpiece for The Old Man Dreams .... MBPI2981 . . 587

Tailpiece for The One Hoss Shay .... MBPI3208 . . 601

Tailpiece for The Origin of the .... MBPI1800 . . 513
Jumping-Jack

Tailpiece for The Painted Pitcher .... PDPI0079 . . . 608

Tailpiece for The Pilgrimage of Truth .... MBPI0824 . . 452

Tailpiece for The Pilgrimage of Truth .... MBPI0826 . . 452

Tailpiece for The Romance of an Ambrotype .. MBPI0745 . . 447

Tailpiece for The Sea Robbers of New York .... MBPI0611 . . 439

Tailpiece for The Star Bearer .... PDPI0054 . . . 606

Tailpiece for The Stool of Fortune .... MBPI1663 . . 504

Tailpiece for The Story of King Arthur .... MBPI2404 . . 551
and His Knights

Tailpiece for The Story of King Arthur .... MBPI2405 . . 551
and His Knights

Tailpiece for The Story of King Arthur .... MBPI2406 . . 551
and His Knights

Tailpiece for The Story of King Arthur .... MBPI2407 . . 551
and His Knights

Tailpiece for The Story of King Arthur .... MBPI2410 . . 551
and His Knights

Tailpiece for The Story of King Arthur .... MBPI2419 . . 552
and His Knights

Tailpiece for The Story of King Arthur .... MBPI2420 . . 552
and His Knights

Tailpiece for The Story of King Arthur .... MBPI2428 . . 552
and His Knights

Tailpiece for The Story of Lesken .... MBPI2066 . . 530

Tailpiece for The Story of Sir Launcelot ...... MBPI2527 . . 558
and his Companions

Tailpiece for The Story of Sir Launcelot ...... MBPI2546 . . 560
and his Companions

Tailpiece for The Story of Sir Launcelot ...... MBPI2560 . . 560
and his Companions

Tailpiece for The Story of Sir Launcelot ...... MBPI2568 . . 561
and his Companions

Tailpiece for The Story of Sir Launcelot ...... MBPI2580 . . 562
and his Companions

Tailpiece for The Story of the Champions .... MBPI2442 . . 553
of the Round Table

Tailpiece for The Story of the Champions .... MBPI2460 . . 554
of the Round Table

Tailpiece for The Story of the Champions .... MBPI2464 . . 554
of the Round Table

Tailpiece for The Story of the Champions .... MBPI2478 . . 555
of the Round Table

Tailpiece for The Story of the Champions .... MBPI2481 . . 556
of the Round Table

Tailpiece for The Story of the Champions .... MBPI2489 . . 556
of the Round Table

Tailpiece for The Story of the Champions .... MBPI2499 . . 557
of the Round Table

Tailpiece for The Story of the Champions .... MBPI2513 . . 558
of the Round Table

Tailpiece for The Story of the Grail and ...... MBPI2600 . . 563
the Passing of Arthur

Tailpiece for The Story of the Grail and ...... MBPI2608 . . 563
the Passing of Arthur

Tailpiece for The Story of the Grail and ...... MBPI2659 . . 567
the Passing of Arthur

Tailpiece for The Two Armies .... MBPI3006 . . 588

Tailpiece for The Yellow of the Leaf .... MBPI0815 . . 451

Tailpiece for Through Inland Waters .... MBPI0699 . . 444

Tailpiece for Through Inland Waters .... MBPI0715 . . 445

A Tailpiece for Through Inland Waters .... MBPI0714 . . 445

Tailpiece for To-Morrow .... MBPI0615 . . 439

Tailpiece for Twelve P.M. .... MBPI0615 . . 439

Tailpiece for Twelve P. M. .... MBPI0565 . . 436

Tailpiece for Washington and the French ..... MBPI0757 . . 448
Craze of '93

Tailpiece for What Shall It Profit? .... MBPI3062 . . 592

Tailpiece for What We All Think .... MBPI2993 . . 588

Index–Titles and Alternate Titles of Pyle's Art

Tailpiece for Wisdom's Wages and Folly's ...... MBPI1593 .. 500
Pay

Tailpiece for Woman's Wit .... MBPI1638 .. 503

Tailpiece, Foreword for Otto of the .... MBPI2282 .. 543
Silver Hand

Tailpiece, Foreword for The Garden Behind ... MBPI2358 .. 548
the Moon

Tailpiece, Foreword for The Story of King ..... MBPI2397 .. 550
Arthur and His Knights

Tailpiece, Foreword for The Story of Sir ..... MBPI2519 .. 558
Launcelot and his Companions

Tailpiece, Foreword for The Story of the ...... MBPI2434 .. 553
Champions of the Round Table

Tailpiece, Introduction for The Price of .... MBPI0078 .. 405
Blood

Tailpiece, List of Illustrations for .... MBPI2933 .. 584
Dorothy Q

Tailpiece, List of Illustrations for Otto .... MBPI2279 .. 543
of the Silver Hand

Tailpiece, List of Illustrations for .... MBPI2157 .. 535
Pepper & Salt

Tailpiece, List of Illustrations for The .... MBPI2093 .. 531
Merry Adventures of Robin Hood

Tailpiece, List of Illustrations for The .... MBPI2799 .. 575
One Hoss Shay

Tailpiece, List of Illustrations for The .... MBPI2399 .. 550
Story of King Arthur and His Knights

Tailpiece, List of Illustrations for The .... MBPI2523 .. 558
Story of Sir Launcelot and his Companions

Tailpiece, List of Illustrations for The .... MBPI2438 .. 553
Story of the Champions of the Round Table

Tailpiece, List of Illustrations for The .... MBPI2604 .. 563
Story of the Grail and the Passing of Arthur

Tailpiece, List of Illustrations for The .... MBPI2172 .. 536
Wonder Clock

Tailpiece, Part I for The Autocrat of the .... MBPI2973 .. 586
Breakfast-Table

Tailpiece, Part I for The Merry .... MBPI2103 .. 532
Adventures of Robin Hood

Tailpiece, Part III for The Merry .... MBPI2114 .. 533
Adventures of Robin Hood

Tailpiece, Part IV for The Merry .... MBPI2120 .. 533
Adventures of Robin Hood

Tailpiece, Part V for The Merry .... MBPI2125 .. 533
Adventures of Robin Hood

Tailpiece, Part VI for The Merry .... MBPI2130 .. 534
Adventures of Robin Hood

Tailpiece, Part VII for The Merry .... MBPI2135 .. 534
Adventures of Robin Hood

Tailpiece, Part VIII for The Merry .... MBPI2140 .. 534
Adventures of Robin Hood

Tailpiece, Preface for Dorothy Q .... MBPI2931 .. 584

Tailpiece, Preface for Pepper & Salt .... MBPI2153 .. 535

Tailpiece, Preface for The Merry .... MBPI2090 .. 531
Adventures of Robin Hood

Tailpiece, Preface for The One Hoss Shay ..... MBPI2797 .. 575

Tailpiece, Prologue for The Merry .... MBPI2097 .. 532
Adventures of Robin Hood

Tailpiece, Prologue for The Story of King ..... MBPI2403 .. 551
Arthur and His Knights

Tailpiece, Sketch Four for By Land and .... MBPI0657 .. 442
Sea

Tailpiece, Sketch One for By Land and Sea ..... MBPI0658 .. 442

Tailpiece, Sketch Three for By Land and ...... MBPI0666 .. 442
Sea

Tailpiece, Sketch Two for By Land and Sea ..... MBPI0662 .. 442

Tailpiece, Table of Contents for Pepper & ..... MBPI2155 .. 535
Salt

Tailpiece, Table of Contents for The .... MBPI2170 .. 536
Wonder Clock

Tailpiece, Table of Contents for Twilight ...... MBPI0974 .. 461
Land

Tailpiece, The End for The Wonder Clock .... MBPI2272 .. 542

"Take care, my friend, take care" .... MBPI1002 .. 463

A Tale of a Tub, with title, ... MBPI1347 .. 485
illustrations and verse

The Talisman .... MBPI1056 .. 466

"The tall man in black knocked upon the .... MBPI1732 .. 509
gate"

"The tall man was lying at his feet, ... MBPI1758 .. 510
huddled hideously on the floor"

"The tall stranger with the club-foot .... MBPI1246 .. 478
stood before her"

A Tea Party .... MBPI2755 .. 573

Telling The News of the Indian Raid .... MBPI0326 .. 421

Temperament .... MBPI3060 .. 592

Thanksgiving Day (entering politely) .... MBPI1335 .. 484

That night his straw stack caught fire .... MBPI1153 .. 473

"That prince or potentate of the old .... MBPI0379 .. 424
sugar king period"

Theatrical costumes designed by Howard .... PDPI0043 ... 606
Pyle

Theatrical costumes designed by Howard .... PDPI0105 ... 610
Pyle

"'Thee hasn't killed him?' timidly .... MBPI1201 .. 476
inquired the girl"

"Their first meeting happened at the .... MBPI0108 .. 407
club"

"Theirs was a spirited encounter upon the .... MBPI1070 .. 467
beach of Teviot Bay

"Then a great mashing blow on my face ..... MBPI1925 .. 521
ended my fight"

"Then appeared suddenly, a little beyond .... MBPI0096 .. 406
the light of the lamp, the spirit of Kurban Sahib"

"Then Beppo carried the Princess ashore" ..... MBPI1734 .. 509

"Then came Mistress Margaret unto me and .. MBPI0343 .. 422
put a letter into my hand"

"Then came the tug of war" .... MBPI0174 .. 411

"Then dost thou not know why I am here?" ... MBPI2319 .. 545
said the Baron

"Then faced her the leonine chief" .... MBPI1911 .. 520

Index–Titles and Alternate Titles of Pyle's Art

"Then he tells his news, in the ruddy . . . . MBPI0268 . . 417
  glow"

"'Then I will come,' said he" . . . . MBPI1839 . . 515

"Then prepare to die" . . . . MBPI1637 . . 503

Then sang Sire Edward . . . . MBPI1000 . . 463

"Then She Dropped Down at His Feet" . . . . MBPI0768 . . 448

"Then something decidedly like a spill" . . . . . . MBPI2814 . . 576

"Then the Hofrath emerged from the . . . . MBPI1208 . . 476
  balcony, and etiquette forbade a longer interview"

Then the old man's lips began to move . . . . . . MBPI3194 . . 600

Then the real fight began . . . . MBPI1033 . . 465

"Then there was a crash and clatter of an . . . . MBPI0111 . . 407
  overturned chair"

Then they began to pull . . . . MBPI1357 . . 485

"Then turned to the table where master . . . . . MBPI1772 . . 511
  and pupil sat absorbed"

"Then Uncle Tom lifted her in his big, ... MBPI1325 . . 483
  strong arms"

Then Winfried told the story of Bethlehem . . . . MBPI0500 . . 432

"Theophilus Went Right Up the Step and . . . . . . MBPI0769 . . 449
  Tugged at the Bell"

Theophilus went right up the step and . . . . MBPI0769 . . 449
  tugged at the bell

Theophylact Bache saving Graydon from the . MBPI0276 . . 418
  Mob in 1776

"There, half stretched on the wet . . . . MBPI1930 . . 521
  blood-stained grass, lay Philip Cross"

"There he watched and guarded while the . . . MBPI1684 . . 506
  others slept"

"There, in the corner, I beheld the . . . . MBPI1260 . . 479
  famous pirate, Captain Edward England"

"There is a charm," said the nurse at . . . . MBPI0905 . . 457
  last

"There is a flock of yellow birds around . . . . . . MBPI0547 . . 435
  her head"

"There is a time to fight and that time . . . . MBPI2017 . . 527
  has now come"

"There sat an old woman at a wheel . . . . MBPI1714 . . 508
  spinning"

There sat three terrible giants . . . . MBPI1561 . . 498

"There sprang from the midst of the smoke . . MBPI1584 . . 499
  a beautiful bird"

There stood the Faery Prince . . . . MBPI1101 . . 469

There they sat, just as little children . . . . MBPI2285 . . 543
  of the town might sit upon their father's doorstep

"There was a passageway yawning before . . . MBPI1626 . . 502
  him"

There was Captain Washington... . . . . MBPI2667 . . 567

"There was exchange of thrust and parry" . . . . MBPI3191 . . 600

"There was feasting and merrymaking" . . . . . . MBPI1694 . . 506

"There was instant silence" . . . . MBPI0033 . . 403

"There's something in there" . . . . MBPI1315 . . 483

Thereafter she clung about Randver . . . . MBPI1089 . . 469

"Thereupon, lifting up his eyes again, he . . . . . MBPI0341 . . 422
  began once more wrestling with the spirit in prayer"

"Thereupon the poor woman screamed aloud, MBPI0569 . . 436
  and cried out that he was a murderer"

These Songs Will Perish . . . . MBPI3177 . . 599

Theseus caught the monster off his guard . . . . MBPI3182 . . 599

"Thetis, the mother of Achilles, was an . . . . MBPI2783 . . 574
  ocean-nymph"

"They are baffled, not defeated" . . . . MBPI2914 . . 583

They awaited the order for the charge . . . . MBPI1087 . . 468

"They beheld their master lying upon his . . . . MBPI0160 . . 410
  face under the table"

"They bore him away to a bench at the far . . . MBPI1676 . . 505
  end of the room"

They brought in their dead and wounded on . MBPI0918 . . 458
  hay wagons

"They called the cats" . . . . MBPI2852 . . 579

"They came...at their master's call" . . . . MBPI2857 . . 579

They carried fruit and vegetables . . . . MBPI0993 . . 463

"They could hear him twenty miles" . . . . MBPI2856 . . 579

"They danced around and around the chest" . . MBPI1720 . . 508

"They entered the vestibule of the . . . . MBPI1710 . . 507
  palace"

"They follow at his heels" . . . . MBPI2835 . . 578

"They found her still sitting in the same . . . . . MBPI1833 . . 515
  place"

They have a so-called native king . . . . MBPI0992 . . 462

"They kissed one another" . . . . MBPI1619 . . 502

"They lead him, limping, to the track" . . . . MBPI2828 . . 577

"They led me, taking hold of my collar, ... MBPI0281 . . 418
  and by my arms"

"They ploughed their fields with an armed . . . MBPI0355 . . 423
  sentry beside them"

"They questioned him with malevolent . . . . . . MBPI1098 . . 469
  persistence"

"They read only upon occasion, when the . . . . MBPI0674 . . 443
  weather darkened"

"They sat down and chatted in an easy, ... MBPI1207 . . 476
  friendly fashion"

They sat down under a tree in a quiet . . . . MBPI1360 . . 485
  corner of the palace grounds

"They saw Arnold de Villeneuve, the great . . . MBPI0143 . . 409
  master, lying upon the floor"

"They say I fainted" . . . . MBPI2924 . . 583

"They scrambled up the parapet and went . . . MBPI3111 . . 595
  surging over the crest, pell mell, upon The British"

They set before him a loaf of bread and a . . . . MBPI1573 . . 499
  bowl of milk

"They stood and looked across the chasm . . . MBPI0105 . . 407
  at him"

They stood staring at the violent sky . . . . MBPI0935 . . 459

"They surged above the breast-work" . . . . MBPI2923 . . 583

"They talked it over–with me sitting on . . . . . . MBPI1073 . . 468
  the horse"

"They told each other about it" . . . . MBPI0774 . . 449

"They used to drill every evening" . . . . MBPI1814 . . 514

"They wait and answer not" . . . . MBPI2907 . . 582

Index–Titles and Alternate Titles of Pyle's Art

"They were creeping round to four" . . . . MBPI2921 . . 583

"They were dressed in loose sackcloth . . . . MBPI0400 . . 425
    shirt and drawers"

They were overtaken by Falmouth himself . . . . MBPI0962 . . 461

They would stand hours together . . . . MBPI1172 . . 474

"They're losing ground" . . . . MBPI2836 . . 578

The Things You Will Learn From The Yellow . . . MBPI2014 . . 526
    And Brown

The Third Sketch . . . . MBPI0012 . . 401

The Third Verse Describeth Also the . . . . MBPI2718 . . 570
    Coming of the Bold Knight

"This is Enoch Wade, gentlemen," said the . . . . MBPI1916 . . 520
    baronet

This Is It with initial A . . . . MBPI2977 . . 587

"This is my daughter,' said the . . . . MBPI1713 . . 508
    merchant"

"This is no courting night" . . . . MBPI0545 . . 435

This is the way that one in Cap and . . . . MBPI2150 . . 535
    Motley stops for awhile along the stony Path of Life to make
    you laugh

This last picture . . . . MBPI0899 . . 457

This Verse Speaketh Also of Lancelot the . . . . . MBPI2717 . . 570
    Bold

Thomas Jefferson . . . . MBPI1993 . . 525

Thomas Jefferson Looking Over the Rough . . . . MBPI1993 . . 525
    Draught of the Declaration of Independence

Thomas Jefferson Writing the Declaration . . . . MBPI1993 . . 525
    of Independence

"Thomas Moon began to lay about him with . . . MBPI0287 . . 418
    his Sword"

"Thomas Moon Knocked Down the First . . . . . . MBPI0287 . . 418
    Spaniard He Met"

Thompson, the Clerk of Congress, ... MBPI0728 . . 446
    announcing to Washington, at Mount Vernon, his election to
    the Presidency

Thomson, The Clerk of Congress, Announces . . . MBPI0728 . . 446
    to Washington at Mount Vernon His Election to the Presidency

Thomson, the Clerk of Congress, ... MBPI0728 . . 446
    announcing to Washington, at Mount Vernon, his election to the
    Presidency

"Thou art a wonder of wonders" . . . . MBPI1715 . . 508

"Thou ugly toad," said the woman . . . . MBPI2327 . . 546

A Thousand Miles a Day . . . . MBPI3179 . . 599

"The three fellows were brought aft to . . . . MBPI1259 . . 479
    the quarterdeck, where Captain Croker stood, just below the
    rail of the deck above"

Three Fortunes, with title, illustrations . . . . . . MBPI1351 . . 485
    and verse

The three giants come to blows . . . . MBPI1454 . . 491

The three giants fight one another like . . . . MBPI1454 . . 491
    fury

The Three Little Pigs and the Ogre . . . . MBPI1497 . . 494

"Three men seized him" . . . . MBPI1647 . . 503

The three rogues lend Caspar sundry . . . . MBPI1511 . . 495
    things so that he may go to the king's castle

The three share the money amongst them . . . . . . MBPI1510 . . 495

The Three Students . . . . MBPI1720 . . 508

Through Inland Waters, An Illustrated . . . . MBPI0684 . . 443
    Title

Thus the Princess cometh forth from the . . . . . . MBPI1514 . . 495
    Castle at twelve o'clock at night

Thus the Princess sits and weeps and . . . . MBPI1531 . . 496
    weeps

The Tiger . . . . PDPI0001 . . . 603

The Tile House, New Castle, Delaware . . . . MBOI0008 . . 612

Time . . . . MBPI0616 . . 439

"'Tis an unfair race, O master," cried . . . . MBPI1115 . . 470
    Ephialtes

" ' 'Tis enough,' cried out Parson Jones, ... MBPI1166 . . 473
    'To make us both rich men' "

"'Tis enough to make us both rich men" . . . . . . MBPI1166 . . 473

Title and illustrated initial H for Hans . . . . MBPI1380 . . 487
    Hecklemann's Luck

Title and illustrated initial H for How . . . . MBPI1388 . . 487
    Dame Margery Twist saw more than was good for her

Title for Grandmother's Story of Bunker . . . . . MBPI2891 . . 581
    Hill Battle

Title page decoration for First Year Book . . . . . MBPI2392 . . 550
    of The Bibliophile Society

Title page decoration for Pepper & Salt . . . . MBPI2151 . . 535

Title page decoration for Stops of . . . . MBPI3022 . . 589
    Various Quills

Title page decoration for Stops of . . . . MBPI3023 . . 589
    Various Quills

Title page decoration for The Lady of . . . . MBPI2697 . . 569
    Shalott

Title page decoration for The Merry . . . . MBPI2088 . . 531
    Adventures of Robin Hood

Title page decoration for The Odes & . . . . MBPI3186 . . 600
    Epodes of Horace

Title page decoration for The Story of . . . . MBPI2396 . . 550
    King Arthur and His Knights

Title page decoration for The Travels of . . . . . . MBPI0058 . . 404
    the Soul

Title page decoration for The Wonder . . . . MBPI2166 . . 536
    Clock

Title page decoration for Twelfth Night . . . . . . MBPI3217 . . 602
    at Eagleroost

Title page decoration for Twelfth Night . . . . MBPI3217 . . 602
    at The Century

Title page for The Story of Sir Launcelot . . . . . . MBPI2396 . . 550
    and his Companions

Title page for The Story of the Champions . . . . . MBPI2396 . . 550
    of the Round Table

Title page for The Story of the Grail and . . . . . . MBPI2396 . . 550
    the Passing of Arthur

Title page illustration for Yankee Doodle . . . . . MBPI2665 . . 567

Title with decoration for The True . . . . MBPI0883 . . 456
    Captain Kidd

Title with decorations for The Yellow of . . . . . . MBPI0812 . . 451
    the Leaf

Index–Titles and Alternate Titles of Pyle's Art

Title with decorations, Mother Carey's .... MBPI0874 .. 455
    Chickens

Title with decorations, Saint Brendan's .... MBPI0871 .. 455
    Island

Title with decorations, The Fairy Morgana ..... MBPI0868 .. 455

Title with decorations, The Flying .... MBPI0877 .. 455
    Dutchman

Title with illustrated initial E for The .... MBPI1866 .. 517
    Story of King Arthur and His Knights

Title with illustrated initial F for The .... MBPI1875 .. 518
    Story of King Arthur and His Knights

Title with illustrated initial H for The .... MBPI1844 .. 516
    Story of King Arthur and His Knights

Title with illustrated initial I for The .... MBPI1861 .. 517
    Story of King Arthur and His Knights

Title with illustrated initial K for The .... MBPI1853 .. 516
    Story of King Arthur and His Knights

Title with illustrated initial K for The .... MBPI1855 .. 516
    Story of King Arthur and His Knights

Title with illustrated initial K for The .... MBPI1858 .. 517
    Story of King Arthur and His Knights

Title with illustrated initial K for The .... MBPI1880 .. 518
    Story of King Arthur and His Knights

Title with illustrated initial P for The .... MBPI1888 .. 518
    Story of King Arthur and His Knights

Title with illustrated initial S for The .... MBPI1848 .. 516
    Story of King Arthur and His Knights

Title with illustrated initial S for The .... MBPI1851 .. 516
    Story of King Arthur and His Knights

Title with illustrated initial S for The .... MBPI1883 .. 518
    Story of King Arthur and His Knights

Title with illustrated initial S for The .... MBPI1885 .. 518
    Story of King Arthur and His Knights

Title with illustrated initial S for The .... MBPI1893 .. 519
    Story of King Arthur and His Knights

Title with illustrated initial S for The .... MBPI1898 .. 519
    Story of King Arthur and His Knights

Title with illustrated initial S for The .... MBPI1900 .. 519
    Story of King Arthur and His Knights

Title with illustrated initial S for The .... MBPI1903 .. 519
    Story of King Arthur and His Knights

Title with illustrated initial S for The .... MBPI1905 .. 520
    Story of King Arthur and His Knights

Title with illustrated initial T for The .... MBPI1840 .. 515
    Story of King Arthur and His Knights

Title with illustrated initial T for The .... MBPI1863 .. 517
    Story of King Arthur and His Knights

Title with illustrated initial T for The .... MBPI1868 .. 517
    Story of King Arthur and His Knights

Title with illustrated initial T for The .... MBPI1870 .. 517
    Story of King Arthur and His Knights

Title with illustrated initial T for The .... MBPI1873 .. 518
    Story of King Arthur and His Knights

Title with illustrated initial T for The .... MBPI1878 .. 518
    Story of King Arthur and His Knights

Title with illustrated initial T for The .... MBPI1890 .. 519

    Story of King Arthur and His Knights

Title with illustrated initial T for The .... MBPI1895 .. 519
    Story of King Arthur and His Knights

Title with illustrated initial T for The .... MBPI1907 .. 520
    Story of King Arthur and His Knights

To Have and to Hold .... MBPI3231 .. 602

To High-born Poets .... MBPI3169 .. 599

"To limber out each stiffened joint" .... MBPI2829 .. 577

To Louise Michel .... MBPI3147 .. 597

"To sea in a bowl!" exclaimed the puzzled .... MBPI2072 .. 530
    Pembroke

To William Watson .... MBPI3143 .. 597

To Zisk, I .... MBPI1361 .. 486

To Zisk, II .... MBPI1362 .. 486

To-Morrow .... MBPI0555 .. 435

"Toiled homeward with his treasure" .... MBPI0486 .. 431

The Toilers .... MBPI3170 .. 599

The Toll Gate .... MBPI0210 .. 414

"Too early voyager with too frail an oar" .... MBPI2793 .. 575

"The Tories seize the omen" .... MBPI2884 .. 581

Tory Refugees .... MBPI0852 .. 454

Tory Refugees on their way to Canada .... MBPI0852 .. 454

The Tory .... MBPI1002 .. 463

Tow of Canal Boats .... MBPI0687 .. 443

"The Town Pump" by Nathaniel Hawthorne ... MBPI2660 .. 567

A Trade At The Tavern, In The Olden Time ..... MBPI2080 .. 530

Transporting powder from the Fort .... MBPI0334 .. 421

"The Travel of The Soul" drawn after .... MBPI0056 .. 404
    Howard Pyle

Traveling by Stage Coach .... MBPI0213 .. 414

Traveling in the Olden Time .... MBPI0330 .. 421

The traveller found the stone behind the .... MBPI1156 .. 473
    hedge a resting-place

The Travels of the Soul .... MBPI0054 .. 404

The Travels of the Soul .... MBPI0055 .. 404

The Travels of the Soul .... MBPI0057 .. 404

The Travels of the Soul .... MBPI0056 .. 404

The Trial of Strength .... MBPI2745 .. 572

Tristram succors the Lady Moeya .... MBPI2466 .. 555

The triumphal entry into Rheims .... MBPI0921 .. 458

The troopers, too, would gallop up... .... MBPI2686 .. 568

"The troopers too would gallop up..." .... MBPI2686 .. 568

The Trotting Match .... MBPI2975 .. 586

The Troubadour .... MBPI0896 .. 456

"The truant tapster" .... MBPI2881 .. 581

Truth and the Jester .... MBPI0821 .. 452

Truth and the Sage .... MBPI0819 .. 452

Truth Before the High Priest .... MBPI0818 .. 452

Truth before the King .... MBPI0817 .. 452

Truth Before the King .... MBPI0817 .. 452

Truth Before the Magician .... MBPI0818 .. 452

Truth Before the Sage .... MBPI0819 .. 452

Truth before the Seer .... MBPI0819 .. 452

Truth in the Fool's Lodge .... MBPI0821 .. 452

Index–Titles and Alternate Titles of Pyle's Art

Truth in the House of the Fool . . . . MBPI0821 . . 452

Truth in the Temple . . . . MBPI0818 . . 452

Truth is Received by the Jester . . . . MBPI0821 . . 452

Truth is Rejected by the High Priest . . . . MBPI0818 . . 452

Truth is Rejected by the King . . . . MBPI0817 . . 452

Truth is Rejected by the Wise Man . . . . MBPI0819 . . 452

Truth Leaves her Heavenly Home . . . . MBPI0816 . . 451

Truth Leaves Her Heavenly Home . . . . MBPI0816 . . 451

Truth Leaves Her Home . . . . MBPI0816 . . 451

Truth Leaves the Fairies' Wonderland . . . . MBPI0816 . . 451

Truth Wanders in the World . . . . MBPI0820 . . 452

Truth Wanders, Lost, in the World . . . . MBPI0820 . . 452

Truth Wanders, Lost in the World . . . . MBPI0820 . . 452

Truth Went on Her Way Alone . . . . MBPI0820 . . 452

"A turbaned coolie and his wife" . . . . MBPI0380 . . 424

"A turbaned negro woman sat with her . . . . . . MBPI0408 . . 426
    knitting"

Turpin and King . . . . MBPI0447 . . 428

"'Twas a strange tale she had ended" . . . . MBPI0890 . . 456

'Tween decks of the slaver . . . . MBPI0994 . . 463

Twelve P. M. . . . . MBPI3029 . . 590

The Two Armies with initial A . . . . MBPI3005 . . 588

Two at a Fireside . . . . MBPI3141 . . 597

The Two Brothers and the Landlord divide . . . MBPI1510 . . 495
    the money

Two Knights do Battle before Cameliard . . . . . . MBPI1871 . . 517

"Two negro women stood gossiping and . . . . MBPI0415 . . 426
    cooling their feet"

Two Opinions, with title, illustrations . . . . MBPI1330 . . 484
    and verse

The two rode away together . . . . MBPI1129 . . 471

The Umbrella–A Curious Present . . . . MBPI0260 . . 417

Umr Singh . . . . MBPI0095 . . 406

Uncle and Nephew–"Well, Jacky, you shall . . . . MBPI1824 . . 514
    have that hundred pounds, you shall"

Uncle Bear and the Great Red Fox after . . . . . . MBPI1527 . . 496
    Farmer John's Apples

Uncle Bear and the Great Red Fox visit . . . . MBPI1526 . . 496
    the farmer's store-house

Uncle Benny . . . . MBPI2040 . . 528

Uncle Ken . . . . MBPI2036 . . 528

Uncle Sam . . . . MBPI0215 . . 414

Uncle Sammy and Joe . . . . MBPI1752 . . 510

Undergraduate Life in 1679 . . . . MBPI1979 . . 524

The United States Captain Boarding the . . . . . . MBPI1032 . . 465
    "Active"

Unpropitious Skies . . . . MBPI1175 . . 474

Untitled Panel . . . . MBPI3233 . . 603

Untitled Panel . . . . MBPI3236 . . 603

Untitled Panel . . . . MBPI3237 . . 603

Unused color design for Howard Pyle . . . . PDPI0028 . . . 605
    bookplate

"The Unwelcome Suitor" . . . . MBPI0777 . . 449

An Unwelcome Toast . . . . MBPI1281 . . 481

Upon the last stage of the journey they . . . . . MBPI0075 . . 405
    stopped for dinner at a tavern

Uther-Pendragon . . . . MBPI2402 . . 551

A Valentine to Phillis . . . . MBPI1227 . . 477

The Valley . . . . MBPI3160 . . 598

"The variety and fatigues of his . . . . MBPI0439 . . 428
    business"

"The veil of sleep fell on him, And his . . . . MBPI2794 . . 575
    thought a dream became"

Venturesome Boldness, with title, ... MBPI1364 . . 486
    illustrations and verse

Verse 1. Ye Jovial Huntsman . . . . MBPI0491 . . 431

Verse 2. Ye Fat, Rich Man . . . . MBPI0492 . . 431

Verse 3. Ye Gallant Soldier . . . . MBPI0493 . . 431

Verse 4. Ye Jolly Country Boy . . . . MBPI0494 . . 431

Verse I, A Pastoral Without Words . . . . MBPI1936 . . 521

Verse II, A Pastoral Without Words . . . . MBPI1938 . . 522

Verse III, A Pastoral Without Words . . . . MBPI1940 . . 522

Verse IV, A Pastoral Without Words . . . . MBPI1942 . . 522

A Verse with a Moral but No Name, with . . . . . MBPI1345 . . 485
    title, illustrations and verse

"A very little old man seated in a very . . . . . . MBPI1790 . . 512
    large chair"

A Very Merry Christmas In The "Good Old . . . . PDPI0039 . . . 606
    Times"

"A vessel of brass full of money" . . . . MBPI1703 . . 507

A Victim to Science, with title, ... MBPI1331 . . 484
    illustrations and verse

"The victims of the witchcraft delusion" . . . . . . MBPI0122 . . 408

Vidal–Poet and Satirist . . . . MBPI0896 . . 456

A view in Jamaica . . . . PDPI0016 . . . 604

A View on the Northern Canal . . . . MBPI0712 . . 445

Viewing the Battle of Bunker Hill . . . . MBPI0849 . . 454

Viewing the Battle of Bunker's Hill . . . . MBPI0849 . . 454

Vignette for A Maid's Choice . . . . MBPI3065 . . 592

Vignette for A Maid's Choice . . . . MBPI3066 . . 592

Vignette for A Maid's Choice . . . . MBPI3067 . . 592

Vignette for A Maid's Choice . . . . MBPI3068 . . 592

Vignette for A Maid's Choice . . . . MBPI3069 . . 592

Vignette for A Maid's Choice . . . . MBPI3070 . . 592

Vignette for A Maid's Choice . . . . MBPI3071 . . 592

Vignette for A Maid's Choice . . . . MBPI3072 . . 592

Vignette for A Maid's Choice . . . . MBPI3073 . . 593

Vignette for A Maid's Choice . . . . MBPI3074 . . 593

Vignette for A Maid's Choice . . . . MBPI3075 . . 593

Vignette for A Maid's Choice . . . . MBPI3076 . . 593

Vignette for A Maid's Choice . . . . MBPI3077 . . 593

Vignette for A Maid's Choice . . . . MBPI3078 . . 593

Vignette for A Maid's Choice . . . . MBPI3079 . . 593

Vignette for A Maid's Choice . . . . MBPI3080 . . 593

Vignette for A Maid's Choice . . . . MBPI3081 . . 593

Vignette for A Maid's Choice . . . . MBPI3082 . . 593

Vignette for A Maid's Choice . . . . MBPI3083 . . 593

Vignette for A Maid's Choice . . . . MBPI3084 . . 593

Index–Titles and Alternate Titles of Pyle's Art

VIGNETTE FOR A MAID'S CHOICE

Vignette for A Maid's Choice	MBPI3085	593
Vignette for A Maid's Choice	MBPI3086	593
Vignette for A Maid's Choice	MBPI3087	593
Vignette for A Maid's Choice	MBPI3088	593
Vignette for A Maid's Choice	MBPI3089	594
Vignette for A Maid's Choice	MBPI3090	594
Vignette for A Maid's Choice	MBPI3091	594
Vignette for A Maid's Choice	MBPI3092	594
Vignette for A Maid's Choice	MBPI3093	594
Vignette for A Maid's Choice	MBPI3094	594
Vignette for A Maid's Choice	MBPI3095	594
Vignette for A Maid's Choice	MBPI3096	594
Vignette for A Maid's Choice	MBPI3097	594
Vignette for A Maid's Choice	MBPI3098	594
Vignette for A Maid's Choice	MBPI3099	594
Vignette for A Maid's Choice	MBPI3100	594
Vignette for A Puppet of Fate	MBPI0796	450
Vignette for A Puppet of Fate	MBPI0798	450
Vignette for A Puppet of Fate	MBPI0799	450
Vignette for A Puppet of Fate	MBPI0800	450
Vignette for A Puppet of Fate	MBPI0801	451
Vignette for A Puppet of Fate	MBPI0803	451
Vignette for A Puppet of Fate	MBPI0806	451
Vignette for A Soldier of Fortune	MBPI0592	437
Vignette for A Soldier of Fortune	MBPI0593	438
Vignette for A Soldier of Fortune	MBPI0595	438
Vignette for A Soldier of Fortune	MBPI0596	438
Vignette for A Soldier of Fortune	MBPI0598	438
Vignette for A Soldier of Fortune	MBPI0599	438
Vignette for A Soldier of Fortune	MBPI0600	438
Vignette for A Soldier of Fortune	MBPI0601	438
Vignette for A Soldier of Fortune	MBPI0603	438
Vignette for A Soldier of Fortune	MBPI0604	438
Vignette for A Soldier of Fortune	MBPI0605	438
Vignette for A Soldier of Fortune	MBPI0606	438
Vignette for A Wonder Book	MBPI3180	599
Vignette for Among the Sand Hills	MBPI0519	433
Vignette for Among the Sand Hills	MBPI0521	433
Vignette for Among the Sand Hills	MBPI0524	433
Vignette for Among the Sand Hills	MBPI0526	433
Vignette for Among the Sand Hills	MBPI0528	433
Vignette for Among the Sand Hills	MBPI0529	434
Vignette for Among the Sand Hills	MBPI0531	434
Vignette for Among the Sand Hills	MBPI0534	434
Vignette for Among the Sand Hills	MBPI0536	434
Vignette for Among the Sand Hills	MBPI0537	434
Vignette for Among the Sand Hills	MBPI0538	434
Vignette for Among the Sand Hills	MBPI0540	434
Vignette for Among the Sand Hills	MBPI0541	434
Vignette for Among the Sand Hills	MBPI0543	434
Vignette for Ill-Luck and the Fiddler	MBPI1586	500
Vignette for Ill-Luck and the Fiddler	MBPI1587	500
Vignette for Ill-Luck and the Fiddler	MBPI1588	500
Vignette for Ill-Luck and the Fiddler	MBPI1589	500

VIGNETTE FOR THE QUAKER LADY

Vignette for Ill-Luck and the Fiddler	MBPI1590	500
Vignette for Ill-Luck and the Fiddler	MBPI1591	500
Vignette for King Custom	MBPI0858	454
Vignette for newspaper head	PDPI0020	604
Vignette for Peter Rugg Ye Bostonian	MBPI1948	522
Vignette for Peter Rugg Ye Bostonian	MBPI1949	522
Vignette for Peter Rugg Ye Bostonian	MBPI1950	522
Vignette for Peter Rugg Ye Bostonian	MBPI1951	522
Vignette for Peter Rugg Ye Bostonian	MBPI1952	522
Vignette for Peter Rugg Ye Bostonian	MBPI1953	523
Vignette for Peter Rugg Ye Bostonian	MBPI1954	523
Vignette for Peter Rugg Ye Bostonian	MBPI1955	523
Vignette for Peter Rugg Ye Bostonian	MBPI1956	523
Vignette for Peter Rugg Ye Bostonian	MBPI1957	523
Vignette for Peter Rugg Ye Bostonian	MBPI1958	523
Vignette for Sailors and Landsmen, A Story of 1812	MBPI1272	480
Vignette for Sailors and Landsmen, A Story of 1812	MBPI1273	480
Vignette for Sailors and Landsmen, A Story of 1812	MBPI1274	480
Vignette for Sailors and Landsmen, A Story of 1812	MBPI1275	480
Vignette for Sailors and Landsmen, A Story of 1812	MBPI1276	480
Vignette for Sailors and Landsmen, A Story of 1812	MBPI1277	480
Vignette for Sailors and Landsmen, A Story of 1812	MBPI1278	480
Vignette for Sailors and Landsmen, A Story of 1812	MBPI1279	480
Vignette for Sailors and Landsmen, A Story of 1812	MBPI1280	480
Vignette for The Chase of the Tide	MBPI1755	510
Vignette for The Cocklane Ghost	MBPI0579	437
Vignette for The Cocklane Ghost	MBPI0580	437
Vignette for The Cocklane Ghost	MBPI0581	437
Vignette for The Cocklane Ghost	MBPI0582	437
Vignette for The Cocklane Ghost	MBPI0583	437
Vignette for The Cocklane Ghost	MBPI0584	437
Vignette for The Cocklane Ghost	MBPI0585	437
Vignette for The Cocklane Ghost	MBPI0586	437
Vignette for The Cocklane Ghost	MBPI0587	437
Vignette for The Cocklane Ghost	MBPI0588	437
Vignette for The Cocklane Ghost	MBPI0589	437
Vignette for The Quaker Lady	MBPI0453	429
Vignette for The Quaker Lady	MBPI0454	429
Vignette for The Quaker Lady	MBPI0455	429
Vignette for The Quaker Lady	MBPI0456	429
Vignette for The Quaker Lady	MBPI0457	429
Vignette for The Quaker Lady	MBPI0458	429
Vignette for The Quaker Lady	MBPI0459	429
Vignette for The Quaker Lady	MBPI0460	429
Vignette for The Quaker Lady	MBPI0461	429

Index–Titles and Alternate Titles of Pyle's Art

Vignette for The Quaker Lady . . . . MBPI0462 . . 429
Vignette for The Quaker Lady . . . . MBPI0463 . . 429
Vignette for The Quaker Lady . . . . MBPI0464 . . 429
Vignette for The Quaker Lady . . . . MBPI0465 . . 430
Vignette for The Quaker Lady . . . . MBPI0466 . . 430
Vignette for The Quaker Lady . . . . MBPI0467 . . 430
Vignette for The Quaker Lady . . . . MBPI0468 . . 430
Vignette for The Romance of an Ambrotype . . . MBPI0734 . . 446
Vignette for The Romance of an Ambrotype . . . MBPI0735 . . 446
Vignette for The Romance of an Ambrotype . . . MBPI0736 . . 446
Vignette for The Romance of an Ambrotype . . . MBPI0737 . . 447
Vignette for The Romance of an Ambrotype . . . MBPI0738 . . 447
Vignette for The Romance of an Ambrotype . . . MBPI0739 . . 447
Vignette for The Romance of an Ambrotype . . . MBPI0740 . . 447
Vignette for The Romance of an Ambrotype . . . MBPI0741 . . 447
Vignette for The Romance of an Ambrotype . . . MBPI0742 . . 447
Vignette for The Romance of an Ambrotype . . . MBPI0743 . . 447
Vignette for The Romance of an Ambrotype . . . MBPI0744 . . 447
Vignette for The Salem Wolf . . . . MBPI1078 . . 468
Vignette for The Salem Wolf . . . . MBPI1079 . . 468
Vignette for The Salem Wolf . . . . MBPI1082 . . 468
Vignette for The Salem Wolf . . . . MBPI1083 . . 468
Vignette for The Salem Wolf . . . . MBPI1085 . . 468
Vignette for The Soldiering of Beniah . . . . MBPI1816 . . 514
    Stidham
Vignette for The Soldiering of Beniah . . . . MBPI1817 . . 514
    Stidham
Vignette for The Soldiering of Beniah . . . . MBPI1818 . . 514
    Stidham
Vignette for The Soldiering of Beniah . . . . MBPI1819 . . 514
    Stidham
Vignette for The Soldiering of Beniah . . . . . . MBPI1820 . . 514
    Stidham
Vignette for The Soldiering of Beniah . . . . MBPI1821 . . 514
    Stidham
Vignette for The Soldiering of Beniah . . . . MBPI1822 . . 514
    Stidham
Vignette for The Soldiering of Beniah . . . . MBPI1823 . . 514
    Stidham
Vignette for The Sword of Hildebrand . . . . MBPI1371 . . 486
Vignette for The Sword of Hildebrand . . . . MBPI1372 . . 486
Vignette for The Sword of Hildebrand . . . . MBPI1373 . . 486
Vignette for The Sword of Hildebrand . . . . MBPI1374 . . 486
Vignette for The Sword of Hildebrand . . . . MBPI1375 . . 486
Vignette for Through Inland Waters . . . . MBPI0685 . . 443
Vignette for Through Inland Waters . . . . MBPI0686 . . 443
Vignette for Through Inland Waters . . . . MBPI0689 . . 444
Vignette for Through Inland Waters . . . . MBPI0690 . . 444
Vignette for Through Inland Waters . . . . MBPI0691 . . 444
Vignette for Through Inland Waters . . . . MBPI0692 . . 444
Vignette for Through Inland Waters . . . . MBPI0693 . . 444
Vignette for Through Inland Waters . . . . MBPI0694 . . 444
Vignette for Through Inland Waters . . . . MBPI0695 . . 444
Vignette for Through Inland Waters . . . . MBPI0696 . . 444

Vignette for Through Inland Waters . . . . MBPI0697 . . 444
Vignette for Through Inland Waters . . . . MBPI0698 . . 444
Vignette for Through Inland Waters . . . . MBPI0701 . . 444
Vignette for Through Inland Waters . . . . MBPI0702 . . 444
Vignette for Through Inland Waters . . . . MBPI0703 . . 444
Vignette for Through Inland Waters . . . . MBPI0704 . . 444
Vignette for Through Inland Waters . . . . MBPI0705 . . 445
Vignette for Through Inland Waters . . . . MBPI0707 . . 445
Vignette for Through Inland Waters . . . . MBPI0708 . . 445
Vignette for Through Inland Waters . . . . MBPI0709 . . 445
Vignette for Through Inland Waters . . . . MBPI0710 . . 445
Vignette for Through Inland Waters . . . . MBPI0711 . . 445
Vignette for Through Inland Waters . . . . MBPI0713 . . 445
Vignette for Through Inland Waters . . . . MBPI0714 . . 445
Vignette for Wisdom's Wages and Folly's . . . . . MBPI1593 . . 500
    Pay
Vignette for Wisdom's Wages and Folly's . . . . . MBPI1594 . . 500
    Pay
Vignette for Wisdom's Wages and Folly's . . . . . MBPI1595 . . 500
    Pay
Vignette for Wisdom's Wages and Folly's . . . . . MBPI1596 . . 500
    Pay
Vignette for Wisdom's Wages and Folly's . . . . . MBPI1597 . . 500
    Pay
Vignette for Wisdom's Wages and Folly's . . . . . MBPI1598 . . 500
    Pay
Vignette for Wisdom's Wages and Folly's . . . . . MBPI1599 . . 500
    Pay
Vignette for Ye True Story of Granny . . . . MBPI1235 . . 478
    Greene of Salem Town
Vignette, Sam Lawson's House . . . . MBPI0497 . . 432
Vignette, the Old Natick Church . . . . MBPI0496 . . 431
Vignette with illustrated initial C for . . . . MBPI1244 . . 478
    The Strange Adventures of Carl Spich
Vignette, woman on a houseboat . . . . PDPI0033 . . . 605
"Villon–The singer Fate fashioned to her . . . . . MBPI0915 . . 458
    liking"
The vines were dying . . . . MBPI1149 . . 472
A Virginia Plantation Wharf . . . . MBPI0672 . . 442
The Virginians . . . . MBPI1125 . . 471
Vision . . . . MBPI3038 . . 590
"The Vision of Echard" . . . . MBPI2794 . . 575
Visit of Pilgrims to the Shore . . . . MBPI0293 . . 419
The visit to André . . . . MBPI0039 . . 403
Vitia and the Governor . . . . MBPI1063 . . 467
Vivien bewitches Merlin . . . . MBPI2414 . . 551
The Voiceless with initial W . . . . MBPI3020 . . 589
"The Waif" . . . . MBPI1771 . . 511
Wail of the Wandering Dead . . . . MBPI3123 . . 596
Waiting for his Share . . . . MBPI1322 . . 483
Walking the plank . . . . MBPI0353 . . 423
War-Ships of Lord Nelson's Time, The . . . . MBPI0043 . . 403
    Battle of Copenhagen

Index–Titles and Alternate Titles of Pyle's Art

"War-Ships of Lord Nelson's Time The Battle of..."

"War-Ships of Lord Nelson's Time The .... MBPI0043 . . 403
Battle of Copenhagen"

Warning Settlers of the Approach of .... MBPI0326 . . 421
Indians

Was this...King Henry's self? Margery .... MBPI2069 . . 530
dropped to her knee

Washington and Clinton at the Festivities ..... MBPI0308 . . 420
Celebrating the Evacuation of New York

Washington and His Generals at Newburg ..... MBPI0304 . . 419

Washington and his Generals in .... MBPI0304 . . 419
Consultation March 15, 1783

Washington and Mary Philipse .... MBPI0679 . . 443

Washington and Nellie Custis .... MBPI0726 . . 446

Washington and Nelly Custis .... MBPI0726 . . 446

Washington and Nelly Custis on Her .... MBPI0726 . . 446
Wedding Day

Washington and Rochambeau before the .... MBPI0851 . . 454
trenches at Yorktown

Washington and Rochambeau in the Trenches .. MBPI0851 . . 454
at Yorktown

Washington and Steuben at Valley Forge ...... MBPI0717 . . 445

Washington bringing his Mother into the .... MBPI0723 . . 446
Ballroom, Fredericksburg

Washington Firing the First Gun at the ...... MBPI2001 . . 526
Siege of Yorktown

Washington In His Garden at Mount Vernon ... MBPI0721 . . 446

Washington in the Garden at Mount Vernon .. MBPI0721 . . 446

Washington met by his neighbors on his .... MBPI0359 . . 423
way to the Inauguration

Washington Receiving the Announcement of ... MBPI0728 . . 446
His Election to the First Presidency of the United States

Washington Receiving the Announcement of ... MBPI0728 . . 446
His Election to the First Presidency

Washington refuses the Colt .... MBPI2080 . . 530

Washington refusing a Dictatorship .... MBPI0303 . . 419

Washington Taking Leave of His Officers, ... MBPI1241 . . 478
Dec. 4, 1783

Washington, the Young Surveyor .... MBPI2792 . . 575

Washington Told of His Election to .... MBPI0728 . . 446
Presidency

Washington's Birth-Day, with title and .... MBPI1209 . . 476
verses inserted

Washington's Head-Quarters, Valley Forge ..... MBPI0243 . . 416

Washington's Private Office at Valley .... MBPI0242 . . 416
Forge

Washington's Private Papers, 1777 .... MBPI0242 . . 416

Washington's Retreat .... MBPI1994 . . 525

Washington's Retreat Across New Jersey .... MBPI1994 . . 525

Washington's Retreat from Great Meadows .... MBPI0676 . . 443

Washington's Retreat from Great Meadows .... MBPI0676 . . 443
1754

"Washington's Retreat Through the .... MBPI1994 . . 525
Jerseys"

Watching the Battle from the Steeple .... MBPI2890 . . 581

"Where they sit in long rows with baskets..."

Watching the Battle of Bunker Hill .... MBPI0849 . . 454

Watching the Battle of Bunker Hill for .... MBPI0849 . . 454
Our Guests Unknown

Watching the Fight at Bunker Hill .... MBPI0849 . . 454

Wayne Homestead .... MBOI0009 . . 612

We Are Well-Nigh Breathless All .... MBPI2865 . . 580

"We came to know each other" .... MBPI2928 . . 583

"We can see each massive column" .... MBPI2916 . . 583

"We climbed the creaking stair" .... MBPI2900 . . 582

"We escaped in the boat" .... MBPI0635 . . 440

"We looked, poor timid creatures" .... MBPI2919 . . 583

"We men-folk thought the music as sweet ... MBPI1915 . . 520
as that of the Cherubim"

We started to run back to the raft for .... MBPI2010 . . 526
our lives

The Weary Reapers Beneath the Moon Hear .. MBPI2708 . . 570
Her Singing

Weather-Breeder .... MBPI3056 . . 591

The Wedding .... MBPI0663 . . 442

"Well, dat nigger cheat de burer–he .... MBPI0173 . . 411
s-t-o-l-e, Massa!"

"Went Plodding Along to see his sick .... MBPI0759 . . 448
people"

Went Plodding Out to See His People Who .... MBPI0759 . . 448
Were Sick

"Went whirling over rocks and waterfalls" ..... MBPI1669 . . 505

"The werewolf...skulked for a moment in the MBPI1740 . . 509
shadow of the yews, and...Yseult plucked old Siegfried's
spear from her girdle"

The Werewolf .... MBPI1740 . . 509

The Wharf of Dreams .... MBPI3146 . . 597

"What a racket they made at the gate" .... MBPI1318 . . 483

"What are my lord's commands?" .... MBPI1662 . . 504

"What are you doing here, Father Goat?" ...... MBPI1525 . . 496

"What do you want, Master?" .... MBPI1506 . . 495

What happened to the Master .... MBPI1476 . . 493

What happened to the Master of Black Arts .... MBPI1476 . . 493
after all his tricks

What Shall It Profit? .... MBPI3061 . . 592

What She Sees in the Mirror .... MBPI2711 . . 570

What We All Think with initial T .... MBPI2992 . . 587

"'What will you have?' said the Genie" .... MBPI1721 . . 508

When All the World Was Young .... MBPI1066 . . 467

When the World Was Young .... MBPI1066 . . 467

"When thou strikest that lower cut at the ...... MBPI1672 . . 505
legs, recover thyself quickly"

"When Thou strikest that lower cut at the ..... MBPI1672 . . 505
legs, recover thyself more quickly."

When thou strikest that lower cut at the .... MBPI1672 . . 505
legs, recover thyself quickly

"Where did you come from, little boy?" ...... MBPI2370 . . 549
she said

"Where they sit in long rows with baskets .... MBPI0381 . . 424
of oranges"

Index–Titles and Alternate Titles of Pyle's Art

Which shall be Captain? . . . . MBPI1114 . . 470

"Which shall it be first–Sausages or . . . . MBPI1526 . . 496
    Pudding?"

"While his eyes still glowed fiery wrath, ... MBPI1924 . . 521
    the trembling lips became piteous in their inability to form
    words"

"While I lay there with my horse upon me, . . . MBPI2298 . . 544
    Baron Frederick ran me down with his lance"

While she stood looking the cow died . . . . MBPI1148 . . 472

While yet her cheek was bright with . . . . MBPI2776 . . 574
    summer bloom

The Whirlwind Road . . . . MBPI3126 . . 596

The White Bird recognizes the Prince . . . . MBPI1563 . . 498

The White Champion meets two Knights at . . MBPI1874 . . 518
    the Mill

Whither? . . . . MBPI0099 . . 407

Whitman starting for Washington . . . . MBPI2763 . . 573

"Who are we that Heaven should make of . . . MBPI1071 . . 467
    the old sea a fowling net?"

"'Who are you? and off with your hat!' I . . . . . . MBPI1926 . . 521
    said to the man, sharply"

"Who are you?" thundered the giant . . . . MBPI3183 . . 599

"Who is the lucky miss, my little . . . . MBPI0967 . . 461
    villain?"

"Who stuffed that white owl?" . . . . MBPI0197 . . 413

The whole world goes afield today . . . . MBPI1092 . . 469

"Why don't you end it?" . . . . MBPI3112 . . 595

"Why don't you show him?" . . . . MBPI2027 . . 527

"Why Seek Ye the Living Among the Dead?" . . . MBPI0101 . . 407

"Why, what is this? Whence came this?" . . . . . . MBPI0120 . . 408

The Wicket of Paradise . . . . MBPI0054 . . 404

"The widow dropped her eyes" . . . . MBPI0482 . . 431

The Widow Spurlock . . . . MBPI0472 . . 430

"Will you forgive my having followed . . . . MBPI0004 . . 401
    you?"

William Cobbett's School . . . . MBPI0261 . . 417

William Kidd, Pirate . . . . MBPI0885 . . 456

William Penn and his Commissioners in the . . MBPI0286 . . 418
    cabin of the "Welcome"

"William Penn the Younger" . . . . MBPI2070 . . 530

"William Penn's Second Visit to his . . . . MBPI1230 . . 477
    Colony 1699"

Wings . . . . PDPI0094 . . . 609

The Winning of a Sword and a Queen . . . . MBPI1865 . . 517

"A wise man stopped to enquire the cause . . . MBPI1624 . . 502
    of his sorrow"

A "Witch" . . . . MBPI0220 . . 414

The witch and ye woman of honey & meal . . . . . MBPI1445 . . 491

The Witch & the woman of honey & barley . . . MBPI1445 . . 491
    meal

Witchcraft . . . . MBPI1098 . . 469

Witchcraft, 1692 . . . . MBPI0322 . . 421

Witchcraft, 1884 . . . . MBPI0323 . . 421

With a cry, Shallum flung up his arms and . . . . MBPI0936 . . 459
    jumped

"With a plate of mince-pie in his lap, ... MBPI1322 . . 483
    and Bush, the big house-dog, sitting beside him"

With great amity the two walked off . . . . MBPI0979 . . 462
    together

"With their heads close together" . . . . MBPI0474 . . 430

"The withered hags were free" . . . . MBPI2854 . . 579

Within sound of the shouting waters . . . . MBPI1914 . . 520

A wolf had not been seen at Salem for . . . . . . MBPI1074 . . 468
    thirty years

Woman at a Spinning Wheel . . . . PDPI0058 . . . 607

Woman carrying urn . . . . PDPI0063 . . . 607

"The woman turned fiercely upon the . . . . MBPI0338 . . 422
    Chieftain"

Women at the Polls in New Jersey in the . . . . . MBPI1192 . . 475
    Good Old Times

The Wood Carver . . . . MBPI0655 . . 441

A Wood Nymph . . . . MBPI1008 . . 463

A Woodland Fountain . . . . MBPI1007 . . 463

The Woodland Pool . . . . MBPI1007 . . 463

"The Word of the Lord came to me, saying . . . MBPI0279 . . 418
    'Cry, Woe to the bloody City of Litchfield!'"

A Wounded Enemy . . . . MBPI1931 . . 521

A Wreck from the Sea . . . . MBPI0667 . . 442

"Wreck in the Offing!" . . . . MBPI1178 . . 474

The Wreck . . . . MBPI0532 . . 434

The Wreck . . . . MBPI0667 . . 442

Writing on some loose sheets of paper . . . . . . MBPI1095 . . 469
    that he held on his knee

Ye Antient Gunne . . . . MBPI0226 . . 415

Ye End for Ye True Story of Granny Greene . . . MBPI1240 . . 478
    of Salem Town

Ye King . . . . MBPI1434 . . 490

Ye Pirate Bold . . . . MBPI0001 . . 401

Ye Pirate Bold, as imagined by a Quaker . . . . . PDPI0018 . . . 604
    Gentleman

Ye Prince & Ye Swan Maiden . . . . MBPI1444 . . 491

Ye Queen of Hearts . . . . PDPI0014 . . . 604

Ye Romantic Adventures of Three Tailors, ... MBPI1329 . . 484
    with title, illustrations and verse

Ye sad story concerning one innocent . . . . MBPI1378 . . 487
    little Lamb and four wicked Wolves, with title, illustrations
    and verse

Ye School for Men . . . . MBPI1356 . . 485

Ye Song of Ye Foolish Old Woman, with . . . . . . MBPI1365 . . 486
    title, illustrations and verse

Ye Song of Ye Gossips, with title, ... MBPI1363 . . 486
    illustrations and verse

Ye Song of Ye Rajah & Ye Fly, with title, ... MBPI1366 . . 486
    illustrations and verse

Ye Story of a Blue China Plate, with . . . . MBPI1377 . . 487
    title, illustrations and verse

Ye Two Wishes, with title, illustrations . . . . MBPI1367 . . 486
    and verse

Ye Virginia Gentleman of the Olden Time . . . . . MBPI0675 . . 443

Yorktown . . . . MBPI0851 . . 454

"You can hear the black cat's purr" . . . . MBPI2858 . . 579

" 'You Design Murder?' Richard Asked" . . . . MBPI1009 . . 464

"You next!" . . . . MBPI0083 . . 406

"You're a good old–fellow–come, let us . . . . . . MBPI2850 . . 579
    go"

The Young Baron leaves his Home . . . . MBPI1352 . . 485

Young De Lesken . . . . MBPI2057 . . 529

The Young Emperor's Entrance to the . . . . MBPI2073 . . 530
    Circus Maximus

"The young fellow lounged in a rattan . . . . . . MBPI0107 . . 407
    chair"

Young Flowering Trees . . . . MBPI3236 . . 603

The young King bringeth ye cup of water . . . . . . MBPI1552 . . 497
    of life to the beautiful Queen

The Young King caresses ye white dove . . . . MBPI1558 . . 498

The Young King goeth down into the pit . . . . MBPI1556 . . 498
    and bringeth up ye maiden

The young King looks upon ye beautiful . . . . MBPI1550 . . 497
    picture which the Stranger showeth him.

The young Knight of the Lea overcomes the . . MBPI2122 . . 533
    Knight of Lancaster

"The young man fell upon his knees" . . . . MBPI1711 . . 507

"The young man prostrated himself in the . . . MBPI1636 . . 503
    dust"

Young Men coming to Call . . . . MBPI0735 . . 446

Young Richard Partington cometh to seek . . . MBPI2132 . . 534
    Merry Robin Hood

Young Robin goes to the Shooting Match . . . . . MBPI2095 . . 531

The Young Smith forges the best Life has . . . . . . MBPI1548 . . 497
    to give

Young William Penn meets the disapproval . . MBPI2070 . . 530
    of his Father, the Admiral

Young Woman in Elizabethan Dress . . . . PDPI0061 . . . 607

Young woman standing under tree . . . . PDPI0034 . . . 605

"The youthful sire" . . . . MBPI2871 . . 580

"Zadok and his master" . . . . MBPI1701 . . 507

Zekle and Huldy . . . . MBPI3205 . . 601

Index–Titles of Pyle's Art In Chronological Sequence

List includes all known published and unpublished completed works of art. Titles are listed chronologically by year.

1871

Vignette for newspaper head .... PDPI0020 . .1871
Medieval Scene .... PDPI0049 . .1875
"But the Proudest and Grandest of All the .... PDPI0104 . .1875
    Flock Was Gobble, Our Gorgeous Turkey-Cock."
"'Ah me!' said the Parson, 'I wish I were .... MBPI2019 . .1876
    young'"
"Alas! he had turned to a terrible boy" .... MBPI2020 . .1876
The Sly Fox .... PDPI0051 . .1876
St. Valentine's Day in Merrie Old England ...... MBPI1174 . .1877
Queen of the May–Unpropitious Skies .... MBPI1175 . .1877
"One of Those City Fellows"–A Hundred ...... MBPI1176 . .1877
    Years Ago
The Gosling states his opinion of the .... MBPI1776 . .1877
    Cock
The Gosling is punished .... MBPI1777 . .1877
The Fox and the Tablet .... MBPI1778 . .1877
The Swineherd who knew curious things ..... MBPI1779 . .1877
Gottenlieb's music works a charm .... MBPI1780 . .1877
Pictorial Puzzle .... MBPI1781 . .1877
The King and his Prime Minister .... MBPI1782 . .1877
Fritz guides the Baron .... MBPI1783 . .1877
"I have brought you the Baron's head" .... MBPI1784 . .1877
The Princess and her Pigs .... MBPI1785 . .1877
"Poor Piggy led the way" .... MBPI1786 . .1877
The Royal Bodyguard .... MBPI1787 . .1877
Tailpiece for Drummer Fritz and His .... MBPI1788 . .1877
    Exploits
Peter asks the fatal question .... MBPI2021 . .1877
Grief and indignation .... MBPI2022 . .1877
"I'll do it!" .... MBPI2023 . .1877
"Do you see this knife?" .... MBPI2024 . .1877
The Notary beckons .... MBPI2025 . .1877
"She's yours" .... MBPI2026 . .1877
"Why don't you show him?" .... MBPI2027 . .1877
The reconciliation .... MBPI2028 . .1877
The Sailor from Constantinople .... MBPI2029 . .1877
"Horror! Devastation! Agony!" .... MBPI2030 . .1877
The Sailor is saved .... MBPI2031 . .1877
The End .... MBPI2032 . .1877
Catching a pony .... MBPI2033 . .1877
A son of the soil .... MBPI2034 . .1877
The lady of the house .... MBPI2035 . .1877
Uncle Ken .... MBPI2036 . .1877
Old Dan Tucker .... MBPI2037 . .1877
The majesty of the law .... MBPI2038 . .1877
Crossing to Assateague .... MBPI2039 . .1877
Uncle Benny .... MBPI2040 . .1877
The pony pen .... MBPI2041 . .1877
J. A. M. Whealton .... MBPI2042 . .1877
Family Cares .... MBPI2043 . .1877
Bliss .... MBPI2044 . .1877
In the Park .... MBPI2045 . .1877
A Quotation from "King Lear" .... MBPI2046 . .1877
The Frightful Accident .... PDPI0071 . .1877

1878

Carnival, Philadelphia, 1778 .... MBPI0167 . .1878
"The little pink finger and the huge .... MBPI0168 . .1878
    black index came to a full stop under this commandment"
At Daddy Bayne's .... MBPI0169 . .1878
"She walked on after saying this, musing" ..... MBPI0170 . .1878
"She went by without looking at him" .... MBPI0171 . .1878
Fermina opens the casket .... MBPI0172 . .1878
"Well, dat nigger cheat de burer–he .... MBPI0173 . .1878
    s-t-o-l-e, Massa!"
"Then came the tug of war" .... MBPI0174 . .1878
Entangled .... MBPI1177 . .1878
"Wreck in the Offing!" .... MBPI1178 . .1878
Lost in the Snow .... MBPI1179 . .1878
A Matrimonial Difficulty–Legal .... MBPI1180 . .1878
    Intervention
An Interrupted Performance .... MBPI1191 . .1878
Kitty and Turkish Merchant .... MBPI1789 . .1878
"A very little old man seated in a very .... MBPI1790 . .1878
    large chair"
"He examined with astonishment and .... MBPI1791 . .1878
    delight"
"A page was appointed to escort it" .... MBPI1792 . .1878
"The king sat upon a chair of state, with ...... MBPI1793 . .1878
    a learned judge at each side"
An Old-time May-Day in "Merrie England" ..... MBPI1794 . .1878
Illustration for How Willy-Wolly Went .... MBPI1795 . .1878
    A-Fishing
Illustration for How Willy-Wolly Went .... MBPI1796 . .1878
    A-Fishing
Illustration for How Willy-Wolly Went .... MBPI1797 . .1878
    A-Fishing
The Fox, the Monkey, and the Pig .... MBPI1798 . .1878
Spearing Eels in Eel Bay .... MBPI2047 . .1878
French Canadian .... MBPI2048 . .1878
Ruins of Old Fort, Carleton's Island .... MBPI2049 . .1878
Catching Muskallonge .... MBPI2050 . .1878
Camping Out .... MBPI2051 . .1878
Billy Patterson .... MBPI2052 . .1878
Joseph Gladd .... MBPI2053 . .1878
McCue .... MBPI2054 . .1878
Cooking a Camp Dinner .... MBPI2055 . .1878
George Campbell .... MBPI2056 . .1878
Young De Lesken .... MBPI2057 . .1878
Mistress Betty .... MBPI2058 . .1878
Dietrich examines the disaster from a .... MBPI2059 . .1878
    distance
"He kissed the little hand" .... MBPI2060 . .1878
Kobus and his pupil .... MBPI2061 . .1878
Jan's courtship .... MBPI2062 . .1878
De Lesken entertaining .... MBPI2063 . .1878
Kobus brings news of Mynheer Jan .... MBPI2064 . .1878
Jan returns .... MBPI2065 . .1878
Tailpiece for The Story of Lesken .... MBPI2066 . .1878
Something Fresh .... PDPI0038 . .1878

Index–Titles of Pyle's Art In Chronological Sequence

1879

Dinner-bell at an Eastville Tavern .... MBPI0175 ..1879
The Country Clerk, Eastville .... MBPI0176 ..1879
Old records .... MBPI0177 ..1879
Aunt Saber .... MBPI0178 ..1879
Peace and War .... MBPI0179 ..1879
Oyster shuckers .... MBPI0180 ..1879
Dredging for oysters .... MBPI0181 ..1879
Strawberry picking .... MBPI0182 ..1879
Cooking shanty .... MBPI0183 ..1879
Aunt Sally .... MBPI0184 ..1879
Fishing shanty .... MBPI0185 ..1879
George, the cook .... MBPI0186 ..1879
Interior of fishing station .... MBPI0187 ..1879
In the Northern Market–"Peaches, one ...... MBPI0188 ..1879
   cent"
A farm "Pluck" .... MBPI0189 ..1879
Group of nomadic "Plucks" .... MBPI0190 ..1879
The peeling-room .... MBPI0191 ..1879
Raising cypress logs in the Dismal Swamp .... MBPI0192 ..1879
Making shingles .... MBPI0193 ..1879
The Phantom Horseman .... MBPI0194 ..1879
The Captain of the Yacht "Delaware" .... MBPI0195 ..1879
A bit of sentiment .... MBPI0196 ..1879
"Who stuffed that white owl?" .... MBPI0197 ..1879
"I'm an owl; you're another" .... MBPI0198 ..1879
"As she spoke, she took his hand, and .... MBPI0199 ..1879
   then paused one moment"
"Laying the old violin tenderly beneath ...... MBPI0200 ..1879
   his chin"
Peter plays the fiddle for the Tavern .... MBPI0201 ..1879
   Folk
Tacy Kelp .... MBPI0202 ..1879
Representing the manner of Peter's .... MBPI0203 ..1879
   Courtship
Jonathan Quidd .... MBPI0204 ..1879
"The little boys cheered vigorously as he ..... MBPI0205 ..1879
   pushed off"
"Here it turned, and said 'Knowest thou ...... MBPI0206 ..1879
   who I am?'"
Tailpiece for The Last Revel in Printz .... MBPI0207 ..1879
   Hall
A complimentary Address to Old .... MBPI0208 ..1879
   Hickory–Interior of Ben Bean's ("Barton") House
Arrival of the Coach at an Old Stage .... MBPI0209 ..1879
   Station
An Old Government Toll-Gate, with .... MBPI0210 ..1879
   Westward-Bound Express
An Old Stager .... MBPI0211 ..1879
Ruins of Old Post Tavern .... MBPI0212 ..1879
Old National Pike Bridge .... MBPI0213 ..1879
Leander .... MBPI0214 ..1879
Uncle Sam .... MBPI0215 ..1879
Preparing for Highwaymen .... MBPI0216 ..1879
An Old Smithy .... MBPI0217 ..1879
Old Way-Side Tavern .... MBPI0218 ..1879
An Old Mile-Stone .... MBPI0219 ..1879
Old Hempstead House .... MBPI0220 ..1879
A Revolutionary Recruiting .... MBPI0221 ..1879
   Office–Privateersmen in New London

1880

A Garden Party given to General .... MBPI0222 ..1879
   Washington
Portrait Gallery in Shaw Mansion .... MBPI0223 ..1879
An Old Time Cup of Coffee .... MBPI0224 ..1879
Patty Hempstead in her Gran'ther's .... MBPI0225 ..1879
   waistcoat
Ye Antient Gunne .... MBPI0226 ..1879
Old tiled Fire Place, Winthrop House .... MBPI0227 ..1879
Mather Byles preaching to Quakers .... MBPI0228 ..1879
Captain Kidd's gift to Mercy Redmond .... MBPI0229 ..1879
The Song of Captain Kidd .... MBPI0230 ..1879
The Robin's Vesper, with title and poem ..... MBPI1181 ..1879
   inserted
A Love Affair of the Olden .... MBPI1182 ..1879
   Time–Consulting the Wise Woman
The Milkmaid's Song, with title and poem .... MBPI1183 ..1879
   inserted
The Dance of the Veterans .... MBPI1184 ..1879
"Breaking the News" .... MBPI1185 ..1879
"As good as new" .... MBPI1799 ..1879
Tailpiece for The Origin of the .... MBPI1800 ..1879
   Jumping-Jack
The Gourd and the Oak .... MBPI1801 ..1879
Bluetree declines Lord Diddledaddle's .... MBPI1803 ..1879
   offer
A Bowl of Milk for Robin Goodfellow .... MBPI1804 ..1879
A Great Black Bear came out of the Woods .... MBPI1805 ..1879
Gretelein and the Elf King .... MBPI1806 ..1879
"A Person of Consequence, carefully fed ...... MBPI1808 ..1879
   and attended to"
Illustration for McGuffey's Fifth .... MBPI2660 ..1879
   Eclectic Reader
Illustration for McGuffey's Fifth .... MBPI2661 ..1879
   Eclectic Reader
The Quack .... MBPI2662 ..1879
The Home-made Press .... MBPI3242 ..1879
The Tiger .... PDPI0001 ..1879
Woman at a Spinning Wheel .... PDPI0058 ..1879
Old Fire-Place, Aunt Saber's Kitchen .... PDPI0097 ..1879
Night Haul of The Seine .... PDPI0099 ..1879
The Old Chimney-Corner .... MBPI0231 ..1880
The Botanist .... MBPI0232 ..1880
The Old Bartram Homestead .... MBPI0233 ..1880
Old Corner Cupboard .... MBPI0234 ..1880
Old Inscription .... MBPI0235 ..1880
The Christ Thorn .... MBPI0236 ..1880
The Garden Path .... MBPI0237 ..1880
Departure for New York .... MBPI0238 ..1880
Along the Chester Valley .... MBPI0240 ..1880
Old Valley Forge Bridge .... MBPI0241 ..1880
Washington's Private Papers, 1777 .... MBPI0242 ..1880
Washington's Head-Quarters, Valley Forge ..... MBPI0243 ..1880
General Wayne's Grave .... MBPI0244 ..1880
Old St. David's Church .... MBPI0245 ..1880
Drawing-Room, Wayne Homestead .... MBPI0246 ..1880
Paoli Monument .... MBPI0247 ..1880
Melissy .... MBPI0248 ..1880
John Dubois's drive to Newburgh .... MBPI0249 ..1880

Index–Titles of Pyle's Art In Chronological Sequence

1880

Sunday in Old Catskill . . . . MBPI0250 . .1880
Dinner at Cornelius Dubois's . . . . MBPI0251 . .1880
"Perhaps she sat there while she stoned . . . . . . MBPI0252 . .1880
    her raisins"
"It is all a mistake, my friend, a . . . . MBPI0253 . .1880
    grievous mistake"
Hale receiving instructions from . . . . MBPI0254 . .1880
    Washington
"I only regret that I have but one life . . . . MBPI0255 . .1880
    to lose for my country"
"I saw her face white even in all that . . . . MBPI0256 . .1880
    immense ruddy glare"
Going to Church . . . . MBPI0258 . .1880
The Umbrella–A Curious Present . . . . MBPI0260 . .1880
The Outcast's Return . . . . MBPI1186 . .1880
The Song of the Whip-poor-Will, with . . . . MBPI1187 . .1880
    title and poem inserted
Illustrated initial E for The Song of The . . . . . . MBPI1188 . .1880
    Whip-poor-Will
Illustrated initial B for The Song of The . . . . . . MBPI1189 . .1880
    Whip-poor-Will
The First Public Reading of the . . . . MBPI1190 . .1880
    Declaration of Independence
Women at the Polls in New Jersey in the . . . . . MBPI1192 . .1880
    Good Old Times
Christmas Morning in Old New York . . . . MBPI1193 . .1880
Miss Nancy takes leave of the officers . . . . MBPI1304 . .1880
Early settlers going to meeting . . . . MBPI1305 . .1880
Isaac Bradley carrying Joseph into the . . . . MBPI1306 . .1880
    settlement
The escape of Hannah Dustin . . . . MBPI1307 . .1880
"Lieutenant Wyman, creeping up, put a . . . . MBPI1308 . .1880
    bullet through him"
"Crack! Crack! went the guns of the . . . . MBPI1309 . .1880
    Indians"
Cutting off a queue to bind a wound . . . . MBPI1310 . .1880
Franklin on his way to France . . . . MBPI1311 . .1880
Battle between the "Bon Homme Richard" . . . . MBPI1312 . .1880
    and the "Serapis"
Decatur and his men boarding the gun-boat . . MBPI1313 . .1880
A Christmas Carol, with title, ... MBPI1314 . .1880
    illustrations, and verse
Bugler at Fort Macon . . . . PDPI0032 . .1880
A Very Merry Christmas In The "Good Old . . . . . PDPI0039 . .1880
    Times"
Illustrated initial A for A Very Merry . . . . PDPI0040 . .1880
    Christmas in The "Good Old Times"
"The Rejection" . . . . MBPI0127 . .1881
Old Swedes Church, Wilmington . . . . MBPI0257 . .1881
At Evening . . . . MBPI0259 . .1881
William Cobbett's School . . . . MBPI0261 . .1881
The Destruction of the Sign . . . . MBPI0262 . .1881
The British in Wilmington . . . . MBPI0263 . .1881
"I never had wood that I liked half so . . . . MBPI0264 . .1881
    well–do see who has nice crooked fuel to sell"
New-Year's Hymn to St. Nicholas . . . . MBPI0265 . .1881
Mynheer's Morning Horn . . . . MBPI0266 . .1881
"He stops at the Sign of the Weathervane" . . . . MBPI0267 . .1881

1881

"Then he tells his news, in the ruddy . . . . MBPI0268 . .1881
    glow"
A Mountain Farm-House . . . . MBPI0269 . .1881
The Lowland Brook . . . . MBPI0270 . .1881
An Autumn Evening . . . . MBPI0271 . .1881
The Mountain Orchard . . . . MBPI0272 . .1881
The Corn Fields on the Hill-Side . . . . MBPI0273 . .1881
New Year's Day Seventy Years Ago–The Last . . MBPI1194 . .1881
    Evening Caller
St. Valentine's Day in the Morning . . . . MBPI1195 . .1881
Politics in the Olden Times–General . . . . MBPI1196 . .1881
    Jackson, President-elect, on his way to Washington
Shad-Fishing on the Lower Delaware at . . . . . . MBPI1197 . .1881
    Night–The Last Haul Before Dawn
The Surrender of Cornwallis . . . . MBPI1198 . .1881
"He was doubtless a tramp" . . . . MBPI1199 . .1881
"Suppose you let me take care of this . . . . MBPI1200 . .1881
    young lady in future?"
"'Thee hasn't killed him?' timidly . . . . MBPI1201 . .1881
    inquired the girl"
The Christmas Tree, title inserted . . . . MBPI1202 . .1881
"There's something in there" . . . . MBPI1315 . .1881
Paul Revere at Lexington . . . . MBPI1316 . .1881
"And blew as he'd not blown since he was . . . . MBPI1317 . .1881
    born"
"What a racket they made at the gate" . . . . MBPI1318 . .1881
"It seemed to lie sound asleep, with a . . . . MBPI1319 . .1881
    snow blanket all over its roof"
"I'm Bijah" . . . . MBPI1320 . .1881
"Do you live with Santa Claus in his own . . . . . MBPI1321 . .1881
    house?"
"With a plate of mince-pie in his lap, ... MBPI1322 . .1881
    and Bush, the big house-dog, sitting beside him"
"Grandfather came in with a back-load of . . . . MBPI1323 . .1881
    sleds"
"He crawled forward, and looked down . . . . . . MBPI1324 . .1881
    through the scuttle hole"
"Edmund Burton, you are a genius!" . . . . MBPI1809 . .1881
The Boys consult Jack-in-the-Box . . . . MBPI1810 . .1881
Jupiter and the Philosopher . . . . MBPI1811 . .1881
"One of the policemen produced a . . . . MBPI1812 . .1881
    bull's-eye lantern"
"The clown counted the money" . . . . MBPI1813 . .1881
Front cover design for Yankee Doodle . . . . MBPI2663 . .1881
Frontispiece for Yankee Doodle . . . . MBPI2664 . .1881
Title page illustration for Yankee Doodle . . . . . MBPI2665 . .1881
Father and I went down to camp... . . . . MBPI2666 . .1881
There was Captain Washington... . . . . MBPI2667 . .1881
And then the feathers in his hat... . . . . MBPI2668 . .1881
Illustration for Yankee Doodle . . . . MBPI2669 . .1881
My Jemima. . . . . MBPI2670 . .1881
And then they had a swampin gun... . . . . MBPI2671 . .1881
And every time they fired it off... . . . . MBPI2672 . .1881
Illustration for Yankee Doodle . . . . MBPI2673 . .1881
It made a noise like father's gun... . . . . MBPI2674 . .1881
I went as near to it myself... . . . . MBPI2675 . .1881
Illustration for Yankee Doodle . . . . MBPI2676 . .1881
Cousin Simon grew so bold... . . . . MBPI2677 . .1881

Index–Titles of Pyle's Art In Chronological Sequence

1881

It scared me so I shrinked off... . . . . MBPI2678 . .1881

And there I see a pumpkin shell... . . . . MBPI2679 . .1881

Illustration for Yankee Doodle . . . . MBPI2680 . .1881

And every time they touched it off... . . . . MBPI2681 . .1881

And there I see a little keg... . . . . MBPI2682 . .1881

And then they'd fife away like fun... . . . . MBPI2683 . .1881

And some had ribbons red as blood... . . . . MBPI2684 . .1881

Illustration for Yankee Doodle . . . . MBPI2685 . .1881

The troopers, too, would gallop up... . . . . MBPI2686 . .1881

Old Uncle Sam come then to change... . . . . . . MBPI2687 . .1881

Illustration for Yankee Doodle . . . . MBPI2688 . .1881

For 'lasses cake, to carry home... . . . . MBPI2689 . .1881

I see another snarl of men... . . . . MBPI2690 . .1881

It scared me so, I hooked it off... . . . . MBPI2691 . .1881

Nor turned about till I got home... . . . . MBPI2692 . .1881

Illustration for Yankee Doodle . . . . MBPI2693 . .1881

Back cover design for Yankee Doodle . . . . MBPI2694 . .1881

Decorative illustrations for The Lady of . . . . MBPI2695 . .1881
    Shalott

Decorative illustrations for The Lady of . . . . MBPI2696 . .1881
    Shalott

Title page decoration for The Lady of . . . . MBPI2697 . .1881
    Shalott

Decorative illustration for The Lady of . . . . MBPI2698 . .1881
    Shalott

Part I for The Lady of Shalott . . . . MBPI2699 . .1881

A Description of the Castle . . . . MBPI2700 . .1881

The people passing the Island . . . . MBPI2701 . .1881

The Fairy Lady of Shalott in the Space of . . . . . MBPI2702 . .1881
    Flowers

A Description of the Same . . . . MBPI2703 . .1881

The Boats Passing Along the River . . . . MBPI2704 . .1881

Illustration for The Lady of Shalott . . . . MBPI2705 . .1881

Decorative illustrations for The Lady of . . . . MBPI2706 . .1881
    Shalott

How the Reapers Hear Her Singing . . . . MBPI2707 . .1881

The Weary Reapers Beneath the Moon Hear . . MBPI2708 . .1881
    Her Singing

Part II for The Lady of Shalott . . . . MBPI2709 . .1881

How the Lady Weaveth Day by Day . . . . MBPI2710 . .1881

What She Sees in the Mirror . . . . MBPI2711 . .1881

Still the Poem Speaketh of the Sights . . . . MBPI2712 . .1881
    Within the Mirror

All These Things She Weaveth Into the Web . . . MBPI2713 . .1881

Illustration for The Lady of Shalott . . . . MBPI2714 . .1881

Part III for The Lady of Shalott . . . . MBPI2715 . .1881

In This Verse is Spoken of the Coming of . . . . . MBPI2716 . .1881
    Sir Lancelot the Bold

This Verse Speaketh Also of Lancelot the . . . . . MBPI2717 . .1881
    Bold

The Third Verse Describeth Also the . . . . MBPI2718 . .1881
    Coming of the Bold Knight

The Fourth Verse Describing the Gallant . . . . . . MBPI2719 . .1881
    Knight Sir Lancelot the Bold

Illustration for The Lady of Shalott . . . . MBPI2720 . .1881

Decorative illustration for The Lady of . . . . MBPI2721 . .1881
    Shalott

The Lady Brings the Curse Upon Her . . . . MBPI2722 . .1881

1882

Illustration for The Lady of Shalott . . . . MBPI2723 . .1881

Part IV for The Lady of Shalott . . . . MBPI2724 . .1881

In Which the Fairy Lady Seeks the River . . . . . . MBPI2725 . .1881

Illustration for The Lady of Shalott . . . . MBPI2726 . .1881

Decorative illustration for The Lady of . . . . MBPI2727 . .1881
    Shalott

Illustration and text for The Lady of . . . . MBPI2728 . .1881
    Shalott

Illustration and text for The Lady of . . . . MBPI2729 . .1881
    Shalott

The Lady Dieth Floating Adown the Stream . . . MBPI2730 . .1881

The Dead Lady Floateth Down Ye Stream . . . . MBPI2731 . .1881
    Toward Camelot

Decorative illustration for The Lady of . . . . MBPI2732 . .1881
    Shalott

Illustration and text for The Lady of . . . . MBPI2733 . .1881
    Shalott

Illustration for The Lady of Shalott . . . . MBPI2734 . .1881

Decorative illustration for The Lady of . . . . MBPI2735 . .1881
    Shalott

Illustration and text for The Lady of . . . . MBPI2736 . .1881
    Shalott

Illustration for The Lady of Shalott . . . . MBPI2737 . .1881

The end for The Lady of Shalott . . . . MBPI2738 . .1881

Decoration for The Lady of Shalott . . . . MBPI2739 . .1881

Front cover design for Lady of Shalott . . . . MBPI2740 . .1881

Spine design for Lady of Shalott . . . . MBPI2741 . .1881

Suspicious Strangers . . . . PDPI0017 . .1881

The Indians Aiming at the Loop-Holes . . . . PDPI0031 . .1881

Pennsylvania Avenue . . . . PDPI0035 . .1881

A Race for Life . . . . PDPI0068 . .1881

Cor Cordia: A Christmas Greeting from Thy . . . PDPI0102 . .1881
    Husband

"The Clang of the Yankee Reaper, on . . . . MBPI0239 . .1882
    Salisbury Plain!"

Isaac Sears addressing the Mob . . . . MBPI0274 . .1882

The Press-Gang in New York . . . . MBPI0275 . .1882

Theophylact Bache saving Graydon from the . . MBPI0276 . .1882
    Mob in 1776

"I often took my Bible and sat in hollow . . . . . . MBPI0278 . .1882
    trees"

"The Word of the Lord came to me, saying . . . . MBPI0279 . .1882
    'Cry, Woe to the bloody City of Litchfield!'"

"I sat in a hay-stack, and said nothing . . . . MBPI0280 . .1882
    for some hours"

"They led me, taking hold of my collar, ... MBPI0281 . .1882
    and by my arms"

"The Admiral lost all control of himself, ... MBPI0282 . .1882
    and in a rage ordered his son to quit the house"

Quaker and King at Whitehall 1681 . . . . MBPI0283 . .1882

The Departure of the "Welcome" . . . . MBPI0284 . .1882

A burial at sea on board the "Welcome" . . . . . . MBPI0285 . .1882

William Penn and his Commissioners in the . . MBPI0286 . .1882
    cabin of the "Welcome"

"Holding forth the missive, he stood by, ... MBPI1203 . .1882
    breathless and speechless"

"Heart of gold! kindest of men!" . . . . MBPI1204 . .1882

"Hilda, airily mounting a high pair of . . . . MBPI1205 . .1882
    steps, proceeded to catalogue the various articles that she
    now dropped one by one into Grettel's wide-spread apron"

Index–Titles of Pyle's Art In Chronological Sequence

1882

"Glancing at the white-robed girlish .... MBPI1206 ..1882
figure before him, with evident admiration, he made a
becoming obeisance"

"They sat down and chatted in an easy, ... MBPI1207 ..1882
friendly fashion"

"Then the Hofrath emerged from the .... MBPI1208 ..1882
balcony, and etiquette forbade a longer interview"

Washington's Birth-Day, with title and .... MBPI1209 ..1882
verses inserted

"The old man's face changed suddenly, and .. MBPI1210 ..1882
he pressed his hand hard upon the arm of the hair-cloth
sofa"

"Breaking from her companions with an ..... MBPI1211 ..1882
excited exclamation, Mlle. Bland grasped the old woman by
the wrists"

The Dead Stowaway .... MBPI1212 ..1882

The Sea-Gull's Song .... MBPI1213 ..1882

Headpiece with initial D for Christmas .... MBPI1214 ..1882
Time Two Hundred Years Ago

Christmas presents for the Squire .... MBPI1215 ..1882

The Arrival at the Blue Boar Inn .... MBPI1216 ..1882

The stirrup-cup .... MBPI1217 ..1882

The Mummers .... MBPI1218 ..1882

The Snapdragon .... MBPI1219 ..1882

Bringing in the Yule-Log .... MBPI1220 ..1882

The Glee Singers .... MBPI1221 ..1882

The Return from Church, Christmas Morning .. MBPI1222 ..1882

Christmas Pudding .... MBPI1223 ..1882

The Contra-Dance .... MBPI1224 ..1882

The Duel .... MBPI1225 ..1882

The Elopement .... MBPI1226 ..1882

"Then Uncle Tom lifted her in his big, ... MBPI1325 ..1882
strong arms"

"A child, sunburned, and with many .... MBPI1770 ..1882
fluttering shreds of raiment"

"She hadn't on anything but a little .... MBPI1771 ..1882
nightgown, the same as if they'd snatched her out o' the
berth, with no time to dress her"

"Then turned to the table where master ...... MBPI1772 ..1882
and pupil sat absorbed"

Sylvia's troubles .... MBPI1773 ..1882

"She wasn't no kin when I marr'ed her, ... MBPI1774 ..1882
but we've lived together over thirty year"

The fight in the fog .... MBPI1775 ..1882

The Forging of Balmung .... MBPI2742 ..1882

The Death of Fafnir .... MBPI2743 ..1882

The Awakening of Brunhild .... MBPI2744 ..1882

The Trial of Strength .... MBPI2745 ..1882

The Quarrel of the Queens .... MBPI2746 ..1882

The Death of Siegfried .... MBPI2747 ..1882

"Ho, Drummer! quick, silence yon Capet" ...... MBPI2748 ..1882

"Awful, and proud, and erect" .... MBPI2749 ..1882

"She looked from the bars of her prison" ...... MBPI2750 ..1882

"Aunt Mary Expressing Her Mind" .... MBPI2751 ..1882

"The Mourning Clam-Man" .... MBPI2752 ..1882

The Beloved Pastor .... MBPI2754 ..1882

"Thomas Moon began to lay about him with MBPI0287 ..1883
his Sword"

1883

Drake's Attack on San Domingo .... MBPI0288 ..1883

"Jacques Cartier setting up a Cross at .... MBPI0289 ..1883
Gaspé"

Dominique de Gourgues avenging the .... MBPI0290 ..1883
Murder of the Huguenot Colony

"He brought both Catholic Priests and .... MBPI0291 ..1883
Huguenot Ministers, who disputed heartily on the Way"

"He rested his Musket" .... MBPI0292 ..1883

The Landing of the Pilgrims .... MBPI0293 ..1883

Arrival of the Young Women at Jamestown .... MBPI0294 ..1883

Endicott cutting the cross out of the .... MBPI0295 ..1883
English flag

Death of King Philip .... MBPI0296 ..1883

Governor Andros and the Boston People ...... MBPI0297 ..1883

A Quaker Exhorter in New England .... MBPI0298 ..1883

Arresting a Witch .... MBPI0299 ..1883

Peter Stuyvesant tearing the Letter .... MBPI0300 ..1883
demanding the Surrender of New York

The "Boston Massacre" .... MBPI0301 ..1883

An out-of-door Tea Party in Colonial New ..... MBPI0302 ..1883
England

Washington refusing a Dictatorship .... MBPI0303 ..1883

Washington and his Generals in .... MBPI0304 ..1883
Consultation March 15, 1783

Lexington Green–"If they want a War, let ..... MBPI0305 ..1883
it begin here"

Sergeant Jasper at the Battle of Fort .... MBPI0306 ..1883
Moultrie

The last boat-load of the British leaving ...... MBPI0307 ..1883
New York

The civil procession, headed by General ...... MBPI0308 ..1883
Washington and Governor Clinton

"The Master caused vs to haue some Beere" ... MBPI0309 ..1883

The Puritan Governor interrupting the .... MBPI0310 ..1883
Christmas sports

A Valentine to Phillis .... MBPI1227 ..1883

A Love Feast Among the Dunkers .... MBPI1228 ..1883

Scene in a Tavern on the Old Albany Post ..... MBPI1229 ..1883
Road

A Conference with the Colonists .... MBPI1230 ..1883

"Autumn Leaves" .... MBPI1231 ..1883

Evacuation Day One Hundred Years Ago– .... MBPI1232 ..1883
The Continental Army Marching Down
the Old Bowery, New York,
November 25, 1783

Headpiece with title for Ye True Story of ...... MBPI1233 ..1883
Granny Greene of Salem Town

Illustrated initial S for Ye True Story .... MBPI1234 ..1883
of Granny Greene of Salem Town

Vignette for Ye True Story of Granny .... MBPI1235 ..1883
Greene of Salem Town

Granny Greene seeketh the Life of ye Hen ..... MBPI1236 ..1883

Dame Charity Greene meeteth Ye Strange .... MBPI1237 ..1883
Little Man

Granny Greene Falleth Into Ill Repute .... MBPI1238 ..1883

The Arrest .... MBPI1239 ..1883

Ye End for Ye True Story of Granny Greene .... MBPI1240 ..1883
of Salem Town

Index–Titles of Pyle's Art In Chronological Sequence

1883

Washington Taking Leave of His Officers, ... MBPI1241 ..1883
Dec. 4, 1783
"The Ant and the Grasshopper" .... MBPI1242 ..1883
Robin on his way to Nottingham .... MBPI1326 ..1883
Robin meets a fair lady .... MBPI1327 ..1883
Robin encounters John Little .... MBPI1328 ..1883
Ye Romantic Adventures of Three Tailors, ... MBPI1329 ..1883
with title, illustrations and verse
Two Opinions, with title, illustrations .... MBPI1330 ..1883
and verse
A Victim to Science, with title, ... MBPI1331 ..1883
illustrations and verse
Headpiece with title for The Revolt of .... MBPI1332 ..1883
the Holidays
Fred .... MBPI1333 ..1883
Dora–Dorothy .... MBPI1334 ..1883
Thanksgiving Day (entering politely) .... MBPI1335 ..1883
Enter Fourth of July bowing and followed .... MBPI1336 ..1883
by Washington's Birthday
The Chorus of the Six Jolly Feeders .... MBPI1337 ..1883
The Military Ballet dance .... MBPI1338 ..1883
Easter & Saturday .... MBPI1339 ..1883
Four Pages armed with spears attendant ...... MBPI1340 ..1883
Enter New Years Day saluting .... MBPI1341 ..1883
Santa Claus bursts into the room from the .... MBPI1342 ..1883
chimney followed by the Elves & Fairies. Tableau
A Disappointment, with title, ... MBPI1343 ..1883
illustrations and verse
Half-title decoration for The Merry .... MBPI2086 ..1883
Adventures of Robin Hood
The Merry Friar carrieth Robin across the ..... MBPI2087 ..1883
Water
Title page decoration for The Merry .... MBPI2088 ..1883
Adventures of Robin Hood
Headpiece, Preface for The Merry .... MBPI2089 ..1883
Adventures of Robin Hood
Tailpiece, Preface for The Merry .... MBPI2090 ..1883
Adventures of Robin Hood
Headpiece, Table of Contents for The .... MBPI2091 ..1883
Merry Adventures of Robin Hood
Headpiece, List of Illustrations for The .... MBPI2092 ..1883
Merry Adventures of Robin Hood
Tailpiece, List of Illustrations for The .... MBPI2093 ..1883
Merry Adventures of Robin Hood
Robin Hood meeteth the tall Stranger on ..... MBPI2094 ..1883
the Bridge
Young Robin goes to the Shooting Match ..... MBPI2095 ..1883
Illustrated initial I for The Merry .... MBPI2096 ..1883
Adventures of Robin Hood
Tailpiece, Prologue for The Merry .... MBPI2097 ..1883
Adventures of Robin Hood
Robin and the Tinker at the Blue Boar Inn ..... MBPI2098 ..1883
The Sheriff of Nottingham plotting .... MBPI2099 ..1883
against Robin sends a messenger to Lincoln
Illustrated initial N for The Merry .... MBPI2100 ..1883
Adventures of Robin Hood
The Sheriff of Nottingham cometh before .... MBPI2101 ..1883
the King at London

1883

The Aged Palmer gives Young David of .... MBPI2102 ..1883
Doncaster news of Will Stutely
Tailpiece, Part I for The Merry .... MBPI2103 ..1883
Adventures of Robin Hood
Robin turns butcher and sells his meat in ..... MBPI2104 ..1883
Nottingham
Robin buys the Butcher's Meat .... MBPI2105 ..1883
Illustrated initial N for The Merry .... MBPI2106 ..1883
Adventures of Robin Hood
Little John overcomes Eric o' Lincoln .... MBPI2107 ..1883
The Mighty Fight betwixt Little John and ..... MBPI2108 ..1883
the Cook
The stout bout between Little John and ...... MBPI2109 ..1883
Arthur a Bland
Little John knoweth not which road to .... MBPI2110 ..1883
take
Illustrated initial I for The Merry .... MBPI2111 ..1883
Adventures of Robin Hood
Merry Robin stops a Stranger in Scarlet .... MBPI2112 ..1883
The Four Yeomen have Merry Sport with a ... MBPI2113 ..1883
Stout Miller
Tailpiece, Part III for The Merry .... MBPI2114 ..1883
Adventures of Robin Hood
Allan a Dale lieth beside the Fountain .... MBPI2115 ..1883
Allan a Dale tells his Story .... MBPI2116 ..1883
Illustrated initial I for The Merry .... MBPI2117 ..1883
Adventures of Robin Hood
The Merry Friar sings a goodly song .... MBPI2118 ..1883
Robin Hood steps betwixt Sir Stephen and ... MBPI2119 ..1883
his Bride
Tailpiece, Part IV for The Merry .... MBPI2120 ..1883
Adventures of Robin Hood
Merry Robin stops a Sorrowful Knight .... MBPI2121 ..1883
The young Knight of the Lea overcomes the .. MBPI2122 ..1883
Knight of Lancaster
Illustrated initial S for The Merry .... MBPI2123 ..1883
Adventures of Robin Hood
Sir Richard pleadeth before the Prior of ...... MBPI2124 ..1883
Emmet
Tailpiece, Part V for The Merry .... MBPI2125 ..1883
Adventures of Robin Hood
Little John in ye guise of a Friar stops .... MBPI2126 ..1883
three Lasses
Little John journeys in Holy Company .... MBPI2127 ..1883
Illustrated initial C for The Merry .... MBPI2128 ..1883
Adventures of Robin Hood
Merry Robin clad as a Beggar stops the ...... MBPI2129 ..1883
Corn Engrosser by the Cross nigh Ollerton
Tailpiece, Part VI for The Merry .... MBPI2130 ..1883
Adventures of Robin Hood
Allan a Dale Singeth Before Our Good .... MBPI2131 ..1883
Queen Eleanor
Young Richard Partington cometh to seek .... MBPI2132 ..1883
Merry Robin Hood
Illustrated initial T for The Merry .... MBPI2133 ..1883
Adventures of Robin Hood
Stout Robin hath a narrow escape .... MBPI2134 ..1883
Tailpiece, Part VII for The Merry .... MBPI2135 ..1883
Adventures of Robin Hood

Index–Titles of Pyle's Art In Chronological Sequence

1883

Robin Hood slayeth Guy of Gisbourne .... MBPI2136 ..1883

Robin and Little John go their ways in .... MBPI2137 ..1883
    search of Adventure

Illustrated initial A for The Merry .... MBPI2138 ..1883
    Adventures of Robin Hood

Merry Robin hath the worst of a Bargain ...... MBPI2139 ..1883

Tailpiece, Part VIII for The Merry .... MBPI2140 ..1883
    Adventures of Robin Hood

Robin shooteth his Last Shaft .... MBPI2141 ..1883

So Ye Great Reaper reapeth among the ...... MBPI2142 ..1883
    Flowers

Illustrated initial A for The Merry .... MBPI2143 ..1883
    Adventures of Robin Hood

Finis for The Merry Adventures of Robin ...... MBPI2144 ..1883
    Hood

Cover design for The Merry Adventures of .... MBPI2145 ..1883
    Robin Hood

Spine design for The Merry Adventures of .... MBPI2146 ..1883
    Robin Hood

Grandfather and Little Benny .... MBPI2753 ..1883

Illustration for Swinton's Fifth Reader .... MBPI2755 ..1883
    and Speaker

Illustration for Swinton's Fifth Reader .... MBPI2756 ..1883
    and Speaker

Inaugural Procession .... MBPI2757 ..1883

A Kentucky Wedding .... MBPI2758 ..1883

Scene in the Theatre in Philadelphia 1794 ..... MBPI2759 ..1883

Decoration and illustrated initial T for .... PDPI0025 ..1883
    Quill and Grill Club Invitation

Seal decoration for Quill and Grill Club .... PDPI0026 ..1883
    Invitation

"The Serenade" .... PDPI0037 ..1883

"May I have the pleasure for the next" .... PDPI0084 ..1883

The French Officers at Newport .... MBPI0311 ..1884

Shay's Mob in possession of a Court House .... MBPI0312 ..1884

At Mrs. Washington's Reception .... MBPI0313 ..1884

Impressment of American Seamen .... MBPI0314 ..1884

Among the Daffodillies .... MBPI0315 ..1884

"So saying, she turned and left me" .... MBPI0316 ..1884

"Bringing in the May" .... MBPI0317 ..1884

President Johnson teaching his first .... MBPI0318 ..1884
    class

Hamilton addressing the mob .... MBPI0319 ..1884

The Search for Toinette .... MBPI0320 ..1884

Headpiece for Witchcraft .... MBPI0321 ..1884

Witchcraft, 1692 .... MBPI0322 ..1884

Witchcraft, 1884 .... MBPI0323 ..1884

"The Cherokees Are Coming" .... MBPI0326 ..1884

"He seized and held the treasure near the .... MBPI1243 ..1884
    light"

The Accident of Birth, with title, ... MBPI1344 ..1884
    illustrations and verse

A Verse with a Moral but No Name, with ...... MBPI1345 ..1884
    title, illustrations and verse

"I am the Grand Duke" .... MBPI1346 ..1884

A Tale of a Tub, with title, ... MBPI1347 ..1884
    illustrations and verse

Pride in Distress, with title, ... MBPI1348 ..1884
    illustrations and verse

1885

Moral Blindness, with title, ... MBPI1349 ..1884
    illustrations and verse

Serious Advice, with title, illustrations .... MBPI1350 ..1884
    and verse

Three Fortunes, with title, illustrations .... MBPI1351 ..1884
    and verse

The Young Baron leaves his Home .... MBPI1352 ..1884

An old woman & a young girl coming .... MBPI1353 ..1884
    towards the Castle

Instantly there appeared before her a .... MBPI1354 ..1884
    strange being

Blow ye horn for ye ferry man .... MBPI1355 ..1884

Ye School for Men .... MBPI1356 ..1884

Then they began to pull .... MBPI1357 ..1884

Instantly there stood by her side a .... MBPI1358 ..1884
    School Trustee

Fitting a long arrow to his bow he sent .... MBPI1359 ..1884
    it directly through the foremost horseman

They sat down under a tree in a quiet .... MBPI1360 ..1884
    corner of the palace grounds

To Zisk, I .... MBPI1361 ..1884

To Zisk, II .... MBPI1362 ..1884

Ye Song of Ye Gossips, with title, ... MBPI1363 ..1884
    illustrations and verse

Venturesome Boldness, with title, ... MBPI1364 ..1884
    illustrations and verse

Ye Song of Ye Foolish Old Woman, with .... MBPI1365 ..1884
    title, illustrations and verse

Ye Song of Ye Rajah & Ye Fly, with title, ... MBPI1366 ..1884
    illustrations and verse

Ye Two Wishes, with title, illustrations .... MBPI1367 ..1884
    and verse

Superficial Culture, with title, ... MBPI1368 ..1884
    illustrations and verse

Play & Earnest, with title, illustrations .... MBPI1369 ..1884
    and verse

Headpiece with initial T for The Sword of ..... MBPI1370 ..1884
    Hildebrand

Vignette for The Sword of Hildebrand .... MBPI1371 ..1884

Vignette for The Sword of Hildebrand .... MBPI1372 ..1884

Vignette for The Sword of Hildebrand .... MBPI1373 ..1884

Vignette for The Sword of Hildebrand .... MBPI1374 ..1884

Vignette for The Sword of Hildebrand .... MBPI1375 ..1884

The Force of Need, with title, ... MBPI1376 ..1884
    illustrations and verse

Dutch and Indians trading .... MBPI2760 ..1884

Roger Williams in exile .... MBPI2761 ..1884

The Indian and the Pioneer .... MBPI2762 ..1884

Whitman starting for Washington .... MBPI2763 ..1884

Notes: Descriptive and Biographic .... MBPI2764 ..1884

Young woman standing under tree .... PDPI0034 ..1884

"All eyes were turned to Abraham .... PDPI0055 ..1884
    Davenport. He rose, slow cleaving with his steady voice the
    intolerable hush."

Daisies .... MBPI0128 ..1885

A Quaker Wedding .... MBPI0129 ..1885

Spring Blossoms .... MBPI0324 ..1885

Rescue of Sevier .... MBPI0325 ..1885

Index–Titles of Pyle's Art In Chronological Sequence

1885

1885

Death of the Indian Chief Alexander . . . . MBPI0327 . .1885

"Roger Feverel had kindled it for the . . . . MBPI0328 . .1885
first time"

"Her glance fell, under his steady gaze" . . . . . . MBPI0329 . .1885

Vignette with illustrated initial C for . . . . MBPI1244 . .1885
The Strange Adventures of Carl Spich

"Maybe the snow deadened his footsteps, ... MBPI1245 . .1885
maybe it was the Devil"

"The tall stranger with the club-foot . . . . MBPI1246 . .1885
stood before her"

"He stopped when he had come close to . . . . . MBPI1247 . .1885
Carl"

"I am going to run away with you" . . . . MBPI1248 . .1885

"She came close to him and laid her hand . . . . MBPI1249 . .1885
lovingly on his arm"

"The Squire went on as though he had not . . . MBPI1250 . .1885
heard"

"He held his hammer poised for a moment" . . . MBPI1251 . .1885

"The fingers of the hand were clutched . . . . . . MBPI1252 . .1885
like a claw"

Ye Story of a Blue China Plate, with . . . . MBPI1377 . .1885
title, illustrations and verse

Ye sad story concerning one innocent . . . . MBPI1378 . .1885
little Lamb and four wicked Wolves, with title, illustrations
and verse

Overconfidence, with title, illustrations . . . . MBPI1379 . .1885
and verse

Title and illustrated initial H for Hans . . . . MBPI1380 . .1885
Hecklemann's Luck

Hans Hecklemann . . . . MBPI1381 . .1885

Catherine . . . . MBPI1382 . .1885

Hans Hecklemann goes to the cottage of . . . . . MBPI1383 . .1885
the Old Wise-Woman in search of his Luck

Hans Hecklemann and the Old Wise-Woman . . MBPI1384 . .1885

Hans finds his Luck . . . . MBPI1385 . .1885

Hans Hecklemann ploughs for Gold . . . . MBPI1386 . .1885

Profession & Practice, with title, ... MBPI1387 . .1885
illustrations and verse

Title and illustrated initial H for How . . . . MBPI1388 . .1885
Dame Margery Twist saw more than was good for her

Dame Twist drinketh tea . . . . MBPI1389 . .1885

The Little Man and the Great Horse . . . . MBPI1390 . .1885

Dame Twist visits a Strange Patient . . . . MBPI1391 . .1885

Dame Margery Twist goeth to see the merry . . MBPI1392 . .1885
doings at the Fair

Dame Twist drives away the Little Folks . . . . . . MBPI1393 . .1885

Dame Twist sees the Little Man in Green . . . . . MBPI1394 . .1885
for the last time

A Newspaper Puff, with title, ... MBPI1395 . .1885
illustrations and verse

Headpiece with title for Clever Peter & . . . . . . MBPI1396 . .1885
the Two Bottles

Clever Peter & the Little Gentleman in . . . . MBPI1397 . .1885
Black

Clever Peter rides to the King's Palace . . . . MBPI1398 . .1885
upon his fine Horse

Peter Eats With the King and Princess . . . . MBPI1399 . .1885

Clever Peter and the Unlucky Bottle . . . . MBPI1400 . .1885

Clever Peter opens the Unlucky Bottle for . . . . MBPI1401 . .1885
the King and Princess

Fancy and Fact, with title, illustrations . . . . MBPI1402 . .1885
and verse

Headpiece with title and initial F for . . . . MBPI1403 . .1885
Farmer Griggs's Boggart

Farmer Georgie Griggs . . . . MBPI1404 . .1885

Dame Mally Griggs . . . . MBPI1405 . .1885

Farmer Griggs and the Boggart . . . . MBPI1406 . .1885

The Departure . . . . MBPI1407 . .1885

Farmer Griggs and the Wise Man . . . . MBPI1408 . .1885

The Boggart Rejoices . . . . MBPI1409 . .1885

Headpiece with title and illustrated . . . . MBPI1410 . .1885
initial O–The Skillful Huntsman

Jacob's Mother & the Herr Mayor . . . . MBPI1411 . .1885

Jacob and The Red One . . . . MBPI1412 . .1885

Jacob shoots at– . . . . MBPI1413 . .1885

–the Magpie . . . . MBPI1414 . .1885

Jacob and the Magic Plough . . . . MBPI1415 . .1885

Jacob and the Red One go hunting together . . MBPI1416 . .1885

Jacob and Gretchen get the best of the . . . . . . MBPI1417 . .1885
Red One and go home together happily

Headpiece with title for Claus & His . . . . MBPI1418 . .1885
Wonderful Staff

Claus and the White Snake . . . . MBPI1419 . .1885

Claus and the Master of Black-Arts . . . . MBPI1420 . .1885

The Master is Angry . . . . MBPI1421 . .1885

Claus listens to the talk of the two . . . . MBPI1422 . .1885
ravens

Claus and the Manikin . . . . MBPI1423 . .1885

Hans discovers Claus's Luck . . . . MBPI1424 . .1885

Headpiece with title and initial T for . . . . MBPI1425 . .1885
The Apple of Contentment

The little man asks for his cap . . . . MBPI1426 . .1885

Christine's Mother and Sisters wish for . . . . MBPI1427 . .1885
the Apple

Christine and the Apple . . . . MBPI1428 . .1885

The King talks with the Wise Man . . . . MBPI1429 . .1885

The King reaches for the Apple . . . . MBPI1430 . .1885

The King's Steward and Christine . . . . MBPI1431 . .1885

Christine gives the Apple to the King . . . . MBPI1432 . .1885

Headpiece with title for The Bird in the . . . . . . MBPI1433 . .1885
Linden Tree

Ye King . . . . MBPI1434 . .1885

Prince John . . . . MBPI1435 . .1885

The Prince aids the Old Woman . . . . MBPI1436 . .1885

The Great Ugly Troll finds the Prince by . . . . . . MBPI1437 . .1885
the Fire

The Gooseherd & her Daughter meet the . . . . . MBPI1438 . .1885
Princess at the Roadside

The Prince looks through the Magic Key . . . . . . MBPI1439 . .1885

The Old King Rejoices at His New . . . . MBPI1440 . .1885
Daughter-in-Law

Headpiece with title for The Swan Maiden . . . . MBPI1441 . .1885

The Swan carries the Prince away . . . . MBPI1442 . .1885

The Prince and the Old Witch with three . . . . . MBPI1443 . .1885
eyes

Ye Prince & Ye Swan Maiden . . . . MBPI1444 . .1885

Index–Titles of Pyle's Art In Chronological Sequence

1885

The Witch & the woman of honey & barley . . . MBPI1445 . .1885
  meal
Headpiece with illustrated initial K for . . . . MBPI1446 . .1885
  The Book of Balbo
The Children are sent to the Asylum . . . . MBPI1447 . .1885
The jolly red-faced Man comes to Town . . . . MBPI1448 . .1885
Rambustius reads the Book of Balbo . . . . MBPI1449 . .1885
The King finds his children . . . . MBPI1450 . .1885
Headpiece with title for How One Turned . . . . MBPI1451 . .1885
  His Trouble to Some Account
The Soldier and his Trouble . . . . MBPI1452 . .1885
The Soldier brings his Trouble before the . . . . . MBPI1453 . .1885
  King
The three giants come to blows . . . . MBPI1454 . .1885
The Rich Man finds Money and Trouble . . . . MBPI1455 . .1885
Headpiece with title for How Boots . . . . MBPI1456 . .1885
  Befooled the King
Peter goes to befool the King . . . . MBPI1457 . .1885
Paul goes Home again . . . . MBPI1458 . .1885
The Old Woman breaks things . . . . MBPI1459 . .1885
The Councilor finds the Wisdom Sack . . . . MBPI1460 . .1885
Boots tricks the Princess into showing . . . . MBPI1461 . .1885
  herself
Headpiece with title for How Three Went . . . . . MBPI1462 . .1885
  Out into the Wide World
The Gray Goose meets the Sausage . . . . MBPI1463 . .1885
The Fox calls on the Cock . . . . MBPI1464 . .1885
The Fox calls on the Sausage . . . . MBPI1465 . .1885
The Fox's Wife makes his bed . . . . MBPI1466 . .1885
Prince Charles sprang to his side: "If he . . . . MBPI2068 . .1885
  goes, so do I!"
This is the way that one in Cap and . . . . MBPI2150 . .1885
  Motley stops for awhile along the stony Path of Life to make
  you laugh
Headpiece, Lexington . . . . MBPI2765 . .1885
The Embarkation . . . . MBPI2766 . .1885
"Blazing and clanging from thicket and . . . . . . MBPI2767 . .1885
  wall"
"For they all thought he was dying, as . . . . MBPI2768 . .1885
  they gathered round him crying"
Howard Pyle script book label . . . . PDPI0005 . .1885
Design for unused Howard Pyle bookplate . . . . PDPI0027 . .1885
Illustration for The Adventure of a Mouse . . . . . PDPI0103 . .1885
The Flight of the Swallow . . . . MBPI0130 . .1886
Illustrated initial T for The Flight of . . . . MBPI0131 . .1886
  the Swallow
Tailpiece for The Flight of the Swallow . . . . MBPI0132 . .1886
Traveling in the Olden Time . . . . MBPI0330 . .1886
Governor Huntington attacked by wolves . . . . . MBPI0331 . .1886
Paul Revere bringing news to Sullivan . . . . MBPI0332 . .1886
Surrender of Fort William and Mary . . . . MBPI0333 . .1886
Transporting powder from the Fort . . . . MBPI0334 . .1886
Bringing the powder to Bunker Hill . . . . MBPI0335 . .1886
The Landing of Cadillac . . . . MBPI0336 . .1886
The Ojibway Maiden disclosing Pontiac's . . . . . MBPI0337 . .1886
  Plot
"'Tis an unfair race, O master," cried . . . . MBPI1115 . .1886
  Ephialtes

1886

"Come hither, lads," she said . . . . MBPI1116 . .1886
Headpiece with title for The Princess . . . . MBPI1467 . .1886
  Golden-Hair and the Great Black Raven
The King meets the Great Black Raven in . . . . . MBPI1468 . .1886
  the Forest
The Princess drinks from the Golden Cup . . . . . MBPI1469 . .1886
The Princess comes to Gruff's Door . . . . MBPI1470 . .1886
The Princess finds her dear Prince again . . . . . . MBPI1471 . .1886
Headpiece with title for The Clever . . . . MBPI1472 . .1886
  Student and the Master of Black Arts
The Princess walking beside the Sea . . . . MBPI1473 . .1886
The Student and the Princess . . . . MBPI1474 . .1886
The Master of Black Arts with a Hen . . . . MBPI1475 . .1886
What happened to the Master . . . . MBPI1476 . .1886
Headpiece with title for Peterkin and the . . . . . MBPI1477 . .1886
  Little Gray Hare
Peterkin's brothers marvel at his fine . . . . MBPI1478 . .1886
  trappings
Peterkin makes off with the Giant's Goose . . . . MBPI1479 . .1886
Peterkin brings the Silver Bell to the . . . . MBPI1480 . .1886
  King
Peterkin dressed as a lass, and the Giant . . . . . MBPI1481 . .1886
Headpiece with title for How the Good . . . . MBPI1482 . .1886
  Gifts were Used by Two
Saint Nicholas at the Rich Man's Door . . . . MBPI1483 . .1886
Saint Nicholas at the Poor Man's House . . . . . . MBPI1484 . .1886
The Poor Man and St. Christopher . . . . MBPI1485 . .1886
The Rich Man and the Two Saints . . . . MBPI1486 . .1886
Headpiece with title for Mother . . . . MBPI1487 . .1886
  Hildegarde
Mother Hildegarde and the Princess . . . . MBPI1488 . .1886
The Princess peeped into the Jar . . . . MBPI1489 . .1886
The Princess and the Pigeons . . . . MBPI1490 . .1886
Mother Hildegarde carries away the Baby . . . . MBPI1491 . .1886
Headpiece with title for Master Jacob . . . . MBPI1492 . .1886
Master Jacob brings his Pig to Market . . . . MBPI1493 . .1886
Master Jacob goes to Town with his Goat . . . . MBPI1494 . .1886
The little tin horn has no effect . . . . MBPI1495 . .1886
Master Jacob and the three Cronies meet . . . . MBPI1496 . .1886
  in the Woods
Headpiece with title for How Three Little . . . . . MBPI1497 . .1886
  Pigs Had the Best of the Great Wicked Ogre
"Have you a roasted apple to put in my . . . . . . MBPI1498 . .1886
  mouth?"
"Do you find the hole?" asked the Little . . . . . . MBPI1499 . .1886
  Pig
"The Ogre shut his eyes and began to . . . . MBPI1500 . .1886
  count"
"Here comes the farmer and his men to see . . MBPI1501 . .1886
  what all the stir is about"
Headpiece with title for The Staff and . . . . MBPI1502 . .1886
  the Fiddle
"Give the poor old Woman a penny or two" . . . MBPI1503 . .1886
"'Rub-a-dub-dub!' says the Fiddler" . . . . MBPI1504 . .1886
A Princess as pretty as a ripe Apple . . . . MBPI1505 . .1886
"What do you want, Master?" . . . . MBPI1506 . .1886
Headpiece with title for The Simpleton . . . . . . MBPI1507 . .1886
  and his Little Black Hen

Index–Titles of Pyle's Art In Chronological Sequence

1886

Caspar and the cunning Landlord . . . . MBPI1508 . .1886

Caspar finds the Gold in the Willow-Tree . . . . . . MBPI1509 . .1886

The Two Brothers and the Landlord divide . . . . MBPI1510 . .1886
the money

Caspar and the Three rascals go to see . . . . MBPI1511 . .1886
the King

Headpiece with title for King Stork . . . . MBPI1512 . .1886

The Drummer carries the Old Man across . . . . . MBPI1513 . .1886
the River

The Princess starts for the Witch's House . . . . . . MBPI1514 . .1886

The Drummer with his Cap of Darkness in . . . . MBPI1515 . .1886
the Witch's House

The Drummer captures the one-eyed Raven . . . MBPI1516 . .1886

Headpiece with title for How the . . . . MBPI1517 . .1886
Princess's Pride was Broken

The Gooseherd plays with a Golden Ball . . . . . . MBPI1518 . .1886

The King peeps over the hedge . . . . MBPI1519 . .1886

The Princess goes to Market with her Eggs . . . . MBPI1520 . .1886

King Florimel greets the Princess . . . . MBPI1521 . .1886

Was this...King Henry's self? Margery . . . . MBPI2069 . .1886
dropped to her knee

Young William Penn meets the disapproval . . . MBPI2070 . .1886
of his Father, the Admiral

On the great terrace of Donegal Castle . . . . MBPI2071 . .1886

"To sea in a bowl!" exclaimed the puzzled . . . . MBPI2072 . .1886
Pembroke

The Young Emperor's Entrance to the . . . . MBPI2073 . .1886
Circus Maximus

"The dark and shadowy outline of a man" . . . . . MBPI2074 . .1886

"A great day this, my young friend," said . . . . . . MBPI2075 . .1886
Mr. John Adams of Massachusetts

Surprised by the Hero of Seventy . . . . MBPI2079 . .1886
Fights–The Good Lord James of Douglas

Front cover design for Pepper & Salt . . . . MBPI2147 . .1886

Back cover design for Pepper & Salt . . . . MBPI2148 . .1886

Half-title decoration for Pepper & Salt . . . . MBPI2149 . .1886

Title page decoration for Pepper & Salt . . . . . . MBPI2151 . .1886

Headpiece, Preface for Pepper & Salt . . . . MBPI2152 . .1886

Tailpiece, Preface for Pepper & Salt . . . . MBPI2153 . .1886

Headpiece, Table of Contents for Pepper & . . . . MBPI2154 . .1886
Salt

Tailpiece, Table of Contents for Pepper & . . . . . MBPI2155 . .1886
Salt

Headpiece, List of Illustrations for . . . . MBPI2156 . .1886
Pepper & Salt

Tailpiece, List of Illustrations for . . . . MBPI2157 . .1886
Pepper & Salt

How Hans was caught . . . . MBPI2158 . .1886

Decoration for Pepper & Salt . . . . MBPI2159 . .1886

Decoration for Pepper & Salt . . . . MBPI2160 . .1886

Decoration for Pepper & Salt . . . . MBPI2161 . .1886

Decoration for Pepper & Salt . . . . MBPI2162 . .1886

Illustration for Swinton's Advanced Third . . . . . MBPI2769 . .1886
Reader

"Her native songs for him she sung" . . . . MBPI2770 . .1886

Headband for A History of New York . . . . MBPI2771 . .1886

Illustrated initial A for A History of . . . . MBPI2772 . .1886
New York

1887

Tailpiece for A History of New York . . . . MBPI2773 . .1886

Spine design for Pepper & Salt . . . . PDPI0077 . .1886

"The woman turned fiercely upon the . . . . MBPI0338 . .1887
Chieftain"

Joseph Brown leading his company to . . . . MBPI0339 . .1887
Nicojack

"I sat gazing upon her as she leaned . . . . MBPI0340 . .1887
forward"

"Thereupon, lifting up his eyes again, he . . . . . MBPI0341 . .1887
began once more wrestling with the spirit in prayer"

"Still she looked upon me, though . . . . MBPI0342 . .1887
silently and pale as death"

"Then came Mistress Margaret unto me and . . MBPI0343 . .1887
put a letter into my hand"

Capture of Elizabeth and Frances Callaway . . . MBPI0344 . .1887
and Jemima Boone

Defence of the Station . . . . MBPI0345 . .1887

On the Tortugas . . . . MBPI0346 . .1887

Capture of the Galleon . . . . MBPI0347 . .1887

Henry Morgan Recruiting for the Attack . . . . . . MBPI0348 . .1887

The Sacking of Panama . . . . MBPI0349 . .1887

Avary sells his jewels . . . . MBPI0350 . .1887

Marooned . . . . MBPI0351 . .1887

Blackbeard buries his treasure . . . . MBPI0352 . .1887

Walking the plank . . . . MBPI0353 . .1887

Aaron Burr's Wooing . . . . MBPI0354 . .1887

"Mr. Longways looked up under his brows . . . . MBPI1253 . .1887
at me with a very curious leer"

"'Boat ahoy!' I cried out, and then . . . . MBPI1254 . .1887
levelled my pistol and fired"

"'Captain Mackra,' said he, coldly, 'you . . . . MBPI1255 . .1887
were pleased to put upon me last night a gross and uncalled
for insult.'"

"So soon as they saw me they fell to . . . . MBPI1256 . .1887
screaming and clung to one another"

"'I am Captain John Mackra,' said I, and . . . . . . MBPI1257 . .1887
I sat down upon the gunwale of the boat"

"I rose slowly from my chair, and stood . . . . MBPI1258 . .1887
with my hand leaning upon the table"

"The three fellows were brought aft to . . . . MBPI1259 . .1887
the quarterdeck, where Captain Croker stood, just below the
rail of the deck above"

"There, in the corner, I beheld the . . . . MBPI1260 . .1887
famous pirate, Captain Edward England"

Dame Bridget's Prophecy . . . . MBPI1522 . .1887

Headpiece with title for How Two Went . . . . . . MBPI1523 . .1887
into Partnership

The Great Red Fox at the Store-house . . . . MBPI1524 . .1887

"What are you doing here, Father Goat?" . . . . . . MBPI1525 . .1887

"Which shall it be first–Sausages or . . . . MBPI1526 . .1887
Pudding?"

Uncle Bear and the Great Red Fox after . . . . . . MBPI1527 . .1887
Farmer John's Apples

Headpiece with title for Bearskin . . . . MBPI1528 . .1887

The basket with the baby in it drifted . . . . MBPI1529 . .1887
down the river

Bearskin and the Princess . . . . MBPI1530 . .1887

The Princess wept and wept . . . . MBPI1531 . .1887

Index–Titles of Pyle's Art In Chronological Sequence

1887

Bearskin and the Swineherd had a fine .... MBPI1532 ..1887
feast together

Illustration for Hugo Grotius and His .... MBPI1533 ..1887
Book Chest

Headpiece with title for Cousin Greylegs, ... MBPI1534 ..1887
Ye Great Red Fox and Grandfather Mole

"The Great Red Fox and Cousin Greylegs ..... MBPI1535 ..1887
were great cronies"

Cousin Greylegs steals away with the bag .... MBPI1536 ..1887
of nails

Brother Fox comes near tramping on the ..... MBPI1537 ..1887
Mole's House

The Great Red Fox shut his teeth and .... MBPI1538 ..1887
grinned

Headpiece and title for Which is Best? .... MBPI1539 ..1887

So the Rich Man left him in his blindness ..... MBPI1540 ..1887

He touched the lock with the little black ..... MBPI1541 ..1887
stone

The Poor Brother opens the chest .... MBPI1542 ..1887

The Rich Brother takes the diamond from .... MBPI1543 ..1887
the statue's hand

Headpiece with title for The Best that .... MBPI1544 ..1887
Life Has to Give

"'So you are stealing my pine cones,' .... MBPI1545 ..1887
said he"

He snatched it and ran .... MBPI1546 ..1887

The Blacksmith carries the Golden Tree to .... MBPI1547 ..1887
the Queen

And that was the end of the Dwarf .... MBPI1548 ..1887

Headpiece with title for The Water of .... MBPI1549 ..1887
Life

A Stranger shows the King the portrait of .... MBPI1550 ..1887
a beautiful Princess

The Faithful Servant is borne on the .... MBPI1551 ..1887
wings of the North Wind

The King gives the Water of Life to the .... MBPI1552 ..1887
beautiful Princess

The King goes to cut off the Faithful .... MBPI1553 ..1887
Servant's arm

Headpiece with title for The Step-mother ..... MBPI1554 ..1887

The Step-daughter follows the Golden Ball .... MBPI1555 ..1887

The King rescues the Maiden from a deep .... MBPI1556 ..1887
pit

The Step-mother changes the Queen into a .. MBPI1557 ..1887
White Dove

The King caresses the White Dove .... MBPI1558 ..1887

Headpiece with title for The White Bird .... MBPI1559 ..1887

The door was opened by a poor man .... MBPI1560 ..1887

There sat three terrible giants .... MBPI1561 ..1887

The Prince takes the Sword of Brightness ..... MBPI1562 ..1887

The White Bird recognizes the Prince .... MBPI1563 ..1887

Headpiece with title for One Good Turn ...... MBPI1564 ..1887
Deserves Another

The Fisher Lad catches a strange fish .... MBPI1565 ..1887

The Fisher Lad comes to the Gray Master's .... MBPI1566 ..1887
house

The Gray Master is caught in the stream ...... MBPI1567 ..1887
and is swept away

The Princess finds the Fisher Lad with .... MBPI1568 ..1887
the key of Wish-House

Gambetta Proclaiming the Republic of .... MBPI1909 ..1887
France

Looking into the Prussian Lines from the ..... MBPI1910 ..1887
Chateau de la Muette

"Then faced her the leonine chief" .... MBPI1911 ..1887

Washington refuses the Colt .... MBPI2080 ..1887

The Star Bearer .... MBPI2081 ..1887

Marginal decoration with title for The .... MBPI2082 ..1887
Star Bearer

Marginal decoration for The Star Bearer .... MBPI2083 ..1887

Marginal decoration for The Star Bearer .... MBPI2084 ..1887

Sat, like a Fate, and watched the flying .... MBPI2774 ..1887
thread

She heard the stir of his black mantle .... MBPI2775 ..1887
trailing in the dust

While yet her cheek was bright with .... MBPI2776 ..1887
summer bloom

Breathed through her lips a sad and .... MBPI2777 ..1887
tremulous tune

Death and Winter closed the autumn scene ... MBPI2778 ..1887

Pyrrhus Finds Philoctetes in a Cave .... MBPI2779 ..1887

Odysseus and His Mother .... MBPI2780 ..1887

Apollo Slaying the Python .... MBPI2781 ..1887

Meleager Refuses to Help in the Defence ..... MBPI2782 ..1887
of the City

The Silver-Footed Thetis Rising from the ...... MBPI2783 ..1887
Waves

The Swineherd Telling His Story to .... MBPI2784 ..1887
Odysseus

Alpheus and Arethusa .... MBPI2785 ..1887

Odysseus Advises King Tyndareus .... MBPI2786 ..1887
Concerning Helen's Suitors

Deianeira and the Dying Centaur Nessus ...... MBPI2787 ..1887

Prometheus .... MBPI2788 ..1887

Palamedes Tests the Madness of Odysseus .... MBPI2789 ..1887

Odysseus and Menelaus Persuading .... MBPI2790 ..1887
Agamemnon to Sacrifice Iphigenia

The Boys present the Salmagundi to Heer .... MBPI2791 ..1887
Governor Stuyvesant

Design for The Grolier Club bookplate .... PDPI0042 ..1887

Illustrated initial T for The Star Bearer .... PDPI0053 ..1887

Tailpiece for The Star Bearer .... PDPI0054 ..1887

The Burning of the Guillotine Before the ..... PDPI0070 ..1887
Statue of Voltaire

"They ploughed their fields with an armed ... MBPI0355 ..1888
sentry beside them"

Finding the body of Joseph Hay in the .... MBPI0356 ..1888
Trail

Coureurs de Bois .... MBPI0357 ..1888

Morgan at Porto Bello .... MBPI0358 ..1888

Headpiece with title for The Three .... MBPI1569 ..1888
Fortunes

He was an old man no longer, but a .... MBPI1570 ..1888
Blessed Angel

The Angel and the Youngest Brother said ..... MBPI1571 ..1888
"Good-bye" and trudged away

Index–Titles of Pyle's Art In Chronological Sequence

1888

A great, ugly, poisonous snake crept out ...... MBPI1572 ..1888
of a hole in the wall

They set before him a loaf of bread and a .... MBPI1573 ..1888
bowl of milk

Headpiece with illustrated initial T for .... MBPI1574 ..1888
The Princess on the Glass Hill

The Prince pours water into the barrel .... MBPI1575 ..1888

The Prince bathes in the fountain .... MBPI1576 ..1888

The Prince kills the Dragon .... MBPI1577 ..1888

The Prince wins the Golden Apple and the ... MBPI1578 ..1888
Silver Pear

The Saving of King Ingé .... MBPI2085 ..1888

Cover design for The Wonder Clock .... MBPI2163 ..1888

Half-title decoration for The Wonder .... MBPI2164 ..1888
Clock

Frontispiece for The Wonder Clock .... MBPI2165 ..1888

Title page decoration for The Wonder .... MBPI2166 ..1888
Clock

Headpiece, Preface for The Wonder Clock ..... MBPI2167 ..1888

Illustrated initial I, Preface for The .... MBPI2168 ..1888
Wonder Clock

Headpiece, Table of Contents for The .... MBPI2169 ..1888
Wonder Clock

Tailpiece, Table of Contents for The .... MBPI2170 ..1888
Wonder Clock

Headpiece, List of Illustrations for The .... MBPI2171 ..1888
Wonder Clock

Tailpiece, List of Illustrations for The .... MBPI2172 ..1888
Wonder Clock

Illustrated initial T for Bearskin .... MBPI2173 ..1888

Illustrated initial T with heading for .... MBPI2174 ..1888
Bearskin

Illustrated initial B with heading for .... MBPI2175 ..1888
Bearskin

Illustrated initial O for The Water of .... MBPI2176 ..1888
Life

Illustrated initial T with heading for .... MBPI2177 ..1888
The Water of Life

Illustrated initial T with heading for .... MBPI2178 ..1888
The Water of Life

Illustrated initial T with heading for .... MBPI2179 ..1888
The Water of Life

Illustrated initial T for How One Turned .... MBPI2180 ..1888
His Trouble to Some Account

Illustrated initial T with heading for .... MBPI2181 ..1888
How One Turned His Trouble to Some Account

Illustrated initial H with heading for .... MBPI2182 ..1888
How One Turned His Trouble to Some Account

Illustrated initial T for How Three Went .... MBPI2183 ..1888
Out into the Wide World

Illustrated initial T with heading for .... MBPI2184 ..1888
How Three Went Out into the Wide World

Illustrated initial T with heading for .... MBPI2185 ..1888
How Three Went Out into the Wide World

Illustrated initial T for The Clever .... MBPI2186 ..1888
Student and the Master of Black Arts

Illustrated initial A with heading for .... MBPI2187 ..1888
The Clever Student and the Master of Black Arts

Illustrated initial T with heading for .... MBPI2188 ..1888
The Clever Student and the Master of Black Arts

Illustrated initial T with heading for .... MBPI2189 ..1888
The Clever Student and the Master of Black Arts

Illustrated initial W with heading for .... MBPI2190 ..1888
The Wonder Clock

Decoration for The Wonder Clock .... MBPI2191 ..1888

Illustrated initial O for The Princess .... MBPI2192 ..1888
Golden-Hair and the Great Black Raven

Illustrated initial T with heading for .... MBPI2193 ..1888
The Princess Golden-Hair and the Great Black Raven

Illustrated initial P with heading for .... MBPI2194 ..1888
The Princess Golden-Hair and the Great Black Raven

Illustrated initial P with heading for .... MBPI2195 ..1888
The Princess Golden-Hair and the Great Black Raven

Illustrated initial T with heading for .... MBPI2196 ..1888
The Princess Golden-Hair and the Great Black Raven

Illustrated initial I for Cousin .... MBPI2197 ..1888
Greylegs, Ye Great Red Fox and Grandfather Mole

Illustrated initial C with heading for .... MBPI2198 ..1888
Cousin Greylegs, Ye Great Red Fox and Grandfather Mole

Illustrated initial C with heading for .... MBPI2199 ..1888
Cousin Greylegs, Ye Great Red Fox and Grandfather Mole

Illustrated initial O for One Good Turn .... MBPI2200 ..1888
Deserves Another

Illustrated initial F with heading for .... MBPI2201 ..1888
One Good Turn Deserves Another

Illustrated initial T with heading for .... MBPI2202 ..1888
One Good Turn Deserves Another

Illustrated initial T with heading for .... MBPI2203 ..1888
One Good Turn Deserves Another

Illustrated initial T with heading for .... MBPI2204 ..1888
One Good Turn Deserves Another

Illustrated initial O for The White Bird .... MBPI2205 ..1888

Illustrated initial T with heading for .... MBPI2206 ..1888
The White Bird

Illustrated initial T with heading for .... MBPI2207 ..1888
The White Bird

Illustrated initial T with heading for .... MBPI2208 ..1888
The White Bird

Illustrated initial T with heading for .... MBPI2209 ..1888
The White Bird

Illustrated initial T for How the Good .... MBPI2210 ..1888
Gifts were Used by Two

Illustrated initial S with heading for .... MBPI2211 ..1888
How the Good Gifts were Used by Two

Illustrated initial S with heading for .... MBPI2212 ..1888
How the Good Gifts were Used by Two

Illustrated initial T with heading for .... MBPI2213 ..1888
How the Good Gifts were Used by Two

Decoration for The Wonder Clock .... MBPI2214 ..1888

Illustrated initial O for How Boots .... MBPI2215 ..1888
Befooled the King

Illustrated initial P with heading for .... MBPI2216 ..1888
How Boots Befooled the King

Illustrated initial P with heading for .... MBPI2217 ..1888
How Boots Befooled the King

Illustrated initial T with heading for .... MBPI2218 ..1888
How Boots Befooled the King

Index–Titles of Pyle's Art In Chronological Sequence

1888

Illustrated initial T with heading for .... MBPI2219 ..1888
How Boots Befooled the King
Decoration for The Wonder Clock .... MBPI2220 ..1888
Illustrated initial O for The Step-mother .... MBPI2221 ..1888
Illustrated initial T with heading for .... MBPI2222 ..1888
The Step-mother
Illustrated initial T with heading for .... MBPI2223 ..1888
The Step-mother
Illustrated initial T with heading for .... MBPI2224 ..1888
The Step-mother
Illustrated initial O for Master Jacob .... MBPI2225 ..1888
Illustrated initial M with heading for .... MBPI2226 ..1888
Master Jacob
Illustrated initial T with heading for .... MBPI2227 ..1888
Master Jacob
Illustrated initial M with heading for .... MBPI2228 ..1888
Master Jacob
Illustrated initial T for Peterkin and .... MBPI2229 ..1888
the Little Grey Hare
Illustrated initial P with heading for .... MBPI2230 ..1888
Peterkin and the Little Grey Hare
Illustrated initial P with heading for .... MBPI2231 ..1888
Peterkin and the Little Grey Hare
Illustrated initial P with heading for .... MBPI2232 ..1888
Peterkin and the Little Grey Hare
Illustrated initial O for Mother .... MBPI2233 ..1888
Hildegarde
Illustrated initial T with heading for .... MBPI2234 ..1888
Mother Hildegarde
Illustrated initial T with heading for .... MBPI2235 ..1888
Mother Hildegarde
Illustrated initial T with heading for .... MBPI2236 ..1888
Mother Hildegarde
Illustrated initial M with heading for .... MBPI2237 ..1888
Mother Hildegarde
Illustrated initial T for Which is Best? .... MBPI2238 ..1888
Illustrated initial H with heading for .... MBPI2239 ..1888
Which is Best?
Illustrated initial T with heading for .... MBPI2240 ..1888
Which is Best?
Illustrated initial T with heading for .... MBPI2241 ..1888
Which is Best?
Decoration for The Wonder Clock .... MBPI2242 ..1888
Illustrated initial T for The Simpleton .... MBPI2243 ..1888
and his Little Black Hen
Illustrated initial T with heading for .... MBPI2244 ..1888
The Simpleton and his Little Black Hen
Illustrated initial T with heading for .... MBPI2245 ..1888
The Simpleton and his Little Black Hen
Illustrated initial O for The Swan Maiden ...... MBPI2246 ..1888
Illustrated initial T with heading for .... MBPI2247 ..1888
The Swan Maiden
Illustrated initial T with heading for .... MBPI2248 ..1888
The Swan Maiden
Illustrated initial T with heading for .... MBPI2249 ..1888
The Swan Maiden
Illustrated initial T for The Three .... MBPI2250 ..1888
Little Pigs and the Ogre

1888

Illustrated initial T with heading for .... MBPI2251 ..1888
The Three Little Pigs and the Ogre
Illustrated initial T with heading for .... MBPI2252 ..1888
The Three Little Pigs and the Ogre
Decoration for The Wonder Clock .... MBPI2253 ..1888
Illustrated initial T for The Staff and .... MBPI2254 ..1888
the Fiddle
Illustrated initial T with heading for .... MBPI2255 ..1888
The Staff and the Fiddle
Illustrated initial T with heading for .... MBPI2256 ..1888
The Staff and the Fiddle
Illustrated initial T with heading for .... MBPI2257 ..1888
The Staff and the Fiddle
Illustrated initial T for How the .... MBPI2258 ..1888
Princess's Pride was broken
Illustrated initial T with heading for .... MBPI2259 ..1888
How the Princess's Pride was broken
Illustrated initial T with heading for .... MBPI2260 ..1888
How the Princess's Pride was broken
Illustrated initial T for How Two went .... MBPI2261 ..1888
into Partnership
Illustrated initial T with heading for .... MBPI2262 ..1888
How Two went into Partnership
Illustrated initial U with heading for .... MBPI2263 ..1888
for How Two went into Partnership
Illustrated initial T for King Stork .... MBPI2264 ..1888
Illustrated initial T with heading for .... MBPI2265 ..1888
King Stork
Illustrated initial T with heading for .... MBPI2266 ..1888
King Stork
Illustrated initial T with heading for .... MBPI2267 ..1888
King Stork
Illustrated initial T for The Best that .... MBPI2268 ..1888
Life has to give
Illustrated initial T with heading for .... MBPI2269 ..1888
The Best that Life has to give
Illustrated initial T with heading for .... MBPI2270 ..1888
The Best that Life has to give
Illustrated initial T with heading for .... MBPI2271 ..1888
The Best that Life has to give
Tailpiece, The End for The Wonder Clock .... MBPI2272 ..1888
Cover design for Otto of the Silver Hand ...... MBPI2273 ..1888
Half-title decoration for Otto of the .... MBPI2274 ..1888
Silver Hand
In the Belfry .... MBPI2275 ..1888
Headpiece, Contents for Otto of the .... MBPI2276 ..1888
Silver Hand
Tailpiece, Contents for Otto of the .... MBPI2277 ..1888
Silver Hand
Headpiece, List of Illustrations for Otto .... MBPI2278 ..1888
of the Silver Hand
Tailpiece, List of Illustrations for Otto .... MBPI2279 ..1888
of the Silver Hand
Headpiece, Foreword for Otto of the .... MBPI2280 ..1888
Silver Hand
Illustrated initial B, Foreword for Otto .... MBPI2281 ..1888
of the Silver Hand
Tailpiece, Foreword for Otto of the .... MBPI2282 ..1888
Silver Hand

Index–Titles of Pyle's Art In Chronological Sequence

1888

Headpiece, Chapter I for Otto of the . . . . MBPI2283 . .1888
    Silver Hand

Illustrated initial U for Otto of the . . . . MBPI2284 . .1888
    Silver Hand

There they sat, just as little children . . . . MBPI2285 . .1888
    of the town might sit upon their father's doorstep

Tailpiece, Chapter I for Otto of the . . . . MBPI2286 . .1888
    Silver Hand

Headpiece, Chapter II for Otto of the . . . . MBPI2287 . .1888
    Silver Hand

Illustrated initial B for Otto of the . . . . MBPI2288 . .1888
    Silver Hand

Away they rode with clashing hoofs and . . . . . MBPI2289 . .1888
    ringing armor

Tailpiece, Chapter II for Otto of the . . . . MBPI2290 . .1888
    Silver Hand

Headpiece, Chapter III for Otto of the . . . . MBPI2291 . .1888
    Silver Hand

Illustrated initial B for Otto of the . . . . MBPI2292 . .1888
    Silver Hand

No one was within but old Ursela, who sat . . . . MBPI2293 . .1888
    crooning over a fire

Tailpiece, Chapter III for Otto of the . . . . MBPI2294 . .1888
    Silver Hand

Headpiece, Chapter IV for Otto of the . . . . MBPI2295 . .1888
    Silver Hand

Illustrated initial W for Otto of the . . . . MBPI2296 . .1888
    Silver Hand

Abbot Otto of St. Michaelsburg was a . . . . MBPI2297 . .1888
    gentle, patient, pale-faced old man

"While I lay there with my horse upon me, ... MBPI2298 . .1888
    Baron Frederick ran me down with his lance"

Tailpiece, Chapter IV for Otto of the . . . . MBPI2299 . .1888
    Silver Hand

Headpiece, Chapter V for Otto of the . . . . MBPI2300 . .1888
    Silver Hand

Illustrated initial S for Otto of the . . . . MBPI2301 . .1888
    Silver Hand

The poor simple Brother sitting under the . . . . MBPI2302 . .1888
    pear tree close to the bee-hives, rocking the little baby in his
    arms

Always it was one picture that little . . . . MBPI2303 . .1888
    Otto sought

Tailpiece, Chapter V for Otto of the . . . . MBPI2304 . .1888
    Silver Hand

Headpiece, Chapter VI for Otto of the . . . . MBPI2305 . .1888
    Silver Hand

Illustrated initial T for Otto of the . . . . MBPI2306 . .1888
    Silver Hand

Poor Brother John came forward and took . . . MBPI2307 . .1888
    the boy's hand

Otto lay close to her feet upon a . . . . MBPI2308 . .1888
    bear-skin

Tailpiece, Chapter VI for Otto of the . . Titles . . MBPI2309 . .1888
    Silver Hand

Headpiece, Chapter VII for Otto of the . . . . MBPI2310 . .1888
    Silver Hand

Illustrated initial T for Otto of the . . . . MBPI2311 . .1888
    Silver Hand

1888

The grim Baron sat silent with his chin . . . . MBPI2312 . .1888
    resting upon his clenched fist

Slowly raising himself upon the narrow . . . . . . MBPI2313 . .1888
    foot-hold, he peeped cautiously within

Schwartz Carl, holding his arbelast in . . . . MBPI2314 . .1888
    his hand, stood silently watching

He strode forward into the room and laid . . . . MBPI2315 . .1888
    his hand heavily on the boy's shoulder

Tailpiece, Chapter VII for Otto of the . . . . MBPI2316 . .1888
    Silver Hand

Headpiece, Chapter VIII for Otto of the . . . . MBPI2317 . .1888
    Silver Hand

Illustrated initial A for Otto of the . . . . MBPI2318 . .1888
    Silver Hand

"Then dost thou not know why I am here?" . . . MBPI2319 . .1888
    said the Baron

Headpiece, Chapter IX for Otto of the . . . . MBPI2320 . .1888
    Silver Hand

Illustrated initial F for Otto of the . . . . MBPI2321 . .1888
    Silver Hand

Fritz, the swineherd, sat eating his late . . . . MBPI2322 . .1888
    supper of porridge

Hans held up a necklace of blue and white . . . MBPI2323 . .1888
    beads

Tailpiece, Chapter IX for Otto of the . . . . MBPI2324 . .1888
    Silver Hand

Headpiece, Chapter X for Otto of the . . . . MBPI2325 . .1888
    Silver Hand

Illustrated initial H for Otto of the . . . . MBPI2326 . .1888
    Silver Hand

"Thou ugly toad," said the woman . . . . MBPI2327 . .1888

The man was Long Jacob, the bowman . . . . MBPI2328 . .1888

In an instant he was flung back and down . . . . MBPI2329 . .1888

Tailpiece, Chapter X for Otto of the . . . . MBPI2330 . .1888
    Silver Hand

Headpiece, Chapter XI for Otto of the . . . . MBPI2331 . .1888
    Silver Hand

Illustrated initial L for Otto of the . . . . MBPI2332 . .1888
    Silver Hand

The next moment they were hanging in . . . . . . MBPI2333 . .1888
    mid-air

Tailpiece, Chapter XI for Otto of the . . . . MBPI2334 . .1888
    Silver Hand

Headpiece, Chapter XII for Otto of the . . . . MBPI2335 . .1888
    Silver Hand

Illustrated initial B for Otto of the . . . . MBPI2336 . .1888
    Silver Hand

He was gazing straight before him with a . . . . MBPI2337 . .1888
    set and stony face

Tailpiece, Chapter XII for Otto of the . . . . MBPI2338 . .1888
    Silver Hand

Headpiece, Chapter XIII for Otto of the . . . . MBPI2339 . .1888
    Silver Hand

Illustrated initial A for Otto of the . . . . MBPI2340 . .1888
    Silver Hand

In the middle of the narrow way stood the . . . MBPI2341 . .1888
    motionless, steel-clad figure

For a moment they stood swaying . . . . MBPI2342 . .1888
    backward and forward

Index–Titles of Pyle's Art In Chronological Sequence

1888

Tailpiece, Chapter XIII for Otto of the ....MBPI2343 ..1888
Silver Hand

Headpiece, Chapter XIV for Otto of the ....MBPI2344 ..1888
Silver Hand

Illustrated initial T for Otto of the ....MBPI2345 ..1888
Silver Hand

It was the great Emperor Rudolph ....MBPI2346 ..1888

Tailpiece, Chapter XIV for Otto of the ....MBPI2347 ..1888
Silver Hand

He took her hand and set it to his lips ....MBPI2348 ..1888

Headpiece, Afterword for Otto of the ....MBPI2349 ..1888
Silver Hand

Illustrated initial T for Otto of the ....MBPI2350 ..1888
Silver Hand

Washington, the Young Surveyor ....MBPI2792 ..1888

Cover design for The Tuesday Club ....MBPI3210 ..1888

Headpiece for The Tuesday Club ....MBPI3211 ..1888

Decoration for The Tuesday Club ....MBPI3212 ..1888

Washington met by his neighbors on his .....MBPI0359 ..1889
way to the Inauguration

The Inauguration ....MBPI0360 ..1889

Celebration on the Night of the ....MBPI0361 ..1889
Inauguration

An Old Lancaster House ....MBPI0362 ..1889

A Dormitory in the Sisters' House, ...MBPI0363 ..1889
Ephrata

The Kloster ....MBPI0364 ..1889

Going to Meeting ....MBPI0365 ..1889

The Kiss of Peace ....MBPI0366 ..1889

My Cicerone ....MBPI0367 ..1889

"It was to represent the Narrow Way" ....MBPI0368 ..1889

"It was along this wall that the wounded .....MBPI0369 ..1889
soldiers sat"

Interior of Chapel ....MBPI0370 ..1889

Headpiece with title and illustrated ....MBPI1579 ..1889
initial T for That Which is Done Never Dies

"A golden swan leaped into the air" ....MBPI1580 ..1889

"As it sang it sang so sweetly and so ....MBPI1581 ..1889
sadly"

"The Princess sits in the window and ....MBPI1582 ..1889
sings"

"The King opened the closet door and ....MBPI1583 ..1889
brought forth the true bride"

"There sprang from the midst of the smoke ..MBPI1584 ..1889
a beautiful bird"

Headpiece with title for Ill-Luck and the ......MBPI1585 ..1889
Fiddler

Vignette for Ill-Luck and the Fiddler ....MBPI1586 ..1889

Vignette for Ill-Luck and the Fiddler ....MBPI1587 ..1889

Vignette for Ill-Luck and the Fiddler ....MBPI1588 ..1889

Vignette for Ill-Luck and the Fiddler ....MBPI1589 ..1889

Vignette for Ill-Luck and the Fiddler ....MBPI1590 ..1889

Vignette for Ill-Luck and the Fiddler ....MBPI1591 ..1889

Headpiece with title for Wisdom's Wages .....MBPI1592 ..1889
and Folly's Pay

Vignette for Wisdom's Wages and Folly's ......MBPI1593 ..1889
Pay

Vignette for Wisdom's Wages and Folly's ......MBPI1594 ..1889
Pay

1890

Vignette for Wisdom's Wages and Folly's ......MBPI1595 ..1889
Pay

Vignette for Wisdom's Wages and Folly's ......MBPI1596 ..1889
Pay

Vignette for Wisdom's Wages and Folly's ......MBPI1597 ..1889
Pay

Vignette for Wisdom's Wages and Folly's ......MBPI1598 ..1889
Pay

Vignette for Wisdom's Wages and Folly's ......MBPI1599 ..1889
Pay

"A moment later there was a great ....MBPI1912 ..1889
hammering on the oak door"

"Five red-coated soldiers on horse-back, ...MBPI1913 ..1889
with another cloaked to the eyes... Clustering about these, a
motley score of poor people, young and old"

Within sound of the shouting waters ....MBPI1914 ..1889

"We men-folk thought the music as sweet ....MBPI1915 ..1889
as that of the Cherubim"

"This is Enoch Wade, gentlemen," said the ....MBPI1916 ..1889
baronet

"Good-by, big brother," she said softly ....MBPI1917 ..1889

"He told them, when we chanced to sit ....MBPI1918 ..1889
around the fires of an evening, most remarkable stories of
field and forest"

"At sight of me the good soul gave a ....MBPI1919 ..1889
guttural exclamation, and stared at me open-mouthed"

Breton Peasants at a Wayside Cross ....MBPI1932 ..1889

The Messiah cover design for The Tuesday ....MBPI3213 ..1889
Club

Cover design without border for Tuesday .....PDPI0066 ..1889
Club

"She stood like a bronze. Gabriel was ....MBPI0371 ..1890
beside her, his naked cutlass in his hand"

"'And you would not give me a chance to ....MBPI0372 ..1890
tell you,'–she repeated, pleadingly,–touching his arm"

Illustrated initial I for Jamaica, New ....MBPI0373 ..1890
and Old

"Popping ineffectual round-shot after ....MBPI0374 ..1890
her"

"The dim, shadowy forms of vessels riding ....MBPI0375 ..1890
at anchor in the night"

"A hot, broad, all-pervading glare of ....MBPI0376 ..1890
sunlight"

"A lodging-house very well known to all ......MBPI0377 ..1890
Jamaica travellers"

Spanish Galleon ....MBPI0378 ..1890

"That prince or potentate of the old ....MBPI0379 ..1890
sugar king period"

"A turbaned coolie and his wife" ....MBPI0380 ..1890

"Where they sit in long rows with baskets ....MBPI0381 ..1890
of oranges"

"Sitting with piles of great pots and ....MBPI0382 ..1890
bowls and queer jars of red earthenware"

"A curious group traveling along a hot ....MBPI0383 ..1890
dusty road"

In the market place ....MBPI0384 ..1890

"In mid-harbor the tainted crafts were ....MBPI0385 ..1890
burned in sight of all"

Index–Titles of Pyle's Art In Chronological Sequence

1890

Gallows Point . . . . MBPI0386 . .1890
"The beautiful sweeping curve of harbor" . . . . . MBPI0387 . .1890
"Squatted on a log, and talked in a sad, ... MBPI0388 . .1890
    melancholy manner"
"The abbot and the town major personating   MBPI0389 . .1890
    conquered Spain"
The Mangrove . . . . MBPI0390 . .1890
"One time it was alive with the great . . . . MBPI0391 . .1890
    lumbering coaches"
"Around the archways and the square stone . . MBPI0392 . .1890
    pillars, buzzing like angry hornets"
"It is the Cathedral of St. Katherine" . . . . MBPI0393 . .1890
"Sic transit gloria mundi" . . . . MBPI0394 . .1890
Headpiece for Jamaica, New and Old . . . . MBPI0395 . .1890
Illustrated initial P for Jamaica, New . . . . MBPI0396 . .1890
    and Old
"The Governor was among the very first to . . . MBPI0397 . .1890
    set foot upon the deck"
"The embrasures are blind and empty" . . . . MBPI0398 . .1890
"Here and there one comes upon an old . . . . . MBPI0399 . .1890
    house"
"They were dressed in loose sackcloth . . . . MBPI0400 . .1890
    shirt and drawers"
"A store stood with open front toward the . . . . MBPI0401 . .1890
    road"
"An old man, lean and naked" . . . . MBPI0402 . .1890
"An ancient sibyl-like figure" . . . . MBPI0403 . .1890
"A crowd gathered around" . . . . MBPI0404 . .1890
"Plantation houses standing back from the . . . MBPI0405 . .1890
    roadside"
"It is the leader, and all the others . . . . MBPI0406 . .1890
    follow it"
"The long straggling aqueduct" . . . . MBPI0407 . .1890
"A turbaned negro woman sat with her . . . . . . MBPI0408 . .1890
    knitting"
"The crooked winding road that leads into . . . MBPI0409 . .1890
    the village"
"He sat down by the garden gate" . . . . MBPI0410 . .1890
"And thither children brought donkeys . . . . MBPI0411 . .1890
    every morning"
"In all houses one finds the filter and . . . . MBPI0412 . .1890
    the water jar"
"Coffee mill, surrounded by flat stone . . . . MBPI0413 . .1890
    terraces"
"A great section of bamboo trunk balanced . . MBPI0414 . .1890
    upon her head"
"Two negro women stood gossiping and . . . . . MBPI0415 . .1890
    cooling their feet"
"The only picturesque object in the whole . . . MBPI0416 . .1890
    horrid expanse"
The bugle call . . . . MBPI0417 . .1890
Illustrated initial A for Old New York . . . . MBPI0418 . .1890
    Taverns
The Old-time Landlord . . . . MBPI0419 . .1890
"The King's Head, kept by one Roger . . . . MBPI0420 . .1890
    Baker"
"Elizabeth Jourdain, who lodged Her . . . . MBPI0421 . .1890
    Majesty's soldiers"

1890

Game of Bowls . . . . MBPI0422 . .1890
"'The Dog's Head in the Pot' (of great . . . . MBPI0423 . .1890
    antiquity)"
"It crossed the river to the Long Island . . . . MBPI0424 . .1890
    side of the Brooklyn Ferry"
Brownejohn's Wharf . . . . MBPI0425 . .1890
"Each to be honored with bumpers . . . . MBPI0426 . .1890
    innumerable of rich wine and punch"
In the reading-room . . . . MBPI0427 . .1890
"The rival editors" . . . . MBPI0428 . .1890
"John Still, 'an honest barber and . . . . MBPI0429 . .1890
    peruke-maker from London'"
"The ball began with French dances" . . . . MBPI0430 . .1890
"The chair was carried by hand and the . . . . . . MBPI0431 . .1890
    harness was worn by the bearers"
"Cards and gaming were features" . . . . MBPI0432 . .1890
The ferry . . . . MBPI0433 . .1890
"Cargoes of favorite vintages" . . . . MBPI0434 . .1890
"The drum beat in the streets of the . . . . MBPI0435 . .1890
    city"
"The first violin would be played by a . . . . MBPI0436 . .1890
    'gentleman lately arrived'"
At the Vauxhall . . . . MBPI0437 . .1890
"Exchanged thrusts with the merciless . . . . MBPI0438 . .1890
    Junius"
"The variety and fatigues of his . . . . MBPI0439 . .1890
    business"
Meeting of Captain Tollemache and Captain . . MBPI0440 . .1890
    Pennington at the New York Arms
"John Cape takes down the quaint old . . . . MBPI0441 . .1890
    sign"
"The men who met at Hampden Hall" . . . . MBPI0442 . .1890
Tailpiece for Old New York Taverns . . . . MBPI0443 . .1890
The Chapman . . . . MBPI0444 . .1890
Claude DuVal proposes a Dance on the . . . . . . MBPI0445 . .1890
    Heath
Sir James Thornhill painting Jack . . . . MBPI0446 . .1890
    Sheppard's portrait
Turpin and King . . . . MBPI0447 . .1890
Jonathan in the Wood Street Compter . . . . MBPI0448 . .1890
    Prison
Jonathan as an Enemy arresting a Thief . . . . . . MBPI0449 . .1890
Jonathan and a Client–The Lady with the . . . . . MBPI0450 . .1890
    Green Pocket-book
On the Way to Tyburn . . . . MBPI0451 . .1890
Headpiece with title for The Quaker Lady . . . . . MBPI0452 . .1890
Vignette for The Quaker Lady . . . . MBPI0453 . .1890
Vignette for The Quaker Lady . . . . MBPI0454 . .1890
Vignette for The Quaker Lady . . . . MBPI0455 . .1890
Vignette for The Quaker Lady . . . . MBPI0456 . .1890
Vignette for The Quaker Lady . . . . MBPI0457 . .1890
Vignette for The Quaker Lady . . . . MBPI0458 . .1890
Vignette for The Quaker Lady . . . . MBPI0459 . .1890
Vignette for The Quaker Lady . . . . MBPI0460 . .1890
Vignette for The Quaker Lady . . . . MBPI0461 . .1890
Vignette for The Quaker Lady . . . . MBPI0462 . .1890
Vignette for The Quaker Lady . . . . MBPI0463 . .1890
Vignette for The Quaker Lady . . . . MBPI0464 . .1890

Index–Titles of Pyle's Art In Chronological Sequence

1890

Vignette for The Quaker Lady . . . . MBPI0465 . .1890
Vignette for The Quaker Lady . . . . MBPI0466 . .1890
Vignette for The Quaker Lady . . . . MBPI0467 . .1890
Vignette for The Quaker Lady . . . . MBPI0468 . .1890
The Magic Flute . . . . MBPI0469 . .1890
"He had beautiful manners" . . . . MBPI0470 . .1890
"His long nightly labors" . . . . MBPI0471 . .1890
The Widow Spurlock . . . . MBPI0472 . .1890
Old Arsena . . . . MBPI0473 . .1890
"With their heads close together" . . . . MBPI0474 . .1890
"He began to play" . . . . MBPI0475 . .1890
Hanging the violin . . . . MBPI0476 . .1890
David . . . . MBPI0477 . .1890
"He prayed with unusual fervor" . . . . MBPI0478 . .1890
Mr. Leuba . . . . MBPI0479 . .1890
"Executing an intricate passage" . . . . MBPI0480 . .1890
"A small crowd had collected around the . . . . . MBPI0481 . .1890
    entrance to the Museum"
"The widow dropped her eyes" . . . . MBPI0482 . .1890
"It was a very gay dinner" . . . . MBPI0483 . .1890
The parson came down the street driving . . . . MBPI0484 . .1890
    his flock of boys
Before the picture . . . . MBPI0485 . .1890
"Toiled homeward with his treasure" . . . . MBPI0486 . .1890
"Buried his head on her bosom" . . . . MBPI0487 . .1890
At David's bedside . . . . MBPI0488 . .1890
"His head bowed on his folded arms" . . . . MBPI0489 . .1890
Headpiece with title for The Salt of Life . . . . . . MBPI1600 . .1890
"Away with you, and never let me see your . . . MBPI1601 . .1890
    face again"
"An old man looked down into the water" . . . . MBPI1602 . .1890
"The Queen raised the veil and looked at . . . . . MBPI1603 . .1890
    the Prince"
"Away the boat went, swifter than the . . . . MBPI1604 . .1890
    wind"
"Beat the statue with her steel-tipped . . . . MBPI1605 . .1890
    whip"
"The raven spread his wings and flew" . . . . MBPI1606 . .1890
"At last they dashed against one another" . . . . MBPI1607 . .1890
"The statue became flesh and blood" . . . . MBPI1608 . .1890
"He had a noble feast set for them" . . . . MBPI1609 . .1890
Headpiece with title for Empty Bottles . . . . MBPI1610 . .1890
"Making strange figures upon the table" . . . . . MBPI1611 . .1890
"'Now,' said the Master, 'take me by the . . . . . . MBPI1612 . .1890
    belt'"
"He gazed and gazed until his heart . . . . MBPI1613 . .1890
    melted within him"
"The dragon leaped into the air" . . . . MBPI1614 . .1890
"He raised the dagger to strike" . . . . MBPI1615 . .1890
Headpiece with title for Where to Lay the . . . . MBPI1616 . .1890
    Blame
"The old man began to utter strange . . . . MBPI1617 . .1890
    spells"
"He caught something that weighed heavily . . MBPI1618 . .1890
    as lead"
"They kissed one another" . . . . MBPI1619 . .1890
"The chief treasurer emptied a bag of . . . . MBPI1620 . .1890
    money into the fur cap"

1890

"Down fell the fisherman" . . . . MBPI1621 . .1890
Headpiece with title for Not a Pin to . . . . MBPI1622 . .1890
    Choose
"He was like one bereft of wits" . . . . MBPI1623 . .1890
"A wise man stopped to enquire the cause . . . MBPI1624 . .1890
    of his sorrow"
"A great crowd of horses laden with balls . . . . . MBPI1625 . .1890
    and bundles of rich stuffs"
"There was a passageway yawning before . . . . MBPI1626 . .1890
    him"
"Out leaped a great hideous Genie" . . . . MBPI1627 . .1890
"Bread as white as snow, and a piece of . . . . . . MBPI1628 . .1890
    cheese"
"Blazing with diamonds and rubies and . . . . . . MBPI1629 . .1890
    emeralds"
"The Princess looked over the edge of the . . . . MBPI1630 . .1890
    balcony"
"'Sire,' said the Ambassador, 'I will . . . . MBPI1631 . .1890
    answer now for my master'"
Headpiece with title for Woman's Wit . . . . MBPI1632 . .1890
"A box of adamant" . . . . MBPI1633 . .1890
"The little man set him to work on the . . . . MBPI1634 . .1890
    bench"
"It was the King's daughter passing by" . . . . . . MBPI1635 . .1890
"The young man prostrated himself in the . . . . MBPI1636 . .1890
    dust"
"Then prepare to die" . . . . MBPI1637 . .1890
Tailpiece for Woman's Wit . . . . MBPI1638 . .1890
Headpiece with title for Good Gifts and a . . . . . MBPI1639 . .1890
    Fool's Folly
"An old man with a beard as white as . . . . MBPI1640 . .1890
    snow"
"Away flew the carpet swifter than the . . . . MBPI1641 . .1890
    wind"
"Every day there was feasting and dancing . . . MBPI1642 . .1890
    and singing"
"He balanced the earthen jar on his head" . . . . MBPI1643 . .1890
"Around and around they spun and whirled" . . MBPI1644 . .1890
"He lay there sighing and groaning" . . . . MBPI1645 . .1890
Headpiece with title for All Things Are . . . . MBPI1646 . .1890
    as Fate Wills
"Three men seized him" . . . . MBPI1647 . .1890
"The King and the beggar feasted" . . . . MBPI1648 . .1890
"He knocked upon the brazen gate" . . . . MBPI1649 . .1890
"The beggar crawled out" . . . . MBPI1650 . .1890
"He was seated upon a throne" . . . . MBPI1651 . .1890
Headpiece with title for Much Shall Have . . . . . MBPI1652 . .1890
    More and Little Shall Have Less
"He spread the money out on the table" . . . . . . MBPI1653 . .1890
"Sat down by the road-side to eat his . . . . MBPI1654 . .1890
    pie"
"He met a poor woman coming home from . . MBPI1655 . .1890
    market"
"'Keep the bag of money for yourself,' . . . . MBPI1656 . .1890
    said the King"
Headpiece with title for The Stool of . . . . MBPI1657 . .1890
    Fortune
"If the shot had cracked the sky he could . . . . . MBPI1658 . .1890
    not have been more frightened"

Index–Titles of Pyle's Art In Chronological Sequence

1890

"Away flew the stool" . . . . MBPI1659 . .1890

"The prettiest princess the sun ever . . . . MBPI1660 . .1890
shone upon"

"Riding in his gilded coach" . . . . MBPI1661 . .1890

"What are my lord's commands?" . . . . MBPI1662 . .1890

Tailpiece for The Stool of Fortune . . . . MBPI1663 . .1890

Headpiece with title for The Captain's . . . . MBPI1763 . .1890
Well

Illustration for The Captain's Well . . . . MBPI1764 . .1890

Illustration for The Captain's Well . . . . MBPI1765 . .1890

Illustration for The Captain's Well . . . . MBPI1766 . .1890

Illustration for The Captain's Well . . . . MBPI1767 . .1890

"He lay silent and still, with his face . . . . MBPI1768 . .1890
half buried in the sand"

"The negro boy, arms whirling wide in . . . . MBPI1920 . .1890
air, shot over the side of the cliff"

"The blow–the whole crushing series of . . . . . . MBPI1921 . .1890
blows–had fallen!"

"She was silent for a moment, her eyes . . . . MBPI1922 . .1890
seeking the floor"

"The dignified sober figure of Abraham . . . . . . MBPI1923 . .1890
Ten Broeck appeared in our wrathful circle"

"While his eyes still glowed fiery wrath, ... MBPI1924 . .1890
the trembling lips became piteous in their inability to form
words"

"Then a great mashing blow on my face . . . . . . MBPI1925 . .1890
ended my fight"

"'Who are you? and off with your hat!' I . . . . . . MBPI1926 . .1890
said to the man, sharply"

"Is your hanging-party ready?" he said . . . . MBPI1927 . .1890

"I turned the sheet over and over in my . . . . . . MBPI1928 . .1890
hands, re-reading lines here and there"

"'I wish to God we were well out of this . . . . . . MBPI1929 . .1890
all,' he said, almost gloomily"

"There, half stretched on the wet . . . . MBPI1930 . .1890
blood-stained grass, lay Philip Cross"

"My hatred of him seemed suddenly to have MBPI1931 . .1890
taken to itself wings"

Decorative title for A Pastoral Without . . . . MBPI1933 . .1890
Words

Subtitle, A Pastoral Without Words . . . . MBPI1934 . .1890

Decorative title, Verse I for A Pastoral . . . . MBPI1935 . .1890
Without Words

Verse I, A Pastoral Without Words . . . . MBPI1936 . .1890

Decorative title, Verse II for A Pastoral . . . . MBPI1937 . .1890
Without Words

Verse II, A Pastoral Without Words . . . . MBPI1938 . .1890

Decorative title, Verse III for A . . . . MBPI1939 . .1890
Pastoral Without Words

Verse III, A Pastoral Without Words . . . . MBPI1940 . .1890

Decorative title, Verse IV for A Pastoral . . . . . . MBPI1941 . .1890
Without Words

Verse IV, A Pastoral Without Words . . . . MBPI1942 . .1890

Decorative title, L'Envoy for A Pastoral . . . . MBPI1943 . .1890
Without Words

L'Envoy, A Pastoral Without Words . . . . MBPI1944 . .1890

Illustrated initial F with decoration for . . . . PDPI0019 . .1890
The Captain's Well

1891

The Flute Player . . . . PDPI0052 . .1890

Ye Pirate Bold . . . . MBPI0001 . .1891

"He was a tall dark gentleman dressed in . . . . . MBPI0133 . .1891
black from head to foot"

"He suddenly began an uncouth grotesque . . MBPI0134 . .1891
dance"

"At that moment she looked up" . . . . MBPI0135 . .1891

"'I am thy Uncle,' said the strange . . . . MBPI0136 . .1891
gentleman"

"He lighted a match and dropped it into . . . . . MBPI0137 . .1891
the vase"

"Oliver gave a piping cry" . . . . MBPI0138 . .1891

"At the open doorway stood Gaspard and . . . . MBPI0139 . .1891
his master"

"Creeping cautiously forward, Oliver came . . . . MBPI0140 . .1891
to the chimney-place"

"'Good day, Monsieur,' said a familiar . . . . MBPI0141 . .1891
voice"

"The question was so sudden and so . . . . MBPI0142 . .1891
startling that Oliver sank back in his seat"

"They saw Arnold de Villeneuve, the great . . . . MBPI0143 . .1891
master, lying upon the floor"

"Such was the workshop in which the two . . . . MBPI0144 . .1891
labored together"

"She held the book to the flames whilest . . . . . MBPI0145 . .1891
talking, her eyes fixed intently upon it"

"He leaned over and looked into her face" . . . . MBPI0146 . .1891

"He saw within an oval mirror, set in a . . . . MBPI0147 . .1891
heavy frame of copper"

"And stripped the false body off of him . . . . . . MBPI0148 . .1891
as you would strip off a man's coat"

"The innkeeper served him in person" . . . . MBPI0149 . .1891

"'Mad!' said Oliver, 'why am I mad?'" . . . . MBPI0150 . .1891

"Oliver spread out the gems upon the . . . . MBPI0151 . .1891
table with his hand"

"He is clad in a loose dressing-robe of . . . . MBPI0152 . .1891
figured cloth and lies in bed reading his book"

"'Do you know,' said the Marquis, 'what a . . . . . MBPI0153 . .1891
thing it is that you ask?'"

"He sank upon his knees beside her" . . . . MBPI0154 . .1891

"She drew her down until the girl kneeled . . . . MBPI0155 . .1891
upon the floor beside the sofa"

"Monsieur the Count de St. Germaine" . . . . MBPI0156 . .1891

"The Count de St. Germaine, without . . . . MBPI0157 . .1891
removing his eyes from his victim, took another deep, luxurious pinch of snuff"

"Oliver fixed his gaze upon the smooth . . . . . . MBPI0158 . .1891
brilliant surface of the glass"

"He saw a dull heavy yellow smoke arise . . . . . MBPI0159 . .1891
to the ceiling"

"They beheld their master lying upon his . . . . . MBPI0160 . .1891
face under the table"

"Suddenly someone touched Oliver lightly . . . MBPI0161 . .1891
upon the shoulder"

"He found in his clinched hand a lace . . . . MBPI0162 . .1891
cravat"

"'Celeste!' breathed Oliver through the . . . . MBPI0163 . .1891
crack in the door"

Index–Titles of Pyle's Art In Chronological Sequence

1891

"Over his shoulder he carried something . . . . . MBPI0164 . .1891
limp, like an empty skin, or a bundle of clothes tied together"

Headpiece with title for The First . . . . MBPI0165 . .1891
Thanksgiving

Illustrated initial O for The First . . . . MBPI0166 . .1891
Thanksgiving

A Maid's Choice . . . . MBPI0490 . .1891

Verse 1. Ye Jovial Huntsman . . . . MBPI0491 . .1891

Verse 2. Ye Fat, Rich Man . . . . MBPI0492 . .1891

Verse 3. Ye Gallant Soldier . . . . MBPI0493 . .1891

Verse 4. Ye Jolly Country Boy . . . . MBPI0494 . .1891

Headpiece for The Two Cornets of Monmouth MBPI1261 . .1891

"On sped the light chestnut, with the . . . . MBPI1262 . .1891
little officer bending almost to the saddle-bow"

Headpiece with title for The Fruit of . . . . MBPI1664 . .1891
Happiness

"He came to the cross-roads and the stone . . . MBPI1665 . .1891
cross"

"He drew out his pipe, and began to play" . . . . MBPI1666 . .1891

"In came the gang of thieves" . . . . MBPI1667 . .1891

"All was a red blaze behind them" . . . . MBPI1668 . .1891

"Went whirling over rocks and waterfalls" . . . . . MBPI1669 . .1891

The Flight from Falworth Castle . . . . MBPI1670 . .1891

"Myles as in a dream kneeled, and . . . . MBPI1671 . .1891
presented the letter"

Illustration for Men of Iron . . . . MBPI1672 . .1891

"At last they had the poor boy down" . . . . MBPI1673 . .1891

"Myles pushed the door further open" . . . . MBPI1674 . .1891

In the "Eyry" . . . . MBPI1675 . .1891

"They bore him away to a bench at the far . . . . MBPI1676 . .1891
end of the room"

"But tell me, Robin Ingoldsby, dost know . . . . . MBPI1677 . .1891
aught more of this matter?"

"'Belike thou sought to take this lad's . . . . MBPI1678 . .1891
life,' said Sir James"

"Stories and jests recited by some . . . . MBPI1679 . .1891
strolling mummer or minstrel"

Myles entertains the Lady Anne and the . . . . . . MBPI1680 . .1891
Lady Alice with his adventures

"Myles found himself standing beside the . . . . MBPI1681 . .1891
bed"

The Earl of Mackworth receives King Henry . . . MBPI1682 . .1891
IV

"Lord George led him to where the King . . . . . MBPI1683 . .1891
stood"

"There he watched and guarded while the . . . MBPI1684 . .1891
others slept"

Illustration for Men of Iron . . . . MBPI1685 . .1891

Illustration for Men of Iron . . . . MBPI1686 . .1891

Prior Edward and Myles in the Priory . . . . MBPI1687 . .1891
Garden

The Challenge . . . . MBPI1688 . .1891

Illustration for Men of Iron . . . . MBPI1689 . .1891

"He held tightly to the saddle-bow of the . . . . MBPI1690 . .1891
fallen man's horse"

Headpiece with title for The Enchanted . . . . . . MBPI1691 . .1891
Island

"Selim the Fisherman finds a leaden box" . . . . . MBPI1692 . .1891

"The old man rapped on the door three . . . . . . MBPI1693 . .1891
times"

"There was feasting and merrymaking" . . . . MBPI1694 . .1891

"Selim the Baker lands on the desert . . . . MBPI1696 . .1891
island"

"'Come with me,' said the little old man" . . . . . . MBPI1697 . .1891

"He called the wisest men of the island . . . . . . MBPI1698 . .1891
to him"

"Down she came from the pedestal where . . . MBPI1699 . .1891
she stood"

Tailpiece for The Enchanted Island . . . . MBPI1700 . .1891

The First Christmas Tree . . . . MBPI1945 . .1891

"It poised for an instant above the . . . . MBPI1946 . .1891
child's fair head–death cruel and imminent"

Headpiece with title for Peter Rugg Ye . . . . MBPI1947 . .1891
Bostonian

Vignette for Peter Rugg Ye Bostonian . . . . MBPI1948 . .1891

Vignette for Peter Rugg Ye Bostonian . . . . MBPI1949 . .1891

Vignette for Peter Rugg Ye Bostonian . . . . MBPI1950 . .1891

Vignette for Peter Rugg Ye Bostonian . . . . MBPI1951 . .1891

Vignette for Peter Rugg Ye Bostonian . . . . MBPI1952 . .1891

Vignette for Peter Rugg Ye Bostonian . . . . MBPI1953 . .1891

Vignette for Peter Rugg Ye Bostonian . . . . MBPI1954 . .1891

Vignette for Peter Rugg Ye Bostonian . . . . MBPI1955 . .1891

Vignette for Peter Rugg Ye Bostonian . . . . MBPI1956 . .1891

Vignette for Peter Rugg Ye Bostonian . . . . MBPI1957 . .1891

Vignette for Peter Rugg Ye Bostonian . . . . MBPI1958 . .1891

The Deacon . . . . MBPI2795 . .1891

"The Deacon inquired of the village folk" . . . . . MBPI2803 . .1891

"All at once the horses stood still" . . . . MBPI2813 . .1891

"Then something decidedly like a spill" . . . . MBPI2814 . .1891

"The famous trotting ground" . . . . MBPI2818 . .1891

"The lovely bonnets beamed their smiles" . . . . . MBPI2823 . .1891

"See how tall they 've grown" . . . . MBPI2851 . .1891

Vignette for A Maid's Choice . . . . MBPI3065 . .1891

Vignette for A Maid's Choice . . . . MBPI3066 . .1891

Vignette for A Maid's Choice . . . . MBPI3067 . .1891

Vignette for A Maid's Choice . . . . MBPI3068 . .1891

Vignette for A Maid's Choice . . . . MBPI3069 . .1891

Vignette for A Maid's Choice . . . . MBPI3070 . .1891

Vignette for A Maid's Choice . . . . MBPI3071 . .1891

Vignette for A Maid's Choice . . . . MBPI3072 . .1891

Vignette for A Maid's Choice . . . . MBPI3073 . .1891

Vignette for A Maid's Choice . . . . MBPI3074 . .1891

Vignette for A Maid's Choice . . . . MBPI3075 . .1891

Vignette for A Maid's Choice . . . . MBPI3076 . .1891

Vignette for A Maid's Choice . . . . MBPI3077 . .1891

Vignette for A Maid's Choice . . . . MBPI3078 . .1891

Vignette for A Maid's Choice . . . . MBPI3079 . .1891

Vignette for A Maid's Choice . . . . MBPI3080 . .1891

Vignette for A Maid's Choice . . . . MBPI3081 . .1891

Vignette for A Maid's Choice . . . . MBPI3082 . .1891

Vignette for A Maid's Choice . . . . MBPI3083 . .1891

Vignette for A Maid's Choice . . . . MBPI3084 . .1891

Vignette for A Maid's Choice . . . . MBPI3085 . .1891

Vignette for A Maid's Choice . . . . MBPI3086 . .1891

Vignette for A Maid's Choice . . . . MBPI3087 . .1891

Vignette for A Maid's Choice . . . . MBPI3088 . .1891

Index–Titles of Pyle's Art In Chronological Sequence

1891

Vignette for A Maid's Choice .... MBPI3089 . .1891
Vignette for A Maid's Choice .... MBPI3090 . .1891
Vignette for A Maid's Choice .... MBPI3091 . .1891
Vignette for A Maid's Choice .... MBPI3092 . .1891
Vignette for A Maid's Choice .... MBPI3093 . .1891
Vignette for A Maid's Choice .... MBPI3094 . .1891
Vignette for A Maid's Choice .... MBPI3095 . .1891
Vignette for A Maid's Choice .... MBPI3096 . .1891
Vignette for A Maid's Choice .... MBPI3097 . .1891
Vignette for A Maid's Choice .... MBPI3098 . .1891
Vignette for A Maid's Choice .... MBPI3099 . .1891
Vignette for A Maid's Choice .... MBPI3100 . .1891
The Deacon's Masterpiece: or the .... PDPI0059 . .1891
    Wonderful "One-Hoss-Shay" with initial H
Peter Rugg Ye Bostonian .... PDPI0060 . .1891
Headpiece with title, A Relay Tavern .... PDPI0067 . .1891
Beach Scene .... PDPI0080 . .1891
"In the Garden" .... MBPI0104 . .1892
"They stood and looked across the chasm .... MBPI0105 . .1892
    at him"
Spine design for Men of Iron .... MBPI0277 . .1892
Reading the Declaration before .... MBPI0501 . .1892
    Washington's Army, New York, July 9, 1776
Headpiece with title for How the .... MBPI0502 . .1892
    Declaration was Received in the Old Thirteen
At Philadelphia, Pennsylvania .... MBPI0503 . .1892
At Princeton, New Jersey .... MBPI0504 . .1892
At Dover, Delaware .... MBPI0505 . .1892
In New York (At Headquarters) .... MBPI0506 . .1892
At Boston, Massachusetts .... MBPI0507 . .1892
At Portsmouth, New Hampshire .... MBPI0508 . .1892
At Newport, Rhode Island .... MBPI0509 . .1892
In Connecticut .... MBPI0510 . .1892
At Williamsburg, Virginia .... MBPI0511 . .1892
At Halifax, North Carolina .... MBPI0512 . .1892
At Baltimore, Maryland .... MBPI0513 . .1892
At Charleston, South Carolina .... MBPI0514 . .1892
At Savannah, Georgia .... MBPI0515 . .1892
Headpiece with title and decorative .... MBPI0516 . .1892
    border for Two Moods
Headpiece for Among the Sand Hills .... MBPI0517 . .1892
Illustrated initial T for Among the Sand ...... MBPI0518 . .1892
    Hills
Vignette for Among the Sand Hills .... MBPI0519 . .1892
Illustrated initial S for Among the Sand ...... MBPI0520 . .1892
    Hills
Vignette for Among the Sand Hills .... MBPI0521 . .1892
Illustrated initial T for Among the Sand ...... MBPI0522 . .1892
    Hills
The Sand Hills .... MBPI0523 . .1892
Vignette for Among the Sand Hills .... MBPI0524 . .1892
Illustrated initial F for Among the Sand ...... MBPI0525 . .1892
    Hills
Vignette for Among the Sand Hills .... MBPI0526 . .1892
Illustrated initial B for Among the Sand ...... MBPI0527 . .1892
    Hills
Vignette for Among the Sand Hills .... MBPI0528 . .1892
Vignette for Among the Sand Hills .... MBPI0529 . .1892

1892

Illustrated initial S for Among the Sand .... MBPI0530 . .1892
    Hills
Vignette for Among the Sand Hills .... MBPI0531 . .1892
The Wreck .... MBPI0532 . .1892
Illustrated initial C for Among the Sand ...... MBPI0533 . .1892
    Hills
Vignette for Among the Sand Hills .... MBPI0534 . .1892
Illustrated initial B for Among the Sand ...... MBPI0535 . .1892
    Hills
Vignette for Among the Sand Hills .... MBPI0536 . .1892
Vignette for Among the Sand Hills .... MBPI0537 . .1892
Vignette for Among the Sand Hills .... MBPI0538 . .1892
Illustrated initial T for Among the Sand ...... MBPI0539 . .1892
    Hills
Vignette for Among the Sand Hills .... MBPI0540 . .1892
Vignette for Among the Sand Hills .... MBPI0541 . .1892
Illustrated initial N for Among the Sand ...... MBPI0542 . .1892
    Hills
Vignette for Among the Sand Hills .... MBPI0543 . .1892
The Lily Lake .... MBPI0544 . .1892
"This is no courting night" .... MBPI0545 . .1892
"Hey, black cat! hey, my pretty black .... MBPI0546 . .1892
    cat"
"There is a flock of yellow birds around .... MBPI0547 . .1892
    her head"
"Father, Father!" .... MBPI0548 . .1892
Headpiece for A Thread Without a Knot .... MBPI1263 . .1892
Stopping the Christmas Stage .... MBPI1264 . .1892
"Zadok and his master" .... MBPI1701 . .1892
"An old man who had a curious necklace ..... MBPI1702 . .1892
    for sale"
"A vessel of brass full of money" .... MBPI1703 . .1892
"A great tall Demon" .... MBPI1704 . .1892
"He fell on his face and kissed the .... MBPI1705 . .1892
    ground"
"The Demon leaped from the earth" .... MBPI1706 . .1892
"A basin filled with jewels" .... MBPI1707 . .1892
"A palace of marble and gold" .... MBPI1708 . .1892
"'I think everybody has gone mad,' said ...... MBPI1709 . .1892
    the young man"
"They entered the vestibule of the .... MBPI1710 . .1892
    palace"
"The young man fell upon his knees" .... MBPI1711 . .1892
"Drew a circle upon the ground with his ..... MBPI1712 . .1892
    finger-tip"
"'This is my daughter,' said the .... MBPI1713 . .1892
    merchant"
"There sat an old woman at a wheel .... MBPI1714 . .1892
    spinning"
"Thou art a wonder of wonders" .... MBPI1715 . .1892
"A dense cloud of blue smoke rose in the ..... MBPI1716 . .1892
    air"
"'I am ready,' said the young man .... MBPI1717 . .1892
    steadily"
"Flew away swifter than the wind" .... MBPI1718 . .1892
"They used to drill every evening" .... MBPI1814 . .1892
Headpiece with title and initial W for .... MBPI1815 . .1892
    The Soldiering of Beniah Stidham

Index–Titles of Pyle's Art In Chronological Sequence

1892

Vignette for The Soldiering of Beniah .... MBPI1816 ..1892
    Stidham

Vignette for The Soldiering of Beniah .... MBPI1817 ..1892
    Stidham

Vignette for The Soldiering of Beniah .... MBPI1818 ..1892
    Stidham

Vignette for The Soldiering of Beniah .... MBPI1819 ..1892
    Stidham

Vignette for The Soldiering of Beniah .... MBPI1820 ..1892
    Stidham

Vignette for The Soldiering of Beniah .... MBPI1821 ..1892
    Stidham

Vignette for The Soldiering of Beniah .... MBPI1822 ..1892
    Stidham

Vignette for The Soldiering of Beniah .... MBPI1823 ..1892
    Stidham

Headpiece for The Little Maid at the Door ..... MBPI2076 ..1892

Illustrated initial J for The Little Maid .... MBPI2077 ..1892
    at the Door

"I see naught but a little maid at the .... MBPI2078 ..1892
    door"

Cover design for Men of Iron .... MBPI2351 ..1892

"Enter Oliver and Mademoiselle Celeste" ...... MBPI2352 ..1892

"The Sachem's Daughter" .... MBPI2793 ..1892

"The Vision of Echard" .... MBPI2794 ..1892

Headpiece, Preface for The One Hoss Shay .... MBPI2796 ..1892

Tailpiece, Preface for The One Hoss Shay ...... MBPI2797 ..1892

Headpiece, List of Illustrations for The .... MBPI2798 ..1892
    One Hoss Shay

Tailpiece, List of Illustrations for The .... MBPI2799 ..1892
    One Hoss Shay

Half-title for The Deacon's Masterpiece .... MBPI2800 ..1892

The Masterpiece .... MBPI2801 ..1892

"A chaise breaks down" .... MBPI2802 ..1892

"Naow she'll dew" .... MBPI2804 ..1892

"She was a wonder, and nothing less" .... MBPI2805 ..1892

"Deacon and deaconess dropped away" ...... MBPI2806 ..1892

"Eighteen Hundred" .... MBPI2807 ..1892

"Fifty-five" .... MBPI2808 ..1892

"Its hundredth year" .... MBPI2809 ..1892

"A general flavor of mild decay" .... MBPI2810 ..1892

"In another hour it will be worn out" .... MBPI2811 ..1892

"The parson takes a drive" .... MBPI2812 ..1892

"Just as bubbles do when they burst" .... MBPI2815 ..1892

"End of the wonderful one-hoss-shay" .... MBPI2816 ..1892

Half-title for How the Old Horse Won the ..... MBPI2817 ..1892
    Bet

"Many a noted steed" .... MBPI2819 ..1892

"The Sunday swell" .... MBPI2820 ..1892

"The jointed tandem" .... MBPI2821 ..1892

"So shy with us, so free with these" .... MBPI2822 ..1892

"I'll bet you two to one" .... MBPI2824 ..1892

"Harnessed in his one-hoss-shay" .... MBPI2825 ..1892

"The sexton...led forth the horse" .... MBPI2826 ..1892

"A sight to see" .... MBPI2827 ..1892

"They lead him, limping, to the track" .... MBPI2828 ..1892

"To limber out each stiffened joint" .... MBPI2829 ..1892

"Something like a stride" .... MBPI2830 ..1892

1893

"A mighty stride he swung" .... MBPI2831 ..1892

"Off went a shoe" .... MBPI2832 ..1892

"And now the stand he rushes by" .... MBPI2833 ..1892

"And off they spring" .... MBPI2834 ..1892

"They follow at his heels" .... MBPI2835 ..1892

"They're losing ground" .... MBPI2836 ..1892

"He's distanced all the lot" .... MBPI2837 ..1892

"Some took his time" .... MBPI2838 ..1892

"Back in the one-hoss-shay he went" .... MBPI2839 ..1892

"A horse can trot, for all he's old" .... MBPI2840 ..1892

Half-title for The Broomstick Train .... MBPI2841 ..1892

"Clear the track" .... MBPI2842 ..1892

"An Essex Deacon dropped in to call" .... MBPI2843 ..1892

"The old dwellings" .... MBPI2844 ..1892

"The small square windows" .... MBPI2845 ..1892

"Dark, dim, Dante-like solitudes" .... MBPI2846 ..1892

"Norman's Woe" .... MBPI2847 ..1892

"The Screeching Woman of Marblehead" ...... MBPI2848 ..1892

"It is n't fair" .... MBPI2849 ..1892

"You're a good old–fellow–come, let us .... MBPI2850 ..1892
    go"

"They called the cats" .... MBPI2852 ..1892

"The Essex people had dreadful times" .... MBPI2853 ..1892

"The withered hags were free" .... MBPI2854 ..1892

"A strange sea-monster stole their bait" .... MBPI2855 ..1892

"They could hear him twenty miles" .... MBPI2856 ..1892

"They came...at their master's call" .... MBPI2857 ..1892

"You can hear the black cat's purr" .... MBPI2858 ..1892

"Catch a gleam from her wicked eye" .... MBPI2859 ..1892

Tailpiece for The Broomstick Train .... MBPI2860 ..1892

The Last Leaf .... MBPI2861 ..1892

The One Hoss Shay .... MBPI2862 ..1892

Dorothy Q .... MBPI2863 ..1892

The Boston Tea Party .... MBPI2864 ..1892

Grandmother's Story of Bunker Hill Battle ..... MBPI2865 ..1892

Dorothy Q .... MBPI2866 ..1892

An Old North-Ender .... MBPI2888 ..1892

"We looked, poor timid creatures" .... MBPI2919 ..1892

Hosea and the "cruetin Sarjunt" .... MBPI3203 ..1892

Hosea and the Parson .... MBPI3204 ..1892

Zekle and Huldy .... MBPI3205 ..1892

"Sunthin in the Pastoral Line" .... MBPI3206 ..1892

Illustration for A Transferred Romance .... MBPI3241 ..1892

The Rivals .... MBPI0007 ..1893

The First Sketch .... MBPI0008 ..1893

Illustrated initial A for The First .... MBPI0009 ..1893
    Sketch

The Second Sketch .... MBPI0010 ..1893

Illustrated initial A for The Second .... MBPI0011 ..1893
    Sketch

The Third Sketch .... MBPI0012 ..1893

Illustrated initial T for The Third .... MBPI0013 ..1893
    Sketch

The Fourth Sketch .... MBPI0014 ..1893

Illustrated initial T for The Fourth .... MBPI0015 ..1893
    Sketch

The Fifth Sketch .... MBPI0016 ..1893

Illustrated initial A for The Fifth .... MBPI0017 ..1893
    Sketch

1893

1893

The Sixth Sketch . . . . MBPI0018 . .1893

Illustrated initial T for The Sixth . . . . MBPI0019 . .1893
   Sketch

In the Bookseller's Shop . . . . MBPI0126 . .1893

Question . . . . MBPI0549 . .1893

Headpiece with title for Monochromes . . . . MBPI0550 . .1893

Illustrated initial S for Question . . . . MBPI0551 . .1893

Tailpiece for Question . . . . MBPI0552 . .1893

Living . . . . MBPI0553 . .1893

Illustrated initial H for Living . . . . MBPI0554 . .1893

To-Morrow . . . . MBPI0555 . .1893

Illustrated initial O for To-Morrow . . . . MBPI0556 . .1893

Tailpiece for Friends and Foes . . . . MBPI0557 . .1893

From Generation to Generation . . . . MBPI0558 . .1893

Illustrated initial I for From Generation . . . . MBPI0559 . .1893
   to Generation

Tailpiece for From Generation to . . . . MBPI0560 . .1893
   Generation

The Bewildered Guest . . . . MBPI0561 . .1893

Illustrated initial I for The Bewildered . . . . MBPI0562 . .1893
   Guest

Hope . . . . MBPI0563 . .1893

Illustrated initial Y for Hope . . . . MBPI0564 . .1893

Tailpiece for Hope . . . . MBPI0565 . .1893

Illustrated initial D for Respite . . . . MBPI0566 . .1893

Respite . . . . MBPI0567 . .1893

"He sat down beside her on the bench" . . . . MBPI0568 . .1893

"Thereupon the poor woman screamed aloud, MBPI0569 . .1893
   and cried out that he was a murderer"

Along the Canal in Old Manhattan . . . . MBPI0570 . .1893

Headpiece with title and illustrated . . . . MBPI0571 . .1893
   initial T for The Evolution of New York

On the River Front . . . . MBPI0572 . .1893

Tailpiece for The Evolution of New York . . . . MBPI0573 . .1893

Headpiece, In 1776, The Conflagration . . . . MBPI0574 . .1893

A Privateersman Ashore . . . . MBPI0575 . .1893

Opening of the Erie Canal . . . . MBPI0576 . .1893

Tailpiece for The Evolution of New York . . . . MBPI0577 . .1893

Headpiece with title and illustrated . . . . MBPI0578 . .1893
   initial T for The Cocklane Ghost

Vignette for The Cocklane Ghost . . . . MBPI0579 . .1893

Vignette for The Cocklane Ghost . . . . MBPI0580 . .1893

Vignette for The Cocklane Ghost . . . . MBPI0581 . .1893

Vignette for The Cocklane Ghost . . . . MBPI0582 . .1893

Vignette for The Cocklane Ghost . . . . MBPI0583 . .1893

Vignette for The Cocklane Ghost . . . . MBPI0584 . .1893

Vignette for The Cocklane Ghost . . . . MBPI0585 . .1893

Vignette for The Cocklane Ghost . . . . MBPI0586 . .1893

Vignette for The Cocklane Ghost . . . . MBPI0587 . .1893

Vignette for The Cocklane Ghost . . . . MBPI0588 . .1893

Vignette for The Cocklane Ghost . . . . MBPI0589 . .1893

Tailpiece for The Cocklane Ghost . . . . MBPI0590 . .1893

Headpiece with initial O for A Soldier of . . . . . . MBPI0591 . .1893
   Fortune

Vignette for A Soldier of Fortune . . . . MBPI0592 . .1893

Vignette for A Soldier of Fortune . . . . MBPI0593 . .1893

A Night in the Village Street . . . . MBPI0594 . .1893

Vignette for A Soldier of Fortune . . . . MBPI0595 . .1893

Vignette for A Soldier of Fortune . . . . MBPI0596 . .1893

Dragging the Duke out of the Coach . . . . MBPI0597 . .1893

Vignette for A Soldier of Fortune . . . . MBPI0598 . .1893

Vignette for A Soldier of Fortune . . . . MBPI0599 . .1893

Vignette for A Soldier of Fortune . . . . MBPI0600 . .1893

Vignette for A Soldier of Fortune . . . . MBPI0601 . .1893

The Fight for the Crown . . . . MBPI0602 . .1893

Vignette for A Soldier of Fortune . . . . MBPI0603 . .1893

Vignette for A Soldier of Fortune . . . . MBPI0604 . .1893

Vignette for A Soldier of Fortune . . . . MBPI0605 . .1893

Vignette for A Soldier of Fortune . . . . MBPI0606 . .1893

Illustration for Stamford's Soprano . . . . MBPI1265 . .1893

Scene in the Town Jail . . . . MBPI1266 . .1893

"Close your doors! close your doors! her . . . . . . MBPI1722 . .1893
   Highness the Princess comes to ride"

"Seeing no enemy, and themselves falling . . . . MBPI1959 . .1893
   every moment from the fire"

The Death of Braddock . . . . MBPI1960 . .1893

"For a while no one said a word" . . . . MBPI1961 . .1893

January and May . . . . MBPI1962 . .1893

Decorative border with title for January . . . . . . MBPI1963 . .1893
   and May

Half-title for Dorothy Q . . . . MBPI2867 . .1893

Painting the Picture . . . . MBPI2868 . .1893

"Girlish bust, but womanly air" . . . . MBPI2869 . .1893

"Hint and promise of stately mien" . . . . MBPI2870 . .1893

"The youthful sire" . . . . MBPI2871 . .1893

"Soft is the breath of a maiden's Yes" . . . . MBPI2872 . .1893

"Lady and lover" . . . . MBPI2873 . .1893

"The Boston teapot bubbled" . . . . MBPI2874 . .1893

Half-title for A Ballad of the Boston . . . . MBPI2875 . .1893
   Tea-Party

A cup of Tea . . . . MBPI2876 . .1893

"Many a six foot grenadier–The flattened . . . . . MBPI2877 . .1893
   grass had measured"

"Her tearful memories treasured" . . . . MBPI2878 . .1893

"Behold the guests advancing" . . . . MBPI2879 . .1893

"The lively barber" . . . . MBPI2880 . .1893

"The truant tapster" . . . . MBPI2881 . .1893

"The cooper's boys" . . . . MBPI2882 . .1893

"The lusty young Fort-Hillers" . . . . MBPI2883 . .1893

"The Tories seize the omen" . . . . MBPI2884 . .1893

"The Mohawk band is swarming" . . . . MBPI2885 . .1893

"So gracious, sweet, and purring" . . . . MBPI2886 . .1893

"The quiet dame" . . . . MBPI2887 . .1893

Tailpiece for A Ballad of the Boston . . . . MBPI2889 . .1893
   Tea-Party

Watching the Battle from the Steeple . . . . MBPI2890 . .1893

Title for Grandmother's Story of Bunker . . . . . . MBPI2891 . .1893
   Hill Battle

The Grandmother . . . . MBPI2892 . .1893

Half-title for Grandmother's Story of . . . . MBPI2893 . .1893
   Bunker-Hill Battle

"Lord Percy's hunted soldiers" . . . . MBPI2894 . .1893

"Says grandma, 'What's the matter?'" . . . . MBPI2895 . .1893

"The Mohawks killed her father" . . . . MBPI2896 . .1893

"'Don't you fret and worry any'" . . . . MBPI2897 . .1893

"Down my hair went as I hurried" . . . . MBPI2898 . .1893

Index–Titles of Pyle's Art In Chronological Sequence

1893

"The Corporal marched before" . . . . MBPI2899 . .1893
"We climbed the creaking stair" . . . . MBPI2900 . .1893
"The earthwork hid them from us" . . . . MBPI2901 . .1893
"The cannons' deafening thrill" . . . . MBPI2902 . .1893
"Like a gentleman of leisure" . . . . MBPI2903 . .1893
"The belted grenadiers" . . . . MBPI2904 . .1893
"The barges gliding onward" . . . . MBPI2905 . .1893
"Again they formed in order" . . . . MBPI2906 . .1893
"They wait and answer not" . . . . MBPI2907 . .1893
"The Corporal, our old cripple" . . . . MBPI2908 . .1893
Dan'l Malcolm's Grave . . . . MBPI2909 . .1893
"In the hush of expectation" . . . . MBPI2910 . .1893
"Like a thunder-cloud it breaks" . . . . MBPI2911 . .1893
"A headlong crowd is flying" . . . . MBPI2912 . .1893
"Are they beaten?" . . . . MBPI2913 . .1893
"They are baffled, not defeated" . . . . MBPI2914 . .1893
"The roofs of Charlestown blazing" . . . . MBPI2915 . .1893
"We can see each massive column" . . . . MBPI2916 . .1893
"The ominous calm is broken" . . . . MBPI2917 . .1893
"The frightened braves of Howe" . . . . MBPI2918 . .1893
"'Have a drop of old Jamaiky'" . . . . MBPI2920 . .1893
"They were creeping round to four" . . . . MBPI2921 . .1893
"In close array they come" . . . . MBPI2922 . .1893
"They surged above the breast-work" . . . . MBPI2923 . .1893
"They say I fainted" . . . . MBPI2924 . .1893
"'Here's a soldier bleeding'" . . . . MBPI2925 . .1893
"Brought him from the battle" . . . . MBPI2926 . .1893
"I saw his eyes were blue" . . . . MBPI2927 . .1893
"We came to know each other" . . . . MBPI2928 . .1893
"His picture Copley painted" . . . . MBPI2929 . .1893
Headpiece with illustrated initial D, ... MBPI2930 . .1893
   Preface for Dorothy Q
Tailpiece, Preface for Dorothy Q . . . . MBPI2931 . .1893
Headpiece, List of Illustrations for . . . . MBPI2932 . .1893
   Dorothy Q
Tailpiece, List of Illustrations for . . . . MBPI2933 . .1893
   Dorothy Q
Decorative heading for Dorothy Q . . . . MBPI2934 . .1893
Decorative border for Dorothy Q . . . . MBPI2935 . .1893
Decorative heading for Dorothy Q . . . . MBPI2936 . .1893
Decorative border for Dorothy Q . . . . MBPI2937 . .1893
Decorative heading for Dorothy Q . . . . MBPI2938 . .1893
Decorative border for Dorothy Q . . . . MBPI2939 . .1893
Decorative heading for Dorothy Q . . . . MBPI2940 . .1893
Decorative border for Dorothy Q . . . . MBPI2941 . .1893
Decorative heading for Dorothy Q . . . . MBPI2942 . .1893
Decorative border for Dorothy Q . . . . MBPI2943 . .1893
Decorative border with title for A Ballad . . . . . . MBPI2944 . .1893
   of the Boston-Tea Party
Decorative border for A Ballad of the . . . . MBPI2945 . .1893
   Boston-Tea Party
Decorative heading for A Ballad of the . . . . MBPI2946 . .1893
   Boston-Tea Party
Tailpiece for A Ballad of the Boston-Tea . . . . . . MBPI2947 . .1893
   Party
Decorative heading for A Ballad of the . . . . MBPI2948 . .1893
   Boston-Tea Party
Tailpiece for A Ballad of the Boston-Tea . . . . . . MBPI2949 . .1893
   Party

1894

Decorative heading for A Ballad of the . . . . MBPI2950 . .1893
   Boston-Tea Party
Decorative heading for A Ballad of the . . . . MBPI2951 . .1893
   Boston-Tea Party
Tailpiece for A Ballad of the Boston-Tea . . . . . . MBPI2952 . .1893
   Party
Decorative heading for A Ballad of the . . . . MBPI2953 . .1893
   Boston-Tea Party
Tailpiece for A Ballad of the Boston-Tea . . . . . . MBPI2954 . .1893
   Party
Decorative heading for A Ballad of the . . . . MBPI2955 . .1893
   Boston-Tea Party
Tailpiece for A Ballad of the Boston-Tea . . . . . . MBPI2956 . .1893
   Party
Decorative heading for A Ballad of the . . . . MBPI2957 . .1893
   Boston-Tea Party
Tailpiece for A Ballad of the Boston-Tea . . . . . . MBPI2958 . .1893
   Party
Decorative heading for A Ballad of the . . . . MBPI2959 . .1893
   Boston-Tea Party
Tailpiece for A Ballad of the Boston-Tea . . . . . . MBPI2960 . .1893
   Party
Balboa's Discovery of the Pacific . . . . MBPI2961 . .1893
Tailpiece, Part I for The Autocrat of the . . . . MBPI2973 . .1893
   Breakfast-Table
Headpiece with initial T, Part III for . . . . MBPI2978 . .1893
   The Autocrat of the Breakfast-Table
Tailpiece for The Chambered Nautilus . . . . MBPI2985 . .1893
The Old Violin . . . . MBPI2987 . .1893
Mare Rubrum with initial F . . . . MBPI2988 . .1893
General Prescott . . . . PDPI0013 . .1893
"He turned the slab-like leaves rapidly" . . . . MBPI0106 . .1894
"The young fellow lounged in a rattan . . . . MBPI0107 . .1894
   chair"
"Their first meeting happened at the . . . . MBPI0108 . .1894
   club"
"DuMoreau was leaning part way across the . . MBPI0109 . .1894
   table"
"He glared at the girl in the dim light" . . . . MBPI0110 . .1894
"Then there was a crash and clatter of an . . . . . MBPI0111 . .1894
   overturned chair"
"He had found the Captain agreeable and . . . . MBPI0607 . .1894
   companionable"
Headpiece with title and illustrated . . . . MBPI0608 . .1894
   initial T for The Sea Robbers of New York
"Pirates used to do that to their . . . . MBPI0609 . .1894
   Captains now and then"
Kidd at Gardiner's Island . . . . MBPI0610 . .1894
Tailpiece for The Sea Robbers of New York . . . . MBPI0611 . .1894
Illustration for Stops of Various Quills . . . . MBPI0612 . .1894
Headpiece with title for Stops of Various . . . . . MBPI0613 . .1894
   Quills
Illustrated initial W for Sphinx . . . . MBPI0614 . .1894
Tailpiece for Twelve P.M. . . . . MBPI0615 . .1894
Time . . . . MBPI0616 . .1894
Illustrated initial D for Time . . . . MBPI0617 . .1894
Society . . . . MBPI0618 . .1894
Illustrated initial Y for Society . . . . MBPI0619 . .1894

Index–Titles of Pyle's Art In Chronological Sequence

1894

Tailpiece for Society . . . . MBPI0620 . .1894
Heredity . . . . MBPI0621 . .1894
Illustrated initial T for Heredity . . . . MBPI0622 . .1894
In the Dark . . . . MBPI0623 . .1894
Solitude . . . . MBPI0624 . .1894
Illustrated initial A for Solitude . . . . MBPI0625 . .1894
Change . . . . MBPI0626 . .1894
Illustrated initial S for Change . . . . MBPI0627 . .1894
Tailpiece for Change . . . . MBPI0628 . .1894
Midway . . . . MBPI0629 . .1894
Illustrated initial S for Midway . . . . MBPI0630 . .1894
Calvary . . . . MBPI0631 . .1894
Illustrated initial I for Calvary . . . . MBPI0632 . .1894
"'Austin,' she said, 'I have come to tell . . . . MBPI1267 . .1894
    you our engagement is at an end'"
"I was conscious only of her own eyes . . . . MBPI1268 . .1894
    looking down at me, gray, deep, inscrutable"
"I stopped, for the woman's head had . . . . MBPI1269 . .1894
    fallen back–she had fainted"
Illustration for The Parasite . . . . MBPI1270 . .1894
Headpiece with title for Sailors and . . . . MBPI1271 . .1894
    Landsmen, A Story of 1812
Vignette for Sailors and Landsmen, A . . . . MBPI1272 . .1894
    Story of 1812
Vignette for Sailors and Landsmen, A . . . . MBPI1273 . .1894
    Story of 1812
Vignette for Sailors and Landsmen, A . . . . MBPI1274 . .1894
    Story of 1812
Vignette for Sailors and Landsmen, A . . . . MBPI1275 . .1894
    Story of 1812
Vignette for Sailors and Landsmen, A . . . . MBPI1276 . .1894
    Story of 1812
Vignette for Sailors and Landsmen, A . . . . MBPI1277 . .1894
    Story of 1812
Vignette for Sailors and Landsmen, A . . . . MBPI1278 . .1894
    Story of 1812
Vignette for Sailors and Landsmen, A . . . . MBPI1279 . .1894
    Story of 1812
Vignette for Sailors and Landsmen, A . . . . MBPI1280 . .1894
    Story of 1812
Headpiece with title for A Piece of Good . . . . . MBPI1719 . .1894
    Luck
"They danced around and around the chest" . . MBPI1720 . .1894
"'What will you have?' said the Genie" . . . . MBPI1721 . .1894
"The Genie had flown with her through the . . MBPI1723 . .1894
    air"
"Next morning the Prime Minister looked . . . . MBPI1724 . .1894
    like a shorn sheep"
"Jacob's magnificent court suit" . . . . MBPI1725 . .1894
"As for the King, he could not believe . . . . MBPI1726 . .1894
    his eyes when he saw it"
"Jacob and the King left in the desert by . . . . . MBPI1727 . .1894
    the Genie"
"The Genie snatched the Minister up and . . . . MBPI1728 . .1894
    flew away with him"
Headpiece with title for The Good of a . . . . MBPI1729 . .1894
    Few Words
"Feasting and drinking and junketing and . . . MBPI1730 . .1894
    merry-making"

1894

"'Look at yonder poor man,' said she to . . . . . . MBPI1731 . .1894
    her nurse"
"The tall man in black knocked upon the . . . . . MBPI1732 . .1894
    gate"
"'Now,' said the King, 'now you are . . . . MBPI1733 . .1894
    married'"
"Then Beppo carried the Princess ashore" . . . . MBPI1734 . .1894
"Again Sebastian served a feast" . . . . MBPI1735 . .1894
"Beppo offers the King milk" . . . . MBPI1736 . .1894
"'Alas, my poor friend!' said he" . . . . MBPI1737 . .1894
"The King laid his hands on Beppo's . . . . MBPI1738 . .1894
    shoulders"
"'Do you not know me?' said she; 'I am . . . . MBPI1739 . .1894
    the Queen'"
Uncle and Nephew–"Well, Jacky, you shall . . . . MBPI1824 . .1894
    have that hundred pounds, you shall"
"'He'll come to by and by; he's only . . . . MBPI1825 . .1894
    stunned a trifle,' said the Captain"
"'Now then, Gentlemen, how much do you . . . MBPI1826 . .1894
    bid for this boy?' said the auctioneer"
"'Speak up, boy,–speak up,' said the . . . . MBPI1827 . .1894
    gentleman"
"Mr. Parker stood looking at his visitor . . . . MBPI1828 . .1894
    with his usual calm reserve"
"I don't want to be anybody's servant, ... MBPI1829 . .1894
    lady, and wouldn't if I could help it"
"He picked up the bird and held it out at . . . . MBPI1830 . .1894
    arm's length"
"He led Jack up to a man who sat on a . . . . MBPI1831 . .1894
    barrel"
"Jack followed the Captain and the young . . . . MBPI1832 . .1894
    lady up the crooked path to the house"
Illustration with illustrated initial M . . . . MBPI1964 . .1894
    for McAndrew's Hymn
Illustration for McAndrew's Hymn . . . . MBPI1965 . .1894
Headpiece for McAndrew's Hymn . . . . MBPI1966 . .1894
Illustrated initial L for McAndrew's Hymn . . . . MBPI1967 . .1894
"I heard a land-breeze ca'" . . . . MBPI1968 . .1894
Headpiece for McAndrew's Hymn . . . . MBPI1969 . .1894
Tailpiece for McAndrew's Hymn . . . . MBPI1970 . .1894
"The Meeting of Cortes and Montezuma" . . . . . MBPI2962 . .1894
Oliver Wendell Holmes at age of 41 . . . . MBPI2963 . .1894
Headpiece, List of Ilustrations for The . . . . MBPI2964 . .1894
    Autocrat of the Breakfast-Table
Headpiece with initial T, Preface for The . . . . . MBPI2965 . .1894
    Autocrat of the Breakfast-Table
Headpiece with initial T for Autocrat's . . . . MBPI2966 . .1894
    Autobiography
Tailpiece for Autocrat's Autobiography . . . . MBPI2967 . .1894
Headpiece with initial I, Part I for The . . . . MBPI2968 . .1894
    Autocrat of the Breakfast-Table
The Mutual Admiration Society . . . . MBPI2969 . .1894
Album Verses with initial W . . . . MBPI2970 . .1894
The Man of Family . . . . MBPI2971 . .1894
Latter-Day Warnings with initial W . . . . MBPI2972 . .1894
Headpiece with initial I, Part II for The . . . . MBPI2974 . .1894
    Autocrat of the Breakfast-Table
The Trotting Match . . . . MBPI2975 . .1894

Index–Titles of Pyle's Art In Chronological Sequence

1894

Sun and Shadow with initial A . . . . MBPI2976 . .1894
This Is It with initial A . . . . MBPI2977 . .1894
At the Club . . . . MBPI2979 . .1894
The Old Man Dreams with initial O . . . . MBPI2980 . .1894
Tailpiece for The Old Man Dreams . . . . MBPI2981 . .1894
Headpiece with initial I, Part IV for The . . . . MBPI2982 . .1894
    Autocrat of the Breakfast-Table
A Reminiscence of the Marigold . . . . MBPI2983 . .1894
The Chambered Nautilus with initial T . . . . MBPI2984 . .1894
Headpiece with initial A, Part V for The . . . . MBPI2986 . .1894
    Autocrat of the Breakfast-Table
Tailpiece for Mare Rubrum . . . . MBPI2989 . .1894
Headpiece with initial S, Part VI for The . . . . MBPI2990 . .1894
    Autocrat of the Breakfast-Table
The Closed Door . . . . MBPI2991 . .1894
What We All Think with initial T . . . . MBPI2992 . .1894
Tailpiece for What We All Think . . . . MBPI2993 . .1894
Oliver Wendell Holmes at the age of 76 . . . . MBPI2994 . .1894
Headpiece with initial T, Part VII for . . . . MBPI2995 . .1894
    The Autocrat of the Breakfast-Table
The Last Blossom with initial T . . . . MBPI2996 . .1894
The Professor in his Boat . . . . MBPI2997 . .1894
The Living Temple . . . . MBPI2998 . .1894
Headpiece with initial S, Part VIII for . . . . MBPI2999 . .1894
    The Autocrat of the Breakfast-Table
Into the River . . . . MBPI3000 . .1894
Spring Has Come with initial T . . . . MBPI3001 . .1894
Headpiece with initial I, Part IX for The . . . . MBPI3002 . .1894
    Autocrat of the Breakfast-Table
First Love . . . . MBPI3003 . .1894
A Good Time Going . . . . MBPI3004 . .1894
The Two Armies with initial A . . . . MBPI3005 . .1894
Tailpiece for The Two Armies . . . . MBPI3006 . .1894
Headpiece with initial T, Part X for The . . . . MBPI3007 . .1894
    Autocrat of the Breakfast-Table
The First Walk . . . . MBPI3008 . .1894
Musa with initial O . . . . MBPI3009 . .1894
Tailpiece for Musa . . . . MBPI3010 . .1894
Headpiece with initial T, Part XI for The . . . . MBPI3011 . .1894
    Autocrat of the Breakfast-Table
Headpiece for The Deacon's Masterpiece . . . . . . MBPI3012 . .1894
Æstivation with initial I . . . . MBPI3013 . .1894
The Mountain Home . . . . MBPI3014 . .1894
Contentment with initial L . . . . MBPI3015 . .1894
Tailpiece for The Autocrat of the . . . . MBPI3016 . .1894
    Breakfast-Table
Headpiece with initial I, Part XII for . . . . MBPI3017 . .1894
    The Autocrat of the Breakfast-Table
Headpiece with title for Parson Turell's . . . . MBPI3018 . .1894
    Legacy
Parson Turell's legacy . . . . MBPI3019 . .1894
The Voiceless with initial W . . . . MBPI3020 . .1894
Tailpiece for The Autocrat of the . . . . MBPI3021 . .1894
    Breakfast-Table
Design for The Players bookplate . . . . MBPI3223 . .1894
"I saw him pass his sword through the . . . . MBPI0002 . .1895
    mate's body"
"He put the glass to his lips and drank . . . . MBPI0003 . .1895
    at one gulp"

1895

"Will you forgive my having followed . . . . MBPI0004 . .1895
    you?"
The Surrender of Captain Pearson on the . . . . . MBPI0020 . .1895
    Deck of the "Bonhomme Richard"
The Bonhomme Richard and Ye Serapis . . . . MBPI0021 . .1895
Headpiece with title and initial T for . . . . MBPI0022 . .1895
    Paul Jones
Paul Jones raising the Rattlesnake Flag . . . . MBPI0023 . .1895
    on the "Alfred"
Tailpiece for Paul Jones . . . . MBPI0024 . .1895
"The Admiral came in his gig of state" . . . . MBPI0025 . .1895
Headpiece with title for The . . . . MBPI0026 . .1895
    Constitution's Last Fight
The Constitution's Last Fight . . . . MBPI0027 . .1895
Tailpiece for The Constitution's Last . . . . MBPI0028 . .1895
    Fight
Maid Marian's Song with title . . . . MBPI0029 . .1895
Maid Marian's Song . . . . MBPI0030 . .1895
"Some of the by-standers said 'She is . . . . MBPI0633 . .1895
    drunk, it will soon pass away'"
"The choicest pieces of her cargo were . . . . MBPI0634 . .1895
    sold at auction"
"We escaped in the boat" . . . . MBPI0635 . .1895
"And again my Captain took the biggest" . . . . . MBPI0636 . .1895
Headpiece with title and illustrated . . . . MBPI0637 . .1895
    initial O for New York Colonial Privateers
"Barbarously murdered the first, and . . . . MBPI0638 . .1895
    grievously wounded the latter"
Tailpiece for New York Colonial . . . . MBPI0639 . .1895
    Privateers
Headpiece with title for Society . . . . MBPI0640 . .1895
Marginal decoration for Society . . . . MBPI0641 . .1895
Tailpiece for Society . . . . MBPI0642 . .1895
Frontispiece for Pebbles . . . . MBPI0643 . .1895
Headpiece with title for Pebbles . . . . MBPI0644 . .1895
Illustrated initial I for The Burden . . . . MBPI0645 . .1895
Hope . . . . MBPI0646 . .1895
Sympathy . . . . MBPI0647 . .1895
Illustrated initial F for Sympathy . . . . MBPI0648 . .1895
Reward and Punishment . . . . MBPI0649 . .1895
Parable . . . . MBPI0650 . .1895
Illustrated initial T for Parable . . . . MBPI0651 . .1895
Statistics . . . . MBPI0652 . .1895
Illustrated initial S for Statistics . . . . MBPI0653 . .1895
Tailpiece for Statistics . . . . MBPI0654 . .1895
In the Wood-Carver's Shop . . . . MBPI0655 . .1895
Headpiece with title for By Land and Sea . . . . . MBPI0656 . .1895
Tailpiece, Sketch Four for By Land and . . . . MBPI0657 . .1895
    Sea
Tailpiece, Sketch One for By Land and Sea . . . . MBPI0658 . .1895
A Sailor's Sweetheart . . . . MBPI0659 . .1895
Headpiece, Sketch Two for By Land and Sea . . . MBPI0660 . .1895
Illustrated initial I, Sketch Two for By . . . . MBPI0661 . .1895
    Land and Sea
Tailpiece, Sketch Two for By Land and Sea . . . . MBPI0662 . .1895
The Sailor's Wedding . . . . MBPI0663 . .1895
Headpiece, Sketch Three for By Land and . . . . . MBPI0664 . .1895
    Sea

Index–Titles of Pyle's Art In Chronological Sequence

1895

Illustrated initial T, Sketch One for By .... MBPI0665 ..1895
Land and Sea
Tailpiece, Sketch Three for By Land and .... MBPI0666 ..1895
Sea
A Wreck from the Sea .... MBPI0667 ..1895
Headpiece, Sketch Four for By Land and ...... MBPI0668 ..1895
Sea
Illustrated initial E, Sketch Four for By .... MBPI0669 ..1895
Land and Sea
Tailpiece, Table of Contents for Twilight .... MBPI0974 ..1895
Land
An Unwelcome Toast .... MBPI1281 ..1895
"The men brought Selim up in front of the ... MBPI1695 ..1895
statue"
"They found her still sitting in the same ...... MBPI1833 ..1895
place"
Governor Spottiswood visits Colonel .... MBPI1834 ..1895
Parker
Jack and Dred rescue Eleanor–The Start ...... MBPI1835 ..1895
The pirates fire upon the fugitives .... MBPI1836 ..1895
"Colonel Parker reached out and laid his ..... MBPI1837 ..1895
hand upon Jack's shoulder; 'Ay,' said he,
'tis a good, honest face'"
Blackbeard's last fight .... MBPI1838 ..1895
"'Then I will come,' said he" .... MBPI1839 ..1895
Illustration for A Forgotten Tale .... MBPI1971 ..1895
Illustration for A Forgotten Tale .... MBPI1972 ..1895
The Brooks Forces evacuating the State ...... MBPI1973 ..1895
House at Little Rock
The rush from the New York Stock Exchange .. MBPI1974 ..1895
on September 18, 1873
Dennis Kearney being drawn through the .... MBPI1975 ..1895
streets of San Francisco after his release from the House of
Correction
November, 1776 .... MBPI1976 ..1895
The Enemy at the Door .... MBPI1977 ..1895
Cover design for The Garden Behind the ..... MBPI2353 ..1895
Moon
In the garden behind the moon .... MBPI2354 ..1895
Headband for The Garden Behind the Moon .. MBPI2355 ..1895
Headband, Illustrations for The Garden .... MBPI2356 ..1895
Behind the Moon
Headpiece, Foreword for The Garden Behind   MBPI2357 ..1895
the Moon
Tailpiece, Foreword for The Garden Behind ... MBPI2358 ..1895
the Moon
Headpiece, Chapter I for The Garden .... MBPI2359 ..1895
Behind the Moon
Headband, Chapter II for The Garden .... MBPI2360 ..1895
Behind the Moon
Headband, Chapter III for The Garden .... MBPI2361 ..1895
Behind the Moon
Headband, Chapter IV for The Garden .... MBPI2362 ..1895
Behind the Moon
David looked up into Hans Krout's face ...... MBPI2363 ..1895
Headband, Chapter V for The Garden Behind . MBPI2364 ..1895
the Moon
Suddenly a half-door opened and there ...... MBPI2365 ..1895
stood a little man

Headband, Chapter VI for The Garden .... MBPI2366 ..1895
Behind the Moon
David sat down on the wooden bench and ... MBPI2367 ..1895
took up a big blue star
Headband, Chapter VII for The Garden .... MBPI2368 ..1895
Behind the Moon
He was standing at an open window .... MBPI2369 ..1895
"Where did you come from, little boy?" .... MBPI2370 ..1895
she said
Headband, Chapter VIII for The Garden .... MBPI2371 ..1895
Behind the Moon
Headband, Chapter IX for The Garden .... MBPI2372 ..1895
Behind the Moon
Headband, Chapter X for The Garden Behind . MBPI2373 ..1895
the Moon
Headband, Chapter XI for The Garden .... MBPI2374 ..1895
Behind the Moon
Headband, Chapter XII for The Garden .... MBPI2375 ..1895
Behind the Moon
Quick as a flash, David leaped out and ...... MBPI2376 ..1895
upon it
Headband, Chapter XIII for The Garden .... MBPI2377 ..1895
Behind the Moon
Headband, Chapter XIV for The Garden .... MBPI2378 ..1895
Behind the Moon
Headband, Chapter XV for The Garden .... MBPI2379 ..1895
Behind the Moon
Fast flew the black winged horse .... MBPI2380 ..1895
Headband, Chapter XVI for The Garden .... MBPI2381 ..1895
Behind the Moon
The giant fell crashing upon the stones .... MBPI2382 ..1895
Cover design for Stops of Various Quills .... MBPI2383 ..1895
Headband, Chapter XVIII for The Garden ...... MBPI2384 ..1895
Behind the Moon
Headband, Chapter XIX for The Garden .... MBPI2385 ..1895
Behind the Moon
She placed her hands on his shoulders .... MBPI2386 ..1895
Cover design for Twilight Land .... MBPI2387 ..1895
Ita Primo Ita Semper .... MBPI2388 ..1895
Dedication for Twilight Land .... MBPI2389 ..1895
Headpiece, Table of Contents for Twilight ..... MBPI2390 ..1895
Land
Headpiece with illustrated initial I, ... MBPI2391 ..1895
Introduction for Twilight Land
Spine design for Stops of Various Quills .... MBPI2622 ..1895
Title page decoration for Stops of .... MBPI3022 ..1895
Various Quills
Title page decoration for Stops of .... MBPI3023 ..1895
Various Quills
Headpiece, Table of Contents for Stops of .... MBPI3024 ..1895
Various Quills
Tailpiece for Midway .... MBPI3025 ..1895
Tailpiece for The Bewildered Guest .... MBPI3026 ..1895
Company .... MBPI3027 ..1895
Tailpiece for Company .... MBPI3028 ..1895
Twelve P. M. .... MBPI3029 ..1895
Tailpiece for In The Dark .... MBPI3030 ..1895
Tailpiece for Solitude .... MBPI3031 ..1895

Index–Titles of Pyle's Art In Chronological Sequence

1895

Conscience . . . . MBPI3032 . .1895
Illustrated initial J for Conscience . . . . MBPI3033 . .1895
Tailpiece for Conscience . . . . MBPI3034 . .1895
Tailpiece for Reward And Punishment . . . . MBPI3035 . .1895
Illustration for Parable . . . . MBPI3036 . .1895
Tailpiece for Parable . . . . MBPI3037 . .1895
Vision . . . . MBPI3038 . .1895
Decoration for Society . . . . MBPI3039 . .1895
Friends and Foes . . . . MBPI3040 . .1895
Sphinx . . . . MBPI3041 . .1895
Materials of a Story . . . . MBPI3042 . .1895
The King Dines . . . . MBPI3043 . .1895
Illustrated initial T for The King Dines . . . . MBPI3044 . .1895
Labor And Capital . . . . MBPI3045 . .1895
Tailpiece for Labor And Capital . . . . MBPI3046 . .1895
Equality . . . . MBPI3047 . .1895
Judgment Day . . . . MBPI3048 . .1895
Mortality . . . . MBPI3049 . .1895
Another Day . . . . MBPI3050 . .1895
Tailpiece for Another Day . . . . MBPI3051 . .1895
Some One Else . . . . MBPI3052 . .1895
Illustrated initial L for Stops of . . . . MBPI3053 . .1895
    Various Quills
Life . . . . MBPI3054 . .1895
Tailpiece for Life . . . . MBPI3055 . .1895
Weather-Breeder . . . . MBPI3056 . .1895
Peonage . . . . MBPI3057 . .1895
Race . . . . MBPI3058 . .1895
Tailpiece for Race . . . . MBPI3059 . .1895
Temperament . . . . MBPI3060 . .1895
What Shall It Profit? . . . . MBPI3061 . .1895
Tailpiece for What Shall It Profit? . . . . MBPI3062 . .1895
Illustrated initial B for Stops of . . . . MBPI3063 . .1895
    Various Quills
Headband for Stops of Various Quills . . . . MBPI3064 . .1895
Spine design for Twilight Land . . . . PDPI0030 . .1895
And we kept those fellows alee, astern . . . . PDPI0072 . .1895
For many a mile we sailed . . . . PDPI0073 . .1895
Her decks are red with her gallant dead . . . . PDPI0074 . .1895
"The gigantic monster dragged the hacked . . MBPI0005 . .1896
    and headless corpse of his victim up the staircase"
"A man in it, standing upright, and . . . . MBPI0006 . .1896
    something lying in a lump at the bow"
"Didst thou tell them I taught thee?" . . . . MBPI0031 . .1896
"I will teach thee to answer thy elders" . . . . MBPI0032 . .1896
Vignette, the Old Natick Church . . . . MBPI0496 . .1896
Vignette, Sam Lawson's House . . . . MBPI0497 . .1896
Sam Lawson telling stories . . . . MBPI0498 . .1896
Headpiece with title and illustrated . . . . MBPI0671 . .1896
    initial G for In Washington's Day
A Virginia Plantation Wharf . . . . MBPI0672 . .1896
"Even Sir William Berkeley, the . . . . MBPI0673 . .1896
    redoubtable Cavalier Governor, saw he must yield"
"They read only upon occasion, when the . . . . MBPI0674 . .1896
    weather darkened"
Ye Virginia Gentleman of the Olden Time . . . . . MBPI0675 . .1896
Washington's Retreat from Great Meadows . . . . MBPI0676 . .1896
Headpiece for Colonel Washington . . . . MBPI0677 . .1896

1896

The Burial of Braddock . . . . MBPI0678 . .1896
Washington and Mary Philipse . . . . MBPI0679 . .1896
Tailpiece for Colonel Washington . . . . MBPI0680 . .1896
Leaving Mount Vernon for the Congress of . . . MBPI0681 . .1896
    the Colonies
The Old Capitol at Williamsburg . . . . MBPI0682 . .1896
In the Old Raleigh Tavern . . . . MBPI0683 . .1896
Head and sidepiece with illustrated . . . . MBPI0684 . .1896
    initial T for Through Inland Waters
Vignette for Through Inland Waters . . . . MBPI0685 . .1896
Vignette for Through Inland Waters . . . . MBPI0686 . .1896
A Floating Town . . . . MBPI0687 . .1896
Headpiece with subtitle for Through . . . . MBPI0688 . .1896
    Inland Waters
Vignette for Through Inland Waters . . . . MBPI0689 . .1896
Vignette for Through Inland Waters . . . . MBPI0690 . .1896
Vignette for Through Inland Waters . . . . MBPI0691 . .1896
Vignette for Through Inland Waters . . . . MBPI0692 . .1896
Vignette for Through Inland Waters . . . . MBPI0693 . .1896
Vignette for Through Inland Waters . . . . MBPI0694 . .1896
Vignette for Through Inland Waters . . . . MBPI0695 . .1896
Vignette for Through Inland Waters . . . . MBPI0696 . .1896
Vignette for Through Inland Waters . . . . MBPI0697 . .1896
Vignette for Through Inland Waters . . . . MBPI0698 . .1896
Tailpiece for Through Inland Waters . . . . MBPI0699 . .1896
Headpiece with title and initial T for . . . . MBPI0700 . .1896
    Through Inland Waters
Vignette for Through Inland Waters . . . . MBPI0701 . .1896
Vignette for Through Inland Waters . . . . MBPI0702 . .1896
Vignette for Through Inland Waters . . . . MBPI0703 . .1896
Vignette for Through Inland Waters . . . . MBPI0704 . .1896
Vignette for Through Inland Waters . . . . MBPI0705 . .1896
Illustration for Through Inland Waters . . . . MBPI0706 . .1896
Vignette for Through Inland Waters . . . . MBPI0707 . .1896
Vignette for Through Inland Waters . . . . MBPI0708 . .1896
Vignette for Through Inland Waters . . . . MBPI0709 . .1896
Vignette for Through Inland Waters . . . . MBPI0710 . .1896
Vignette for Through Inland Waters . . . . MBPI0711 . .1896
Illustration for Through Inland Waters . . . . MBPI0712 . .1896
Vignette for Through Inland Waters . . . . MBPI0713 . .1896
Vignette for Through Inland Waters . . . . MBPI0714 . .1896
Tailpiece for Through Inland Waters . . . . MBPI0715 . .1896
Headpiece with title for General . . . . MBPI0716 . .1896
    Washington
Washington and Steuben at Valley Forge . . . . . . MBPI0717 . .1896
Lady Washington's Arrival at . . . . MBPI0718 . .1896
    Headquarters, Cambridge
The Escape of Arnold . . . . MBPI0719 . .1896
Carpenter's Hall, Philadelphia . . . . MBPI0720 . .1896
Washington in the Garden at Mount Vernon . . MBPI0721 . .1896
Headpiece with title for First in Peace . . . . MBPI0722 . .1896
Washington bringing his Mother into the . . . . MBPI0723 . .1896
    Ballroom, Fredericksburg
Mustered out–A rest on the way home . . . . MBPI0724 . .1896
Tailpiece for First in Peace . . . . MBPI0725 . .1896
Washington and Nelly Custis . . . . MBPI0726 . .1896
Headpiece with title for The First . . . . MBPI0727 . .1896
    President of the United States

Index–Titles of Pyle's Art In Chronological Sequence

1896

Thompson, the Clerk of Congress, ... MBPI0728 . . 1896
   announcing to Washington, at Mount Vernon, his election to
   the Presidency
The Death of Washington . . . . MBPI0729 . . 1896
Tailpiece for The First President of the . . . . MBPI0730 . . 1896
   United States
Christmas 1896, Cover Design . . . . MBPI0731 . . 1896
Headpiece with title for The Romance of . . . . . MBPI0732 . . 1896
   an Ambrotype
Illustrated initial T for The Romance of . . . . MBPI0733 . . 1896
   an Ambrotype
Vignette for The Romance of an Ambrotype . . . MBPI0734 . . 1896
Vignette for The Romance of an Ambrotype . . . MBPI0735 . . 1896
Vignette for The Romance of an Ambrotype . . . MBPI0736 . . 1896
Vignette for The Romance of an Ambrotype . . . MBPI0737 . . 1896
Vignette for The Romance of an Ambrotype . . . MBPI0738 . . 1896
Vignette for The Romance of an Ambrotype . . . MBPI0739 . . 1896
Vignette for The Romance of an Ambrotype . . . MBPI0740 . . 1896
Vignette for The Romance of an Ambrotype . . . MBPI0741 . . 1896
Vignette for The Romance of an Ambrotype . . . MBPI0742 . . 1896
Vignette for The Romance of an Ambrotype . . . MBPI0743 . . 1896
Vignette for The Romance of an Ambrotype . . . MBPI0744 . . 1896
Tailpiece for The Romance of an Ambrotype . . MBPI0745 . . 1896
Headband with title for Tom Chist and the . . . . MBPI1161 . . 1896
   Treasure Box
Such a wreck was a Godsend to the poor . . . . . MBPI1162 . . 1896
   and needy settlers
"And twenty one and twenty two" . . . . MBPI1163 . . 1896
The pirate captain looked impassively on . . . . . MBPI1164 . . 1896
Over the next rise he ran, and so on over . . . . . MBPI1165 . . 1896
   the sliding, shifting ground, panting and gasping
"'Tis enough to make us both rich men" . . . . . . MBPI1166 . . 1896
"I knew it, I knew it," exclaimed the . . . . MBPI1167 . . 1896
   great man
"Captain Malyoe shot Captain Brand . . . . MBPI1282 . . 1896
   through the head"
Headpiece with title for The Ghost of . . . . MBPI1283 . . 1896
   Captain Brand
Illustrated initial B for The Ghost of . . . . MBPI1284 . . 1896
   Captain Brand
Headpiece for The Ghost of Captain Brand . . . . MBPI1285 . . 1896
Headpiece for The Ghost of Captain Brand . . . . MBPI1286 . . 1896
Headpiece for The Ghost of Captain Brand . . . . MBPI1287 . . 1896
"She would sit quite still, permitting . . . . MBPI1288 . . 1896
   Barnaby to gaze"
Headpiece for The Ghost of Captain Brand . . . . MBPI1289 . . 1896
"The werewolf...skulked for a moment in the MBPI1740 . . 1896
   shadow of the yews, and...Yseult plucked old Siegfried's
   spear from her girdle"
"My dear," said General Washington, ... MBPI1741 . . 1896
   "Captain Prescott's behavior was inexcusable"
Anthony Von Corlear, The Trumpeter of New . . MBPI2067 . . 1896
   Amsterdam
Vignette, woman on a houseboat . . . . PDPI0033 . . 1896
The Garfield Ambulance Train on its way . . . . . PDPI0056 . . 1896
   to Elberon, N.J.
"There was instant silence" . . . . MBPI0033 . . 1897
In Aunt Gainor's Garden . . . . MBPI0034 . . 1897

1897

Aunt Gainor . . . . MBPI0035 . . 1897
In the presence of Washington . . . . MBPI0036 . . 1897
In the Prison . . . . MBPI0037 . . 1897
"Here, André! A Spy!" . . . . MBPI0038 . . 1897
The visit to André . . . . MBPI0039 . . 1897
Arnold and his wife . . . . MBPI0040 . . 1897
The Duel . . . . MBPI0041 . . 1897
"Is it Yes or No, Darthea?" . . . . MBPI0042 . . 1897
Headpiece for The Battle of Copenhagen . . . . . MBPI0043 . . 1897
Nelson sealing his letter to the Crown . . . . MBPI0044 . . 1897
   Prince of Denmark
Tailpiece for The Battle of Copenhagen . . . . MBPI0045 . . 1897
The Mizzen Top of the "Redoubtable" . . . . MBPI0046 . . 1897
The fields around lay bare to the moon . . . . MBPI0499 . . 1897
Then Winfried told the story of Bethlehem . . . . MBPI0500 . . 1897
The Assembly Ball . . . . MBPI0746 . . 1897
Headpiece with title for The Assembly . . . . MBPI0747 . . 1897
   Ball
Illustrated initial I for The Assembly . . . . MBPI0748 . . 1897
   Ball
Tailpiece for The Assembly Ball . . . . MBPI0749 . . 1897
Love and Death . . . . MBPI0750 . . 1897
Headpiece for Love and Death . . . . MBPI0751 . . 1897
Tailpiece for Love and Death . . . . MBPI0752 . . 1897
A Banquet to Genet . . . . MBPI0753 . . 1897
Headpiece, Arrival of Genet at Gray's . . . . MBPI0754 . . 1897
   Ferry
The News of the Execution of Louis XVI . . . . MBPI0755 . . 1897
Citizen Genet formally presented to . . . . MBPI0756 . . 1897
   Washington
Tailpiece for Washington and the French . . . . . MBPI0757 . . 1897
   Craze of '93
Headpiece with title for The Buccaneers . . . . . . MBPI1168 . . 1897
He asked this figure of war to step aside . . . . . MBPI1169 . . 1897
   for him
The crowd scattered . . . . MBPI1170 . . 1897
He leaped to the wheel . . . . MBPI1171 . . 1897
They would stand hours together . . . . MBPI1172 . . 1897
"I've kept my ears open to all your . . . . MBPI1290 . . 1897
   doings"
How the Devil Haunted the Meeting-House, . . MBPI1291 . . 1897
   Part I.
How the Devil Stole the Collector's Snuff . . . . . MBPI1292 . . 1897
   Box, Part II.
The Strange Adventures of a Young . . . . MBPI1293 . . 1897
   Gentleman of Quality, Part III.
A Romantic Episode in the Life of a Young . . . . MBPI1294 . . 1897
   Lady, Part IV.
How the Devil Was Cast Out of the . . . . MBPI1295 . . 1897
   Meeting-House, Part V.
Tailpiece for A True History of the Devil . . . . MBPI1296 . . 1897
   at New Hope
Spirit of Spring . . . . MBPI1742 . . 1897
Esmond and the Prince . . . . MBPI1978 . . 1897
Undergraduate Life in 1679 . . . . MBPI1979 . . 1897
Father Hennepin Celebrating Mass . . . . MBPI3101 . . 1897
Assassination of LaSalle . . . . MBPI3102 . . 1897
The Return from Deerfield . . . . MBPI3103 . . 1897

Index–Titles of Pyle's Art In Chronological Sequence

1897

Lygia and Vinicius in the Garden of Aulus . . . . . MBPI3104 . .1897
The Punishment of Chilo by Vinicius . . . . MBPI3105 . .1897
Nero holding a Golden Lute, with Rome in . . . . MBPI3106 . .1897
    Flames
"Peractum est!" . . . . MBPI3107 . .1897
The Conversion of Chilo . . . . MBPI3108 . .1897
"Quo Vadis, Domine!" . . . . MBPI3109 . .1897
Cover design for Report of the Board of . . . . . . PDPI0057 . .1897
    Park Commissioners, Wilmington, Delaware
Cover border design for The Ladies' Home . . . . PDPI0100 . .1897
    Journal
Decoration with title for Poisoned Ice . . . . MBPI0071 . .1898
Headpiece for Poisoned Ice . . . . MBPI0072 . .1898
On the edge of the ring, guarded, stood . . . . . . MBPI0073 . .1898
    Brother Bartholome and the Carmelite
Tailpiece for Poisoned Ice . . . . MBPI0074 . .1898
Upon the last stage of the journey they . . . . . . MBPI0075 . .1898
    stopped for dinner at a tavern
Headpiece with title for The Price of . . . . MBPI0076 . .1898
    Blood
Illustrated initial I for The Price of . . . . MBPI0077 . .1898
    Blood
Tailpiece, Introduction for The Price of . . . . MBPI0078 . .1898
    Blood
Illustrated initial T for The Price of . . . . MBPI0079 . .1898
    Blood
Headpiece for The Price of Blood . . . . MBPI0080 . .1898
Headpiece, Chapter II for The Price of . . . . MBPI0081 . .1898
    Blood
Illustrated initial A for The Price of . . . . MBPI0082 . .1898
    Blood
Headpiece, Chapter III for The Price of . . . . MBPI0083 . .1898
    Blood
Illustrated initial O for The Price of . . . . MBPI0084 . .1898
    Blood
Headpiece, Chapter IV for The Price of . . . . MBPI0085 . .1898
    Blood
Illustrated initial E for The Price of . . . . MBPI0086 . .1898
    Blood
Headpiece, Chapter V for The Price of . . . . MBPI0087 . .1898
    Blood
Illustrated initial T for The Price of . . . . MBPI0088 . .1898
    Blood
Tailpiece for The Birds of Cirencester . . . . MBPI0495 . .1898
Decoration with title for Old Chester . . . . MBPI0758 . .1898
    Tales
Headpiece for "The Promises of Dorthea" . . . . . MBPI0759 . .1898
"She seemed 'a tall white lily,' he said" . . . . MBPI0760 . .1898
"'Change it? My name?' she said" . . . . MBPI0761 . .1898
Headpiece for "Good For the Soul" . . . . MBPI0762 . .1898
Headpiece for "Miss Maria" . . . . MBPI0763 . .1898
"'And who's going to support 'em?' . . . . MBPI0764 . .1898
    demanded Mrs. Barkley"
"Judge Morrison read these harmless . . . . MBPI0765 . .1898
    jingles, chuckling and sneering"
Headpiece for "The Thief" . . . . MBPI0766 . .1898
Headpiece for "The Child's Mother" . . . . MBPI0767 . .1898
"Mary turned white, then she dropped . . . . . . .MBPI0768 . .1898
    down at his feet"

1898

Headpiece for "Justice and the Judge" . . . . MBPI0769 . .1898
"'So you're hanging the locusts?' . . . . MBPI0770 . .1898
    inquired the Judge, contemptuously"
Headpiece for "Where the Laborers Are . . . . . . MBPI0771 . .1898
    Few"
"I had enemies in my line" . . . . MBPI0772 . .1898
Headpiece for "Sally" . . . . MBPI0773 . .1898
"They told each other about it" . . . . MBPI0774 . .1898
Headpiece for "The Unexpectedness of Mr. . . . MBPI0775 . .1898
    Horace Shields"
"Mr. Horace looked at her with instant . . . . MBPI0776 . .1898
    sympathy"
"And you shall not hinder me" . . . . MBPI0777 . .1898
Headpiece for Old Captain . . . . MBPI0778 . .1898
Illustration for Old Captain . . . . MBPI0779 . .1898
Illustration for Old Captain . . . . MBPI0780 . .1898
Illustration for Old Captain . . . . MBPI0781 . .1898
Illustration for Old Captain . . . . MBPI0782 . .1898
Illustration for Old Captain . . . . MBPI0783 . .1898
Illustration for Old Captain . . . . MBPI0784 . .1898
Illustration for Old Captain . . . . MBPI0785 . .1898
Illustration for Old Captain . . . . MBPI0786 . .1898
Tailpiece for Old Captain . . . . MBPI0787 . .1898
Small Game Better Than None . . . . MBPI1297 . .1898
"Bringing fire and terror to roof tree . . . . MBPI1980 . .1898
    and bed"
Headpiece with title and illustrated . . . . MBPI1981 . .1898
    initial T for The Birds of Cirencester
Illustrated initial D for The Birds of . . . . MBPI1982 . .1898
    Cirencester
Illustrated initial A for The Birds of . . . . MBPI1983 . .1898
    Cirencester
Illustrated initial A for The Birds of . . . . MBPI1984 . .1898
    Cirencester
Illustrated initial F for The Birds of . . . . MBPI1985 . .1898
    Cirencester
Illustrated initial S for The Birds of . . . . MBPI1986 . .1898
    Cirencester
Illustrated initial H for The Birds of . . . . MBPI1987 . .1898
    Cirencester
Illustrated initial S for The Birds of . . . . MBPI1988 . .1898
    Cirencester
Illustrated initial F for The Birds of . . . . MBPI1989 . .1898
    Cirencester
Illustrated initial Y for The Birds of . . . . MBPI1990 . .1898
    Cirencester
The Fight on Lexington Common, April 19, . . . MBPI1991 . .1898
    1775
The Battle of Bunker Hill . . . . MBPI1992 . .1898
Thomas Jefferson Writing the Declaration . . . . MBPI1993 . .1898
    of Independence
The Retreat Through the Jerseys . . . . MBPI1994 . .1898
The Burial of General Fraser . . . . MBPI1995 . .1898
The Attack Upon the Chew House . . . . MBPI1996 . .1898
Clark on his way to Kaskaskia . . . . MBPI1997 . .1898
The Meeting of Greene and Gates at . . . . MBPI1998 . .1898
    Charlotte, N.C.
The Evacuation of Charleston by the . . . . MBPI1999 . .1898
    British December 14, 1782

Index–Titles of Pyle's Art In Chronological Sequence

1898

Arnold Tells his Wife of the Discovery of ...... MBPI2000 ..1898
his Treason
Washington Firing the First Gun at the .... MBPI2001 ..1898
Siege of Yorktown
Benjamin Franklin and Richard Oswald .... MBPI2002 ..1898
Discussing the Treaty of Peace at Paris
The Fall of Montcalm .... MBPI3110 ..1898
Cover design for The Cecilia Society .... MBPI3214 ..1898
Portrait of Joshua Clayton .... PDPI0045 ..1898
Dead Men Tell No Tales .... MBPI0089 ..1899
The Burning Ship .... MBPI0100 ..1899
Frontispiece for The Body to the Soul .... MBPI0788 ..1899
Headpiece with title for The Body to the ...... MBPI0789 ..1899
Soul
Marginal decoration for The Body to the ..... MBPI0790 ..1899
Soul
Decoration for The Body to the Soul .... MBPI0791 ..1899
Marginal decoration for The Body to the ..... MBPI0792 ..1899
Soul
Marginal decoration for The Body to the ..... MBPI0793 ..1899
Soul
Tailpiece for The Body to the Soul .... MBPI0794 ..1899
Headpiece with title with illustrated .... MBPI0795 ..1899
initial T for A Puppet of Fate
Vignette for A Puppet of Fate .... MBPI0796 ..1899
Chapter heading with illustrated initial .... MBPI0797 ..1899
N for A Puppet of Fate
Vignette for A Puppet of Fate .... MBPI0798 ..1899
Vignette for A Puppet of Fate .... MBPI0799 ..1899
Vignette for A Puppet of Fate .... MBPI0800 ..1899
Vignette for A Puppet of Fate .... MBPI0801 ..1899
Chapter heading with illustrated initial .... MBPI0802 ..1899
F for A Puppet of Fate
Vignette for A Puppet of Fate .... MBPI0803 ..1899
Illustration for A Puppet of Fate .... MBPI0804 ..1899
Chapter heading with illustrated initial .... MBPI0805 ..1899
A for A Puppet of Fate
Vignette for A Puppet of Fate .... MBPI0806 ..1899
How the Buccaneers Kept Christmas .... MBPI1298 ..1899
George and Martha Washington entertaining   MBPI1743 ..1899
their friends on the lawn at Mount Vernon
"He called on Franklin and received the ...... MBPI1744 ..1899
necessary recognition"
"The good, aged Doctor, the appearance of ... MBPI1745 ..1899
whose rotund figure on the streets was the signal for the
Parisians to doff their hats"
"At the same time he extended toward King .. MBPI1746 ..1899
Louis the precious Memorial"
The Death of Colonel John Laurens .... MBPI1747 ..1899
Front cover design for The Price of Blood ...... MBPI1802 ..1899
Back cover design for The Price of Blood ...... MBPI1807 ..1899
"They scrambled up the parapet and went ... MBPI3111 ..1899
surging over the crest, pell mell, upon The British"
Headpiece for Bi-Centennial .... MBPI3215 ..1899
Commemoration, Holy Trinity, Old Swedes Church
Design for Frederick Haines Curtiss .... MBPI3225 ..1899
bookplate
The Flying Dutchman .... MBPI0090 ..1900

1900

Headpiece with title for A Prelude .... MBPI0807 ..1900
Illustrated initial T for A Prelude .... MBPI0808 ..1900
In Springtime .... MBPI0809 ..1900
Tailpiece for A Prelude .... MBPI0810 ..1900
Headpiece for The Yellow of the Leaf .... MBPI0811 ..1900
Title with decorations for The Yellow of .... MBPI0812 ..1900
the Leaf
Illustrated initial T for The Yellow of .... MBPI0813 ..1900
the Leaf
The falling leaf is at the door; The .... MBPI0814 ..1900
Autumn Wind is on the Hill
Tailpiece for The Yellow of the Leaf .... MBPI0815 ..1900
Truth Leaves the Fairies' Wonderland .... MBPI0816 ..1900
Truth before the King .... MBPI0817 ..1900
Truth in the Temple .... MBPI0818 ..1900
Truth before the Seer .... MBPI0819 ..1900
Truth Went on Her Way Alone .... MBPI0820 ..1900
Truth in the Fool's Lodge .... MBPI0821 ..1900
Headpiece with title for The Pilgrimage ...... MBPI0822 ..1900
of Truth
Illustrated initial F for The Pilgrimage .... MBPI0823 ..1900
of Truth
Tailpiece for The Pilgrimage of Truth .... MBPI0824 ..1900
Illustrated initial T for The Pilgrimage .... MBPI0825 ..1900
of Truth
Tailpiece for The Pilgrimage of Truth .... MBPI0826 ..1900
Illustrated initial T for The Pilgrimage .... MBPI0827 ..1900
of Truth
Headband for The Pilgrimage of Truth .... MBPI0828 ..1900
Headband for The Pilgrimage of Truth .... MBPI0829 ..1900
Illustrated initial B for The Pilgrimage .... MBPI0830 ..1900
of Truth
Illustrated initial O for The Pilgrimage .... MBPI0831 ..1900
of Truth
Illustrated initial H for The Pilgrimage .... MBPI0832 ..1900
of Truth
Landing negroes at Jamestown from Dutch .. MBPI0834 ..1900
man-of-war, 1619
Decoration with title for The Man with .... MBPI1173 ..1900
the Hoe
Cover design for McClure's Magazine .... MBPI1748 ..1900
Headband for At the Turn of the Glass .... MBPI1749 ..1900
At the Turn of the Glass .... MBPI1750 ..1900
Marginal decoration for At the Turn of .... MBPI1751 ..1900
the Glass
"He struck once and again at the bald, ... MBPI1769 ..1900
narrow forehead beneath him"
His niece had found him lying dead .... MBPI2003 ..1900
Another rush of breakers pitching the .... MBPI2004 ..1900
boat, cork-like, into the air
He looked down and sang out, "Lower .... MBPI2005 ..1900
away!"
"Why don't you end it?" .... MBPI3112 ..1900
Half-title decoration for The Man with .... MBPI3113 ..1900
the Hoe and Other Poems
Frontispiece for The Man with the Hoe and ... MBPI3114 ..1900
Other Poems
Headpiece, Dedication for The Man with ..... MBPI3115 ..1900
the Hoe and Other Poems

Index—Titles of Pyle's Art In Chronological Sequence

1900

Headpiece, Prefatory Note for The Man . . . . MBPI3116 . .1900
   with the Hoe and Other Poems
Headpiece, The Contents for The Man with . . . MBPI3117 . .1900
   the Hoe and Other Poems
The Man With the Hoe . . . . MBPI3118 . .1900
A Look Into the Gulf . . . . MBPI3119 . .1900
Brotherhood . . . . MBPI3120 . .1900
Song of the Followers of Pan . . . . MBPI3121 . .1900
Little Brothers of the Ground . . . . MBPI3122 . .1900
Wail of the Wandering Dead . . . . MBPI3123 . .1900
A Prayer . . . . MBPI3124 . .1900
The Poet . . . . MBPI3125 . .1900
The Whirlwind Road . . . . MBPI3126 . .1900
The Desire of Nations . . . . MBPI3127 . .1900
Headband I for The Man with the Hoe and . . . MBPI3128 . .1900
   Other Poems
The Goblin Laugh . . . . MBPI3129 . .1900
Poetry . . . . MBPI3130 . .1900
A Meeting . . . . MBPI3131 . .1900
Infinite Depths . . . . MBPI3132 . .1900
A Leaf From the Devil's Jest-Book . . . . MBPI3133 . .1900
The Paymaster . . . . MBPI3134 . .1900
The Last Furrow . . . . MBPI3135 . .1900
In the Storm . . . . MBPI3136 . .1900
After Reading Shakespeare . . . . MBPI3137 . .1900
Headband II for The Man with the Hoe and . . . MBPI3138 . .1900
   Other Poems
The Poets . . . . MBPI3139 . .1900
Love's Vigil . . . . MBPI3140 . .1900
Two at a Fireside . . . . MBPI3141 . .1900
Headband III for The Man with the Hoe and . . MBPI3142 . .1900
   Other Poems
To William Watson . . . . MBPI3143 . .1900
Man . . . . MBPI3144 . .1900
In High Sierras . . . . MBPI3145 . .1900
The Wharf of Dreams . . . . MBPI3146 . .1900
To Louise Michel . . . . MBPI3147 . .1900
Shepherd Boy and Nereid . . . . MBPI3148 . .1900
A Song at the Start . . . . MBPI3149 . .1900
My Comrade . . . . MBPI3150 . .1900
Joy of the Morning . . . . MBPI3151 . .1900
A Cry in the Night . . . . MBPI3152 . .1900
Fays . . . . MBPI3153 . .1900
In Death Valley . . . . MBPI3154 . .1900
At Dawn . . . . MBPI3155 . .1900
"Follow Me" . . . . MBPI3156 . .1900
In Poppy Fields . . . . MBPI3157 . .1900
The Joy of the Hills . . . . MBPI3158 . .1900
The Invisible Bride . . . . MBPI3159 . .1900
The Valley . . . . MBPI3160 . .1900
The Climb of Life . . . . MBPI3161 . .1900
Midsummer Noon . . . . MBPI3162 . .1900
Griefs . . . . MBPI3163 . .1900
An Old Road . . . . MBPI3164 . .1900
Music . . . . MBPI3165 . .1900
Fay Song . . . . MBPI3166 . .1900
The Old Earth . . . . MBPI3167 . .1900
Divine Adventure . . . . MBPI3168 . .1900

1901

To High-born Poets . . . . MBPI3169 . .1900
The Toilers . . . . MBPI3170 . .1900
On the Gulf of Night . . . . MBPI3171 . .1900
A Harvest Song . . . . MBPI3172 . .1900
The Man Under the Stone . . . . MBPI3173 . .1900
Song to the Divine Mother . . . . MBPI3174 . .1900
From the Hand of a Child . . . . MBPI3175 . .1900
The Rock-Breaker . . . . MBPI3176 . .1900
These Songs Will Perish . . . . MBPI3177 . .1900
Assassination of William of Orange . . . . MBPI3178 . .1900
A Thousand Miles a Day . . . . MBPI3179 . .1900
Vignette for A Wonder Book . . . . MBPI3180 . .1900
"Behold it then!" cried Perseus . . . . MBPI3181 . .1900
Theseus caught the monster off his guard . . . . MBPI3182 . .1900
"Who are you?" thundered the giant . . . . MBPI3183 . .1900
"Let me hasten onward" . . . . MBPI3184 . .1900
Design for The Players bookplate . . . . MBPI3224 . .1900
Design for Howard Pyle bookplate . . . . MBPI3226 . .1900
To Have and to Hold . . . . MBPI3231 . .1900
Cavalier with sword . . . . PDPI0021 . .1900
Unused color design for Howard Pyle . . . . PDPI0028 . .1900
   bookplate
Soldier with spear . . . . PDPI0050 . .1900
Young Woman in Elizabethan Dress . . . . PDPI0061 . .1900
The Sea Fight . . . . PDPI0076 . .1900
Don Quixote's Encounter with the Windmill . . . MBPI0047 . .1901
Headpiece with title and decorated border . . . MBPI0048 . .1901
   for Hope and Memory
Hope and Memory . . . . MBPI0049 . .1901
Headpiece for Hope and Memory . . . . MBPI0050 . .1901
Tailpiece for Hope and Memory . . . . MBPI0051 . .1901
Marginal decoration for Hope and Memory . . . MBPI0052 . .1901
Marginal decoration for Hope and Memory . . . MBPI0053 . .1901
Columbia Speaks . . . . MBPI0091 . .1901
Headpiece for A Sahib's War . . . . MBPI0092 . .1901
Decoration with title for A Sahib's War . . . . MBPI0093 . .1901
Illustrated initial P for A Sahib's War . . . . MBPI0094 . .1901
Umr Singh . . . . MBPI0095 . .1901
"Then appeared suddenly, a little beyond . . . . MBPI0096 . .1901
   the light of the lamp, the spirit of Kurban Sahib"
Tailpiece for A Sahib's War . . . . MBPI0097 . .1901
Headpiece with decoration and title for . . . . . . MBPI0833 . .1901
   Colonies and Nation
Anne Hutchinson preaching in her house in . . MBPI0835 . .1901
   Boston
Arrival of Stuyvesant in New Amsterdam . . . . . MBPI0836 . .1901
The Burning of Jamestown . . . . MBPI0837 . .1901
Ships loading in Albemarle Sound . . . . MBPI0838 . .1901
On the War-Path . . . . MBPI0839 . .1901
A Pennsylvania Cave-Dwelling XVIIth . . . . MBPI0840 . .1901
   Century
An interview between Sir Edmund Andros . . . MBPI0841 . .1901
   and James Blair
Phips recovering the sunken treasure . . . . MBPI0842 . .1901
Sloughter signing the death warrant of . . . . . . MBPI0843 . .1901
   Leisler
Colonel Rhett and Pirate Stede Bonnet . . . . . . MBPI0844 . .1901
The Capitulation of Louisbourg . . . . MBPI0845 . .1901

Index–Titles of Pyle's Art In Chronological Sequence

1901

After the Massacre; Samuel Adams .... MBPI0846 ..1901
    demanding of Governor Hutchinson the instant withdrawal
    of British Troops
Burning of the "Gaspee" .... MBPI0847 ..1901
The Boston Tea Party .... MBPI0848 ..1901
Viewing the Battle of Bunker's Hill .... MBPI0849 ..1901
Fight between "Bonhomme Richard" and ..... MBPI0850 ..1901
    "Serapis"
Washington and Rochambeau before the .... MBPI0851 ..1901
    trenches at Yorktown
Tory Refugees on their way to Canada .... MBPI0852 ..1901
A Political Discussion .... MBPI0853 ..1901
A Dream of Young Summer .... MBPI0854 ..1901
Headpiece for King Custom .... MBPI0855 ..1901
Illustrated initial M for King Custom .... MBPI0856 ..1901
Marginal decoration for King Custom .... MBPI0857 ..1901
Vignette for King Custom .... MBPI0858 ..1901
My Lady of Brede .... MBPI0859 ..1901
Headpiece for Margaret of Cortona .... MBPI0860 ..1901
The Sea Man .... MBPI0861 ..1901
Uncle Sammy and Joe .... MBPI1752 ..1901
Headpiece with title and initial T for .... MBPI1753 ..1901
    The Chase of the Tide
Marginal illustration for The Chase of .... MBPI1754 ..1901
    the Tide
Vignette for The Chase of the Tide .... MBPI1755 ..1901
Illustration for The Chase of the Tide .... MBPI1756 ..1901
"The Sea–He've cotched us!" .... MBPI1757 ..1901
General Wayne endeavoring to quell the ..... MBPI2006 ..1901
    mutiny of the Pennsylvania Regiments at Morristown, N.J.
General Andrew Jackson receiving the .... MBPI2007 ..1901
    plaudits of his motley army after the victory of New Orleans
Spring .... MBPI2505 ..1901
"'Let me go to him!' she shrieked, in her ...... MBPI3185 ..1901
    anguish of soul"
Title page decoration for The Odes & .... MBPI3186 ..1901
    Epodes of Horace
The Poet at Twilight .... MBPI3187 ..1901
Subtitle page decoration for The Odes & ..... MBPI3188 ..1901
    Epodes of Horace
"Euterpe" .... MBPI3189 ..1901
Horace Reading to Maecenas .... MBPI3190 ..1901
"There was exchange of thrust and parry" ..... MBPI3191 ..1901
Lorna Doone .... MBPI3192 ..1901
A Matter of Fate .... PDPI0015 ..1901
Bust profile with chalice .... PDPI0085 ..1901
Bust profile arm extended .... PDPI0086 ..1901
Head I .... PDPI0087 ..1901
Head II .... PDPI0088 ..1901
Head III .... PDPI0089 ..1901
Head I with wings .... PDPI0090 ..1901
Head II with wings .... PDPI0091 ..1901
Head III with wings .... PDPI0092 ..1901
Head IV with wings .... PDPI0093 ..1901
Wings .... PDPI0094 ..1901
Subtitle decoration I .... PDPI0095 ..1901
Subtitle decoration II .... PDPI0096 ..1901
The Wicket of Paradise .... MBPI0054 ..1902

1902

In the Meadows of Youth .... MBPI0055 ..1902
In the Valley of the Shadows .... MBPI0056 ..1902
At the Gates of Life .... MBPI0057 ..1902
Title page decoration for The Travels of .... MBPI0058 ..1902
    the Soul
Headpiece with title The Travels of the .... MBPI0059 ..1902
    Soul
Illustrated initial T for The Travels of .... MBPI0060 ..1902
    the Soul
Headpiece with title In the Meadows of ...... MBPI0061 ..1902
    Youth
Illustrated initial O for In the Meadows .... MBPI0062 ..1902
    of Youth
Tailpiece for In the Meadows of Youth .... MBPI0063 ..1902
Headpiece with title In the Valley of the ...... MBPI0064 ..1902
    Shadows
Illustrated initial N for In the Valley .... MBPI0065 ..1902
    of the Shadows
Tailpiece for In the Valley of the .... MBPI0066 ..1902
    Shadows
Headpiece with title At the Gates of Life ...... MBPI0067 ..1902
Illustrated initial A for At the Gates of .... MBPI0068 ..1902
    Life
Tailpiece for At the Gates of Life .... MBPI0069 ..1902
Song of Peace .... MBPI0098 ..1902
"His Majesty would furnish no more money .. MBPI0112 ..1902
    for treasure hunting"
The settler .... MBPI0113 ..1902
"He fell in love" .... MBPI0114 ..1902
"A fair brick house in the Green Lane of ...... MBPI0115 ..1902
    North Boston"
"Stand off, ye wretches" .... MBPI0116 ..1902
"He had seen great guns in the bottom of .... MBPI0117 ..1902
    the sea"
"Soberly joined himself to the North .... MBPI0118 ..1902
    Church"
"The ships rolled and wallowed in the .... MBPI0119 ..1902
    river"
"Why, what is this? Whence came this?" ...... MBPI0120 ..1902
"An 'Eminent Person from Whitehall' .... MBPI0121 ..1902
    visited him in his chambers"
"The victims of the witchcraft delusion" .... MBPI0122 ..1902
"The Queen granted him an audience" .... MBPI0123 ..1902
Cap'n Goldsack .... MBPI0670 ..1902
Frontispiece for North Folk Legends of .... MBPI0862 ..1902
    the Sea
Decoration with title for North Folk .... MBPI0863 ..1902
    Legends of the Sea
Illustrated initial T for North Folk .... MBPI0864 ..1902
    Legends of the Sea
Decoration with title for North Folk .... MBPI0865 ..1902
    Legends of the Sea
The Fishing of Thor and Hymir .... MBPI0866 ..1902
Headpiece for North Folk Legends of the ..... MBPI0867 ..1902
    Sea
Title with decorations, The Fairy Morgana ..... MBPI0868 ..1902
The Fairy Morgana .... MBPI0869 ..1902
Headpiece for North Folk Legends of the ..... MBPI0870 ..1902
    Sea

Index–Titles of Pyle's Art In Chronological Sequence

1902

Title with decorations, Saint Brendan's .... MBPI0871 ..1902
   Island
Saint Brendan .... MBPI0872 ..1902
Headpiece for North Folk Legends of the ..... MBPI0873 ..1902
   Sea
Title with decorations, Mother Carey's .... MBPI0874 ..1902
   Chickens
Mother Carey .... MBPI0875 ..1902
Headpiece for North Folk Legends of the ..... MBPI0876 ..1902
   Sea
Title with decorations, The Flying .... MBPI0877 ..1902
   Dutchman
Headpiece for The Voice .... MBPI0878 ..1902
An autumn field of which she had dreamed ... MBPI0879 ..1902
She cried out .... MBPI0880 ..1902
She felt her blood tingling in every vein ...... MBPI0881 ..1902
Headpiece for The True Captain Kidd .... MBPI0882 ..1902
Title with decoration for The True .... MBPI0883 ..1902
   Captain Kidd
Illustrated initial W for The True .... MBPI0884 ..1902
   Captain Kidd
Kidd on the Deck of the "Adventure .... MBPI0885 ..1902
   Galley"
Burning the Ship .... MBPI0886 ..1902
Buried Treasure .... MBPI0887 ..1902
Title with illustrated initial T for The .... MBPI1840 ..1902
   Story of King Arthur and His Knights
The Enchanter Merlin .... MBPI1841 ..1902
Headpiece for The Story of King Arthur .... MBPI1842 ..1902
   and His Knights
Illustrated initial A for The Story of .... MBPI1843 ..1902
   King Arthur and His Knights
Title with illustrated initial H for The .... MBPI1844 ..1902
   Story of King Arthur and His Knights
How one clad all in black did a wonder .... MBPI1845 ..1902
   before King Leodegrance of Camilard
Sir Kay overthroweth his Enemies .... MBPI1846 ..1902
Illustrated initial I for The Story of .... MBPI1847 ..1902
   King Arthur and His Knights
Title with illustrated initial S for The .... MBPI1848 ..1902
   Story of King Arthur and His Knights
Sir Kay breaketh his sword at ye .... MBPI1849 ..1902
   Tournament
Headpiece for The Story of King Arthur .... MBPI1850 ..1902
   and His Knights
Title with illustrated initial S for The .... MBPI1851 ..1902
   Story of King Arthur and His Knights
Sir Kay showeth the mystic Sword unto Sir ... MBPI1852 ..1902
   Ector
Title with illustrated initial K for The .... MBPI1853 ..1902
   Story of King Arthur and His Knights
King Leodegrance cometh to the assay of .... MBPI1854 ..1902
   the Sword
Queen Esther inciting the Indians to .... MBPI2008 ..1902
   attack the settlers at Wyoming
The Connecticut Settlers entering the .... MBPI2009 ..1902
   Western Reserve
We started to run back to the raft for .... MBPI2010 ..1902
   our lives

1903

The boat and I went by him with a rush .... MBPI2011 ..1902
Decorative title with illustrated initial .... MBPI2012 ..1902
   S for Sindbad on Burrator
I began to play .... MBPI2013 ..1902
I sat at her feet while she drilled the .... MBPI2014 ..1902
   island language into me
"If I catch you here again you'll need .... MBPI2015 ..1902
   someone to sew you up"
I clutched at his ankle .... MBPI2016 ..1902
"There is a time to fight and that time .... MBPI2017 ..1902
   has now come"
Title page decoration for First Year Book ...... MBPI2392 ..1902
   of The Bibliophile Society
The Bibliophile .... MBPI2393 ..1902
Inauguration of Washington in New York ...... MBPI3193 ..1902
Then the old man's lips began to move .... MBPI3194 ..1902
Illustration for A Report of the truth .... MBPI3195 ..1902
   concerning the last sea-fight of the Revenge
Design for drinking mug .... PDPI0023 ..1902
Tailpiece design and verse for drinking .... PDPI0024 ..1902
   mug
Renaissance Couple .... PDPI0044 ..1902
Christmas Morn .... MBPI0070 ..1903
The Nation Makers .... MBPI0103 ..1903
The Chantey-Man .... MBPI0888 ..1903
"Small heed had we of the fleet, sweet .... MBPI0889 ..1903
   hours"
"'Twas a strange tale she had ended" .... MBPI0890 ..1903
Lady Adeliza came wondering to the .... MBPI0891 ..1903
   balcony
He thought of his love .... MBPI0892 ..1903
In the night .... MBPI0893 ..1903
"Nothing harms me all the day" .... MBPI0894 ..1903
At the gate of the Castle .... MBPI0895 ..1903
Vidal–Poet and Satirist .... MBPI0896 ..1903
In the train of King Alfonzo .... MBPI0897 ..1903
Title with illustrated initial K for The .... MBPI1855 ..1903
   Story of King Arthur and His Knights
How Arthur drew forth Ye Sword .... MBPI1856 ..1903
Headpiece for The Story of King Arthur .... MBPI1857 ..1903
   and His Knights
Title with illustrated initial K for The .... MBPI1858 ..1903
   Story of King Arthur and His Knights
King Arthur of Britain .... MBPI1859 ..1903
Illustrated initial S for The Story of .... MBPI1860 ..1903
   King Arthur and His Knights
Title with illustrated initial I for The .... MBPI1861 ..1903
   Story of King Arthur and His Knights
In the Valley of Delight .... MBPI1862 ..1903
Title with illustrated initial T for The .... MBPI1863 ..1903
   Story of King Arthur and His Knights
The Battle with the Sable Knight .... MBPI1864 ..1903
The Winning of a Sword and a Queen .... MBPI1865 ..1903
Title with illustrated initial E for The .... MBPI1866 ..1903
   Story of King Arthur and His Knights
Excalibur the Sword .... MBPI1867 ..1903
Title with illustrated initial T for The .... MBPI1868 ..1903
   Story of King Arthur and His Knights

1903

The Lady Guinevere .... MBPI1869 ..1903

Title with illustrated initial T for The .... MBPI1870 ..1903
Story of King Arthur and His Knights

Two Knights do Battle before Cameliard ...... MBPI1871 ..1903

Headpiece for The Story of King Arthur .... MBPI1872 ..1903
and His Knights

Title with illustrated initial T for The .... MBPI1873 ..1903
Story of King Arthur and His Knights

The White Champion meets two Knights at ... MBPI1874 ..1903
the Mill

Title with illustrated initial F for The .... MBPI1875 ..1903
Story of King Arthur and His Knights

Four Knights serve the Gardener Lad .... MBPI1876 ..1903

Headpiece for The Story of King Arthur .... MBPI1877 ..1903
and His Knights

Title with illustrated initial T for The .... MBPI1878 ..1903
Story of King Arthur and His Knights

The Gardener Lad takes off his Cap .... MBPI1879 ..1903

Title with illustrated initial K for The .... MBPI1880 ..1903
Story of King Arthur and His Knights

King Arthur meets the Lady Guinevere .... MBPI1881 ..1903

Headpiece for The Story of King Arthur .... MBPI1882 ..1903
and His Knights

Title with illustrated initial S for The .... MBPI1883 ..1903
Story of King Arthur and His Knights

Sir Pellias encounters the Sorrowful Lady ..... MBPI1884 ..1903
in Arroy

Title with illustrated initial S for The .... MBPI1885 ..1903
Story of King Arthur and His Knights

Sir Pellias, the Gentle Knight .... MBPI1886 ..1903

Headpiece for The Story of King Arthur .... MBPI1887 ..1903
and His Knights

Title with illustrated initial P for The .... MBPI1888 ..1903
Story of King Arthur and His Knights

Parcenet covers Sir Pellias with a cloak .... MBPI1889 ..1903

Title with illustrated initial T for The .... MBPI1890 ..1903
Story of King Arthur and His Knights

The Lady of the Lake sits by the Fountain ..... MBPI1891 ..1903
in Arroy

Headpiece for The Story of King Arthur .... MBPI1892 ..1903
and His Knights

Title with illustrated initial S for The .... MBPI1893 ..1903
Story of King Arthur and His Knights

Sir Gawaine sups with ye Lady Ettard .... MBPI1894 ..1903

Title with illustrated initial T for The .... MBPI1895 ..1903
Story of King Arthur and His Knights

The Lady of the Lake finds Sir Pellias .... MBPI1896 ..1903
wounded

Headpiece for The Story of King Arthur .... MBPI1897 ..1903
and His Knights

Title with illustrated initial S for The .... MBPI1898 ..1903
Story of King Arthur and His Knights

Sir Percival of Gales .... MBPI1899 ..1903

Title with illustrated initial S for The .... MBPI1900 ..1903
Story of King Arthur and His Knights

Sir Percival and Sir Pellinore ride .... MBPI1901 ..1903
together

Headpiece, Vivien for The Story of King .... MBPI1902 ..1903
Arthur and His Knights

1903

Title with illustrated initial S for The .... MBPI1903 ..1903
Story of King Arthur and His Knights

Sir Percival overcometh ye Enchantress ...... MBPI1904 ..1903
Vivien

Title with illustrated initial S for The .... MBPI1905 ..1903
Story of King Arthur and His Knights

Sir Kay interrupts ye meditations of Sir .... MBPI1906 ..1903
Percival

Title with illustrated initial T for The .... MBPI1907 ..1903
Story of King Arthur and His Knights

The Lady Yvette the Fair .... MBPI1908 ..1903

"Humbility is the fountain of all wirtue" .... MBPI2018 ..1903

Cover design for The Story of King Arthur .... MBPI2394 ..1903
and His Knights

Spine design for The Story of King Arthur .... MBPI2395 ..1903
and His Knights

Title page decoration for The Story of .... MBPI2396 ..1903
King Arthur and His Knights

Tailpiece, Foreword for The Story of King ..... MBPI2397 ..1903
Arthur and His Knights

Tailpiece, Contents for The Story of King ...... MBPI2398 ..1903
Arthur and His Knights

Tailpiece, List of Illustrations for The .... MBPI2399 ..1903
Story of King Arthur and His Knights

Subtitle page decoration for The Story of ..... MBPI2400 ..1903
King Arthur and His Knights

Illustrated initial U with heading for .... MBPI2401 ..1903
The Story of King Arthur and His Knights

Uther-Pendragon .... MBPI2402 ..1903

Tailpiece, Prologue for The Story of King ...... MBPI2403 ..1903
Arthur and His Knights

Tailpiece for The Story of King Arthur .... MBPI2404 ..1903
and His Knights

Tailpiece for The Story of King Arthur .... MBPI2405 ..1903
and His Knights

Tailpiece for The Story of King Arthur .... MBPI2406 ..1903
and His Knights

Tailpiece for The Story of King Arthur .... MBPI2407 ..1903
and His Knights

Illustrated initial T with heading for .... MBPI2408 ..1903
The Story of King Arthur and His Knights

The Lady of Ye Lake .... MBPI2409 ..1903

Tailpiece for The Story of King Arthur .... MBPI2410 ..1903
and His Knights

Illustrated initial T with heading for .... MBPI2411 ..1903
The Story of King Arthur and His Knights

The Enchantress Vivien .... MBPI2412 ..1903

Illustrated initial V with heading for .... MBPI2413 ..1903
The Story of King Arthur and His Knights

Vivien bewitches Merlin .... MBPI2414 ..1903

Illustrated initial Q with heading for .... MBPI2415 ..1903
The Story of King Arthur and His Knights

Queen Morgana le Fay .... MBPI2416 ..1903

Illustrated initial Q with heading for .... MBPI2417 ..1903
The Story of King Arthur and His Knights

Queen Morgana loses Excalibur his sheath .... MBPI2418 ..1903

Tailpiece for The Story of King Arthur .... MBPI2419 ..1903
and His Knights

Index–Titles of Pyle's Art In Chronological Sequence

1903

Tailpiece for The Story of King Arthur . . . . MBPI2420 . .1903
and His Knights
Illustrated initial S with heading for . . . . MBPI2421 . .1903
The Story of King Arthur and His Knights
Sir Gawaine the Son of Lot, King of . . . . MBPI2422 . .1903
Orkney
Headpiece for The Story of King Arthur . . . . MBPI2423 . .1903
and His Knights
Illustrated initial K with heading for . . . . MBPI2424 . .1903
The Story of King Arthur and His Knights
King Arthur findeth ye old woman in ye . . . . . . MBPI2425 . .1903
hut
Illustrated initial S with heading for . . . . MBPI2426 . .1903
The Story of King Arthur and His Knights
Sir Gawaine finds the beautiful Lady . . . . MBPI2427 . .1903
Tailpiece for The Story of King Arthur . . . . MBPI2428 . .1903
and His Knights
The Garden of Youth . . . . MBPI2506 . .1903
Caxton at his Press . . . . MBPI3196 . .1903
"Friar" Bacon in his Study . . . . MBPI3197 . .1903
Erasmus reading to Colet And More . . . . MBPI3198 . .1903
"Izaak" Walton . . . . MBPI3199 . .1903
Richard DeBury and the Young Edward III . . . . . MBPI3200 . .1903
Subtitle page decoration for Breviary . . . . MBPI3202 . .1903
Treasures
The Genus of Art . . . . MBPI3234 . .1903
Ye Pirate Bold, as imagined by a Quaker . . . . . . PDPI0018 . .1903
Gentleman
Illustration for Odes of Anacreon . . . . PDPI0036 . .1903
Anacreontics
Design for Howard Pyle School of Art . . . . PDPI0062 . .1903
lapel pin
Sea Battle between Two Frigates . . . . PDPI0101 . .1903
Whither? . . . . MBPI0099 . .1904
Her whisper was so soft he only guessed . . . . . MBPI0898 . .1904
the words
This last picture . . . . MBPI0899 . .1904
He stretched out his hand to the curtains . . . . . MBPI0900 . .1904
He found Melite alone . . . . MBPI0901 . .1904
He sang for her as they sat in the . . . . MBPI0902 . .1904
gardens
He climbed the stairs slowly, for he was . . . . . . MBPI0903 . .1904
growing feeble
Estercel . . . . MBPI0904 . .1904
"There is a charm," said the nurse at . . . . MBPI0905 . .1904
last
Eileen slipped the ring into the nest . . . . MBPI0906 . .1904
The Battle of the Stairs . . . . MBPI0907 . .1904
The dark folk trooped to meet them on the . . . MBPI0908 . .1904
shore
Bertha, the much beloved . . . . MBPI0909 . .1904
The drawing of the sword . . . . MBPI0910 . .1904
The rescue of Azilicz . . . . MBPI0911 . .1904
Her head and shoulders hung over the . . . . MBPI0912 . .1904
space without
"She tricked me, little maid" . . . . MBPI0913 . .1904
Catherine de Vaucelles, in her garden . . . . MBPI0914 . .1904
"Villon–The singer Fate fashioned to her . . . . . MBPI0915 . .1904
liking"

1905

"The King himself hauled me out of gaol" . . . . . MBPI0916 . .1904
The charge . . . . MBPI0917 . .1904
They brought in their dead and wounded . . . . MBPI0918 . .1904
on hay wagons
"I thought of you, when I was falling," . . . . MBPI0919 . .1904
he said vaguely
She believed that she had daily speech . . . . . . MBPI0920 . .1904
with angels
The triumphal entry into Rheims . . . . MBPI0921 . .1904
Guarded by rough English soldiers . . . . MBPI0922 . .1904
A lithe, young, slender figure . . . . MBPI0923 . .1904
Parson Rawson spoke to her with a . . . . MBPI0924 . .1904
pleasant chiding
Catherine Duke quickened her steps . . . . MBPI0925 . .1904
"Here is all I have to give thee–It is . . . . MBPI1299 . .1904
the King's Jewel"
"I know thy heart, that thou dost love me . . . . MBPI1300 . .1904
well"
"Not for myself do I seek this vengeance" . . . . . MBPI1301 . .1904
Illustration for The Eclogues of Vergil . . . . MBPI3201 . .1904
The portrait of a young gentleman who . . . . . . PDPI0006 . .1904
always says "Thank you!"
Ye Queen of Hearts . . . . PDPI0014 . .1904
Woman carrying urn . . . . PDPI0063 . .1904
Illustrated initial M for Invitation . . . . PDPI0081 . .1904
Tailpiece for Invitation . . . . PDPI0082 . .1904
Ocean View . . . . PDPI0083 . .1904
"Why Seek Ye the Living Among the Dead?" . . . MBPI0101 . .1905
The Minute Man . . . . MBPI0102 . .1905
Melicent stood motionless like a wild . . . . MBPI0926 . .1905
thing at gaze
A man lay prone there, half turned upon . . . . . MBPI0927 . .1905
his face
Sir John shook his spear at the ladies . . . . MBPI0928 . .1905
who sneered
La Salle christening the country . . . . MBPI0929 . .1905
"Louisiana"
La Salle petitions the King for . . . . MBPI0930 . .1905
permission to explore the Mississippi
She drew bridle, listening–there was no . . . . . . MBPI0931 . .1905
sound
"Are you ever lonely here?" he inquired . . . . MBPI0932 . .1905
"Come, come, your Future Majesty! Cheer . . . . . MBPI0933 . .1905
up!"
I knelt by the whispering, muttering old . . . . . . MBPI0934 . .1905
man
They stood staring at the violent sky . . . . MBPI0935 . .1905
With a cry, Shallum flung up his arms and . . . . MBPI0936 . .1905
jumped
The Crown-Prince Karl, dead by his own . . . . . . MBPI0937 . .1905
hand
Carlotta–tall, white, queenly–a cluster . . . . MBPI0938 . .1905
of flowers in her arms
Her outstretched arms seemed to close . . . . . . MBPI0939 . .1905
upon something
Old Immortality . . . . MBPI0940 . .1905
"I loved the husk of a man" . . . . MBPI0941 . .1905
Headpiece with title for The Fox Brush . . . . MBPI0942 . .1905

Index–Titles of Pyle's Art In Chronological Sequence

1905

So for a heart-beat she saw him . . . . MBPI0943 . .1905
He came to her–in his helmet a fox brush . . . . MBPI0944 . .1905
   spangled with jewels
Headband for The Fox Brush . . . . MBPI0945 . .1905
Marginal decoration, female with . . . . MBPI0946 . .1905
   outstretched arm
Marginal decoration, male with sword and . . . MBPI0947 . .1905
   shield
The doge sat alone in a great carven . . . . MBPI0948 . .1905
   chair
He laid the mantle over the girl's . . . . MBPI0949 . .1905
   shoulders
"He lay awhile conscious of great . . . . MBPI0950 . .1905
   comfort"
"She hung drooping in the great chair of . . . . . MBPI0951 . .1905
   state"
The buccaneer was a picturesque fellow . . . . . . MBPI0952 . .1905
An attack on a galleon . . . . MBPI0953 . .1905
So the treasure was divided . . . . MBPI0954 . .1905
Extorting tribute from the citizens . . . . MBPI0955 . .1905
Headband for The Fate of a Treasure Town . . . . MBPI0956 . .1905
Headpiece for The Fate of a Treasure Town . . . . MBPI0957 . .1905
Illustrated initial A for The Fate of a . . . . MBPI0958 . .1905
   Treasure Town
Marginal decoration, female with ship . . . . MBPI0959 . .1905
Marginal decoration, male with tree . . . . MBPI0960 . .1905
Cover design for The Story of Champions . . . . . MBPI2429 . .1905
   of the Round Table
Spine design for The Story of the . . . . MBPI2430 . .1905
   Champions of the Round Table
Illustrated initial S with heading for . . . . MBPI2431 . .1905
   The Story of the Champions of the Round Table
Sir Launcelot of the Lake . . . . MBPI2432 . .1905
Headpiece, Foreword for The Story of the . . . . . MBPI2433 . .1905
   Champions of the Round Table
Tailpiece, Foreword for The Story of the . . . . . . MBPI2434 . .1905
   Champions of the Round Table
Headpiece, Contents for The Story of the . . . . . MBPI2435 . .1905
   Champions of the Round Table
Tailpiece, Contents for The Story of the . . . . . . MBPI2436 . .1905
   Champions of the Round Table
Headpiece, List of Illustrations for The . . . . MBPI2437 . .1905
   Story of the Champions of the Round Table
Tailpiece, List of Illustrations for The . . . . MBPI2438 . .1905
   Story of the Champions of the Round Table
Illustrated initial T with heading for . . . . MBPI2439 . .1905
   The Story of the Champions of the Round Table
The Lady Nymue beareth away Launcelot . . . . MBPI2440 . .1905
   into the Lake
Headpiece for The Story of the Champions . . . MBPI2441 . .1905
   of the Round Table
Tailpiece for The Story of the Champions . . . . . MBPI2442 . .1905
   of the Round Table
Illustrated initial S with heading for . . . . MBPI2443 . .1905
   The Story of the Champions of the Round Table
Sir Launcelot greets Queen Guinevere . . . . MBPI2444 . .1905
Headpiece for The Story of the Champions . . . MBPI2445 . .1905
   of the Round Table

Illustrated initial S with heading for . . . . MBPI2446 . .1905
   The Story of the Champions of the Round Table
Sir Lionel of Britain . . . . MBPI2447 . .1905
Illustrated initial Q with heading for . . . . MBPI2448 . .1905
   The Story of the Champions of the Round Table
Queen Morgana appears unto Sir Launcelot . . . MBPI2449 . .1905
Illustrated initial S with heading for . . . . MBPI2450 . .1905
   The Story of the Champions of the Round Table
Sir Launcelot doeth battle with Sir . . . . MBPI2451 . .1905
   Turquine
Illustrated initial S with heading for . . . . MBPI2452 . .1905
   The Story of the Champions of the Round Table
Sir Launcelot sits with Sir Hilaire and . . . . MBPI2453 . .1905
   Croisette
Illustrated initial S with heading for . . . . MBPI2454 . .1905
   The Story of the Champions of the Round Table
Sir Launcelot and Elouise the Fair . . . . MBPI2455 . .1905
Illustrated initial S with heading for . . . . MBPI2456 . .1905
   The Story of the Champions of the Round Table
Sir Launcelot climbs to catch the lady's . . . . . . MBPI2457 . .1905
   falcon
Illustrated initial S with heading for . . . . MBPI2458 . .1905
   The Story of the Champions of the Round Table
Sir Launcelot takes the armor of Sir Kay . . . . . . MBPI2459 . .1905
Tailpiece for The Story of the Champions . . . . . MBPI2460 . .1905
   of the Round Table
Illustrated initial S with heading for . . . . MBPI2461 . .1905
   The Story of the Champions of the Round Table
Sir Tristram of Lyonesse . . . . MBPI2462 . .1905
Headpiece for The Story of the Champions . . . MBPI2463 . .1905
   of the Round Table
Tailpiece for The Story of the Champions . . . . . MBPI2464 . .1905
   of the Round Table
Illustrated initial T with heading for . . . . MBPI2465 . .1905
   The Story of the Champions of the Round Table
Tristram succors the Lady Moeya . . . . MBPI2466 . .1905
Headpiece for The Story of the Champions . . . MBPI2467 . .1905
   of the Round Table
Illustrated initial K with heading for . . . . MBPI2468 . .1905
   The Story of the Champions of the Round Table
King Mark of Cornwall . . . . MBPI2469 . .1905
Illustrated initial T with heading for . . . . MBPI2470 . .1905
   The Story of the Champions of the Round Table
The Lady Belle Isoult . . . . MBPI2471 . .1905
Illustrated initial T with heading for . . . . MBPI2472 . .1905
   The Story of the Champions of the Round Table
The Queen of Ireland seeks to slay Sir . . . . MBPI2473 . .1905
   Tristram
Illustrated initial S with heading for . . . . MBPI2474 . .1905
   The Story of the Champions of the Round Table
Sir Tristram harpeth before King Mark . . . . MBPI2475 . .1905
Illustrated initial S with heading for . . . . MBPI2476 . .1905
   The Story of the Champions of the Round Table
Sir Tristram sits with Sir Launcelot . . . . MBPI2477 . .1905
Tailpiece for The Story of the Champions . . . . . MBPI2478 . .1905
   of the Round Table
Illustrated initial B with heading for . . . . MBPI2479 . .1905
   The Story of the Champions of the Round Table

Index–Titles of Pyle's Art In Chronological Sequence

1905

Belle Isoult and Sir Tristram drink the .... MBPI2480 ..1905
  love draught
Tailpiece for The Story of the Champions ..... MBPI2481 ..1905
  of the Round Table
Illustrated initial S with heading for .... MBPI2482 ..1905
  The Story of the Champions of the Round Table
Sir Lamorack of Gales .... MBPI2483 ..1905
Headpiece for The Story of the Champions ... MBPI2484 ..1905
  of the Round Table
Illustrated initial S with heading for .... MBPI2485 ..1905
  The Story of the Champions of the Round Table
Sir Tristram cometh to ye castle of Sir .... MBPI2486 ..1905
  Nabon
Illustrated initial S with heading for .... MBPI2487 ..1905
  The Story of the Champions of the Round Table
Sir Lamorack herds the swine of Sir Nabon .... MBPI2488 ..1905
Tailpiece for The Story of the Champions ..... MBPI2489 ..1905
  of the Round Table
Illustrated initial S with heading for .... MBPI2490 ..1905
  The Story of the Champions of the Round Table
Sir Tristram assaults King Mark .... MBPI2491 ..1905
Headpiece for The Story of the Champions ... MBPI2492 ..1905
  of the Round Table
Illustrated initial S with heading for .... MBPI2493 ..1905
  The Story of the Champions of the Round Table
Sir Kay and the Forest Madman .... MBPI2494 ..1905
Illustrated initial S with heading for .... MBPI2495 ..1905
  The Story of the Champions of the Round Table
Sir Tristram leaps into ye Sea .... MBPI2496 ..1905
Illustrated initial K with heading for .... MBPI2497 ..1905
  The Story of the Champions of the Round Table
King Mark broods mischief .... MBPI2498 ..1905
Tailpiece for The Story of the Champions ..... MBPI2499 ..1905
  of the Round Table
Illustrated initial T with heading for .... MBPI2509 ..1905
  The Story of the Champions of the Round Table
The Demoiselle Blanchefleur .... MBPI2510 ..1905
Tailpiece for The Story of the Champions ..... MBPI2513 ..1905
  of the Round Table
Headpiece, Publisher's Note for The One ...... MBPI3207 ..1905
  Hoss Shay
Tailpiece for The One Hoss Shay .... MBPI3208 ..1905
Design for Edith Kermit Roosevelt .... MBPI3227 ..1905
  bookplate
Design for The Yale Club of New York City .... MBPI3228 ..1905
  bookplate
The Genus of Literature .... MBPI3232 ..1905
Shepherd and Girl .... MBPI3233 ..1905
The Genus of Music .... MBPI3235 ..1905
Young Flowering Trees .... MBPI3236 ..1905
Flowering Tree II .... MBPI3237 ..1905
The Genus of Drama .... MBPI3238 ..1905
Howard Pyle self portrait painting .... PDPI0004 ..1905
Strip of Green for mural panel .... PDPI0011 ..1905
Flowering Tree I .... PDPI0012 ..1905
Headband for The Gods of the Copybook .... PDPI0078 ..1905
  Maxims
A neat and shrivelled gentleman sat at a ..... MBPI0961 ..1906
  desk

1907

They were overtaken by Falmouth himself .... MBPI0962 ..1906
Beatrix and Esmond .... MBPI0963 ..1906
Becky Sharp and Lord Steyne .... MBPI0964 ..1906
So may the future bring its wreath of .... MBPI1302 ..1906
  roses and of bay to you.
Preliminary study for MBPI3240 The .... MBPI1303 ..1906
  Landing of Carteret
"The tall man was lying at his feet, ... MBPI1758 ..1906
  huddled hideously on the floor"
Headband for The Second-Class Passenger .... MBPI1759 ..1906
"I have been reserved for this–to free .... MBPI1760 ..1906
  the land from spiritual tyranny"
"The Lord hath sent me here to die like ...... MBPI1761 ..1906
  Stephen at the feet of Saul"
"At her appearing the multitude was .... MBPI1762 ..1906
  hushed, awed by that air she wore"
Cover design for Twelfth Night at .... MBPI3216 ..1906
  Eagleroost
Title page decoration for Twelfth Night .... MBPI3217 ..1906
  at Eagleroost
Headpiece for Twelfth Night at Eagleroost .... MBPI3218 ..1906
Cover design for Centuria's Greetings .... MBPI3219 ..1906
Headpiece for Centuria's Greetings .... MBPI3220 ..1906
Illustrated initial G for Centuria's .... MBPI3221 ..1906
  Greetings
Poor Richard .... MBPI3222 ..1906
The Battle of Nashville .... MBPI3239 ..1906
A view in Jamaica .... PDPI0016 ..1906
A figure to provoke tears .... MBPI0965 ..1907
Pendennis .... MBPI0966 ..1907
"Who is the lucky miss, my little .... MBPI0967 ..1907
  villain?"
The duel between John Blumer and Cazaio ... MBPI0968 ..1907
"The Bastille is not a very healthy .... MBPI0969 ..1907
  place"
The Death of Cazaio .... MBPI0970 ..1907
The king glared down at her .... MBPI0971 ..1907
Suddenly their comedy turned tragic .... MBPI0972 ..1907
"I am the daughter of that unfortunate .... MBPI0973 ..1907
  Captain Keitt!"
Illustrated initial T for The Ruby of .... MBPI0975 ..1907
  Kishmoor
Jonathan Rugg .... MBPI0976 ..1907
The negress beckoned him to draw nearer .... MBPI0977 ..1907
The little gentleman with one eye .... MBPI0978 ..1907
With great amity the two walked off .... MBPI0979 ..1907
  together
The little gentleman in black emitted a .... MBPI0980 ..1907
  piercing scream
The man with the silver earrings .... MBPI0981 ..1907
The stranger threw himself upon Jonathan ... MBPI0982 ..1907
  with the fury of a madman
The man with the broken nose .... MBPI0983 ..1907
The arms of his captor held him as in a .... MBPI0984 ..1907
  vise
The lady with the silver veil .... MBPI0985 ..1907
Jonathan Rugg was married to Martha Dobbs MBPI0986 ..1907
  the following year

Index–Titles of Pyle's Art In Chronological Sequence

1907

Captain Keitt . . . . MBPI0987 . .1907
Abraham Lincoln . . . . MBPI0988 . .1907
She became as famous for speed as her . . . . . . MBPI0989 . .1907
    short career allowed
Her captain was a Cuban . . . . MBPI0990 . .1907
The cruiser piled on all sail . . . . MBPI0991 . .1907
They have a so-called native king . . . . MBPI0992 . .1907
They carried fruit and vegetables . . . . MBPI0993 . .1907
'Tween decks of the slaver . . . . MBPI0994 . .1907
The rest were shot and thrown overboard . . . . . MBPI0995 . .1907
The mate elevated and sighted the gun . . . . MBPI0996 . .1907
The lighters were soon alongside . . . . MBPI0997 . .1907
She was a solid mass of flame . . . . MBPI0998 . .1907
Meregrett, daughter of Philippe the Bold . . . . . . MBPI0999 . .1907
Then sang Sire Edward . . . . MBPI1000 . .1907
Cover design for The Story of Sir . . . . MBPI2514 . .1907
    Launcelot and his Companions
Spine design for The Story of Sir . . . . MBPI2515 . .1907
    Launcelot and his Companions
Illustrated initial T with heading for . . . . MBPI2516 . .1907
    The Story of Sir Launcelot and his Companions
The Lady Elaine the Fair . . . . MBPI2517 . .1907
Headpiece, Foreword for The Story of Sir . . . . . MBPI2518 . .1907
    Launcelot and his Companions
Tailpiece, Foreword for The Story of Sir . . . . MBPI2519 . .1907
    Launcelot and his Companions
Headpiece, Contents for The Story of Sir . . . . . . MBPI2520 . .1907
    Launcelot and his Companions
Tailpiece, Contents for The Story of Sir . . . . MBPI2521 . .1907
    Launcelot and his Companions
Headpiece, List of Illustrations for The . . . . MBPI2522 . .1907
    Story of Sir Launcelot and his Companions
Tailpiece, List of Illustrations for The . . . . MBPI2523 . .1907
    Story of Sir Launcelot and his Companions
Illustrated initial S with heading for . . . . MBPI2524 . .1907
    The Story of Sir Launcelot and his Companions
Sir Mellegrans interrupts the sport of . . . . MBPI2525 . .1907
    the Queen
Headpiece for The Story of Sir Launcelot . . . . . MBPI2526 . .1907
    and his Companions
Tailpiece for The Story of Sir Launcelot . . . . MBPI2527 . .1907
    and his Companions
Illustrated initial D with heading for . . . . MBPI2528 . .1907
    The Story of Sir Launcelot and his Companions
Denneys and the Hermit help Sir Launcelot . . . MBPI2529 . .1907
    to his armor
Headpiece for The Story of Sir Launcelot . . . . MBPI2530 . .1907
    and his Companions
Illustrated initial H with heading for . . . . MBPI2531 . .1907
    The Story of Sir Launcelot and his Companions
How Sir Launcelot rode errant in a cart . . . . . . MBPI2532 . .1907
Illustrated initial T with heading for . . . . MBPI2533 . .1907
    The Story of Sir Launcelot and his Companions
The Damsel Elose the Fair rescues Sir . . . . MBPI2534 . .1907
    Launcelot
Illustrated initial S with heading for . . . . MBPI2535 . .1907
    The Story of Sir Launcelot and his Companions
Sir Gareth of Orkney . . . . MBPI2536 . .1907

Headpiece for The Story of Sir Launcelot . . . . . MBPI2537 . .1907
    and his Companions
Illustrated initial T with heading for . . . . MBPI2538 . .1907
    The Story of Sir Launcelot and his Companions
The Damsel Lynette . . . . MBPI2539 . .1907
Illustrated initial S with heading for . . . . MBPI2540 . .1907
    The Story of Sir Launcelot and his Companions
Sir Gareth doeth Battle with the Knight . . . . . . MBPI2541 . .1907
    of the River Ford
Illustrated initial T with heading for . . . . MBPI2542 . .1907
    The Story of Sir Launcelot and his Companions
The Lady Layonnesse . . . . MBPI2543 . .1907
Illustrated initial T with heading for . . . . MBPI2544 . .1907
    The Story of Sir Launcelot and his Companions
The Lady Layonnesse cometh to the . . . . MBPI2545 . .1907
    Pavilion of Sir Gareth
Tailpiece for The Story of Sir Launcelot . . . . MBPI2546 . .1907
    and his Companions
Illustrated initial H with heading for . . . . MBPI2547 . .1907
    The Story of Sir Launcelot and his Companions
How Sir Launcelot held discourse with ye . . . . MBPI2548 . .1907
    merry Minstrels
Headpiece for The Story of Sir Launcelot . . . . . MBPI2549 . .1907
    and his Companions
Illustrated initial S with heading for . . . . MBPI2550 . .1907
    The Story of Sir Launcelot and his Companions
Sir Launcelot slayeth the Worm of Corbin . . . . MBPI2551 . .1907
Illustrated initial S with heading for . . . . MBPI2552 . .1907
    The Story of Sir Launcelot and his Companions
Sir Launcelot confideth his Shield to . . . . MBPI2553 . .1907
    Elaine the Fair
Illustrated initial S with heading for . . . . MBPI2554 . .1907
    The Story of Sir Launcelot and his Companions
Sir Launcelot and Sir Lavaine overlook . . . . MBPI2555 . .1907
    the Field of Astolat
Illustrated initial S with heading for . . . . MBPI2556 . .1907
    The Story of Sir Launcelot and his Companions
Sir Gawaine knoweth the shield of Sir . . . . MBPI2557 . .1907
    Launcelot
Illustrated initial S with heading for . . . . MBPI2558 . .1907
    The Story of Sir Launcelot and his Companions
Sir Launcelot leapeth from the window . . . . MBPI2559 . .1907
Tailpiece for The Story of Sir Launcelot . . . . MBPI2560 . .1907
    and his Companions
Illustrated initial T with heading for . . . . MBPI2561 . .1907
    The Story of Sir Launcelot and his Companions
The Madman of the Forest who was Sir . . . . . . MBPI2562 . .1907
    Launcelot
Headpiece for The Story of Sir Launcelot . . . . . MBPI2563 . .1907
    and his Companions
Illustrated initial T with heading for . . . . MBPI2564 . .1907
    The Story of Sir Launcelot and his Companions
The Forest Madman saveth ye Life of King . . . . MBPI2565 . .1907
    Arthur
Illustrated initial T with heading for . . . . MBPI2566 . .1907
    The Story of Sir Launcelot and his Companions
The Lady Elaine the Fair Knoweth Sir . . . . MBPI2567 . .1907
    Launcelot

Index–Titles of Pyle's Art In Chronological Sequence

1907

Tailpiece for The Story of Sir Launcelot .... MBPI2568 ..1907
and his Companions

Illustrated initial S with heading for .... MBPI2569 ..1907
The Story of Sir Launcelot and his Companions

Sir Gawaine, Knight of the Fountain .... MBPI2570 ..1907

Headpiece for The Story of Sir Launcelot ..... MBPI2571 ..1907
and his Companions

Illustrated initial S with heading for .... MBPI2572 ..1907
The Story of Sir Launcelot and his Companions

Sir Ewaine poureth water on the slab .... MBPI2573 ..1907

Illustrated initial T with heading for .... MBPI2574 ..1907
The Story of Sir Launcelot and his Companions

The Damsel Elose giveth a ring to Sir .... MBPI2575 ..1907
Ewaine

Illustrated initial T with heading for .... MBPI2576 ..1907
The Story of Sir Launcelot and his Companions

The Lady of the Fountain .... MBPI2577 ..1907

Illustrated initial A with heading for .... MBPI2578 ..1907
The Story of Sir Launcelot and his Companions

A Damsel bringeth aid unto Sir Ewaine .... MBPI2579 ..1907

Tailpiece for The Story of Sir Launcelot .... MBPI2580 ..1907
and his Companions

Illustrated initial S with heading for .... MBPI2581 ..1907
The Story of Sir Launcelot and his Companions

Sir Lamorack and Sir Percival receive .... MBPI2582 ..1907
their Mother's Blessing

Headpiece for The Story of Sir Launcelot ..... MBPI2583 ..1907
and his Companions

Illustrated initial S with heading for .... MBPI2584 ..1907
The Story of Sir Launcelot and his Companions

Sir Percival and Sir Ector look upon the .... MBPI2585 ..1907
Isle of Joy

Illustrated initial S with heading for .... MBPI2586 ..1907
The Story of Sir Launcelot and his Companions

Sir Lavaine the Son of Pelles .... MBPI2587 ..1907

Illustrated initial M with heading for .... MBPI2588 ..1907
The Story of Sir Launcelot and his Companions

Merlin Prophesieth from a Cloud of Mist ...... MBPI2589 ..1907

Headpiece for The Story of Sir Launcelot ..... MBPI2590 ..1907
and his Companions

Illustrated initial S with heading for .... MBPI2591 ..1907
The Story of Sir Launcelot and his Companions

Sir Bors de Ganis, the good .... MBPI2592 ..1907

Illustrated initial T with heading for .... MBPI2593 ..1907
The Story of Sir Launcelot and his Companions

The Barge of the Dead .... MBPI2594 ..1907

Dofobius .... MBPI3209 ..1907

The Landing of Carteret .... MBPI3240 ..1907

Front cover decorative border for .... PDPI0069 ..1907
McClure's Magazine

"Others have lived through greater woes ..... MBPI1001 ..1908
than ours"

"Take care, my friend, take care" .... MBPI1002 ..1908

The officers would be waiting until she .... MBPI1003 ..1908
should appear

The passing of Dona Victoria .... MBPI1004 ..1908

Rosamund and Sir Gregory .... MBPI1005 ..1908

Queen Ysabeau in her carven chair .... MBPI1006 ..1908

1908

She arrayed herself in silence .... MBPI1007 ..1908

Horse and man plunged heavily after her ..... MBPI1008 ..1908

The coming of Lancaster .... MBPI1009 ..1908

Branwen .... MBPI1010 ..1908

The Newcomes .... MBPI1011 ..1908

The dark, smiling Salim, with his magic .... MBPI1012 ..1908
pack, was welcome

Edric the singer .... MBPI1013 ..1908

Marginal decoration with title for Edric .... MBPI1014 ..1908
and Sylvaine

Marginal decoration for Edric and .... MBPI1015 ..1908
Sylvaine

Marginal decoration for Edric and .... MBPI1016 ..1908
Sylvaine

Marginal decoration for Edric and .... MBPI1017 ..1908
Sylvaine

Marginal decoration for Edric and .... MBPI1018 ..1908
Sylvaine

Marginal decoration for Edric and .... MBPI1019 ..1908
Sylvaine

Marginal decoration for Edric and .... MBPI1020 ..1908
Sylvaine

Marginal decoration for Edric and .... MBPI1021 ..1908
Sylvaine

Marginal decoration for Edric and .... MBPI1022 ..1908
Sylvaine

Marginal decoration for Edric and .... MBPI1023 ..1908
Sylvaine

Marginal decoration for Edric and .... MBPI1024 ..1908
Sylvaine

Marginal decoration for Edric and .... MBPI1025 ..1908
Sylvaine

Marginal decoration for Edric and .... MBPI1026 ..1908
Sylvaine

Marginal decoration for Edric and .... MBPI1027 ..1908
Sylvaine

Marginal decoration for Edric and .... MBPI1028 ..1908
Sylvaine

Tailpiece for Edric and Sylvaine .... MBPI1029 ..1908

"I will have him between these hands" .... MBPI1030 ..1908

In an instant those long fingers closed .... MBPI1031 ..1908
on the Governor

"The American captain with his mate .... MBPI1032 ..1908
boarded us"

Then the real fight began .... MBPI1033 ..1908

Diana Sherley .... MBPI1034 ..1908

"Go, Madam, and leave the Prodigal among .. MBPI1035 ..1908
his husks"

Old Jacob Van Kleek had never favored our ... MBPI1036 ..1908
hero's suit

Decorative title with illustrated initial .... MBPI1037 ..1908
U for The Mysterious Chest

The skeletonlike stranger entered .... MBPI1038 ..1908

It was his belief that the chest was .... MBPI1039 ..1908
certainly haunted

Swinging his lanthorn and followed by his ... MBPI1040 ..1908
laboring assistants

The Reverend Ebenezer Doolittle .... MBPI1041 ..1908

Index–Titles of Pyle's Art In Chronological Sequence

1908

"D'ye see what the wretches have left?" . . . . MBPI1042 . .1908
Gazed down upon the dreadful object . . . . MBPI1043 . .1908
He was greatly addicted to little supper . . . . . . MBPI1044 . .1908
    parties of his own sex
A dreadful spectacle . . . . MBPI1045 . .1908
Old Jacob Van Kleek the money-lender . . . . MBPI1046 . .1908
Illustration for The Mysterious Chest . . . . MBPI1047 . .1908
Our young gentleman of the law . . . . MBPI1048 . .1908
He perused the inscription with great . . . . MBPI1049 . .1908
    particularity
"If this dreadful thing is not taken away . . . . . . MBPI1050 . .1908
    I shall go mad"
Lugged the mysterious chest to the . . . . MBPI1051 . .1908
    lawyer's house
Tailpiece for The Mysterious Chest . . . . MBPI1052 . .1908
The Shell . . . . MBPI1053 . .1908
"The Dancer" . . . . MBPI1054 . .1908
When All the World Was Young . . . . MBPI1066 . .1908
Which shall be Captain? . . . . MBPI1114 . .1908
The Midsummer Moon . . . . MBPI2507 . .1908
Design for Keats-Shelley Memorial . . . . MBPI3229 . .1908
    bookplate
Birthday Tribute to Theodore Roosevelt . . . . . . PDPI0003 . .1908
Design for 1908 Christmas Seal . . . . PDPI0064 . .1908
Design for 1908 Christmas Seal–Rounded . . . . PDPI0065 . .1908
    corners
His eyes fell on the dancer in her . . . . MBPI1055 . .1909
    shimmering scarlet
In place of the apple hung a little . . . . MBPI1056 . .1909
    gilded skull
The precious minutes flew past, but she . . . . . . MBPI1057 . .1909
    was silent
"He watched me as a cat watches a mouse" . . . MBPI1058 . .1909
"He lost his hold and fell, taking me . . . . MBPI1059 . .1909
    with him"
The Duke of Gloucester sent for Edward . . . . . . MBPI1060 . .1909
    Maudelain
The Queen read the Scriptures in the . . . . MBPI1061 . .1909
    vulgar tongue
Dim and faded pictures at times came . . . . MBPI1062 . .1909
    before them
Vitia and the Governor . . . . MBPI1063 . .1909
Sheridan's first interview with Rowand . . . . MBPI1064 . .1909
A lonely duel in the middle of a great, ... MBPI1065 . .1909
    sunny field
The Midnight Court Martial . . . . MBPI1067 . .1909
She put the silver coronet upon her head . . . . . MBPI1068 . .1909
She saw herself for what he had said, and . . . . MBPI1069 . .1909
    swooned
Theirs was a spirited encounter upon the . . . . . MBPI1070 . .1909
    beach of Teviot Bay
"Who are we that Heaven should make of . . . . MBPI1071 . .1909
    the old sea a fowling net?"
It was a comrade from his own regiment . . . . . . MBPI1072 . .1909
"They talked it over–with me sitting on . . . . . . MBPI1073 . .1909
    the horse"
A wolf had not been seen at Salem for . . . . MBPI1074 . .1909
    thirty years

1910

Decorative title with illustrated initial . . . . MBPI1075 . .1909
    T for The Salem Wolf
Once it chased Dr. Wilkinson into the . . . . MBPI1076 . .1909
    very town itself
Marginal illustration for The Salem Wolf . . . . . . MBPI1077 . .1909
Vignette for The Salem Wolf . . . . MBPI1078 . .1909
Vignette for The Salem Wolf . . . . MBPI1079 . .1909
Marginal illustration for The Salem Wolf . . . . . . MBPI1080 . .1909
Marginal illustration for The Salem Wolf . . . . . . MBPI1081 . .1909
Vignette for The Salem Wolf . . . . MBPI1082 . .1909
Vignette for The Salem Wolf . . . . MBPI1083 . .1909
Headpiece for The Salem Wolf . . . . MBPI1084 . .1909
Vignette for The Salem Wolf . . . . MBPI1085 . .1909
The nation is at war and must have men . . . . . . MBPI1086 . .1909
They awaited the order for the charge . . . . MBPI1087 . .1909
The Enchanted Seas . . . . MBPI2508 . .1909
Marooned . . . . MBPI2511 . .1909
Preliminary study for proposed mural for . . . . . PDPI0002 . .1909
    Soldiers and Sailors Memorial Hall of Allegheny County,
    Pennsylvania
The Inquisitive Peasant . . . . PDPI0022 . .1909
Angel of Death . . . . PDPI0029 . .1909
Theatrical costumes designed by Howard . . . . PDPI0043 . .1909
    Pyle
Design for punch bowl . . . . PDPI0046 . .1909
Design for centerpiece . . . . PDPI0047 . .1909
Design for . . . . PDPI0048 . .1909
    candelabra–candlestick–electrolier
Marooned . . . . PDPI0098 . .1909
Theatrical costumes designed by Howard . . . . PDPI0105 . .1909
    Pyle
"I grow old, having no son but Randver" . . . . . . MBPI1088 . .1910
Thereafter she clung about Randver . . . . MBPI1089 . .1910
"I found him and he wasn't alone" . . . . MBPI1090 . .1910
"My boy wanted to do the divin', but . . . . MBPI1091 . .1910
    'twas me that went down"
The whole world goes afield today . . . . MBPI1092 . .1910
Flaggingly the reed pen went up and down . . MBPI1093 . .1910
    the vellum
She told him her adventures in a breath . . . . . . MBPI1094 . .1910
Writing on some loose sheets of paper . . . . MBPI1095 . .1910
    that he held on his knee
"I have broken it," she wailed . . . . MBPI1096 . .1910
"And see that you watch well," he snarled . . . . MBPI1097 . .1910
"They questioned him with malevolent . . . . . . MBPI1098 . .1910
    persistence"
The sea boiled over the wreckage in . . . . MBPI1099 . .1910
    streaky white
Page was at the wheel, steering . . . . MBPI1100 . .1910
There stood the Faery Prince . . . . MBPI1101 . .1910
Decorative title with illustrated initial . . . . MBPI1102 . .1910
    T for Ysobel de Corveaux
Marginal illustration for Ysobel de . . . . MBPI1103 . .1910
    Corveaux
Marginal illustration for Ysobel de . . . . MBPI1104 . .1910
    Corveaux
Marginal illustration for Ysobel de . . . . MBPI1105 . .1910
    Corveaux

Index–Titles of Pyle's Art In Chronological Sequence

Marginal illustration for Ysobel de ....MBPI1106 ..1910
   Corveaux
Marginal illustration for Ysobel de ....MBPI1107 ..1910
   Corveaux
Marginal illustration for Ysobel de ....MBPI1108 ..1910
   Corveaux
Marginal illustration for Ysobel de ....MBPI1109 ..1910
   Corveaux
Marginal illustration for Ysobel de ....MBPI1110 ..1910
   Corveaux
Marginal illustration for Ysobel de ....MBPI1111 ..1910
   Corveaux
Marginal illustration for Ysobel de ....MBPI1112 ..1910
   Corveaux
Headpiece for Ysobel de Coreaux ....MBPI1113 ..1910
The Virginians ....MBPI1125 ..1910
Hendryk Hudson and the Half-Moon ....MBPI2500 ..1910
Peter Stuyvesant and the English Fleet ....MBPI2501 ..1910
Life in an Old Dutch Town ....MBPI2502 ..1910
Dutch Soldier ....MBPI2503 ..1910
English Soldier ....MBPI2504 ..1910
The Mermaid ....MBPI2512 ..1910
Cover design for The Story of the Grail ....MBPI2595 ..1910
   and the Passing of Arthur
Spine design for The Story of the Grail ....MBPI2596 ..1910
   and the Passing of Arthur
Illustrated initial S with heading for ....MBPI2597 ..1910
   The Story of the Grail and the Passing of Arthur
Sir Galahad of the Grail ....MBPI2598 ..1910
Headpiece, Foreword for The Story of the .....MBPI2599 ..1910
   Grail and the Passing of Arthur
Tailpiece for The Story of the Grail and ....MBPI2600 ..1910
   the Passing of Arthur
Headpiece, Contents for The Story of the .....MBPI2601 ..1910
   Grail and the Passing of Arthur
Tailpiece, Contents for The Story of the ....MBPI2602 ..1910
   Grail and the Passing of Arthur
Headpiece, List of Illustrations for The ....MBPI2603 ..1910
   Story of the Grail and the Passing of Arthur
Tailpiece, List of Illustrations for The ....MBPI2604 ..1910
   Story of the Grail and the Passing of Arthur
Illustrated initial S with heading for ....MBPI2605 ..1910
   The Story of the Grail and the Passing of Arthur
Sir Geraint, Son of Erbin ....MBPI2606 ..1910
Headpiece for The Story of the Grail and .....MBPI2607 ..1910
   the Passing of Arthur
Tailpiece for The Story of the Grail and ....MBPI2608 ..1910
   the Passing of Arthur
Illustrated initial E with heading for ....MBPI2609 ..1910
   The Story of the Grail and the Passing of Arthur
Enid and Geraint in the garden ....MBPI2610 ..1910
Headpiece for The Story of the Grail and .....MBPI2611 ..1910
   the Passing of Arthur
Illustrated initial S with heading for ....MBPI2612 ..1910
   The Story of the Grail and the Passing of Arthur
Sir Geraint and the Knight of the ....MBPI2613 ..1910
   Sparrowhawk
Illustrated initial S with heading for ....MBPI2614 ..1910
   The Story of the Grail and the Passing of Arthur

Sir Geraint lies asleep ....MBPI2615 ..1910
Illustrated initial E with heading for ....MBPI2616 ..1910
   The Story of the Grail and the Passing of Arthur
Enid talks with the Earl ....MBPI2617 ..1910
Illustrated initial E with heading for ....MBPI2618 ..1910
   The Story of the Grail and the Passing of Arthur
Enid and Geraint ride past the Town ....MBPI2619 ..1910
   bridge
Illustrated initial T with heading for ....MBPI2620 ..1910
   The Story of the Grail and the Passing of Arthur
The King's Physicians attend Sir Geraint ....MBPI2621 ..1910
Illustrated initial S with heading for ....MBPI2623 ..1910
   The Story of the Grail and the Passing of Arthur
Sir Galahad cometh with the Hermit of the ...MBPI2624 ..1910
   Forest
Headpiece for The Story of the Grail and .....MBPI2625 ..1910
   the Passing of Arthur
Illustrated initial T with heading for ....MBPI2626 ..1910
   The Story of the Grail and the Passing of Arthur
The Lady of the Lake and Sir Galahad ....MBPI2627 ..1910
Illustrated initial S with heading for ....MBPI2628 ..1910
   The Story of the Grail and the Passing of Arthur
Sir Galahad meets Sir Melyas ....MBPI2629 ..1910
Illustrated initial T with heading for ....MBPI2630 ..1910
   The Story of the Grail and the Passing of Arthur
The Grail is manifested, and Sir ....MBPI2631 ..1910
   Launcelot sleepeth
Illustrated initial S with heading for ....MBPI2632 ..1910
   The Story of the Grail and the Passing of Arthur
Sir Percival rideth the black horse ....MBPI2633 ..1910
Illustrated initial S with heading for ....MBPI2634 ..1910
   The Story of the Grail and the Passing of Arthur
Sir Bors rides with the white knight ....MBPI2635 ..1910
Illustrated initial S with heading for ....MBPI2636 ..1910
   The Story of the Grail and the Passing of Arthur
Sir Galahad rides with the Lady ....MBPI2637 ..1910
Illustrated initial T with heading for ....MBPI2638 ..1910
   The Story of the Grail and the Passing of Arthur
The Queen's pages clothe Sir Launcelot ....MBPI2639 ..1910
Headpiece for The Story of the Grail and .....MBPI2640 ..1910
   the Passing of Arthur
Illustrated initial S with heading for ....MBPI2641 ..1910
   The Story of the Grail and the Passing of Arthur
Sir Mador de la Porte ....MBPI2642 ..1910
Illustrated initial S with heading for ....MBPI2643 ..1910
   The Story of the Grail and the Passing of Arthur
Sir Mador begs for his Life ....MBPI2644 ..1910
Illustrated initial S with heading for ....MBPI2645 ..1910
   The Story of the Grail and the Passing of Arthur
Sir Launcelot defends the door ....MBPI2646 ..1910
Illustrated initial T with heading for ....MBPI2647 ..1910
   The Story of the Grail and the Passing of Arthur
The Bishop of Rochester and the King ....MBPI2648 ..1910
Illustrated initial S with heading for ....MBPI2649 ..1910
   The Story of the Grail and the Passing of Arthur
Sir Gawaine challenges Sir Launcelot ....MBPI2650 ..1910
Illustrated initial T with heading for ....MBPI2651 ..1910
   The Story of the Grail and the Passing of Arthur

Index–Titles of Pyle's Art In Chronological Sequence

1910

The Passing of Sir Gawaine . . . . MBPI2652 . .1910
Illustrated initial S with heading for . . . . MBPI2653 . .1910
    The Story of the Grail and the Passing of Arthur
Sir Mordred the traitor . . . . MBPI2654 . .1910
Illustrated initial T with heading for . . . . MBPI2655 . .1910
    The Story of the Grail and the Passing of Arthur
The Passing of Arthur . . . . MBPI2656 . .1910
Illustrated initial T with heading for . . . . MBPI2657 . .1910
    The Story of the Grail and the Passing of Arthur
The Passing of Guinevere . . . . MBPI2658 . .1910
Tailpiece for The Story of the Grail and . . . . MBPI2659 . .1910
    the Passing of Arthur
The Escape . . . . PDPI0007 . .1910
Preliminary study for MBPI2501 Peter . . . . PDPI0008 . .1910
    Stuyvesant and the English Fleet
Preliminary study for MBPI2500 Hendryk . . . . . PDPI0009 . .1910
    Hudson and the Half-Moon
Preliminary study for MBPI2502 Life in an . . . . PDPI0010 . .1910
    Old Dutch Town
"A Study" . . . . PDPI0041 . .1910
River Rocks . . . . PDPI0075 . .1910
General Lee on his famous charger . . . . MBPI1117 . .1911
    "Traveler"
His army broke up and followed him, ... MBPI1118 . .1911
    weeping and sobbing
So long as Gann would follow, his Master . . . . . MBPI1119 . .1911
    would lead
Man and staff sank into the peat mud . . . . MBPI1120 . .1911
Jocelin, with many encomiums, displayed . . . . MBPI1121 . .1911
    his emeralds
"I have loved you for a great while, fair . . . . MBPI1122 . .1911
    Mervisaunt"
She was continually beset by spies . . . . MBPI1123 . .1911
The secret room . . . . MBPI1124 . .1911
"Everything you wish for shall be yours" . . . . . . MBPI1126 . .1911
Decorative title for The Dead Finger . . . . MBPI1127 . .1911
So Beppo's first wish was fulfilled . . . . MBPI1128 . .1911
The two rode away together . . . . MBPI1129 . .1911
Beppo sat in the Notary's house talking . . . . . . MBPI1130 . .1911
    about the will
He saw a great coach approaching . . . . MBPI1131 . .1911
The grand duke gave him a golden chain . . . . . MBPI1132 . .1911
He thrust the cobbler back against the . . . . MBPI1133 . .1911
    door
He was poor as ever . . . . MBPI1134 . .1911
The last of the "Naronic" . . . . MBPI1135 . .1911
Stefano and Serafina at the well . . . . MBPI1136 . .1911
Decorative title for The Painted Pitcher . . . . MBPI1137 . .1911
Montofacini, the Magician . . . . MBPI1138 . .1911
The shopman . . . . MBPI1139 . .1911
The bear would stand upon his hind legs . . . . . MBPI1140 . .1911
    and dance
Nicolo, the tallow chandler . . . . MBPI1141 . .1911
Serafina was leaning from the window . . . . MBPI1142 . .1911
Cassacinci and the runaway horse . . . . MBPI1143 . .1911
The DuPont Powder Wagon . . . . MBPI3230 . .1911
Tailpiece for The Painted Pitcher . . . . PDPI0079 . .1911
Decorative title for The Evil Eye . . . . MBPI1144 . .1912

1913

He was engaged to Caterina . . . . MBPI1145 . .1912
She pointed her finger at Caterina . . . . MBPI1146 . .1912
One of the horses fell dead in the field . . . . MBPI1147 . .1912
While she stood looking the cow died . . . . MBPI1148 . .1912
The vines were dying . . . . MBPI1149 . .1912
"The Evil Eye," he said . . . . MBPI1150 . .1912
Montofacini, the Magician . . . . MBPI1151 . .1912
"I am a ruined man" . . . . MBPI1152 . .1912
That night his straw stack caught fire . . . . MBPI1153 . .1912
He knew not what ailed her or what to do . . . . MBPI1154 . .1912
He was lying on the library floor in the . . . . MBPI1155 . .1912
    morning
The traveller found the stone behind the . . . . . MBPI1156 . .1912
    hedge a resting-place
Nicolo and the Robber . . . . MBPI1157 . .1912
He had lost the soul of M. Fournier . . . . MBPI0124 . .1913
Over her gleaming shoulder her chalky . . . . . . MBPI0125 . .1913
    face lowered at him, with a look of sullen hatred
Herr Vollmer quietly stepped out into the . . . . MBPI1158 . .1913
    street
She began to talk to Huntford about . . . . MBPI1159 . .1913
    himself
The little man raced down the stairs and . . . . . MBPI1160 . .1913
    out into the street

MBPI0001	**Ye Pirate Bold**		**401**
PM1558	Ye Pirate Bold	November, 1911	3
PM0001	Ye Pirate Bold	January, 1912	3
PM1146	Letter and drawing by Howard Pyle	January 1, 1916	10
MBPI0002	**"I saw him pass his sword through the mate's body"**		**401**
PM0727	The Novels and Tales of Robert Louis Stevenson (Kidnapped)	1895	189
PM1040	The Novels, Travels, Essays & Poems of Robert Louis Stevenson	1901	189
MBPI0003	**"He put the glass to his lips and drank at one gulp"**		**401**
PM0728	The Novels and Tales of Robert Louis Stevenson (Strange Case of Dr. Jekyll and Mr. Hyde)	1895	189
PM1464	Art Institute of Chicago, Chicago, Illinois	1903	130, 297
PM1466	Kellogg Public Library, Green Bay, Wisconsin	1904	301
MBPI0004	**"Will you forgive my having followed you?"**		**401**
PM0729	The Novels and Tales of Robert Louis Stevenson (David Balfour)	1895	189
PM1040	The Novels, Travels, Essays & Poems of Robert Louis Stevenson	1901	189
MBPI0005	**"The gigantic monster dragged the hacked and headless corpse of his victim up the staircase"**		**401**
PM0730	In Ole Virginia	1896	171
MBPI0006	**"A man in it, standing upright, and something lying in a lump at the bow"**		**401**
PM0730	In Ole Virginia	1896	171
MBPI0007	**The Rivals**		**401**
PM0007	A Set of Sketches	December, 1893	11
MBPI0008	**The First Sketch**		**401**
PM0007	A Set of Sketches	December, 1893	11
MBPI0009	**Illustrated initial A for The First Sketch**		**401**
PM0007	A Set of Sketches	December, 1893	11
MBPI0010	**The Second Sketch**		**401**
PM0007	A Set of Sketches	December, 1893	11
MBPI0011	**Illustrated initial A for The Second Sketch**		**401**
PM0007	A Set of Sketches	December, 1893	11
MBPI0012	**The Third Sketch**		**401**
PM0007	A Set of Sketches	December, 1893	11
PM0726	Modern Illustration	1895	186
MBPI0013	**Illustrated initial T for The Third Sketch**		**401**
PM0007	A Set of Sketches	December, 1893	11
MBPI0014	**The Fourth Sketch**		**401**
PM0007	A Set of Sketches	December, 1893	11
MBPI0015	**Illustrated initial T for The Fourth Sketch**		**401**
PM0007	A Set of Sketches	December, 1893	11
MBPI0016	**The Fifth Sketch**		**401**
PM0007	A Set of Sketches	December, 1893	11
PM0994	The Century Book of Famous Americans	1896	142
MBPI0017	**Illustrated initial A for The Fifth Sketch**		**402**
PM0007	A Set of Sketches	December, 1893	11
MBPI0018	**The Sixth Sketch**		**402**
PM0007	A Set of Sketches	December, 1893	11
MBPI0019	**Illustrated initial T for The Sixth Sketch**		**402**
PM0007	A Set of Sketches	December, 1893	11
MBPI0020	**The Surrender of Captain Pearson on the Deck of the "Bonhomme Richard"**		**402**
PM0008	Paul Jones	April, 1895	11
PM0798	The Drexel Institute, Philadelphia, Pennsylvania	1897	8, 140, 268, 284
PM0799	St. Botolph Club, Boston, Massachusetts	1897	140, 268, 288
PM1453	Trans-Mississippi and International Exposition, Omaha, Nebraska	1898	293
MBPI0021	**The Bonhomme Richard and Ye Serapis**		**402**
PM0008	Paul Jones	April, 1895	11
PM0742	The Book of the Ocean	1898	136
MBPI0022	**Headpiece with title and initial T for Paul Jones**		**402**
PM0008	Paul Jones	April, 1895	11
MBPI0023	**Paul Jones raising the Rattlesnake Flag on the "Alfred"**		**402**
PM0008	Paul Jones	April, 1895	11
MBPI0024	**Tailpiece for Paul Jones**		**402**

PM0008	Paul Jones	April, 1895	11
PM1260	The Re-Christening of Phoebe	July, 1915	124
PM1150	Auguste Rodin	March, 1918	14
PM1261	The Story of "The Marseillaise"	January, 1919	124
MBPI0025	**"The Admiral came in his gig of state"**		**402**
PM0009	A Business Transaction	June, 1895	12
PM0798	The Drexel Institute, Philadelphia, Pennsylvania	1897	8, 140, 268, 284
PM0799	St. Botolph Club, Boston, Massachusetts	1897	140, 268, 288
PM1149	Forty Years of This Magazine	November, 1910	14
PM1242	Monographs on American Wood Engraving	February, 1918	107
MBPI0026	**Headpiece with title for The Constitution's Last Fight**		**402**
PM0010	The Constitution's Last Fight	September, 1895	12
MBPI0027	**The Constitution's Last Fight**		**402**
PM0010	The Constitution's Last Fight	September, 1895	12
PM0742	The Book of the Ocean	1898	136
MBPI0028	**Tailpiece for The Constitution's Last Fight**		**402**
PM0010	The Constitution's Last Fight	September, 1895	12
MBPI0029	**Maid Marian's Song with title**		**402**
PM0011	Maid Marian's Song	November, 1895	12
MBPI0030	**Maid Marian's Song**		**402**
PM0011	Maid Marian's Song	November, 1895	12
MBPI0031	**"Didst thou tell them I taught thee?"**		**402**
PM0012	Hugh Wynne, Free Quaker	November, 1896	12
PM0734	Hugh Wynne, Free Quaker	1897	170
PM0798	The Drexel Institute, Philadelphia, Pennsylvania	1897	8, 140, 268, 284
PM0799	St. Botolph Club, Boston, Massachusetts	1897	140, 268, 288
PM1554	Works of S. Weir Mitchell: Hugh Wynne	1910	253
MBPI0032	**"I will teach thee to answer thy elders"**		**402**
PM0013	Hugh Wynne, Free Quaker	December, 1896	12
PM0734	Hugh Wynne, Free Quaker	1897	170
PM0798	The Drexel Institute, Philadelphia, Pennsylvania	1897	8, 140, 268, 284
PM0799	St. Botolph Club, Boston, Massachusetts	1897	140, 268, 288
PM1554	Works of S. Weir Mitchell: Hugh Wynne	1910	253
MBPI0033	**"There was instant silence"**		**403**
PM0014	Hugh Wynne, Free Quaker	January, 1897	12
PM0734	Hugh Wynne, Free Quaker	1897	170
PM0798	The Drexel Institute, Philadelphia, Pennsylvania	1897	8, 140, 268, 284
PM0799	St. Botolph Club, Boston, Massachusetts	1897	140, 268, 288
PM1554	Works of S. Weir Mitchell: Hugh Wynne	1910	253
MBPI0034	**In Aunt Gainor's Garden**		**403**
PM0015	Hugh Wynne, Free Quaker	February, 1897	12
PM0734	Hugh Wynne, Free Quaker	1897	170
PM0798	The Drexel Institute, Philadelphia, Pennsylvania	1897	8, 140, 268, 284
PM0799	St. Botolph Club, Boston, Massachusetts	1897	140, 268, 288
PM1554	Works of S. Weir Mitchell: Hugh Wynne	1910	253
MBPI0035	**Aunt Gainor**		**403**
PM0016	Hugh Wynne, Free Quaker	March, 1897	12
PM0734	Hugh Wynne, Free Quaker	1897	170
PM0798	The Drexel Institute, Philadelphia, Pennsylvania	1897	8, 140, 268, 284
PM0799	St. Botolph Club, Boston, Massachusetts	1897	140, 268, 288
PM1131	Advertisement	December, 1899	8
PM1554	Works of S. Weir Mitchell: Hugh Wynne	1910	253
MBPI0036	**In the presence of Washington**		**403**
PM0017	Hugh Wynne, Free Quaker	April, 1897	12
PM0734	Hugh Wynne, Free Quaker	1897	170
PM1133	Book Review	July, 1907	8
PM1143	The Modern Hero in Illustration	July, 1907	10
PM1554	Works of S. Weir Mitchell: Hugh Wynne	1910	253
MBPI0037	**In the Prison**		**403**
PM0018	Hugh Wynne, Free Quaker	May, 1897	12

PM0734	Hugh Wynne, Free Quaker	1897	170
PM1554	Works of S. Weir Mitchell: Hugh Wynne	1910	253
MBPI0038	**"Here, André! A Spy!"**		**403**
PM0019	Hugh Wynne, Free Quaker	June, 1897	13
PM0734	Hugh Wynne, Free Quaker	1897	170
PM1554	Works of S. Weir Mitchell: Hugh Wynne	1910	253
MBPI0039	**The visit to André**		**403**
PM0020	Hugh Wynne, Free Quaker	July, 1897	13
PM0734	Hugh Wynne, Free Quaker	1897	170
PM1554	Works of S. Weir Mitchell: Hugh Wynne	1910	253
MBPI0040	**Arnold and his wife**		**403**
PM0021	Hugh Wynne, Free Quaker	August, 1897	13
PM0734	Hugh Wynne, Free Quaker	1897	170
PM1554	Works of S. Weir Mitchell: Hugh Wynne	1910	253
MBPI0041	**The Duel**		**403**
PM0022	Hugh Wynne, Free Quaker	September, 1897	13
PM0734	Hugh Wynne, Free Quaker	1897	170
PM1554	Works of S. Weir Mitchell: Hugh Wynne	1910	253
MBPI0042	**"Is it Yes or No, Darthea?"**		**403**
PM0023	Hugh Wynne, Free Quaker	October, 1897	13
PM1224	American History In Fiction	October, 1897	99
PM0734	Hugh Wynne, Free Quaker	1897	170
PM1554	Works of S. Weir Mitchell: Hugh Wynne	1910	253
MBPI0043	**Headpiece for The Battle of Copenhagen**		**403**
PM0024	The Battle of Copenhagen	February, 1897	12
PM1258	War-Ships Ancient and Modern	March, 1907	124
PM1522	Boys and Girls Bookshelf: Historic Tales and Golden Deeds	1912	137
MBPI0044	**Nelson sealing his letter to the Crown Prince of Denmark**		**403**
PM0024	The Battle of Copenhagen	February, 1897	12
PM0798	The Drexel Institute, Philadelphia, Pennsylvania	1897	8, 140, 268, 284
PM0799	St. Botolph Club, Boston, Massachusetts	1897	140, 268, 288
PM1592	A Catalogue of Drawings	1897	140, 284
PM1593	A Catalogue of Illustrations	1897	140, 288
MBPI0045	**Tailpiece for The Battle of Copenhagen**		**403**
PM0024	The Battle of Copenhagen	February, 1897	12
MBPI0046	**The Mizzen Top of the "Redoubtable"**		**403**
PM0025	Nelson at Trafalgar	March, 1897	12
MBPI0047	**Don Quixote's Encounter with the Windmill**		**403**
PM0026	Three Pictures of Don Quixote	November, 1901	13
MBPI0048	**Headpiece with title and decorated border for Hope and Memory**		**403**
PM0027	Hope and Memory	November, 1901	13
MBPI0049	**Hope and Memory**		**404**
PM0027	Hope and Memory	November, 1901	13
MBPI0050	**Headpiece for Hope and Memory**		**404**
PM0027	Hope and Memory	November, 1901	13
MBPI0051	**Tailpiece for Hope and Memory**		**404**
PM0027	Hope and Memory	November, 1901	13
MBPI0052	**Marginal decoration for Hope and Memory**		**404**
PM0027	Hope and Memory	November, 1901	13
MBPI0053	**Marginal decoration for Hope and Memory**		**404**
PM0027	Hope and Memory	November, 1901	13
MBPI0054	**The Wicket of Paradise**		**404**
PM0028	The Travels of the Soul	December, 1902	13
PM1464	Art Institute of Chicago, Chicago, Illinois	1903	130, 297
PM1467	Kellogg Public Library, Green Bay, Wisconsin	1904	21, 302
MBPI0055	**In the Meadows of Youth**		**404**
PM0028	The Travels of the Soul	December, 1902	13
PM1464	Art Institute of Chicago, Chicago, Illinois	1903	130, 297
PM1467	Kellogg Public Library, Green Bay, Wisconsin	1904	21, 302
MBPI0056	**In the Valley of the Shadows**		**404**

PM0028	The Travels of the Soul	December, 1902	13
PM1050	Pictorial Composition and the Critical Judgment of Pictures	1903	203
PM1464	Art Institute of Chicago, Chicago, Illinois	1903	130, 297
PM1467	Kellogg Public Library, Green Bay, Wisconsin	1904	21, 302
MBPI0057	**At the Gates of Life**		**404**
PM0028	The Travels of the Soul	December, 1902	13
PM1464	Art Institute of Chicago, Chicago, Illinois	1903	130, 297
PM1467	Kellogg Public Library, Green Bay, Wisconsin	1904	21, 302
MBPI0058	**Title page decoration for The Travels of the Soul**		**404**
PM0028	The Travels of the Soul	December, 1902	13
MBPI0059	**Headpiece with title The Travels of the Soul**		**404**
PM0028	The Travels of the Soul	December, 1902	13
MBPI0060	**Illustrated initial T for The Travels of the Soul**		**404**
PM0028	The Travels of the Soul	December, 1902	13
MBPI0061	**Headpiece with title In the Meadows of Youth**		**404**
PM0028	The Travels of the Soul	December, 1902	13
MBPI0062	**Illustrated initial O for In the Meadows of Youth**		**404**
PM0028	The Travels of the Soul	December, 1902	13
MBPI0063	**Tailpiece for In the Meadows of Youth**		**404**
PM0028	The Travels of the Soul	December, 1902	13
MBPI0064	**Headpiece with title In the Valley of the Shadows**		**404**
PM0028	The Travels of the Soul	December, 1902	13
MBPI0065	**Illustrated initial N for In the Valley of the Shadows**		**405**
PM0028	The Travels of the Soul	December, 1902	13
MBPI0066	**Tailpiece for In the Valley of the Shadows**		**405**
PM0028	The Travels of the Soul	December, 1902	13
MBPI0067	**Headpiece with title At the Gates of Life**		**405**
PM0028	The Travels of the Soul	December, 1902	13
MBPI0068	**Illustrated initial A for At the Gates of Life**		**405**
PM0028	The Travels of the Soul	December, 1902	13
MBPI0069	**Tailpiece for At the Gates of Life**		**405**
PM0028	The Travels of the Soul	December, 1902	13
MBPI0070	**Christmas Morn**		**405**
PM0029	Christmas Morn	December 20, 1903	14
MBPI0071	**Decoration with title for Poisoned Ice**		**405**
PM0030	Poisoned Ice	December 10, 1898	15
MBPI0072	**Headpiece for Poisoned Ice**		**405**
PM0030	Poisoned Ice	December 10, 1898	15
MBPI0073	**On the edge of the ring, guarded, stood Brother Bartholome and the Carmelite**		**405**
PM0030	Poisoned Ice	December 10, 1898	15
PM1468	American Art Galleries, New York, New York	1905	303
PM1479	Hotel Dupont, Wilmington, Delaware	1912	141, 310
PM1481	Panama and Pacific International Exhibition, San Francisco, California	1915	315
MBPI0074	**Tailpiece for Poisoned Ice**		**405**
PM0030	Poisoned Ice	December 10, 1898	15
PM1574	The Real Right Thing	December 16, 1899	15
MBPI0075	**Upon the last stage of the journey they stopped for dinner at a tavern**		**405**
PM0031	The Price of Blood	December 17, 1898	15, 204
PM1399	Advertisement: The Price of Blood	December 17, 1898	73
PM0653	The Price of Blood	1899	15, 204
PM1479	Hotel Dupont, Wilmington, Delaware	1912	141, 310
PM1481	Panama and Pacific International Exhibition, San Francisco, California	1915	315
MBPI0076	**Headpiece with title for The Price of Blood**		**405**
PM0031	The Price of Blood	December 17, 1898	15, 204
MBPI0077	**Illustrated initial I for The Price of Blood**		**405**
PM0031	The Price of Blood	December 17, 1898	15, 204
MBPI0078	**Tailpiece, Introduction for The Price of Blood**		**405**
PM0031	The Price of Blood	December 17, 1898	15, 204
MBPI0079	**Illustrated initial T for The Price of Blood**		**405**
PM0031	The Price of Blood	December 17, 1898	15, 204

MBPI0080	**Headpiece for The Price of Blood**		**405**
PM0031	The Price of Blood	December 17, 1898	15, 204
PM0653	The Price of Blood	1899	15, 204
MBPI0081	**Headpiece, Chapter II for The Price of Blood**		**406**
PM0031	The Price of Blood	December 17, 1898	15, 204
PM0653	The Price of Blood	1899	15, 204
MBPI0082	**Illustrated initial A for The Price of Blood**		**406**
PM0031	The Price of Blood	December 17, 1898	15, 204
MBPI0083	**Headpiece, Chapter III for The Price of Blood**		**406**
PM0031	The Price of Blood	December 17, 1898	15, 204
PM0653	The Price of Blood	1899	15, 204
MBPI0084	**Illustrated initial O for The Price of Blood**		**406**
PM0031	The Price of Blood	December 17, 1898	15, 204
MBPI0085	**Headpiece, Chapter IV for The Price of Blood**		**406**
PM0031	The Price of Blood	December 17, 1898	15, 204
PM0653	The Price of Blood	1899	15, 204
MBPI0086	**Illustrated initial E for The Price of Blood**		**406**
PM0031	The Price of Blood	December 17, 1898	15, 204
MBPI0087	**Headpiece, Chapter V for The Price of Blood**		**406**
PM0031	The Price of Blood	December 17, 1898	15, 204
PM0653	The Price of Blood	1899	15, 204
MBPI0088	**Illustrated initial T for The Price of Blood**		**406**
PM0031	The Price of Blood	December 17, 1898	15, 204
MBPI0089	**Dead Men Tell No Tales**		**406**
PM0032	Dead Men Tell No Tales	December 16, 1899	15
PM1013	The Green Flag & Other Stories	1909	157
MBPI0090	**The Flying Dutchman**		**406**
PM0033	The Flying Dutchman	December 8, 1900	15
PM1479	Hotel Dupont, Wilmington, Delaware	1912	141, 310
PM1481	Panama and Pacific International Exhibition, San Francisco, California	1915	315
MBPI0091	**Columbia Speaks**		**406**
PM0034	Columbia Speaks	January 12, 1901	16
PM0931	Great American Illustrators: Howard Pyle, Illustrator	September, 1907	99, 106
MBPI0092	**Headpiece for A Sahib's War**		**406**
PM0035	A Sahib's War	December 7, 1901	16
MBPI0093	**Decoration with title for A Sahib's War**		**406**
PM0035	A Sahib's War	December 7, 1901	16
MBPI0094	**Illustrated initial P for A Sahib's War**		**406**
PM0035	A Sahib's War	December 7, 1901	16
MBPI0095	**Umr Singh**		**406**
PM0035	A Sahib's War	December 7, 1901	16
MBPI0096	**"Then appeared suddenly, a little beyond the light of the lamp, the spirit of Kurban Sahib"**		**406**
PM0035	A Sahib's War	December 7, 1901	16
MBPI0097	**Tailpiece for A Sahib's War**		**407**
PM0035	A Sahib's War	December 7, 1901	16
MBPI0098	**Song of Peace**		**407**
PM0036	Song of Peace	June 14, 1902	16
MBPI0099	**Whither?**		**407**
PM0037	How Are We Going To Vote This Year?	November 5, 1904	16
MBPI0100	**The Burning Ship**		**407**
PM1542	The Works of Charles Kingsley	1899	251
PM0038	The Burning Ship	December 10, 1904	16
PM1205	Our Leading Illustrators	December 14, 1905	96
PM1468	American Art Galleries, New York, New York	1905	303
PM1404	A Catalogue of Collier's Art Prints	1906	271
PM1428	The Burning Ship	1907	340-341
PM1431	The Burning Ship	1908	340-341
PM1479	Hotel Dupont, Wilmington, Delaware	1912	141, 310
PM1481	Panama and Pacific International Exhibition, San Francisco, California	1915	315
MBPI0101	**"Why Seek Ye the Living Among the Dead?"**		**407**

PM0039	"Why Seek Ye the Living Among the Dead?"	April 15, 1905	16
MBPI0102	**The Minute Man**		**407**
PM1468	American Art Galleries, New York, New York	1905	303
PM0040	The Minute Man	February 17, 1906	16
PM1429	The Minute Man	1907	340
MBPI0103	**The Nation Makers**		**407**
PM1464	Art Institute of Chicago, Chicago, Illinois	1903	130, 297
PM1466	Kellogg Public Library, Green Bay, Wisconsin	1904	301
PM1468	American Art Galleries, New York, New York	1905	303
PM0041	The Nation Makers	June 2, 1906	16
PM1404	A Catalogue of Collier's Art Prints	1906	271
PM0931	Great American Illustrators: Howard Pyle, Illustrator	September, 1907	99, 106
PM1430	The Nation Makers	1907	340-341
PM1320	Collier's 1908 Calendar	1908	278
PM1432	The Nation Makers	1908	340-341
PM1472	Pratt Institute, Brooklyn, New York	1908	106, 306
PM1473	Macbeth Gallery, New York	1908	307
PM1269	Songs We Love: The Star Spangled Banner	1912	213
PM0794	American Art by American Artists	1915	130
PM1616	The Junior Classics: Poems Old and New	1918	174
MBPI0104	**"In the Garden"**		**407**
PM0042	To the Soil of the Earth	June, 1892	17
MBPI0105	**"They stood and looked across the chasm at him"**		**407**
PM0042	To the Soil of the Earth	June, 1892	17
MBPI0106	**"He turned the slab-like leaves rapidly"**		**407**
PM0043	A Modern Magian	August, 1894	17
MBPI0107	**"The young fellow lounged in a rattan chair"**		**407**
PM0043	A Modern Magian	August, 1894	17
MBPI0108	**"Their first meeting happened at the club"**		**407**
PM0043	A Modern Magian	August, 1894	17
MBPI0109	**"DuMoreau was leaning part way across the table"**		**407**
PM0043	A Modern Magian	August, 1894	17
MBPI0110	**"He glared at the girl in the dim light"**		**407**
PM0043	A Modern Magian	August, 1894	17
MBPI0111	**"Then there was a crash and clatter of an overturned chair"**		**407**
PM0043	A Modern Magian	August, 1894	17
MBPI0112	**"His Majesty would furnish no more money for treasure hunting"**		**407**
PM0044	The First Self-Made American	June, 1902	20
MBPI0113	**The settler**		**408**
PM0044	The First Self-Made American	June, 1902	20
MBPI0114	**"He fell in love"**		**408**
PM0044	The First Self-Made American	June, 1902	20
PM0993	The Coast of Freedom	1902	144
PM1561	The Coast of Freedom	1902	272
MBPI0115	**"A fair brick house in the Green Lane of North Boston"**		**408**
PM0044	The First Self-Made American	June, 1902	20
MBPI0116	**"Stand off, ye wretches"**		**408**
PM0044	The First Self-Made American	June, 1902	20
MBPI0117	**"He had seen great guns in the bottom of the sea"**		**408**
PM0044	The First Self-Made American	June, 1902	20
MBPI0118	**"Soberly joined himself to the North Church"**		**408**
PM0044	The First Self-Made American	June, 1902	20
MBPI0119	**"The ships rolled and wallowed in the river"**		**408**
PM0044	The First Self-Made American	June, 1902	20
MBPI0120	**"Why, what is this? Whence came this?"**		**408**
PM0044	The First Self-Made American	June, 1902	20
PM1464	Art Institute of Chicago, Chicago, Illinois	1903	130, 297
PM1470	St. Botolph Club, Boston, Massachusetts	1906	303
MBPI0121	**"An 'Eminent Person from Whitehall' visited him in his chambers"**		**408**
PM0044	The First Self-Made American	June, 1902	20

MBPI0122	**"The victims of the witchcraft delusion"**		**408**
PM0044	The First Self-Made American	June, 1902	20
MBPI0123	**"The Queen granted him an audience"**		**408**
PM0044	The First Self-Made American	June, 1902	20
MBPI0124	**He had lost the soul of M. Fournier**		**408**
PM0045	The Madonna of the Blackbird	January, 1913	20
MBPI0125	**Over her gleaming shoulder her chalky face lowered at him, with a look of sullen hatred**		**408**
PM0045	The Madonna of the Blackbird	January, 1913	20
MBPI0126	**In the Bookseller's Shop**		**408**
PM0006	The Chevalier de Resseguier	May, 1893	11
MBPI0127	**"The Rejection"**		**408**
PM1441	Salmagundi Club, New York, New York	1881	282
PM0047	"The Rejection"	December 9, 1882	21
MBPI0128	**Daisies**		**408**
PM0048	Daisies	May 9, 1885	22
MBPI0129	**A Quaker Wedding**		**409**
PM0049	A Quaker Wedding	December 12, 1885	22
MBPI0130	**The Flight of the Swallow**		**409**
PM0050	The Flight of the Swallow	November 27, 1886	22
MBPI0131	**Illustrated initial T for The Flight of the Swallow**		**409**
PM0050	The Flight of the Swallow	November 27, 1886	22
MBPI0132	**Tailpiece for The Flight of the Swallow**		**409**
PM0050	The Flight of the Swallow	November 27, 1886	22
MBPI0133	**"He was a tall dark gentleman dressed in black from head to foot"**		**409**
PM0051	A Modern Aladdin	May 23, 1891	22, 186
PM0648	A Modern Aladdin	1892	22-24, 185
MBPI0134	**"He suddenly began an uncouth grotesque dance"**		**409**
PM0051	A Modern Aladdin	May 23, 1891	22, 186
PM0648	A Modern Aladdin	1892	22-24, 185
MBPI0135	**"At that moment she looked up"**		**409**
PM0051	A Modern Aladdin	May 23, 1891	22, 186
PM0648	A Modern Aladdin	1892	22-24, 185
MBPI0136	**"'I am thy Uncle,' said the strange gentleman"**		**409**
PM0051	A Modern Aladdin	May 23, 1891	22, 186
PM0648	A Modern Aladdin	1892	22-24, 185
MBPI0137	**"He lighted a match and dropped it into the vase"**		**409**
PM0051	A Modern Aladdin	May 23, 1891	22, 186
PM0648	A Modern Aladdin	1892	22-24, 185
MBPI0138	**"Oliver gave a piping cry"**		**409**
PM0052	A Modern Aladdin	May 30, 1891	22, 186
PM0648	A Modern Aladdin	1892	22-24, 185
MBPI0139	**"At the open doorway stood Gaspard and his master"**		**409**
PM0052	A Modern Aladdin	May 30, 1891	22, 186
PM0648	A Modern Aladdin	1892	22-24, 185
MBPI0140	**"Creeping cautiously forward, Oliver came to the chimney-place"**		**409**
PM0052	A Modern Aladdin	May 30, 1891	22, 186
PM0648	A Modern Aladdin	1892	22-24, 185
MBPI0141	**"'Good day, Monsieur,' said a familiar voice"**		**409**
PM0052	A Modern Aladdin	May 30, 1891	22, 186
PM0648	A Modern Aladdin	1892	22-24, 185
MBPI0142	**"The question was so sudden and so startling that Oliver sank back in his seat"**		**409**
PM0053	A Modern Aladdin	June 6, 1891	22, 186
PM1119	Novels and Tales	January, 1892	6
PM0648	A Modern Aladdin	1892	22-24, 185
MBPI0143	**"They saw Arnold de Villeneuve, the great master, lying upon the floor"**		**409**
PM0053	A Modern Aladdin	June 6, 1891	22, 186
PM0648	A Modern Aladdin	1892	22-24, 185
MBPI0144	**"Such was the workshop in which the two labored together"**		**409**
PM0053	A Modern Aladdin	June 6, 1891	22, 186
PM0648	A Modern Aladdin	1892	22-24, 185

MBPI0145	"She held the book to the flames whilest talking, her eyes fixed intently upon it"		410
PM0053	A Modern Aladdin	June 6, 1891	22, 186
PM0648	A Modern Aladdin	1892	22-24, 185
MBPI0146	"He leaned over and looked into her face"		410
PM0054	A Modern Aladdin	June 13, 1891	23, 186
PM0648	A Modern Aladdin	1892	22-24, 185
MBPI0147	"He saw within an oval mirror, set in a heavy frame of copper"		410
PM0054	A Modern Aladdin	June 13, 1891	23, 186
PM0648	A Modern Aladdin	1892	22-24, 185
MBPI0148	"And stripped the false body off of him as you would strip off a man's coat"		410
PM0054	A Modern Aladdin	June 13, 1891	23, 186
PM0648	A Modern Aladdin	1892	22-24, 185
MBPI0149	"The innkeeper served him in person"		410
PM0054	A Modern Aladdin	June 13, 1891	23, 186
PM0648	A Modern Aladdin	1892	22-24, 185
MBPI0150	"'Mad!' said Oliver, 'why am I mad?'"		410
PM0055	A Modern Aladdin	June 20, 1891	23, 186
PM0648	A Modern Aladdin	1892	22-24, 185
MBPI0151	"Oliver spread out the gems upon the table with his hand"		410
PM0055	A Modern Aladdin	June 20, 1891	23, 186
PM0648	A Modern Aladdin	1892	22-24, 185
MBPI0152	"He is clad in a loose dressing-robe of figured cloth and lies in bed reading his book"		410
PM0055	A Modern Aladdin	June 20, 1891	23, 186
PM0925	Book Review	January, 1892	9
PM0648	A Modern Aladdin	1892	22-24, 185
MBPI0153	"'Do you know,' said the Marquis, 'what a thing it is that you ask?'"		410
PM0056	A Modern Aladdin	June 27, 1891	23, 186
PM0648	A Modern Aladdin	1892	22-24, 185
MBPI0154	"He sank upon his knees beside her"		410
PM0056	A Modern Aladdin	June 27, 1891	23, 186
PM0648	A Modern Aladdin	1892	22-24, 185
MBPI0155	"She drew her down until the girl kneeled upon the floor beside the sofa"		410
PM0056	A Modern Aladdin	June 27, 1891	23, 186
PM0648	A Modern Aladdin	1892	22-24, 185
MBPI0156	"Monsieur the Count de St. Germaine"		410
PM0056	A Modern Aladdin	June 27, 1891	23, 186
PM0648	A Modern Aladdin	1892	22-24, 185
MBPI0157	"The Count de St. Germaine, without removing his eyes from his victim, took another deep, luxurious pinch of snuff"		410
PM0057	A Modern Aladdin	July 4, 1891	23, 186
PM0648	A Modern Aladdin	1892	22-24, 185
MBPI0158	"Oliver fixed his gaze upon the smooth brilliant surface of the glass"		410
PM0057	A Modern Aladdin	July 4, 1891	23, 186
PM0648	A Modern Aladdin	1892	22-24, 185
MBPI0159	"He saw a dull heavy yellow smoke arise to the ceiling"		410
PM0057	A Modern Aladdin	July 4, 1891	23, 186
PM0648	A Modern Aladdin	1892	22-24, 185
MBPI0160	"They beheld their master lying upon his face under the table"		410
PM0057	A Modern Aladdin	July 4, 1891	23, 186
PM0648	A Modern Aladdin	1892	22-24, 185
MBPI0161	"Suddenly someone touched Oliver lightly upon the shoulder"		411
PM0058	A Modern Aladdin	July 11, 1891	23, 186
PM0648	A Modern Aladdin	1892	22-24, 185
MBPI0162	"He found in his clinched hand a lace cravat"		411
PM0058	A Modern Aladdin	July 11, 1891	23, 186
PM0648	A Modern Aladdin	1892	22-24, 185
MBPI0163	"'Celeste!' breathed Oliver through the crack in the door"		411
PM0058	A Modern Aladdin	July 11, 1891	23, 186
PM0648	A Modern Aladdin	1892	22-24, 185
MBPI0164	"Over his shoulder he carried something limp, like an empty skin, or a bundle of clothes tied together"		411

PM0058	A Modern Aladdin	July 11, 1891	23, 186
PM0648	A Modern Aladdin	1892	22-24, 185
MBPI0165	**Headpiece with title for The First Thanksgiving**		**411**
PM0059	The First Thanksgiving	December 5, 1891	24
MBPI0166	**Illustrated initial O for The First Thanksgiving**		**411**
PM0059	The First Thanksgiving	December 5, 1891	24
MBPI0167	**Carnival, Philadelphia, 1778**		**411**
PM0060	The Battle of Monmouth Court-House	June, 1878	24
PM0931	Great American Illustrators: Howard Pyle, Illustrator	September, 1907	99, 106
MBPI0168	**"The little pink finger and the huge black index came to a full stop under this commandment"**		**411**
PM0061	Daddy Will	July, 1878	24
MBPI0169	**At Daddy Bayne's**		**411**
PM0062	Owlet	July, 1878	24
MBPI0170	**"She walked on after saying this, musing"**		**411**
PM0062	Owlet	July, 1878	24
MBPI0171	**"She went by without looking at him"**		**411**
PM0063	Manuel Menendez	August, 1878	24
MBPI0172	**Fermina opens the casket**		**411**
PM0063	Manuel Menendez	August, 1878	24
MBPI0173	**"Well, dat nigger cheat de burer–he s-t-o-l-e, Massa!"**		**411**
PM0064	Ab'm: A Glimpse of Modern Dixie	September, 1878	24
MBPI0174	**"Then came the tug of war"**		**411**
PM0064	Ab'm: A Glimpse of Modern Dixie	September, 1878	24
MBPI0175	**Dinner-bell at an Eastville Tavern**		**411**
PM0065	A Peninsular Canaan. I	May, 1879	24
MBPI0176	**The Country Clerk, Eastville**		**411**
PM0065	A Peninsular Canaan. I	May, 1879	24
MBPI0177	**Old records**		**412**
PM0065	A Peninsular Canaan. I	May, 1879	24
MBPI0178	**Aunt Saber**		**412**
PM0065	A Peninsular Canaan. I	May, 1879	24
MBPI0179	**Peace and War**		**412**
PM0065	A Peninsular Canaan. I	May, 1879	24
MBPI0180	**Oyster shuckers**		**412**
PM0066	A Peninsular Canaan. II	June, 1879	24
MBPI0181	**Dredging for oysters**		**412**
PM0066	A Peninsular Canaan. II	June, 1879	24
MBPI0182	**Strawberry picking**		**412**
PM0066	A Peninsular Canaan. II	June, 1879	24
MBPI0183	**Cooking shanty**		**412**
PM0066	A Peninsular Canaan. II	June, 1879	24
MBPI0184	**Aunt Sally**		**412**
PM0066	A Peninsular Canaan. II	June, 1879	24
MBPI0185	**Fishing shanty**		**412**
PM0066	A Peninsular Canaan. II	June, 1879	24
MBPI0186	**George, the cook**		**412**
PM0066	A Peninsular Canaan. II	June, 1879	24
MBPI0187	**Interior of fishing station**		**412**
PM0066	A Peninsular Canaan. II	June, 1879	24
MBPI0188	**In the Northern Market–"Peaches, one cent"**		**412**
PM0067	A Peninsular Canaan. III	July, 1879	25
MBPI0189	**A farm "Pluck"**		**412**
PM0067	A Peninsular Canaan. III	July, 1879	25
MBPI0190	**Group of nomadic "Plucks"**		**412**
PM0067	A Peninsular Canaan. III	July, 1879	25
MBPI0191	**The peeling-room**		**412**
PM0067	A Peninsular Canaan. III	July, 1879	25
MBPI0192	**Raising cypress logs in the Dismal Swamp**		**412**
PM0067	A Peninsular Canaan. III	July, 1879	25

MBPI0193	**Making shingles**		**413**
PM0067	A Peninsular Canaan. III	July, 1879	25
MBPI0194	**The Phantom Horseman**		**413**
PM0067	A Peninsular Canaan. III	July, 1879	25
MBPI0195	**The Captain of the Yacht "Delaware"**		**413**
PM0067	A Peninsular Canaan. III	July, 1879	25
MBPI0196	**A bit of sentiment**		**413**
PM0067	A Peninsular Canaan. III	July, 1879	25
MBPI0197	**"Who stuffed that white owl?"**		**413**
PM0068	The Owl-Critic	July, 1879	25
MBPI0198	**"I'm an owl; you're another"**		**413**
PM0068	The Owl-Critic	July, 1879	25
MBPI0199	**"As she spoke, she took his hand, and then paused one moment"**		**413**
PM0069	The First Mrs. Petersham	August, 1879	25
MBPI0200	**"Laying the old violin tenderly beneath his chin"**		**413**
PM0070	The Last Revel in Printz Hall	September, 1879	25
MBPI0201	**Peter plays the fiddle for the Tavern Folk**		**413**
PM0070	The Last Revel in Printz Hall	September, 1879	25
MBPI0202	**Tacy Kelp**		**413**
PM0070	The Last Revel in Printz Hall	September, 1879	25
MBPI0203	**Representing the manner of Peter's Courtship**		**413**
PM1297	The Illustrated Magazines for September	August 21, 1879	103
PM0070	The Last Revel in Printz Hall	September, 1879	25
PM0670	Art in America	1880	131
MBPI0204	**Jonathan Quidd**		**413**
PM0070	The Last Revel in Printz Hall	September, 1879	25
MBPI0205	**"The little boys cheered vigorously as he pushed off"**		**413**
PM0070	The Last Revel in Printz Hall	September, 1879	25
MBPI0206	**"Here it turned, and said 'Knowest thou who I am?'"**		**413**
PM0070	The Last Revel in Printz Hall	September, 1879	25
MBPI0207	**Tailpiece for The Last Revel in Printz Hall**		**413**
PM0070	The Last Revel in Printz Hall	September, 1879	25
MBPI0208	**A complimentary Address to Old Hickory–Interior of Ben Bean's ("Barton") House**		**413**
PM0071	The Old National Pike	November, 1879	25
PM1090	Advertisement: Building the Nation	December, 1882	1
PM0682	Building the Nation	1883	138
MBPI0209	**Arrival of the Coach at an Old Stage Station**		**414**
PM0071	The Old National Pike	November, 1879	25
MBPI0210	**An Old Government Toll-Gate, with Westward-Bound Express**		**414**
PM0071	The Old National Pike	November, 1879	25
PM0675	Harper's Popular Cyclopaedia of United States History	1881	164
PM0682	Building the Nation	1883	138
PM0761	Harper's Encyclopaedia of United States History	1902	158
PM0954	Harper's Encyclopaedia of United States History from 458 A.D. to 1915	1915	161
MBPI0211	**An Old Stager**		**414**
PM0071	The Old National Pike	November, 1879	25
MBPI0212	**Ruins of Old Post Tavern**		**414**
PM0071	The Old National Pike	November, 1879	25
MBPI0213	**Old National Pike Bridge**		**414**
PM0071	The Old National Pike	November, 1879	25
PM0682	Building the Nation	1883	138
PM0761	Harper's Encyclopaedia of United States History	1902	158
MBPI0214	**Leander**		**414**
PM0071	The Old National Pike	November, 1879	25
MBPI0215	**Uncle Sam**		**414**
PM0071	The Old National Pike	November, 1879	25
MBPI0216	**Preparing for Highwaymen**		**414**
PM0071	The Old National Pike	November, 1879	25
MBPI0217	**An Old Smithy**		**414**
PM0071	The Old National Pike	November, 1879	25

MBPI0218	**Old Way-Side Tavern**		**414**
PM0071	The Old National Pike	November, 1879	25
PM0682	Building the Nation	1883	138
MBPI0219	**An Old Mile-Stone**		**414**
PM0071	The Old National Pike	November, 1879	25
MBPI0220	**Old Hempstead House**		**414**
PM0072	Sea-Drift from a New England Port	December, 1879	26
PM0671	Old Times in the Colonies	1881	193
PM0761	Harper's Encyclopaedia of United States History	1902	158
PM0954	Harper's Encyclopaedia of United States History from 458 A.D. to 1915	1915	161
MBPI0221	**A Revolutionary Recruiting Office–Privateersmen in New London**		**414**
PM0072	Sea-Drift from a New England Port	December, 1879	26
MBPI0222	**A Garden Party given to General Washington**		**414**
PM1298	Selections from the Illustrated Monthlies for December	December 6, 1879	103
PM0072	Sea-Drift from a New England Port	December, 1879	26
PM0682	Building the Nation	1883	138
MBPI0223	**Portrait Gallery in Shaw Mansion**		**414**
PM0072	Sea-Drift from a New England Port	December, 1879	26
MBPI0224	**An Old Time Cup of Coffee**		**414**
PM0072	Sea-Drift from a New England Port	December, 1879	26
PM0682	Building the Nation	1883	138
MBPI0225	**Patty Hempstead in her Gran'ther's waistcoat**		**415**
PM0072	Sea-Drift from a New England Port	December, 1879	26
MBPI0226	**Ye Antient Gunne**		**415**
PM0072	Sea-Drift from a New England Port	December, 1879	26
MBPI0227	**Old tiled Fire Place, Winthrop House**		**415**
PM0072	Sea-Drift from a New England Port	December, 1879	26
PM0671	Old Times in the Colonies	1881	193
MBPI0228	**Mather Byles preaching to Quakers**		**415**
PM0072	Sea-Drift from a New England Port	December, 1879	26
PM0671	Old Times in the Colonies	1881	193
MBPI0229	**Captain Kidd's gift to Mercy Redmond**		**415**
PM0072	Sea-Drift from a New England Port	December, 1879	26
MBPI0230	**The Song of Captain Kidd**		**415**
PM0072	Sea-Drift from a New England Port	December, 1879	26
MBPI0231	**The Old Chimney-Corner**		**415**
PM0073	Bartram and His Garden	February, 1880	26
MBPI0232	**The Botanist**		**415**
PM0073	Bartram and His Garden	February, 1880	26
MBPI0233	**The Old Bartram Homestead**		**415**
PM0073	Bartram and His Garden	February, 1880	26
MBPI0234	**Old Corner Cupboard**		**415**
PM0073	Bartram and His Garden	February, 1880	26
MBPI0235	**Old Inscription**		**415**
PM0073	Bartram and His Garden	February, 1880	26
MBPI0236	**The Christ Thorn**		**415**
PM0073	Bartram and His Garden	February, 1880	26
MBPI0237	**The Garden Path**		**415**
PM0073	Bartram and His Garden	February, 1880	26
MBPI0238	**Departure for New York**		**415**
PM0073	Bartram and His Garden	February, 1880	26
MBPI0239	**"The Clang of the Yankee Reaper, on Salisbury Plain!"**		**415**
PM0676	Farm Ballads	1882	150
PM1006	Farm Ballads	1905	151
MBPI0240	**Along the Chester Valley**		**415**
PM0074	Some Pennsylvania Nooks	April, 1880	26
MBPI0241	**Old Valley Forge Bridge**		**416**
PM0074	Some Pennsylvania Nooks	April, 1880	26
PM0761	Harper's Encyclopaedia of United States History	1902	158
PM0954	Harper's Encyclopaedia of United States History from 458 A.D. to 1915	1915	161

MBPI0242	**Washington's Private Papers, 1777**		**416**
PM0074	Some Pennsylvania Nooks	April, 1880	26
PM0761	Harper's Encyclopaedia of United States History	1902	158
PM0954	Harper's Encyclopaedia of United States History from 458 A.D. to 1915	1915	161
MBPI0243	**Washington's Head-Quarters, Valley Forge**		**416**
PM0074	Some Pennsylvania Nooks	April, 1880	26
PM0761	Harper's Encyclopaedia of United States History	1902	158
PM0954	Harper's Encyclopaedia of United States History from 458 A.D. to 1915	1915	161
MBPI0244	**General Wayne's Grave**		**416**
PM0074	Some Pennsylvania Nooks	April, 1880	26
PM1039	The Northwest Under Three Flags	1900	188
PM0761	Harper's Encyclopaedia of United States History	1902	158
MBPI0245	**Old St. David's Church**		**416**
PM0074	Some Pennsylvania Nooks	April, 1880	26
MBPI0246	**Drawing-Room, Wayne Homestead**		**416**
PM0074	Some Pennsylvania Nooks	April, 1880	26
PM0682	Building the Nation	1883	138
PM1039	The Northwest Under Three Flags	1900	188
PM0761	Harper's Encyclopaedia of United States History	1902	158
PM0954	Harper's Encyclopaedia of United States History from 458 A.D. to 1915	1915	161
MBPI0247	**Paoli Monument**		**416**
PM0074	Some Pennsylvania Nooks	April, 1880	26
MBPI0248	**Melissy**		**416**
PM0074	Some Pennsylvania Nooks	April, 1880	26
MBPI0249	**John Dubois's drive to Newburgh**		**416**
PM0075	Old Catskill	May, 1880	26
MBPI0250	**Sunday in Old Catskill**		**416**
PM0075	Old Catskill	May, 1880	26
PM0682	Building the Nation	1883	138
MBPI0251	**Dinner at Cornelius Dubois's**		**416**
PM0075	Old Catskill	May, 1880	26
PM0682	Building the Nation	1883	138
MBPI0252	**"Perhaps she sat there while she stoned her raisins"**		**416**
PM0076	"Salgama Condita"	May, 1880	26
MBPI0253	**"It is all a mistake, my friend, a grievous mistake"**		**416**
PM1299	The Illustrated Magazines for May	April 29, 1880	103
PM0076	"Salgama Condita"	May, 1880	26
MBPI0254	**Hale receiving instructions from Washington**		**416**
PM0077	Captain Nathan Hale	June, 1880	27
PM1265	Commemorative of Nathan Hale, Martyr-Spy of the Revolution	1887	144, 344
MBPI0255	**"I only regret that I have but one life to lose for my country"**		**416**
PM0077	Captain Nathan Hale	June, 1880	27
PM1265	Commemorative of Nathan Hale, Martyr-Spy of the Revolution	1887	144, 344
PM1562	Evacuation Day, New York, Novenmber 25, 1893	1893	344
PM0761	Harper's Encyclopaedia of United States History	1902	158
PM0954	Harper's Encyclopaedia of United States History from 458 A.D. to 1915	1915	161
MBPI0256	**"I saw her face white even in all that immense ruddy glare"**		**416**
PM0078	The Driftwood Fire	November, 1880	27
MBPI0257	**Old Swedes Church, Wilmington**		**417**
PM0079	Old-Time Life in a Quaker Town	January, 1881	27
PM0759	A History of the American People	1902	165
PM0761	Harper's Encyclopaedia of United States History	1902	158
PM0954	Harper's Encyclopaedia of United States History from 458 A.D. to 1915	1915	161
PM0795	A History of the American People	1918	166, 170, 273
MBPI0258	**Going to Church**		**417**
PM1439	Salmagundi Club, New York, New York	1880	282
PM0079	Old-Time Life in a Quaker Town	January, 1881	27
PM1020	A History of Wood Engraving	1883	169
PM1411	Going to Church	1900	333-334, 337-338
PM0761	Harper's Encyclopaedia of United States History	1902	158

PM0954	Harper's Encyclopaedia of United States History from 458 A.D. to 1915	1915	161
MBPI0259	**At Evening**		**417**
PM0079	Old-Time Life in a Quaker Town	January, 1881	27
PM0761	Harper's Encyclopaedia of United States History	1902	158
PM0954	Harper's Encyclopaedia of United States History from 458 A.D. to 1915	1915	161
MBPI0260	**The Umbrella–A Curious Present**		**417**
PM1439	Salmagundi Club, New York, New York	1880	282
PM0079	Old-Time Life in a Quaker Town	January, 1881	27
MBPI0261	**William Cobbett's School**		**417**
PM0079	Old-Time Life in a Quaker Town	January, 1881	27
PM0313	Advertisement: Building the Nation	January 16, 1883	76
PM0682	Building the Nation	1883	138
MBPI0262	**The Destruction of the Sign**		**417**
PM0079	Old-Time Life in a Quaker Town	January, 1881	27
MBPI0263	**The British in Wilmington**		**417**
PM0079	Old-Time Life in a Quaker Town	January, 1881	27
MBPI0264	**"I never had wood that I liked half so well–do see who has nice crooked fuel to sell"**		**417**
PM0080	Patient Mercy Jones	January, 1881	27
MBPI0265	**New-Year's Hymn to St. Nicholas**		**417**
PM0081	A Glimpse of an Old Dutch Town	March, 1881	27
PM0682	Building the Nation	1883	138
MBPI0266	**Mynheer's Morning Horn**		**417**
PM0081	A Glimpse of an Old Dutch Town	March, 1881	27
PM0682	Building the Nation	1883	138
PM0988	The Boy Travellers in Northern Europe	1892	137
MBPI0267	**"He stops at the Sign of the Weathervane"**		**417**
PM0082	Tilghman's Ride from Yorktown to Philadelphia	November, 1881	27
MBPI0268	**"Then he tells his news, in the ruddy glow"**		**417**
PM0082	Tilghman's Ride from Yorktown to Philadelphia	November, 1881	27
MBPI0269	**A Mountain Farm-House**		**417**
PM0083	Autumn Sketches in the Pennsylvania Highlands	December, 1881	27
MBPI0270	**The Lowland Brook**		**417**
PM0083	Autumn Sketches in the Pennsylvania Highlands	December, 1881	27
PM1441	Salmagundi Club, New York, New York	1881	282
MBPI0271	**An Autumn Evening**		**417**
PM0083	Autumn Sketches in the Pennsylvania Highlands	December, 1881	27
MBPI0272	**The Mountain Orchard**		**417**
PM0083	Autumn Sketches in the Pennsylvania Highlands	December, 1881	27
MBPI0273	**The Corn Fields on the Hill-Side**		**418**
PM0083	Autumn Sketches in the Pennsylvania Highlands	December, 1881	27
MBPI0274	**Isaac Sears addressing the Mob**		**418**
PM0084	Old New York Coffee-Houses	March, 1882	27
MBPI0275	**The Press-Gang in New York**		**418**
PM0084	Old New York Coffee-Houses	March, 1882	27
MBPI0276	**Theophylact Bache saving Graydon from the Mob in 1776**		**418**
PM0084	Old New York Coffee-Houses	March, 1882	27
MBPI0277	**Spine design for Men of Iron**		**418**
PM0647	Men of Iron	1892	92-94, 182
MBPI0278	**"I often took my Bible and sat in hollow trees"**		**418**
PM0085	The Early Quakers in England and Pennsylvania	November, 1882	28
MBPI0279	**"The Word of the Lord came to me, saying 'Cry, Woe to the bloody City of Litchfield!'"**		**418**
PM0085	The Early Quakers in England and Pennsylvania	November, 1882	28
PM0761	Harper's Encyclopaedia of United States History	1902	158
PM0954	Harper's Encyclopaedia of United States History from 458 A.D. to 1915	1915	161
MBPI0280	**"I sat in a hay-stack, and said nothing for some hours"**		**418**
PM0085	The Early Quakers in England and Pennsylvania	November, 1882	28
MBPI0281	**"They led me, taking hold of my collar, and by my arms"**		**418**
PM0085	The Early Quakers in England and Pennsylvania	November, 1882	28
PM0761	Harper's Encyclopaedia of United States History	1902	158
PM0954	Harper's Encyclopaedia of United States History from 458 A.D. to 1915	1915	161

MBPI0282	"The Admiral lost all control of himself, and in a rage ordered his son to quit the house"		418
PM0085	The Early Quakers in England and Pennsylvania	November, 1882	28
MBPI0283	**Quaker and King at Whitehall 1681**		**418**
PM0085	The Early Quakers in England and Pennsylvania	November, 1882	28
PM0761	Harper's Encyclopaedia of United States History	1902	158
PM0954	Harper's Encyclopaedia of United States History from 458 A.D. to 1915	1915	161
MBPI0284	**The Departure of the "Welcome"**		**418**
PM0085	The Early Quakers in England and Pennsylvania	November, 1882	28
PM0761	Harper's Encyclopaedia of United States History	1902	158
PM0954	Harper's Encyclopaedia of United States History from 458 A.D. to 1915	1915	161
MBPI0285	**A burial at sea on board the "Welcome"**		**418**
PM0085	The Early Quakers in England and Pennsylvania	November, 1882	28
MBPI0286	**William Penn and his Commissioners in the cabin of the "Welcome"**		**418**
PM0085	The Early Quakers in England and Pennsylvania	November, 1882	28
MBPI0287	**"Thomas Moon began to lay about him with his Sword"**		**418**
PM0086	The Old English Seamen	January, 1883	28
PM0687	A Larger History of the United States of America	1886	176
PM0663	Adventures of Pirates and Sea-Rovers	1908	53, 129
MBPI0288	**Drake's Attack on San Domingo**		**418**
PM0086	The Old English Seamen	January, 1883	28
PM0687	A Larger History of the United States of America	1886	176
PM0663	Adventures of Pirates and Sea-Rovers	1908	53, 129
MBPI0289	**"Jacques Cartier setting up a Cross at Gaspé"**		**419**
PM0087	The French Voyageurs	March, 1883	28
PM0686	Indian History For Young Folks	1885	172
PM0761	Harper's Encyclopaedia of United States History	1902	158
PM0954	Harper's Encyclopaedia of United States History from 458 A.D. to 1915	1915	161
MBPI0290	**Dominique de Gourgues avenging the Murder of the Huguenot Colony**		**419**
PM0087	The French Voyageurs	March, 1883	28
PM0687	A Larger History of the United States of America	1886	176
PM0761	Harper's Encyclopaedia of United States History	1902	158
PM0954	Harper's Encyclopaedia of United States History from 458 A.D. to 1915	1915	161
MBPI0291	**"He brought both Catholic Priests and Huguenot Ministers, who disputed heartily on the Way"**		**419**
PM0087	The French Voyageurs	March, 1883	28
PM0687	A Larger History of the United States of America	1886	176
PM0761	Harper's Encyclopaedia of United States History	1902	158
PM0954	Harper's Encyclopaedia of United States History from 458 A.D. to 1915	1915	161
MBPI0292	**"He rested his Musket"**		**419**
PM0087	The French Voyageurs	March, 1883	28
PM0687	A Larger History of the United States of America	1886	176
MBPI0293	**The Landing of the Pilgrims**		**419**
PM0088	An English Nation	April, 1883	28
PM0687	A Larger History of the United States of America	1886	176
PM0948	Swinton's Advanced Fourth Reader	1886	234
PM0714	A School History of the United States	1893	210
PM0761	Harper's Encyclopaedia of United States History	1902	158
PM0954	Harper's Encyclopaedia of United States History from 458 A.D. to 1915	1915	161
PM0795	A History of the American People	1918	166, 170, 273
PM0929	Indian History For Young Folks	1919	172
MBPI0294	**Arrival of the Young Women at Jamestown**		**419**
PM0088	An English Nation	April, 1883	28
PM0687	A Larger History of the United States of America	1886	176
PM0761	Harper's Encyclopaedia of United States History	1902	158
PM0954	Harper's Encyclopaedia of United States History from 458 A.D. to 1915	1915	161
MBPI0295	**Endicott cutting the cross out of the English flag**		**419**
PM0088	An English Nation	April, 1883	28
PM0761	Harper's Encyclopaedia of United States History	1902	158
PM0954	Harper's Encyclopaedia of United States History from 458 A.D. to 1915	1915	161
MBPI0296	**Death of King Philip**		**419**
PM0089	The Hundred Years' War	June, 1883	28

PM0686	Indian History For Young Folks		1885	172
PM0687	A Larger History of the United States of America		1886	176
PM0761	Harper's Encyclopaedia of United States History		1902	158
PM0929	Indian History For Young Folks		1919	172
MBPI0297	**Governor Andros and the Boston People**			**419**
PM0089	The Hundred Years' War	June, 1883		28
PM0687	A Larger History of the United States of America		1886	176
PM0761	Harper's Encyclopaedia of United States History		1902	158
PM0954	Harper's Encyclopaedia of United States History from 458 A.D. to 1915		1915	161
MBPI0298	**A Quaker Exhorter in New England**			**419**
PM0090	The Second Generation of Englishmen in America	July, 1883		28
PM1192	Advertisement: Harper & Brothers Holiday Books	November 28, 1885		70
PM0687	A Larger History of the United States of America		1886	176
PM0761	Harper's Encyclopaedia of United States History		1902	158
PM0954	Harper's Encyclopaedia of United States History from 458 A.D. to 1915		1915	161
MBPI0299	**Arresting a Witch**			**419**
PM0090	The Second Generation of Englishmen in America	July, 1883		28
PM0687	A Larger History of the United States of America		1886	176
PM0761	Harper's Encyclopaedia of United States History		1902	158
MBPI0300	**Peter Stuyvesant tearing the Letter demanding the Surrender of New York**			**419**
PM0090	The Second Generation of Englishmen in America	July, 1883		28
PM0687	A Larger History of the United States of America		1886	176
PM0761	Harper's Encyclopaedia of United States History		1902	158
PM0954	Harper's Encyclopaedia of United States History from 458 A.D. to 1915		1915	161
MBPI0301	**The "Boston Massacre"**			**419**
PM0091	The British Yoke	August, 1883		28
PM0687	A Larger History of the United States of America		1886	176
PM0761	Harper's Encyclopaedia of United States History		1902	158
PM0954	Harper's Encyclopaedia of United States History from 458 A.D. to 1915		1915	161
MBPI0302	**An out-of-door Tea Party in Colonial New England**			**419**
PM0091	The British Yoke	August, 1883		28
PM0049	A Quaker Wedding	December 12, 1885		22
PM0687	A Larger History of the United States of America		1886	176
MBPI0303	**Washington refusing a Dictatorship**			**419**
PM0092	Last Days of Washington's Army at Newburgh	October, 1883		29
PM0696	Old Homestead Poems		1888	192
PM0761	Harper's Encyclopaedia of United States History		1902	158
PM0954	Harper's Encyclopaedia of United States History from 458 A.D. to 1915		1915	161
PM0795	A History of the American People		1918	166, 170, 273
MBPI0304	**Washington and his Generals in Consultation March 15, 1783**			**419**
PM0092	Last Days of Washington's Army at Newburgh	October, 1883		29
PM0761	Harper's Encyclopaedia of United States History		1902	158
PM0954	Harper's Encyclopaedia of United States History from 458 A.D. to 1915		1915	161
PM0795	A History of the American People		1918	166, 170, 273
MBPI0305	**Lexington Green–"If they want a War, let it begin here"**			**420**
PM0093	The Dawning of Independence	October, 1883		29
PM0687	A Larger History of the United States of America		1886	176
PM0761	Harper's Encyclopaedia of United States History		1902	158
PM0773	History of the United States From 986 to 1905		1905	168
PM0954	Harper's Encyclopaedia of United States History from 458 A.D. to 1915		1915	161
MBPI0306	**Sergeant Jasper at the Battle of Fort Moultrie**			**420**
PM0093	The Dawning of Independence	October, 1883		29
PM1579	Selections from Holiday Books	December 16, 1885		103
PM1384	Advertisement: Larger History of the United States	December, 1885		30
PM1610	Book Reviews	December, 1885		9
PM0687	A Larger History of the United States of America		1886	176
PM1339	Harper's Catalogue of Books For Boys & Girls		1887	266
PM0761	Harper's Encyclopaedia of United States History		1902	158
MBPI0307	**The last boat-load of the British leaving New York**			**420**
PM0094	Evacuation of New York by the British, 1783	November, 1883		29

PM0761	Harper's Encyclopaedia of United States History	1902	158
PM0954	Harper's Encyclopaedia of United States History from 458 A.D. to 1915	1915	161
MBPI0308	**The civil procession, headed by General Washington and Governor Clinton**		**420**
PM0094	Evacuation of New York by the British, 1783	November, 1883	29
PM0761	Harper's Encyclopaedia of United States History	1902	158
PM0954	Harper's Encyclopaedia of United States History from 458 A.D. to 1915	1915	161
MBPI0309	**"The Master caused vs to haue some Beere"**		**420**
PM0095	Christmas	December, 1883	29
MBPI0310	**The Puritan Governor interrupting the Christmas sports**		**420**
PM0095	Christmas	December, 1883	29
MBPI0311	**The French Officers at Newport**		**420**
PM0096	The Birth of a Nation	January, 1884	29
PM0687	A Larger History of the United States of America	1886	176
MBPI0312	**Shay's Mob in possession of a Court House**		**420**
PM0096	The Birth of a Nation	January, 1884	29
PM1444	The Grolier Club, New York, New York	1884	283
PM0687	A Larger History of the United States of America	1886	176
PM0759	A History of the American People	1902	165
PM0761	Harper's Encyclopaedia of United States History	1902	158
PM0954	Harper's Encyclopaedia of United States History from 458 A.D. to 1915	1915	161
PM0795	A History of the American People	1918	166, 170, 273
MBPI0313	**At Mrs. Washington's Reception**		**420**
PM0097	Our Country's Cradle	February, 1884	29
PM0687	A Larger History of the United States of America	1886	176
PM1479	Hotel Dupont, Wilmington, Delaware	1912	141, 310
MBPI0314	**Impressment of American Seamen**		**420**
PM0098	The Second War for Independence	April, 1884	29
PM0687	A Larger History of the United States of America	1886	176
PM0759	A History of the American People	1902	165
PM0761	Harper's Encyclopaedia of United States History	1902	158
PM0795	A History of the American People	1918	166, 170, 273
MBPI0315	**Among the Daffodillies**		**420**
PM0099	A May-Day Idyl of the Olden Time	May, 1884	29
MBPI0316	**"So saying, she turned and left me"**		**420**
PM0099	A May-Day Idyl of the Olden Time	May, 1884	29
MBPI0317	**"Bringing in the May"**		**420**
PM0099	A May-Day Idyl of the Olden Time	May, 1884	29
MBPI0318	**President Johnson teaching his first class**		**420**
PM0100	King's College	October, 1884	29
MBPI0319	**Hamilton addressing the mob**		**420**
PM0100	King's College	October, 1884	29
MBPI0320	**The Search for Toinette**		**420**
PM0101	Toinette	December, 1884	29
MBPI0321	**Headpiece for Witchcraft**		**421**
PM0102	Witchcraft	December, 1884	29
MBPI0322	**Witchcraft, 1692**		**421**
PM0102	Witchcraft	December, 1884	29
MBPI0323	**Witchcraft, 1884**		**421**
PM0102	Witchcraft	December, 1884	29
MBPI0324	**Spring Blossoms**		**421**
PM0103	Spring Blossoms	May, 1885	29
MBPI0325	**Rescue of Sevier**		**421**
PM0104	Knoxville in the Olden Time	June, 1885	30
PM0761	Harper's Encyclopaedia of United States History	1902	158
PM0954	Harper's Encyclopaedia of United States History from 458 A.D. to 1915	1915	161
MBPI0326	**"The Cherokees Are Coming"**		**421**
PM1444	The Grolier Club, New York, New York	1884	283
PM0104	Knoxville in the Olden Time	June, 1885	30
PM0761	Harper's Encyclopaedia of United States History	1902	158
PM0954	Harper's Encyclopaedia of United States History from 458 A.D. to 1915	1915	161

MBPI0327	**Death of the Indian Chief Alexander**		**421**
PM0105	An Indian Journey	November, 1885	30
MBPI0328	**"Roger Feverel had kindled it for the first time"**		**421**
PM0106	Esther Feverel	December, 1885	30
MBPI0329	**"Her glance fell, under his steady gaze"**		**421**
PM0106	Esther Feverel	December, 1885	30
MBPI0330	**Traveling in the Olden Time**		**421**
PM0107	The City of Cleveland	March, 1886	30
MBPI0331	**Governor Huntington attacked by wolves**		**421**
PM0107	The City of Cleveland	March, 1886	30
MBPI0332	**Paul Revere bringing news to Sullivan**		**421**
PM0108	The Gunpowder for Bunker Hill	July, 1886	30
PM0761	Harper's Encyclopaedia of United States History	1902	158
PM0954	Harper's Encyclopaedia of United States History from 458 A.D. to 1915	1915	161
MBPI0333	**Surrender of Fort William and Mary**		**421**
PM0108	The Gunpowder for Bunker Hill	July, 1886	30
PM0761	Harper's Encyclopaedia of United States History	1902	158
PM0954	Harper's Encyclopaedia of United States History from 458 A.D. to 1915	1915	161
MBPI0334	**Transporting powder from the Fort**		**421**
PM0108	The Gunpowder for Bunker Hill	July, 1886	30
PM0761	Harper's Encyclopaedia of United States History	1902	158
PM0954	Harper's Encyclopaedia of United States History from 458 A.D. to 1915	1915	161
MBPI0335	**Bringing the powder to Bunker Hill**		**421**
PM0108	The Gunpowder for Bunker Hill	July, 1886	30
PM0761	Harper's Encyclopaedia of United States History	1902	158
PM0954	Harper's Encyclopaedia of United States History from 458 A.D. to 1915	1915	161
MBPI0336	**The Landing of Cadillac**		**421**
PM0109	The City of the Strait	August, 1886	30
PM1039	The Northwest Under Three Flags	1900	188
PM0761	Harper's Encyclopaedia of United States History	1902	158
PM0954	Harper's Encyclopaedia of United States History from 458 A.D. to 1915	1915	161
MBPI0337	**The Ojibway Maiden disclosing Pontiac's Plot**		**422**
PM0109	The City of the Strait	August, 1886	30
PM0929	Indian History For Young Folks	1919	172
MBPI0338	**"The woman turned fiercely upon the Chieftain"**		**422**
PM0110	The Southern Gateway of the Alleghanies	April, 1887	30
PM1447	World's Columbian Exposition, Chicago, Illinois	1893	283
MBPI0339	**Joseph Brown leading his company to Nicojack**		**422**
PM0110	The Southern Gateway of the Alleghanies	April, 1887	30
PM1614	Heroes of National History	1919	164
MBPI0340	**"I sat gazing upon her as she leaned forward"**		**422**
PM0111	Stephen Wycherlie	June, 1887	30
MBPI0341	**"Thereupon, lifting up his eyes again, he began once more wrestling with the spirit in prayer"**		**422**
PM0111	Stephen Wycherlie	June, 1887	30
MBPI0342	**"Still she looked upon me, though silently and pale as death"**		**422**
PM0111	Stephen Wycherlie	June, 1887	30
MBPI0343	**"Then came Mistress Margaret unto me and put a letter into my hand"**		**422**
PM0111	Stephen Wycherlie	June, 1887	30
MBPI0344	**Capture of Elizabeth and Frances Callaway and Jemima Boone**		**422**
PM0112	The Kentucky Pioneers	June, 1887	30
PM0712	Abraham Lincoln	1893	129
PM0929	Indian History For Young Folks	1919	172
MBPI0345	**Defence of the Station**		**422**
PM0112	The Kentucky Pioneers	June, 1887	30
PM0712	Abraham Lincoln	1893	129
PM1076	The Great Adventurers	1915	157
PM0929	Indian History For Young Folks	1919	172
MBPI0346	**On the Tortugas**		**422**
PM0113	Buccaneers and Marooners of the Spanish Main. I	August, 1887	31
MBPI0347	**Capture of the Galleon**		**422**

PM0113	Buccaneers and Marooners of the Spanish Main. I	August, 1887	31
PM0966	The Founder of an American School of Art	February 23, 1907	106
PM1173	Howard Pyle	January, 1912	61
MBPI0348	**Henry Morgan Recruiting for the Attack**		**422**
PM0113	Buccaneers and Marooners of the Spanish Main. I	August, 1887	31
PM0645	The Buccaneers and Marooners of America	1891	138
PM1032	The Memorial Story of America	1894	181
PM1072	Story of America	1894	218
PM1549	The Book of Bravery	1918	135
MBPI0349	**The Sacking of Panama**		**422**
PM0113	Buccaneers and Marooners of the Spanish Main. I	August, 1887	31
PM1031	The Making of a Great Magazine	1889	179
MBPI0350	**Avary sells his jewels**		**422**
PM0114	Buccaneers and Marooners of the Spanish Main. II	September, 1887	31
MBPI0351	**Marooned**		**422**
PM0114	Buccaneers and Marooners of the Spanish Main. II	September, 1887	31
PM0931	Great American Illustrators: Howard Pyle, Illustrator	September, 1907	99, 106
PM1173	Howard Pyle	January, 1912	61
PM1096	Howard Pyle, Biographical Sketches of American Artists	October, 1915	2
MBPI0352	**Blackbeard buries his treasure**		**422**
PM0114	Buccaneers and Marooners of the Spanish Main. II	September, 1887	31
MBPI0353	**Walking the plank**		**423**
PM0114	Buccaneers and Marooners of the Spanish Main. II	September, 1887	31
PM1096	Howard Pyle, Biographical Sketches of American Artists	October, 1915	2
MBPI0354	**Aaron Burr's Wooing**		**423**
PM0115	Aaron Burr's Wooing	October, 1887	31
MBPI0355	**"They ploughed their fields with an armed sentry beside them"**		**423**
PM0116	On the Outposts–1780	February, 1888	31
PM1039	The Northwest Under Three Flags	1900	188
PM0761	Harper's Encyclopaedia of United States History	1902	158
PM0954	Harper's Encyclopaedia of United States History from 458 A.D. to 1915	1915	161
MBPI0356	**Finding the body of Joseph Hay in the Trail**		**423**
PM0116	On the Outposts–1780	February, 1888	31
MBPI0357	**Coureurs de Bois**		**423**
PM0117	Canadian Voyageurs on the Saguenay	March, 1888	31
PM1039	The Northwest Under Three Flags	1900	188
MBPI0358	**Morgan at Porto Bello**		**423**
PM0118	Morgan	December, 1888	31
PM0798	The Drexel Institute, Philadelphia, Pennsylvania	1897	8, 140, 268, 284
PM0799	St. Botolph Club, Boston, Massachusetts	1897	140, 268, 288
MBPI0359	**Washington met by his neighbors on his way to the Inauguration**		**423**
PM0119	Washington's Inauguration	April, 1889	31
MBPI0360	**The Inauguration**		**423**
PM0119	Washington's Inauguration	April, 1889	31
PM0711	A Tour Around New York and My Summer Acre	1893	236
PM0761	Harper's Encyclopaedia of United States History	1902	158
PM0954	Harper's Encyclopaedia of United States History from 458 A.D. to 1915	1915	161
MBPI0361	**Celebration on the Night of the Inauguration**		**423**
PM0119	Washington's Inauguration	April, 1889	31
PM0711	A Tour Around New York and My Summer Acre	1893	236
PM0759	A History of the American People	1902	165
PM0761	Harper's Encyclopaedia of United States History	1902	158
PM0954	Harper's Encyclopaedia of United States History from 458 A.D. to 1915	1915	161
PM0795	A History of the American People	1918	166, 170, 273
MBPI0362	**An Old Lancaster House**		**423**
PM0120	A Peculiar People	October, 1889	31
MBPI0363	**A Dormitory in the Sisters' House, Ephrata**		**423**
PM0120	A Peculiar People	October, 1889	31
MBPI0364	**The Kloster**		**423**
PM0120	A Peculiar People	October, 1889	31

MBPI0365	**Going to Meeting**		**423**
PM0120	A Peculiar People	October, 1889	31
MBPI0366	**The Kiss of Peace**		**423**
PM0120	A Peculiar People	October, 1889	31
MBPI0367	**My Cicerone**		**423**
PM0120	A Peculiar People	October, 1889	31
MBPI0368	**"It was to represent the Narrow Way"**		**423**
PM0120	A Peculiar People	October, 1889	31
MBPI0369	**"It was along this wall that the wounded soldiers sat"**		**424**
PM0120	A Peculiar People	October, 1889	31
MBPI0370	**Interior of Chapel**		**424**
PM0120	A Peculiar People	October, 1889	31
MBPI0371	**"She stood like a bronze. Gabriel was beside her, his naked cutlass in his hand"**		**424**
PM0121	Youma	January, 1890	32
PM1114	Novels for Summer Reading	June, 1890	6
PM0701	Youma: The Story of A West Indian Slave	1890	255
PM1385	Advertisement: Books for Holiday Gifts	December, 1890	35
MBPI0372	**"'And you would not give me a chance to tell you,'–she repeated, pleadingly,–touching his arm"**		**424**
PM0122	Youma	February, 1890	32
PM1565	Howard Pyle, Author-Illustrator 1853-1911	February, 1912	2
MBPI0373	**Illustrated initial I for Jamaica, New and Old**		**424**
PM0123	Jamaica, New and Old. I	January, 1890	32
PM1565	Howard Pyle, Author-Illustrator 1853-1911	February, 1912	2
MBPI0374	**"Popping ineffectual round-shot after her"**		**424**
PM0123	Jamaica, New and Old. I	January, 1890	32
MBPI0375	**"The dim, shadowy forms of vessels riding at anchor in the night"**		**424**
PM0123	Jamaica, New and Old. I	January, 1890	32
MBPI0376	**"A hot, broad, all-pervading glare of sunlight"**		**424**
PM0123	Jamaica, New and Old. I	January, 1890	32
MBPI0377	**"A lodging-house very well known to all Jamaica travellers"**		**424**
PM0123	Jamaica, New and Old. I	January, 1890	32
MBPI0378	**Spanish Galleon**		**424**
PM0123	Jamaica, New and Old. I	January, 1890	32
MBPI0379	**"That prince or potentate of the old sugar king period"**		**424**
PM0123	Jamaica, New and Old. I	January, 1890	32
MBPI0380	**"A turbaned coolie and his wife"**		**424**
PM0123	Jamaica, New and Old. I	January, 1890	32
MBPI0381	**"Where they sit in long rows with baskets of oranges"**		**424**
PM0123	Jamaica, New and Old. I	January, 1890	32
MBPI0382	**"Sitting with piles of great pots and bowls and queer jars of red earthenware"**		**424**
PM0123	Jamaica, New and Old. I	January, 1890	32
MBPI0383	**"A curious group traveling along a hot dusty road"**		**424**
PM0123	Jamaica, New and Old. I	January, 1890	32
MBPI0384	**In the market place**		**424**
PM0123	Jamaica, New and Old. I	January, 1890	32
MBPI0385	**"In mid-harbor the tainted crafts were burned in sight of all"**		**425**
PM0123	Jamaica, New and Old. I	January, 1890	32
MBPI0386	**Gallows Point**		**425**
PM0123	Jamaica, New and Old. I	January, 1890	32
MBPI0387	**"The beautiful sweeping curve of harbor"**		**425**
PM0123	Jamaica, New and Old. I	January, 1890	32
MBPI0388	**"Squatted on a log, and talked in a sad, melancholy manner"**		**425**
PM0123	Jamaica, New and Old. I	January, 1890	32
MBPI0389	**"The abbot and the town major personating conquered Spain"**		**425**
PM0123	Jamaica, New and Old. I	January, 1890	32
MBPI0390	**The Mangrove**		**425**
PM0123	Jamaica, New and Old. I	January, 1890	32
MBPI0391	**"One time it was alive with the great lumbering coaches"**		**425**
PM0123	Jamaica, New and Old. I	January, 1890	32
MBPI0392	**"Around the archways and the square stone pillars, buzzing like angry hornets"**		**425**

PM0123	Jamaica, New and Old. I	January, 1890	32
MBPI0393	"It is the Cathedral of St. Katherine"		425
PM0123	Jamaica, New and Old. I	January, 1890	32
MBPI0394	"Sic transit gloria mundi"		425
PM0123	Jamaica, New and Old. I	January, 1890	32
MBPI0395	Headpiece for Jamaica, New and Old		425
PM0124	Jamaica, New and Old. II	February, 1890	32
MBPI0396	Illustrated initial P for Jamaica, New and Old		425
PM0124	Jamaica, New and Old. II	February, 1890	32
MBPI0397	"The Governor was among the very first to set foot upon the deck"		425
PM0124	Jamaica, New and Old. II	February, 1890	32
MBPI0398	"The embrasures are blind and empty"		425
PM0124	Jamaica, New and Old. II	February, 1890	32
MBPI0399	"Here and there one comes upon an old house"		425
PM0124	Jamaica, New and Old. II	February, 1890	32
MBPI0400	"They were dressed in loose sackcloth shirt and drawers"		425
PM0124	Jamaica, New and Old. II	February, 1890	32
MBPI0401	"A store stood with open front toward the road"		426
PM0124	Jamaica, New and Old. II	February, 1890	32
MBPI0402	"An old man, lean and naked"		426
PM0124	Jamaica, New and Old. II	February, 1890	32
MBPI0403	"An ancient sibyl-like figure"		426
PM0124	Jamaica, New and Old. II	February, 1890	32
MBPI0404	"A crowd gathered around"		426
PM0124	Jamaica, New and Old. II	February, 1890	32
MBPI0405	"Plantation houses standing back from the roadside"		426
PM0124	Jamaica, New and Old. II	February, 1890	32
MBPI0406	"It is the leader, and all the others follow it"		426
PM0124	Jamaica, New and Old. II	February, 1890	32
MBPI0407	"The long straggling aqueduct"		426
PM0124	Jamaica, New and Old. II	February, 1890	32
MBPI0408	"A turbaned negro woman sat with her knitting"		426
PM0124	Jamaica, New and Old. II	February, 1890	32
MBPI0409	"The crooked winding road that leads into the village"		426
PM0124	Jamaica, New and Old. II	February, 1890	32
MBPI0410	"He sat down by the garden gate"		426
PM0124	Jamaica, New and Old. II	February, 1890	32
MBPI0411	"And thither children brought donkeys every morning"		426
PM0124	Jamaica, New and Old. II	February, 1890	32
MBPI0412	"In all houses one finds the filter and the water jar"		426
PM0124	Jamaica, New and Old. II	February, 1890	32
MBPI0413	"Coffee mill, surrounded by flat stone terraces"		426
PM0124	Jamaica, New and Old. II	February, 1890	32
MBPI0414	"A great section of bamboo trunk balanced upon her head"		426
PM0124	Jamaica, New and Old. II	February, 1890	32
MBPI0415	"Two negro women stood gossiping and cooling their feet"		426
PM0124	Jamaica, New and Old. II	February, 1890	32
MBPI0416	"The only picturesque object in the whole horrid expanse"		426
PM0124	Jamaica, New and Old. II	February, 1890	32
MBPI0417	The bugle call		427
PM0124	Jamaica, New and Old. II	February, 1890	32
MBPI0418	Illustrated initial A for Old New York Taverns		427
PM0125	Old New York Taverns	May, 1890	33
MBPI0419	The Old-time Landlord		427
PM0125	Old New York Taverns	May, 1890	33
MBPI0420	"The King's Head, kept by one Roger Baker"		427
PM0125	Old New York Taverns	May, 1890	33
MBPI0421	"Elizabeth Jourdain, who lodged Her Majesty's soldiers"		427
PM0125	Old New York Taverns	May, 1890	33
MBPI0422	Game of Bowls		427

PM0125	Old New York Taverns	May, 1890	33
MBPI0423	**"'The Dog's Head in the Pot' (of great antiquity)"**		**427**
PM0125	Old New York Taverns	May, 1890	33
MBPI0424	**"It crossed the river to the Long Island side of the Brooklyn Ferry"**		**427**
PM0125	Old New York Taverns	May, 1890	33
MBPI0425	**Brownejohn's Wharf**		**427**
PM0125	Old New York Taverns	May, 1890	33
MBPI0426	**"Each to be honored with bumpers innumerable of rich wine and punch"**		**427**
PM0125	Old New York Taverns	May, 1890	33
MBPI0427	**In the reading-room**		**427**
PM0125	Old New York Taverns	May, 1890	33
MBPI0428	**"The rival editors"**		**427**
PM0125	Old New York Taverns	May, 1890	33
MBPI0429	**"John Still, 'an honest barber and peruke-maker from London'"**		**427**
PM0125	Old New York Taverns	May, 1890	33
MBPI0430	**"The ball began with French dances"**		**427**
PM0125	Old New York Taverns	May, 1890	33
MBPI0431	**"The chair was carried by hand and the harness was worn by the bearers"**		**427**
PM0125	Old New York Taverns	May, 1890	33
MBPI0432	**"Cards and gaming were features"**		**427**
PM0125	Old New York Taverns	May, 1890	33
MBPI0433	**The ferry**		**428**
PM0125	Old New York Taverns	May, 1890	33
MBPI0434	**"Cargoes of favorite vintages"**		**428**
PM0125	Old New York Taverns	May, 1890	33
MBPI0435	**"The drum beat in the streets of the city"**		**428**
PM0125	Old New York Taverns	May, 1890	33
MBPI0436	**"The first violin would be played by a 'gentleman lately arrived'"**		**428**
PM0125	Old New York Taverns	May, 1890	33
MBPI0437	**At the Vauxhall**		**428**
PM0125	Old New York Taverns	May, 1890	33
MBPI0438	**"Exchanged thrusts with the merciless Junius"**		**428**
PM0125	Old New York Taverns	May, 1890	33
MBPI0439	**"The variety and fatigues of his business"**		**428**
PM0125	Old New York Taverns	May, 1890	33
MBPI0440	**Meeting of Captain Tollemache and Captain Pennington at the New York Arms**		**428**
PM0125	Old New York Taverns	May, 1890	33
MBPI0441	**"John Cape takes down the quaint old sign"**		**428**
PM0125	Old New York Taverns	May, 1890	33
MBPI0442	**"The men who met at Hampden Hall"**		**428**
PM0125	Old New York Taverns	May, 1890	33
MBPI0443	**Tailpiece for Old New York Taverns**		**428**
PM0125	Old New York Taverns	May, 1890	33
MBPI0444	**The Chapman**		**428**
PM0126	Chapbook Heroes	June, 1890	34
MBPI0445	**Claude DuVal proposes a Dance on the Heath**		**428**
PM0126	Chapbook Heroes	June, 1890	34
MBPI0446	**Sir James Thornhill painting Jack Sheppard's portrait**		**428**
PM0126	Chapbook Heroes	June, 1890	34
MBPI0447	**Turpin and King**		**428**
PM0126	Chapbook Heroes	June, 1890	34
MBPI0448	**Jonathan in the Wood Street Compter Prison**		**428**
PM0127	A Famous Chapbook Villain	July, 1890	34, 189, 252
MBPI0449	**Jonathan as an Enemy arresting a Thief**		**429**
PM0127	A Famous Chapbook Villain	July, 1890	34, 189, 252
MBPI0450	**Jonathan and a Client–The Lady with the Green Pocket-book**		**429**
PM0127	A Famous Chapbook Villain	July, 1890	34, 189, 252
MBPI0451	**On the Way to Tyburn**		**429**
PM0127	A Famous Chapbook Villain	July, 1890	34, 189, 252
MBPI0452	**Headpiece with title for The Quaker Lady**		**429**

PM0128	The Quaker Lady	November, 1890	34
MBPI0453	**Vignette for The Quaker Lady**		**429**
PM0128	The Quaker Lady	November, 1890	34
MBPI0454	**Vignette for The Quaker Lady**		**429**
PM0128	The Quaker Lady	November, 1890	34
MBPI0455	**Vignette for The Quaker Lady**		**429**
PM0128	The Quaker Lady	November, 1890	34
MBPI0456	**Vignette for The Quaker Lady**		**429**
PM0128	The Quaker Lady	November, 1890	34
MBPI0457	**Vignette for The Quaker Lady**		**429**
PM0128	The Quaker Lady	November, 1890	34
MBPI0458	**Vignette for The Quaker Lady**		**429**
PM0128	The Quaker Lady	November, 1890	34
MBPI0459	**Vignette for The Quaker Lady**		**429**
PM0128	The Quaker Lady	November, 1890	34
MBPI0460	**Vignette for The Quaker Lady**		**429**
PM0128	The Quaker Lady	November, 1890	34
MBPI0461	**Vignette for The Quaker Lady**		**429**
PM0128	The Quaker Lady	November, 1890	34
MBPI0462	**Vignette for The Quaker Lady**		**429**
PM0128	The Quaker Lady	November, 1890	34
MBPI0463	**Vignette for The Quaker Lady**		**429**
PM0128	The Quaker Lady	November, 1890	34
MBPI0464	**Vignette for The Quaker Lady**		**429**
PM0128	The Quaker Lady	November, 1890	34
MBPI0465	**Vignette for The Quaker Lady**		**430**
PM0128	The Quaker Lady	November, 1890	34
MBPI0466	**Vignette for The Quaker Lady**		**430**
PM0128	The Quaker Lady	November, 1890	34
MBPI0467	**Vignette for The Quaker Lady**		**430**
PM0128	The Quaker Lady	November, 1890	34
MBPI0468	**Vignette for The Quaker Lady**		**430**
PM0128	The Quaker Lady	November, 1890	34
MBPI0469	**The Magic Flute**		**430**
PM0129	Flute and Violin	December, 1890	35
PM0923	Book Review	June, 1891	9
PM0704	Flute and Violin, and Other Kentucky Tales and Romances	1891	152
MBPI0470	**"He had beautiful manners"**		**430**
PM0129	Flute and Violin	December, 1890	35
PM0704	Flute and Violin, and Other Kentucky Tales and Romances	1891	152
MBPI0471	**"His long nightly labors"**		**430**
PM0129	Flute and Violin	December, 1890	35
PM0704	Flute and Violin, and Other Kentucky Tales and Romances	1891	152
PM1386	A Selection of Books Suitable for Holiday Gifts	December, 1891	36
MBPI0472	**The Widow Spurlock**		**430**
PM0129	Flute and Violin	December, 1890	35
PM0704	Flute and Violin, and Other Kentucky Tales and Romances	1891	152
MBPI0473	**Old Arsena**		**430**
PM0129	Flute and Violin	December, 1890	35
MBPI0474	**"With their heads close together"**		**430**
PM0129	Flute and Violin	December, 1890	35
PM0704	Flute and Violin, and Other Kentucky Tales and Romances	1891	152
MBPI0475	**"He began to play"**		**430**
PM0129	Flute and Violin	December, 1890	35
PM1117	Recent Fiction	June, 1891	6
PM0704	Flute and Violin, and Other Kentucky Tales and Romances	1891	152
MBPI0476	**Hanging the violin**		**430**
PM0129	Flute and Violin	December, 1890	35
PM0704	Flute and Violin, and Other Kentucky Tales and Romances	1891	152
MBPI0477	**David**		**430**

PM0129	Flute and Violin	December, 1890	35
PM0704	Flute and Violin, and Other Kentucky Tales and Romances	1891	152
MBPI0478	**"He prayed with unusual fervor"**		**430**
PM0129	Flute and Violin	December, 1890	35
PM0704	Flute and Violin, and Other Kentucky Tales and Romances	1891	152
MBPI0479	**Mr. Leuba**		**430**
PM0129	Flute and Violin	December, 1890	35
MBPI0480	**"Executing an intricate passage"**		**430**
PM0129	Flute and Violin	December, 1890	35
PM0704	Flute and Violin, and Other Kentucky Tales and Romances	1891	152
MBPI0481	**"A small crowd had collected around the entrance to the Museum"**		**431**
PM0129	Flute and Violin	December, 1890	35
MBPI0482	**"The widow dropped her eyes"**		**431**
PM0129	Flute and Violin	December, 1890	35
PM0704	Flute and Violin, and Other Kentucky Tales and Romances	1891	152
MBPI0483	**"It was a very gay dinner"**		**431**
PM0129	Flute and Violin	December, 1890	35
PM0704	Flute and Violin, and Other Kentucky Tales and Romances	1891	152
MBPI0484	**The parson came down the street driving his flock of boys**		**431**
PM0129	Flute and Violin	December, 1890	35
PM0704	Flute and Violin, and Other Kentucky Tales and Romances	1891	152
PM1386	A Selection of Books Suitable for Holiday Gifts	December, 1891	36
MBPI0485	**Before the picture**		**431**
PM0129	Flute and Violin	December, 1890	35
PM0704	Flute and Violin, and Other Kentucky Tales and Romances	1891	152
MBPI0486	**"Toiled homeward with his treasure"**		**431**
PM0129	Flute and Violin	December, 1890	35
MBPI0487	**"Buried his head on her bosom"**		**431**
PM0129	Flute and Violin	December, 1890	35
PM0704	Flute and Violin, and Other Kentucky Tales and Romances	1891	152
MBPI0488	**At David's bedside**		**431**
PM0129	Flute and Violin	December, 1890	35
PM0704	Flute and Violin, and Other Kentucky Tales and Romances	1891	152
MBPI0489	**"His head bowed on his folded arms"**		**431**
PM0129	Flute and Violin	December, 1890	35
PM0704	Flute and Violin, and Other Kentucky Tales and Romances	1891	152
MBPI0490	**A Maid's Choice**		**431**
PM0130	A Maid's Choice	December, 1891	35
MBPI0491	**Verse 1. Ye Jovial Huntsman**		**431**
PM0130	A Maid's Choice	December, 1891	35
MBPI0492	**Verse 2. Ye Fat, Rich Man**		**431**
PM0130	A Maid's Choice	December, 1891	35
MBPI0493	**Verse 3. Ye Gallant Soldier**		**431**
PM0130	A Maid's Choice	December, 1891	35
MBPI0494	**Verse 4. Ye Jolly Country Boy**		**431**
PM0130	A Maid's Choice	December, 1891	35
MBPI0495	**Tailpiece for The Birds of Cirencester**		**431**
PM0590	The Birds of Cirencester	January, 1898	111
MBPI0496	**Vignette, the Old Natick Church**		**431**
PM0732	The Writings of Harriet Beecher Stowe	1896	254
MBPI0497	**Vignette, Sam Lawson's House**		**432**
PM0733	The Writings of Harriet Beecher Stowe	1896	254
MBPI0498	**Sam Lawson telling stories**		**432**
PM0733	The Writings of Harriet Beecher Stowe	1896	254
MBPI0499	**The fields around lay bare to the moon**		**432**
PM0739	The First Christmas Tree	1897	151
PM0762	The Blue Flower	1902	135
PM1083	The Van Dyke Book	1905	241
MBPI0500	**Then Winfried told the story of Bethlehem**		**432**
PM0739	The First Christmas Tree	1897	151

MBPI0501	**Reading the Declaration before Washington's Army, New York, July 9, 1776**		**432**
PM0132	How the Declaration was Received in the Old Thirteen	July, 1892	36
PM0795	A History of the American People	1918	166, 170, 273
MBPI0502	**Headpiece with title for How the Declaration was Received in the Old Thirteen**		**432**
PM0132	How the Declaration was Received in the Old Thirteen	July, 1892	36
MBPI0503	**At Philadelphia, Pennsylvania**		**432**
PM0132	How the Declaration was Received in the Old Thirteen	July, 1892	36
MBPI0504	**At Princeton, New Jersey**		**432**
PM0132	How the Declaration was Received in the Old Thirteen	July, 1892	36
MBPI0505	**At Dover, Delaware**		**432**
PM0132	How the Declaration was Received in the Old Thirteen	July, 1892	36
MBPI0506	**In New York (At Headquarters)**		**432**
PM0132	How the Declaration was Received in the Old Thirteen	July, 1892	36
MBPI0507	**At Boston, Massachusetts**		**432**
PM0132	How the Declaration was Received in the Old Thirteen	July, 1892	36
MBPI0508	**At Portsmouth, New Hampshire**		**432**
PM0132	How the Declaration was Received in the Old Thirteen	July, 1892	36
MBPI0509	**At Newport, Rhode Island**		**432**
PM0132	How the Declaration was Received in the Old Thirteen	July, 1892	36
MBPI0510	**In Connecticut**		**432**
PM0132	How the Declaration was Received in the Old Thirteen	July, 1892	36
MBPI0511	**At Williamsburg, Virginia**		**432**
PM0132	How the Declaration was Received in the Old Thirteen	July, 1892	36
MBPI0512	**At Halifax, North Carolina**		**432**
PM0132	How the Declaration was Received in the Old Thirteen	July, 1892	36
MBPI0513	**At Baltimore, Maryland**		**433**
PM0132	How the Declaration was Received in the Old Thirteen	July, 1892	36
MBPI0514	**At Charleston, South Carolina**		**433**
PM0132	How the Declaration was Received in the Old Thirteen	July, 1892	36
MBPI0515	**At Savannah, Georgia**		**433**
PM0132	How the Declaration was Received in the Old Thirteen	July, 1892	36
MBPI0516	**Headpiece with title and decorative border for Two Moods**		**433**
PM0133	Two Moods	July, 1892	37
MBPI0517	**Headpiece for Among the Sand Hills**		**433**
PM0134	Among the Sand Hills	September, 1892	37
MBPI0518	**Illustrated initial T for Among the Sand Hills**		**433**
PM0134	Among the Sand Hills	September, 1892	37
MBPI0519	**Vignette for Among the Sand Hills**		**433**
PM0134	Among the Sand Hills	September, 1892	37
MBPI0520	**Illustrated initial S for Among the Sand Hills**		**433**
PM0134	Among the Sand Hills	September, 1892	37
MBPI0521	**Vignette for Among the Sand Hills**		**433**
PM0134	Among the Sand Hills	September, 1892	37
MBPI0522	**Illustrated initial T for Among the Sand Hills**		**433**
PM0134	Among the Sand Hills	September, 1892	37
MBPI0523	**The Sand Hills**		**433**
PM0134	Among the Sand Hills	September, 1892	37
MBPI0524	**Vignette for Among the Sand Hills**		**433**
PM0134	Among the Sand Hills	September, 1892	37
MBPI0525	**Illustrated initial F for Among the Sand Hills**		**433**
PM0134	Among the Sand Hills	September, 1892	37
MBPI0526	**Vignette for Among the Sand Hills**		**433**
PM0134	Among the Sand Hills	September, 1892	37
MBPI0527	**Illustrated initial B for Among the Sand Hills**		**433**
PM0134	Among the Sand Hills	September, 1892	37
MBPI0528	**Vignette for Among the Sand Hills**		**433**
PM0134	Among the Sand Hills	September, 1892	37
PM0279	The Buccaneers	June 29, 1897	64, 214
MBPI0529	**Vignette for Among the Sand Hills**		**434**
PM0134	Among the Sand Hills	September, 1892	37

MBPI0530	**Illustrated initial S for Among the Sand Hills**		**434**
PM0134	Among the Sand Hills	September, 1892	37
MBPI0531	**Vignette for Among the Sand Hills**		**434**
PM0134	Among the Sand Hills	September, 1892	37
MBPI0532	**The Wreck**		**434**
PM0134	Among the Sand Hills	September, 1892	37
MBPI0533	**Illustrated initial C for Among the Sand Hills**		**434**
PM0134	Among the Sand Hills	September, 1892	37
MBPI0534	**Vignette for Among the Sand Hills**		**434**
PM0134	Among the Sand Hills	September, 1892	37
MBPI0535	**Illustrated initial B for Among the Sand Hills**		**434**
PM0134	Among the Sand Hills	September, 1892	37
MBPI0536	**Vignette for Among the Sand Hills**		**434**
PM0134	Among the Sand Hills	September, 1892	37
MBPI0537	**Vignette for Among the Sand Hills**		**434**
PM0134	Among the Sand Hills	September, 1892	37
MBPI0538	**Vignette for Among the Sand Hills**		**434**
PM0134	Among the Sand Hills	September, 1892	37
MBPI0539	**Illustrated initial T for Among the Sand Hills**		**434**
PM0134	Among the Sand Hills	September, 1892	37
MBPI0540	**Vignette for Among the Sand Hills**		**434**
PM0134	Among the Sand Hills	September, 1892	37
PM1187	A Gentleman Adventurer	September, 1898	64
PM1392	Advertisements	December, 1898	46
PM1650	Harper's Round Table for 1898	1898	268
PM1188	An Early Free-Trader	January, 1899	64
MBPI0541	**Vignette for Among the Sand Hills**		**434**
PM0134	Among the Sand Hills	September, 1892	37
MBPI0542	**Illustrated initial N for Among the Sand Hills**		**434**
PM0134	Among the Sand Hills	September, 1892	37
MBPI0543	**Vignette for Among the Sand Hills**		**434**
PM0134	Among the Sand Hills	September, 1892	37
MBPI0544	**The Lily Lake**		**434**
PM0134	Among the Sand Hills	September, 1892	37
MBPI0545	**"This is no courting night"**		**435**
PM0135	Giles Corey, Yeoman	December, 1892	38
PM1122	New Books on Varied Topics	May, 1893	7
PM1137	Giles Corey Yeoman	May, 1893	9
PM0715	Giles Corey, Yeoman	1893	156
MBPI0546	**"Hey, black cat! hey, my pretty black cat"**		**435**
PM0135	Giles Corey, Yeoman	December, 1892	38
PM0715	Giles Corey, Yeoman	1893	156
MBPI0547	**"There is a flock of yellow birds around her head"**		**435**
PM0135	Giles Corey, Yeoman	December, 1892	38
PM0715	Giles Corey, Yeoman	1893	156
MBPI0548	**"Father, Father!"**		**435**
PM0135	Giles Corey, Yeoman	December, 1892	38
PM0715	Giles Corey, Yeoman	1893	156
MBPI0549	**Question**		**435**
PM0136	Monochromes	March, 1893	38
PM0723	Stops of Various Quills	1895	215
MBPI0550	**Headpiece with title for Monochromes**		**435**
PM0136	Monochromes	March, 1893	38
PM0723	Stops of Various Quills	1895	215
MBPI0551	**Illustrated initial S for Question**		**435**
PM0136	Monochromes	March, 1893	38
PM0723	Stops of Various Quills	1895	215
MBPI0552	**Tailpiece for Question**		**435**
PM0136	Monochromes	March, 1893	38
PM0723	Stops of Various Quills	1895	215

MBPI0553	**Living**		**435**
PM0136	Monochromes	March, 1893	38
PM0723	Stops of Various Quills	1895	215
MBPI0554	**Illustrated initial H for Living**		**435**
PM0136	Monochromes	March, 1893	38
PM0723	Stops of Various Quills	1895	215
MBPI0555	**To-Morrow**		**435**
PM0136	Monochromes	March, 1893	38
PM0723	Stops of Various Quills	1895	215
MBPI0556	**Illustrated initial O for To-Morrow**		**435**
PM0136	Monochromes	March, 1893	38
PM0723	Stops of Various Quills	1895	215
MBPI0557	**Tailpiece for Friends and Foes**		**435**
PM0136	Monochromes	March, 1893	38
PM0723	Stops of Various Quills	1895	215
MBPI0558	**From Generation to Generation**		**435**
PM0136	Monochromes	March, 1893	38
PM0723	Stops of Various Quills	1895	215
PM1181	A Laughy-Man	March 2, 1897	64
MBPI0559	**Illustrated initial I for From Generation to Generation**		**435**
PM0136	Monochromes	March, 1893	38
PM0723	Stops of Various Quills	1895	215
MBPI0560	**Tailpiece for From Generation to Generation**		**435**
PM0136	Monochromes	March, 1893	38
PM0723	Stops of Various Quills	1895	215
MBPI0561	**The Bewildered Guest**		**436**
PM0136	Monochromes	March, 1893	38
PM0723	Stops of Various Quills	1895	215
MBPI0562	**Illustrated initial I for The Bewildered Guest**		**436**
PM0136	Monochromes	March, 1893	38
PM0723	Stops of Various Quills	1895	215
MBPI0563	**Hope**		**436**
PM0136	Monochromes	March, 1893	38
PM0723	Stops of Various Quills	1895	215
MBPI0564	**Illustrated initial Y for Hope**		**436**
PM0136	Monochromes	March, 1893	38
PM0723	Stops of Various Quills	1895	215
MBPI0565	**Tailpiece for Hope**		**436**
PM0136	Monochromes	March, 1893	38
PM0723	Stops of Various Quills	1895	215
MBPI0566	**Illustrated initial D for Respite**		**436**
PM0136	Monochromes	March, 1893	38
MBPI0567	**Respite**		**436**
PM0136	Monochromes	March, 1893	38
PM0723	Stops of Various Quills	1895	215
MBPI0568	**"He sat down beside her on the bench"**		**436**
PM0137	Retribution	April, 1893	38
MBPI0569	**"Thereupon the poor woman screamed aloud, and cried out that he was a murderer"**		**436**
PM0137	Retribution	April, 1893	38
MBPI0570	**Along the Canal in Old Manhattan**		**436**
PM0138	The Evolution of New York. I	May, 1893	38
PM1447	World's Columbian Exposition, Chicago, Illinois	1893	283
PM0716	In Old New York	1894	171
PM0798	The Drexel Institute, Philadelphia, Pennsylvania	1897	8, 140, 268, 284
PM0799	St. Botolph Club, Boston, Massachusetts	1897	140, 268, 288
PM1533	Looking Backward on Manhattan, The Canal Street of New Amsterdam and of New York To-Day	November 16, 1913	124
MBPI0571	**Headpiece with title and illustrated initial T for The Evolution of New York**		**436**
PM0138	The Evolution of New York. I	May, 1893	38
PM0761	Harper's Encyclopaedia of United States History	1902	158

MBPI0572	**On the River Front**		**436**
PM0138	The Evolution of New York. I	May, 1893	38
PM0716	In Old New York	1894	171
PM0759	A History of the American People	1902	165
PM0761	Harper's Encyclopaedia of United States History	1902	158
PM0954	Harper's Encyclopaedia of United States History from 458 A.D. to 1915	1915	161
PM0795	A History of the American People	1918	166, 170, 273
MBPI0573	**Tailpiece for The Evolution of New York**		**436**
PM0138	The Evolution of New York. I	May, 1893	38
PM0716	In Old New York	1894	171
PM0761	Harper's Encyclopaedia of United States History	1902	158
PM0954	Harper's Encyclopaedia of United States History from 458 A.D. to 1915	1915	161
MBPI0574	**Headpiece, In 1776, The Conflagration**		**436**
PM0139	The Evolution of New York. II	June, 1893	38
PM0716	In Old New York	1894	171
PM0761	Harper's Encyclopaedia of United States History	1902	158
PM0954	Harper's Encyclopaedia of United States History from 458 A.D. to 1915	1915	161
MBPI0575	**A Privateersman Ashore**		**436**
PM0139	The Evolution of New York. II	June, 1893	38
PM0716	In Old New York	1894	171
MBPI0576	**Opening of the Erie Canal**		**436**
PM0139	The Evolution of New York. II	June, 1893	38
PM0716	In Old New York	1894	171
MBPI0577	**Tailpiece for The Evolution of New York**		**437**
PM0139	The Evolution of New York. II	June, 1893	38
MBPI0578	**Headpiece with title and illustrated initial T for The Cocklane Ghost**		**437**
PM0140	The Cocklane Ghost	August, 1893	39
MBPI0579	**Vignette for The Cocklane Ghost**		**437**
PM0140	The Cocklane Ghost	August, 1893	39
MBPI0580	**Vignette for The Cocklane Ghost**		**437**
PM0140	The Cocklane Ghost	August, 1893	39
MBPI0581	**Vignette for The Cocklane Ghost**		**437**
PM0140	The Cocklane Ghost	August, 1893	39
MBPI0582	**Vignette for The Cocklane Ghost**		**437**
PM0140	The Cocklane Ghost	August, 1893	39
MBPI0583	**Vignette for The Cocklane Ghost**		**437**
PM0140	The Cocklane Ghost	August, 1893	39
MBPI0584	**Vignette for The Cocklane Ghost**		**437**
PM0140	The Cocklane Ghost	August, 1893	39
MBPI0585	**Vignette for The Cocklane Ghost**		**437**
PM0140	The Cocklane Ghost	August, 1893	39
MBPI0586	**Vignette for The Cocklane Ghost**		**437**
PM0140	The Cocklane Ghost	August, 1893	39
MBPI0587	**Vignette for The Cocklane Ghost**		**437**
PM0140	The Cocklane Ghost	August, 1893	39
MBPI0588	**Vignette for The Cocklane Ghost**		**437**
PM0140	The Cocklane Ghost	August, 1893	39
MBPI0589	**Vignette for The Cocklane Ghost**		**437**
PM0140	The Cocklane Ghost	August, 1893	39
MBPI0590	**Tailpiece for The Cocklane Ghost**		**437**
PM0140	The Cocklane Ghost	August, 1893	39
MBPI0591	**Headpiece with initial O for A Soldier of Fortune**		**437**
PM0141	A Soldier of Fortune	December, 1893	39
MBPI0592	**Vignette for A Soldier of Fortune**		**437**
PM0141	A Soldier of Fortune	December, 1893	39
MBPI0593	**Vignette for A Soldier of Fortune**		**438**
PM0141	A Soldier of Fortune	December, 1893	39
MBPI0594	**A Night in the Village Street**		**438**
PM0141	A Soldier of Fortune	December, 1893	39
MBPI0595	**Vignette for A Soldier of Fortune**		**438**

PM0141	A Soldier of Fortune	December, 1893	39
MBPI0596	**Vignette for A Soldier of Fortune**		**438**
PM0141	A Soldier of Fortune	December, 1893	39
MBPI0597	**Dragging the Duke out of the Coach**		**438**
PM0141	A Soldier of Fortune	December, 1893	39
MBPI0598	**Vignette for A Soldier of Fortune**		**438**
PM0141	A Soldier of Fortune	December, 1893	39
MBPI0599	**Vignette for A Soldier of Fortune**		**438**
PM0141	A Soldier of Fortune	December, 1893	39
MBPI0600	**Vignette for A Soldier of Fortune**		**438**
PM0141	A Soldier of Fortune	December, 1893	39
MBPI0601	**Vignette for A Soldier of Fortune**		**438**
PM0141	A Soldier of Fortune	December, 1893	39
MBPI0602	**The Fight for the Crown**		**438**
PM0141	A Soldier of Fortune	December, 1893	39
MBPI0603	**Vignette for A Soldier of Fortune**		**438**
PM0141	A Soldier of Fortune	December, 1893	39
MBPI0604	**Vignette for A Soldier of Fortune**		**438**
PM0141	A Soldier of Fortune	December, 1893	39
MBPI0605	**Vignette for A Soldier of Fortune**		**438**
PM0141	A Soldier of Fortune	December, 1893	39
MBPI0606	**Vignette for A Soldier of Fortune**		**438**
PM0141	A Soldier of Fortune	December, 1893	39
MBPI0607	**"He had found the Captain agreeable and companionable"**		**438**
PM0143	The Sea Robbers of New York	November, 1894	39
MBPI0608	**Headpiece with title and illustrated initial T for The Sea Robbers of New York**		**438**
PM0143	The Sea Robbers of New York	November, 1894	39
PM1179	Advertisement	August, 1895	40
MBPI0609	**"Pirates used to do that to their Captains now and then"**		**439**
PM0143	The Sea Robbers of New York	November, 1894	39
PM0798	The Drexel Institute, Philadelphia, Pennsylvania	1897	8, 140, 268, 284
PM0799	St. Botolph Club, Boston, Massachusetts	1897	140, 268, 288
MBPI0610	**Kidd at Gardiner's Island**		**439**
PM0143	The Sea Robbers of New York	November, 1894	39
PM1345	A Fifty Two Week Feast of Harper's Round Table	1896	267
MBPI0611	**Tailpiece for The Sea Robbers of New York**		**439**
PM0143	The Sea Robbers of New York	November, 1894	39
MBPI0612	**Illustration for Stops of Various Quills**		**439**
PM0144	Stops of Various Quills	December, 1894	40
PM0723	Stops of Various Quills	1895	215
PM1387	Advertisement: Harper & Brothers Holiday Books	December, 1895	41
MBPI0613	**Headpiece with title for Stops of Various Quills**		**439**
PM0144	Stops of Various Quills	December, 1894	40
PM0723	Stops of Various Quills	1895	215
MBPI0614	**Illustrated initial W for Sphinx**		**439**
PM0144	Stops of Various Quills	December, 1894	40
PM0723	Stops of Various Quills	1895	215
MBPI0615	**Tailpiece for Twelve P.M.**		**439**
PM0144	Stops of Various Quills	December, 1894	40
PM0723	Stops of Various Quills	1895	215
MBPI0616	**Time**		**439**
PM0144	Stops of Various Quills	December, 1894	40
PM0723	Stops of Various Quills	1895	215
MBPI0617	**Illustrated initial D for Time**		**439**
PM0144	Stops of Various Quills	December, 1894	40
PM0723	Stops of Various Quills	1895	215
MBPI0618	**Society**		**439**
PM0144	Stops of Various Quills	December, 1894	40
PM0723	Stops of Various Quills	1895	215
PM1387	Advertisement: Harper & Brothers Holiday Books	December, 1895	41

MBPI0619	**Illustrated initial Y for Society**		**439**
PM0144	Stops of Various Quills	December, 1894	40
PM0723	Stops of Various Quills	1895	215
MBPI0620	**Tailpiece for Society**		**439**
PM0144	Stops of Various Quills	December, 1894	40
PM0723	Stops of Various Quills	1895	215
MBPI0621	**Heredity**		**439**
PM0144	Stops of Various Quills	December, 1894	40
PM0723	Stops of Various Quills	1895	215
MBPI0622	**Illustrated initial T for Heredity**		**439**
PM0144	Stops of Various Quills	December, 1894	40
PM0723	Stops of Various Quills	1895	215
MBPI0623	**In the Dark**		**439**
PM0144	Stops of Various Quills	December, 1894	40
PM0723	Stops of Various Quills	1895	215
MBPI0624	**Solitude**		**439**
PM0144	Stops of Various Quills	December, 1894	40
PM0723	Stops of Various Quills	1895	215
MBPI0625	**Illustrated initial A for Solitude**		**440**
PM0144	Stops of Various Quills	December, 1894	40
PM0723	Stops of Various Quills	1895	215
MBPI0626	**Change**		**440**
PM0144	Stops of Various Quills	December, 1894	40
PM0723	Stops of Various Quills	1895	215
MBPI0627	**Illustrated initial S for Change**		**440**
PM0144	Stops of Various Quills	December, 1894	40
PM0723	Stops of Various Quills	1895	215
MBPI0628	**Tailpiece for Change**		**440**
PM0144	Stops of Various Quills	December, 1894	40
PM0723	Stops of Various Quills	1895	215
MBPI0629	**Midway**		**440**
PM0144	Stops of Various Quills	December, 1894	40
PM0723	Stops of Various Quills	1895	215
MBPI0630	**Illustrated initial S for Midway**		**440**
PM0144	Stops of Various Quills	December, 1894	40
PM0723	Stops of Various Quills	1895	215
MBPI0631	**Calvary**		**440**
PM0144	Stops of Various Quills	December, 1894	40
PM0723	Stops of Various Quills	1895	215
MBPI0632	**Illustrated initial I for Calvary**		**440**
PM0144	Stops of Various Quills	December, 1894	40
PM0723	Stops of Various Quills	1895	215
MBPI0633	**"Some of the by-standers said 'She is drunk, it will soon pass away'"**		**440**
PM0145	New York Slave Traders	January, 1895	40
MBPI0634	**"The choicest pieces of her cargo were sold at auction"**		**440**
PM0145	New York Slave Traders	January, 1895	40
MBPI0635	**"We escaped in the boat"**		**440**
PM0145	New York Slave Traders	January, 1895	40
MBPI0636	**"And again my Captain took the biggest"**		**440**
PM0146	New York Colonial Privateers	February, 1895	40
PM0636	When I Was a Little Boy	April, 1912	127
MBPI0637	**Headpiece with title and illustrated initial O for New York Colonial Privateers**		**440**
PM0146	New York Colonial Privateers	February, 1895	40
MBPI0638	**"Barbarously murdered the first, and grievously wounded the latter"**		**440**
PM0146	New York Colonial Privateers	February, 1895	40
MBPI0639	**Tailpiece for New York Colonial Privateers**		**440**
PM0146	New York Colonial Privateers	February, 1895	40
MBPI0640	**Headpiece with title for Society**		**440**
PM0147	Society	March, 1895	40
PM0723	Stops of Various Quills	1895	215

MBPI0641	**Marginal decoration for Society**		**441**
PM0147	Society	March, 1895	40
PM0723	Stops of Various Quills	1895	215
MBPI0642	**Tailpiece for Society**		**441**
PM0147	Society	March, 1895	40
PM0723	Stops of Various Quills	1895	215
MBPI0643	**Frontispiece for Pebbles**		**441**
PM0148	Pebbles	September, 1895	40
PM0723	Stops of Various Quills	1895	215
MBPI0644	**Headpiece with title for Pebbles**		**441**
PM0148	Pebbles	September, 1895	40
PM0723	Stops of Various Quills	1895	215
MBPI0645	**Illustrated initial I for The Burden**		**441**
PM0148	Pebbles	September, 1895	40
PM0723	Stops of Various Quills	1895	215
MBPI0646	**Hope**		**441**
PM0148	Pebbles	September, 1895	40
PM0723	Stops of Various Quills	1895	215
MBPI0647	**Sympathy**		**441**
PM0148	Pebbles	September, 1895	40
PM0723	Stops of Various Quills	1895	215
MBPI0648	**Illustrated initial F for Sympathy**		**441**
PM0148	Pebbles	September, 1895	40
PM0723	Stops of Various Quills	1895	215
PM1125	Book Reviews	December, 1895	7
MBPI0649	**Reward and Punishment**		**441**
PM0148	Pebbles	September, 1895	40
PM0723	Stops of Various Quills	1895	215
MBPI0650	**Parable**		**441**
PM0148	Pebbles	September, 1895	40
PM0723	Stops of Various Quills	1895	215
MBPI0651	**Illustrated initial T for Parable**		**441**
PM0148	Pebbles	September, 1895	40
PM0723	Stops of Various Quills	1895	215
MBPI0652	**Statistics**		**441**
PM0148	Pebbles	September, 1895	40
PM0723	Stops of Various Quills	1895	215
MBPI0653	**Illustrated initial S for Statistics**		**441**
PM0148	Pebbles	September, 1895	40
PM0723	Stops of Various Quills	1895	215
MBPI0654	**Tailpiece for Statistics**		**441**
PM0148	Pebbles	September, 1895	40
PM0723	Stops of Various Quills	1895	215
MBPI0655	**In the Wood-Carver's Shop**		**441**
PM0149	By Land and Sea	December, 1895	41
PM0798	The Drexel Institute, Philadelphia, Pennsylvania	1897	8, 140, 268, 284
PM0799	St. Botolph Club, Boston, Massachusetts	1897	140, 268, 288
PM1455	The New Century Club, Wilmington, Delaware	1899	294
PM1464	Art Institute of Chicago, Chicago, Illinois	1903	130, 297
PM1479	Hotel Dupont, Wilmington, Delaware	1912	141, 310
PM1481	Panama and Pacific International Exhibition, San Francisco, California	1915	315
MBPI0656	**Headpiece with title for By Land and Sea**		**441**
PM0149	By Land and Sea	December, 1895	41
PM1455	The New Century Club, Wilmington, Delaware	1899	294
PM1464	Art Institute of Chicago, Chicago, Illinois	1903	130, 297
PM1479	Hotel Dupont, Wilmington, Delaware	1912	141, 310
MBPI0657	**Tailpiece, Sketch Four for By Land and Sea**		**442**
PM0149	By Land and Sea	December, 1895	41
PM1464	Art Institute of Chicago, Chicago, Illinois	1903	130, 297
MBPI0658	**Tailpiece, Sketch One for By Land and Sea**		**442**

PM0149	By Land and Sea	December, 1895	41
PM1464	Art Institute of Chicago, Chicago, Illinois	1903	130, 297
PM1479	Hotel Dupont, Wilmington, Delaware	1912	141, 310
MBPI0659	**A Sailor's Sweetheart**		**442**
PM0149	By Land and Sea	December, 1895	41
PM0798	The Drexel Institute, Philadelphia, Pennsylvania	1897	8, 140, 268, 284
PM0799	St. Botolph Club, Boston, Massachusetts	1897	140, 268, 288
PM1455	The New Century Club, Wilmington, Delaware	1899	294
PM1464	Art Institute of Chicago, Chicago, Illinois	1903	130, 297
PM0809	Catalogue of Pictures by Howard Pyle	1912	141, 310
PM1479	Hotel Dupont, Wilmington, Delaware	1912	141, 310
PM1096	Howard Pyle, Biographical Sketches of American Artists	October, 1915	2
PM1481	Panama and Pacific International Exhibition, San Francisco, California	1915	315
MBPI0660	**Headpiece, Sketch Two for By Land and Sea**		**442**
PM0149	By Land and Sea	December, 1895	41
PM1186	The Blockaders	August, 1898	64
PM1455	The New Century Club, Wilmington, Delaware	1899	294
PM1464	Art Institute of Chicago, Chicago, Illinois	1903	130, 297
PM1479	Hotel Dupont, Wilmington, Delaware	1912	141, 310
MBPI0661	**Illustrated initial I, Sketch Two for By Land and Sea**		**442**
PM0149	By Land and Sea	December, 1895	41
PM1479	Hotel Dupont, Wilmington, Delaware	1912	141, 310
MBPI0662	**Tailpiece, Sketch Two for By Land and Sea**		**442**
PM0149	By Land and Sea	December, 1895	41
PM1464	Art Institute of Chicago, Chicago, Illinois	1903	130, 297
PM1479	Hotel Dupont, Wilmington, Delaware	1912	141, 310
MBPI0663	**The Sailor's Wedding**		**442**
PM0149	By Land and Sea	December, 1895	41
PM1308	Harper's Magazine for Christmas 1895	1895	271
PM0798	The Drexel Institute, Philadelphia, Pennsylvania	1897	8, 140, 268, 284
PM0799	St. Botolph Club, Boston, Massachusetts	1897	140, 268, 288
PM1455	The New Century Club, Wilmington, Delaware	1899	294
PM1464	Art Institute of Chicago, Chicago, Illinois	1903	130, 297
PM1479	Hotel Dupont, Wilmington, Delaware	1912	141, 310
PM1481	Panama and Pacific International Exhibition, San Francisco, California	1915	315
MBPI0664	**Headpiece, Sketch Three for By Land and Sea**		**442**
PM0149	By Land and Sea	December, 1895	41
PM1455	The New Century Club, Wilmington, Delaware	1899	294
PM1464	Art Institute of Chicago, Chicago, Illinois	1903	130, 297
PM1479	Hotel Dupont, Wilmington, Delaware	1912	141, 310
MBPI0665	**Illustrated initial T, Sketch One for By Land and Sea**		**442**
PM0149	By Land and Sea	December, 1895	41
PM1479	Hotel Dupont, Wilmington, Delaware	1912	141, 310
MBPI0666	**Tailpiece, Sketch Three for By Land and Sea**		**442**
PM0149	By Land and Sea	December, 1895	41
PM1464	Art Institute of Chicago, Chicago, Illinois	1903	130, 297
PM1479	Hotel Dupont, Wilmington, Delaware	1912	141, 310
MBPI0667	**A Wreck from the Sea**		**442**
PM0149	By Land and Sea	December, 1895	41
PM0798	The Drexel Institute, Philadelphia, Pennsylvania	1897	8, 140, 268, 284
PM0799	St. Botolph Club, Boston, Massachusetts	1897	140, 268, 288
PM1455	The New Century Club, Wilmington, Delaware	1899	294
PM1464	Art Institute of Chicago, Chicago, Illinois	1903	130, 297
PM1479	Hotel Dupont, Wilmington, Delaware	1912	141, 310
PM1481	Panama and Pacific International Exhibition, San Francisco, California	1915	315
MBPI0668	**Headpiece, Sketch Four for By Land and Sea**		**442**
PM0149	By Land and Sea	December, 1895	41
PM1455	The New Century Club, Wilmington, Delaware	1899	294
PM1464	Art Institute of Chicago, Chicago, Illinois	1903	130, 297
PM1479	Hotel Dupont, Wilmington, Delaware	1912	141, 310

MBPI0669	**Illustrated initial E, Sketch Four for By Land and Sea**		**442**
PM0149	By Land and Sea	December, 1895	41
PM1479	Hotel Dupont, Wilmington, Delaware	1912	141, 310
MBPI0670	**Cap'n Goldsack**		**442**
PM0194	Cap'n Goldsack	July, 1902	50
MBPI0671	**Headpiece with title and illustrated initial G for In Washington's Day**		**442**
PM0150	In Washington's Day	January, 1896	41
PM0738	George Washington	1897	155
PM0798	The Drexel Institute, Philadelphia, Pennsylvania	1897	8, 140, 268, 284
PM0799	St. Botolph Club, Boston, Massachusetts	1897	140, 268, 288
MBPI0672	**A Virginia Plantation Wharf**		**442**
PM0150	In Washington's Day	January, 1896	41
PM0738	George Washington	1897	155
PM0798	The Drexel Institute, Philadelphia, Pennsylvania	1897	8, 140, 268, 284
PM0799	St. Botolph Club, Boston, Massachusetts	1897	140, 268, 288
PM1501	American Historical Paintings by Howard Pyle	September, 1900	100
PM1503	A Virginia Plantation Wharf	1900	334
PM0761	Harper's Encyclopaedia of United States History	1902	158
MBPI0673	**"Even Sir William Berkeley, the redoubtable Cavalier Governor, saw he must yield"**		**443**
PM0150	In Washington's Day	January, 1896	41
PM0738	George Washington	1897	155
PM0798	The Drexel Institute, Philadelphia, Pennsylvania	1897	8, 140, 268, 284
PM0799	St. Botolph Club, Boston, Massachusetts	1897	140, 268, 288
PM1501	American Historical Paintings by Howard Pyle	September, 1900	100
PM1504	"Even Sir William Berkeley, the redoubtable Cavalier Governor, saw he must yield"	1900	334
PM1173	Howard Pyle	January, 1912	61
MBPI0674	**"They read only upon occasion, when the weather darkened"**		**443**
PM0150	In Washington's Day	January, 1896	41
PM0738	George Washington	1897	155
PM0798	The Drexel Institute, Philadelphia, Pennsylvania	1897	8, 140, 268, 284
PM0799	St. Botolph Club, Boston, Massachusetts	1897	140, 268, 288
PM1501	American Historical Paintings by Howard Pyle	September, 1900	100
PM1505	"They read only upon occasion, when the weather darkened"	1900	334-335
PM1096	Howard Pyle, Biographical Sketches of American Artists	October, 1915	2
MBPI0675	**Ye Virginia Gentleman of the Olden Time**		**443**
PM0150	In Washington's Day	January, 1896	41
PM0738	George Washington	1897	155
MBPI0676	**Washington's Retreat from Great Meadows**		**443**
PM0151	Colonel Washington	March, 1896	42
PM0738	George Washington	1897	155
PM0798	The Drexel Institute, Philadelphia, Pennsylvania	1897	8, 140, 268, 284
PM0799	St. Botolph Club, Boston, Massachusetts	1897	140, 268, 288
PM1501	American Historical Paintings by Howard Pyle	September, 1900	100
PM1506	Washington's Retreat from Great Meadows	1900	334-335
PM1534	Memorable Events in American History	March 29, 1914	125
MBPI0677	**Headpiece for Colonel Washington**		**443**
PM0151	Colonel Washington	March, 1896	42
PM0738	George Washington	1897	155
PM0798	The Drexel Institute, Philadelphia, Pennsylvania	1897	8, 140, 268, 284
PM0799	St. Botolph Club, Boston, Massachusetts	1897	140, 268, 288
PM1501	American Historical Paintings by Howard Pyle	September, 1900	100
PM1520	Braddock's Defeat, Battle of Monongahela	1900	334, 337
MBPI0678	**The Burial of Braddock**		**443**
PM0151	Colonel Washington	March, 1896	42
PM1180	A Virginia Cavalier	October 27, 1896	63
PM0738	George Washington	1897	155
PM0798	The Drexel Institute, Philadelphia, Pennsylvania	1897	8, 140, 268, 284
PM0799	St. Botolph Club, Boston, Massachusetts	1897	140, 268, 288
PM1501	American Historical Paintings by Howard Pyle	September, 1900	100

PM1039	The Northwest Under Three Flags	1900	188
PM1507	The Burial of Braddock	1900	334-335
PM0795	A History of the American People	1918	166, 170, 273
PM1556	A History of The American People	1918	273
MBPI0679	**Washington and Mary Philipse**		**443**
PM0151	Colonel Washington	March, 1896	42
PM0738	George Washington	1897	155
PM0798	The Drexel Institute, Philadelphia, Pennsylvania	1897	8, 140, 268, 284
PM0799	St. Botolph Club, Boston, Massachusetts	1897	140, 268, 288
PM1501	American Historical Paintings by Howard Pyle	September, 1900	100
PM1508	Washington and Mary Philipse	1900	334-335
MBPI0680	**Tailpiece for Colonel Washington**		**443**
PM0151	Colonel Washington	March, 1896	42
PM0738	George Washington	1897	155
PM0798	The Drexel Institute, Philadelphia, Pennsylvania	1897	8, 140, 268, 284
PM0799	St. Botolph Club, Boston, Massachusetts	1897	140, 268, 288
MBPI0681	**Leaving Mount Vernon for the Congress of the Colonies**		**443**
PM0152	At Home in Virginia	May, 1896	42
PM1253	Old Books in New Dress	November 28, 1896	106
PM1194	Advertisement: George Washington	December 5, 1896	72
PM1346	Harper & Brothers' Holiday Books	1896	267
PM1390	Advertisement: Harper & Brothers Holiday Books for 1896	December, 1896	44
PM0738	George Washington	1897	155
PM0798	The Drexel Institute, Philadelphia, Pennsylvania	1897	8, 140, 268, 284
PM0799	St. Botolph Club, Boston, Massachusetts	1897	140, 268, 288
PM1501	American Historical Paintings by Howard Pyle	September, 1900	100
PM1510	Leaving Mount Vernon for the Congress of the Colonies	1900	334-335
PM1173	Howard Pyle	January, 1912	61
PM1534	Memorable Events in American History	March 29, 1914	125
PM0795	A History of the American People	1918	166, 170, 273
MBPI0682	**The Old Capitol at Williamsburg**		**443**
PM0152	At Home in Virginia	May, 1896	42
PM1126	The Real Washington	December, 1896	7
PM0738	George Washington	1897	155
PM0798	The Drexel Institute, Philadelphia, Pennsylvania	1897	8, 140, 268, 284
PM0799	St. Botolph Club, Boston, Massachusetts	1897	140, 268, 288
PM1501	American Historical Paintings by Howard Pyle	September, 1900	100
PM1502	The Old Capitol at Williamsburg	1900	334-337
PM0759	A History of the American People	1902	165
PM0795	A History of the American People	1918	166, 170, 273
MBPI0683	**In the Old Raleigh Tavern**		**443**
PM0152	At Home in Virginia	May, 1896	42
PM0738	George Washington	1897	155
PM0798	The Drexel Institute, Philadelphia, Pennsylvania	1897	8, 140, 268, 284
PM0799	St. Botolph Club, Boston, Massachusetts	1897	140, 268, 288
PM1501	American Historical Paintings by Howard Pyle	September, 1900	100
PM1509	In the Old Raleigh Tavern	1900	334-335
PM0931	Great American Illustrators: Howard Pyle, Illustrator	September, 1907	99, 106
PM1173	Howard Pyle	January, 1912	61
MBPI0684	**Head and sidepiece with illustrated initial T for Through Inland Waters**		**443**
PM0153	Through Inland Waters. I	May, 1896	42
PM0798	The Drexel Institute, Philadelphia, Pennsylvania	1897	8, 140, 268, 284
PM0799	St. Botolph Club, Boston, Massachusetts	1897	140, 268, 288
MBPI0685	**Vignette for Through Inland Waters**		**443**
PM0153	Through Inland Waters. I	May, 1896	42
MBPI0686	**Vignette for Through Inland Waters**		**443**
PM0153	Through Inland Waters. I	May, 1896	42
MBPI0687	**A Floating Town**		**443**
PM0153	Through Inland Waters. I	May, 1896	42
PM0798	The Drexel Institute, Philadelphia, Pennsylvania	1897	8, 140, 268, 284

PM0799	St. Botolph Club, Boston, Massachusetts	1897	140, 268, 288
MBPI0688	**Headpiece with subtitle for Through Inland Waters**		**443**
PM0153	Through Inland Waters. I	May, 1896	42
MBPI0689	**Vignette for Through Inland Waters**		**444**
PM0153	Through Inland Waters. I	May, 1896	42
PM0798	The Drexel Institute, Philadelphia, Pennsylvania	1897	8, 140, 268, 284
PM0799	St. Botolph Club, Boston, Massachusetts	1897	140, 268, 288
MBPI0690	**Vignette for Through Inland Waters**		**444**
PM0153	Through Inland Waters. I	May, 1896	42
MBPI0691	**Vignette for Through Inland Waters**		**444**
PM0153	Through Inland Waters. I	May, 1896	42
MBPI0692	**Vignette for Through Inland Waters**		**444**
PM0153	Through Inland Waters. I	May, 1896	42
MBPI0693	**Vignette for Through Inland Waters**		**444**
PM0153	Through Inland Waters. I	May, 1896	42
MBPI0694	**Vignette for Through Inland Waters**		**444**
PM0153	Through Inland Waters. I	May, 1896	42
PM0798	The Drexel Institute, Philadelphia, Pennsylvania	1897	8, 140, 268, 284
PM0799	St. Botolph Club, Boston, Massachusetts	1897	140, 268, 288
MBPI0695	**Vignette for Through Inland Waters**		**444**
PM0153	Through Inland Waters. I	May, 1896	42
MBPI0696	**Vignette for Through Inland Waters**		**444**
PM0153	Through Inland Waters. I	May, 1896	42
PM0798	The Drexel Institute, Philadelphia, Pennsylvania	1897	8, 140, 268, 284
PM0799	St. Botolph Club, Boston, Massachusetts	1897	140, 268, 288
MBPI0697	**Vignette for Through Inland Waters**		**444**
PM0153	Through Inland Waters. I	May, 1896	42
PM0798	The Drexel Institute, Philadelphia, Pennsylvania	1897	8, 140, 268, 284
PM0799	St. Botolph Club, Boston, Massachusetts	1897	140, 268, 288
MBPI0698	**Vignette for Through Inland Waters**		**444**
PM0153	Through Inland Waters. I	May, 1896	42
PM0798	The Drexel Institute, Philadelphia, Pennsylvania	1897	8, 140, 268, 284
PM0799	St. Botolph Club, Boston, Massachusetts	1897	140, 268, 288
MBPI0699	**Tailpiece for Through Inland Waters**		**444**
PM0153	Through Inland Waters. I	May, 1896	42
PM0798	The Drexel Institute, Philadelphia, Pennsylvania	1897	8, 140, 268, 284
PM0799	St. Botolph Club, Boston, Massachusetts	1897	140, 268, 288
MBPI0700	**Headpiece with title and initial T for Through Inland Waters**		**444**
PM0154	Through Inland Waters. II	June, 1896	42
PM0798	The Drexel Institute, Philadelphia, Pennsylvania	1897	8, 140, 268, 284
PM0799	St. Botolph Club, Boston, Massachusetts	1897	140, 268, 288
MBPI0701	**Vignette for Through Inland Waters**		**444**
PM0154	Through Inland Waters. II	June, 1896	42
MBPI0702	**Vignette for Through Inland Waters**		**444**
PM0154	Through Inland Waters. II	June, 1896	42
MBPI0703	**Vignette for Through Inland Waters**		**444**
PM0154	Through Inland Waters. II	June, 1896	42
MBPI0704	**Vignette for Through Inland Waters**		**444**
PM0154	Through Inland Waters. II	June, 1896	42
MBPI0705	**Vignette for Through Inland Waters**		**445**
PM0154	Through Inland Waters. II	June, 1896	42
MBPI0706	**Illustration for Through Inland Waters**		**445**
PM0154	Through Inland Waters. II	June, 1896	42
PM0798	The Drexel Institute, Philadelphia, Pennsylvania	1897	8, 140, 268, 284
PM0799	St. Botolph Club, Boston, Massachusetts	1897	140, 268, 288
MBPI0707	**Vignette for Through Inland Waters**		**445**
PM0154	Through Inland Waters. II	June, 1896	42
PM0798	The Drexel Institute, Philadelphia, Pennsylvania	1897	8, 140, 268, 284
PM0799	St. Botolph Club, Boston, Massachusetts	1897	140, 268, 288
MBPI0708	**Vignette for Through Inland Waters**		**445**

PM0154	Through Inland Waters. II	June, 1896	42
MBPI0709	**Vignette for Through Inland Waters**		**445**
PM0154	Through Inland Waters. II	June, 1896	42
PM0798	The Drexel Institute, Philadelphia, Pennsylvania	1897	8, 140, 268, 284
PM0799	St. Botolph Club, Boston, Massachusetts	1897	140, 268, 288
MBPI0710	**Vignette for Through Inland Waters**		**445**
PM0154	Through Inland Waters. II	June, 1896	42
MBPI0711	**Vignette for Through Inland Waters**		**445**
PM0154	Through Inland Waters. II	June, 1896	42
PM0798	The Drexel Institute, Philadelphia, Pennsylvania	1897	8, 140, 268, 284
PM0799	St. Botolph Club, Boston, Massachusetts	1897	140, 268, 288
MBPI0712	**Illustration for Through Inland Waters**		**445**
PM0154	Through Inland Waters. II	June, 1896	42
PM0798	The Drexel Institute, Philadelphia, Pennsylvania	1897	8, 140, 268, 284
PM0799	St. Botolph Club, Boston, Massachusetts	1897	140, 268, 288
MBPI0713	**Vignette for Through Inland Waters**		**445**
PM0154	Through Inland Waters. II	June, 1896	42
MBPI0714	**Vignette for Through Inland Waters**		**445**
PM0154	Through Inland Waters. II	June, 1896	42
PM0798	The Drexel Institute, Philadelphia, Pennsylvania	1897	8, 140, 268, 284
PM0799	St. Botolph Club, Boston, Massachusetts	1897	140, 268, 288
MBPI0715	**Tailpiece for Through Inland Waters**		**445**
PM0154	Through Inland Waters. II	June, 1896	42
PM0798	The Drexel Institute, Philadelphia, Pennsylvania	1897	8, 140, 268, 284
PM0799	St. Botolph Club, Boston, Massachusetts	1897	140, 268, 288
MBPI0716	**Headpiece with title for General Washington**		**445**
PM0155	General Washington	July, 1896	43
PM1126	The Real Washington	December, 1896	7
PM0738	George Washington	1897	155
PM0798	The Drexel Institute, Philadelphia, Pennsylvania	1897	8, 140, 268, 284
PM0799	St. Botolph Club, Boston, Massachusetts	1897	140, 268, 288
PM0989	The Boys of '76, A History of the Battles of the Revolution	1897	137
PM1534	Memorable Events in American History	March 29, 1914	125
MBPI0717	**Washington and Steuben at Valley Forge**		**445**
PM0155	General Washington	July, 1896	43
PM0738	George Washington	1897	155
PM0798	The Drexel Institute, Philadelphia, Pennsylvania	1897	8, 140, 268, 284
PM0799	St. Botolph Club, Boston, Massachusetts	1897	140, 268, 288
PM1592	A Catalogue of Drawings	1897	140, 284
PM1593	A Catalogue of Illustrations	1897	140, 288
PM1501	American Historical Paintings by Howard Pyle	September, 1900	100
PM1512	Washington and Steuben at Valley Forge	1900	334, 336
PM1534	Memorable Events in American History	March 29, 1914	125
MBPI0718	**Lady Washington's Arrival at Headquarters, Cambridge**		**445**
PM0155	General Washington	July, 1896	43
PM0738	George Washington	1897	155
PM0798	The Drexel Institute, Philadelphia, Pennsylvania	1897	8, 140, 268, 284
PM0799	St. Botolph Club, Boston, Massachusetts	1897	140, 268, 288
PM1501	American Historical Paintings by Howard Pyle	September, 1900	100
PM1511	Lady Washington's Arrival at Headquarters, Cambridge	1900	334-335
MBPI0719	**The Escape of Arnold**		**445**
PM0155	General Washington	July, 1896	43
PM0738	George Washington	1897	155
PM0798	The Drexel Institute, Philadelphia, Pennsylvania	1897	8, 140, 268, 284
PM0799	St. Botolph Club, Boston, Massachusetts	1897	140, 268, 288
PM1501	American Historical Paintings by Howard Pyle	September, 1900	100
PM1513	The Escape of Arnold	1900	334, 336
PM1211	Howard Pyle, NA, Illustrator, Painter	January, 1912	97
PM1534	Memorable Events in American History	March 29, 1914	125
MBPI0720	**Carpenter's Hall, Philadelphia**		**445**

PM0155	General Washington	July, 1896	43
PM0738	George Washington	1897	155
PM0761	Harper's Encyclopaedia of United States History	1902	158
PM0954	Harper's Encyclopaedia of United States History from 458 A.D. to 1915	1915	161
PM0795	A History of the American People	1918	166, 170, 273
MBPI0721	**Washington in the Garden at Mount Vernon**		**446**
PM0156	First in Peace	September, 1896	43
PM1126	The Real Washington	December, 1896	7
PM0738	George Washington	1897	155
PM0798	The Drexel Institute, Philadelphia, Pennsylvania	1897	8, 140, 268, 284
PM0799	St. Botolph Club, Boston, Massachusetts	1897	140, 268, 288
PM1592	A Catalogue of Drawings	1897	140, 284
PM1593	A Catalogue of Illustrations	1897	140, 288
PM1501	American Historical Paintings by Howard Pyle	September, 1900	100
PM1516	Washington in the Garden at Mount Vernon	1900	334, 336
PM1402	Art Exhibit Catalogue	1903	270
PM1421	Washington in his Garden at Mount Vernon	1903	339
MBPI0722	**Headpiece with title for First in Peace**		**446**
PM0156	First in Peace	September, 1896	43
PM1126	The Real Washington	December, 1896	7
PM0738	George Washington	1897	155
PM0798	The Drexel Institute, Philadelphia, Pennsylvania	1897	8, 140, 268, 284
PM0799	St. Botolph Club, Boston, Massachusetts	1897	140, 268, 288
PM1534	Memorable Events in American History	March 29, 1914	125
MBPI0723	**Washington bringing his Mother into the Ballroom, Fredericksburg**		**446**
PM0156	First in Peace	September, 1896	43
PM0738	George Washington	1897	155
PM0798	The Drexel Institute, Philadelphia, Pennsylvania	1897	8, 140, 268, 284
PM0799	St. Botolph Club, Boston, Massachusetts	1897	140, 268, 288
PM1501	American Historical Paintings by Howard Pyle	September, 1900	100
PM1515	Washington bringing his Mother into the Ballroom, Fredericksburg	1900	334, 336
PM1594	Washington Bringing his Mother into the Ballroom, Fredericksburg	1900	333, 337
PM1534	Memorable Events in American History	March 29, 1914	125
MBPI0724	**Mustered out–A rest on the way home**		**446**
PM0156	First in Peace	September, 1896	43
PM1409	Mustered Out, A Rest On The Way Home	1896	330
PM0738	George Washington	1897	155
PM0798	The Drexel Institute, Philadelphia, Pennsylvania	1897	8, 140, 268, 284
PM0799	St. Botolph Club, Boston, Massachusetts	1897	140, 268, 288
PM1501	American Historical Paintings by Howard Pyle	September, 1900	100
PM1514	Mustered out–A rest on the way home	1900	334, 336
MBPI0725	**Tailpiece for First in Peace**		**446**
PM0156	First in Peace	September, 1896	43
PM0738	George Washington	1897	155
PM0798	The Drexel Institute, Philadelphia, Pennsylvania	1897	8, 140, 268, 284
PM0799	St. Botolph Club, Boston, Massachusetts	1897	140, 268, 288
PM1534	Memorable Events in American History	March 29, 1914	125
MBPI0726	**Washington and Nelly Custis**		**446**
PM0157	The First President of the United States	November, 1896	43
PM0738	George Washington	1897	155
PM0798	The Drexel Institute, Philadelphia, Pennsylvania	1897	8, 140, 268, 284
PM0799	St. Botolph Club, Boston, Massachusetts	1897	140, 268, 288
PM1501	American Historical Paintings by Howard Pyle	September, 1900	100
PM1518	Washington and Nelly Custis	1900	334, 337
PM0867	Howard Pyle–An Appreciation	November 18, 1911	74
PM1534	Memorable Events in American History	March 29, 1914	125
MBPI0727	**Headpiece with title for The First President of the United States**		**446**
PM0157	The First President of the United States	November, 1896	43
PM0738	George Washington	1897	155
PM0798	The Drexel Institute, Philadelphia, Pennsylvania	1897	8, 140, 268, 284

PM0799	St. Botolph Club, Boston, Massachusetts	1897	140, 268, 288
MBPI0728	**Thompson, the Clerk of Congress, announcing to Washington, at Mount Vernon, his election to the Presidency**		**446**
PM0157	The First President of the United States	November, 1896	43
PM0738	George Washington	1897	155
PM0798	The Drexel Institute, Philadelphia, Pennsylvania	1897	8, 140, 268, 284
PM0799	St. Botolph Club, Boston, Massachusetts	1897	140, 268, 288
PM1501	American Historical Paintings by Howard Pyle	September, 1900	100
PM1517	Thompson, the Clerk of Congress, announcing to Washington, at Mount Vernon, his election to the Presidency	1900	334, 336
PM0759	A History of the American People	1902	165
PM0761	Harper's Encyclopaedia of United States History	1902	158
PM1534	Memorable Events in American History	March 29, 1914	125
PM0954	Harper's Encyclopaedia of United States History from 458 A.D. to 1915	1915	161
PM0795	A History of the American People	1918	166, 170, 273
MBPI0729	**The Death of Washington**		**446**
PM0157	The First President of the United States	November, 1896	43
PM0738	George Washington	1897	155
PM0798	The Drexel Institute, Philadelphia, Pennsylvania	1897	8, 140, 268, 284
PM0799	St. Botolph Club, Boston, Massachusetts	1897	140, 268, 288
PM1501	American Historical Paintings by Howard Pyle	September, 1900	100
PM1519	The Death of Washington	1900	334, 337
PM1534	Memorable Events in American History	March 29, 1914	125
MBPI0730	**Tailpiece for The First President of the United States**		**446**
PM0157	The First President of the United States	November, 1896	43
PM0738	George Washington	1897	155
PM0798	The Drexel Institute, Philadelphia, Pennsylvania	1897	8, 140, 268, 284
PM0799	St. Botolph Club, Boston, Massachusetts	1897	140, 268, 288
MBPI0731	**Christmas 1896, Cover Design**		**446**
PM0158	Cover Design	December, 1896	43
MBPI0732	**Headpiece with title for The Romance of an Ambrotype**		**446**
PM0159	The Romance of an Ambrotype	December, 1896	44
PM0798	The Drexel Institute, Philadelphia, Pennsylvania	1897	8, 140, 268, 284
PM0799	St. Botolph Club, Boston, Massachusetts	1897	140, 268, 288
MBPI0733	**Illustrated initial T for The Romance of an Ambrotype**		**446**
PM0159	The Romance of an Ambrotype	December, 1896	44
MBPI0734	**Vignette for The Romance of an Ambrotype**		**446**
PM0159	The Romance of an Ambrotype	December, 1896	44
PM0798	The Drexel Institute, Philadelphia, Pennsylvania	1897	8, 140, 268, 284
PM0799	St. Botolph Club, Boston, Massachusetts	1897	140, 268, 288
MBPI0735	**Vignette for The Romance of an Ambrotype**		**446**
PM0159	The Romance of an Ambrotype	December, 1896	44
PM0798	The Drexel Institute, Philadelphia, Pennsylvania	1897	8, 140, 268, 284
PM0799	St. Botolph Club, Boston, Massachusetts	1897	140, 268, 288
MBPI0736	**Vignette for The Romance of an Ambrotype**		**446**
PM0159	The Romance of an Ambrotype	December, 1896	44
PM0798	The Drexel Institute, Philadelphia, Pennsylvania	1897	8, 140, 268, 284
PM0799	St. Botolph Club, Boston, Massachusetts	1897	140, 268, 288
MBPI0737	**Vignette for The Romance of an Ambrotype**		**447**
PM0159	The Romance of an Ambrotype	December, 1896	44
PM0798	The Drexel Institute, Philadelphia, Pennsylvania	1897	8, 140, 268, 284
PM0799	St. Botolph Club, Boston, Massachusetts	1897	140, 268, 288
MBPI0738	**Vignette for The Romance of an Ambrotype**		**447**
PM0159	The Romance of an Ambrotype	December, 1896	44
PM0798	The Drexel Institute, Philadelphia, Pennsylvania	1897	8, 140, 268, 284
PM0799	St. Botolph Club, Boston, Massachusetts	1897	140, 268, 288
MBPI0739	**Vignette for The Romance of an Ambrotype**		**447**
PM0159	The Romance of an Ambrotype	December, 1896	44
PM0798	The Drexel Institute, Philadelphia, Pennsylvania	1897	8, 140, 268, 284
PM0799	St. Botolph Club, Boston, Massachusetts	1897	140, 268, 288

MBPI0740	**Vignette for The Romance of an Ambrotype**		**447**
PM0159	The Romance of an Ambrotype	December, 1896	44
PM0798	The Drexel Institute, Philadelphia, Pennsylvania	1897	8, 140, 268, 284
PM0799	St. Botolph Club, Boston, Massachusetts	1897	140, 268, 288
MBPI0741	**Vignette for The Romance of an Ambrotype**		**447**
PM0159	The Romance of an Ambrotype	December, 1896	44
PM0798	The Drexel Institute, Philadelphia, Pennsylvania	1897	8, 140, 268, 284
PM0799	St. Botolph Club, Boston, Massachusetts	1897	140, 268, 288
MBPI0742	**Vignette for The Romance of an Ambrotype**		**447**
PM0159	The Romance of an Ambrotype	December, 1896	44
PM0798	The Drexel Institute, Philadelphia, Pennsylvania	1897	8, 140, 268, 284
PM0799	St. Botolph Club, Boston, Massachusetts	1897	140, 268, 288
MBPI0743	**Vignette for The Romance of an Ambrotype**		**447**
PM0159	The Romance of an Ambrotype	December, 1896	44
PM0798	The Drexel Institute, Philadelphia, Pennsylvania	1897	8, 140, 268, 284
PM0799	St. Botolph Club, Boston, Massachusetts	1897	140, 268, 288
MBPI0744	**Vignette for The Romance of an Ambrotype**		**447**
PM0159	The Romance of an Ambrotype	December, 1896	44
PM0798	The Drexel Institute, Philadelphia, Pennsylvania	1897	8, 140, 268, 284
PM0799	St. Botolph Club, Boston, Massachusetts	1897	140, 268, 288
MBPI0745	**Tailpiece for The Romance of an Ambrotype**		**447**
PM0159	The Romance of an Ambrotype	December, 1896	44
PM0798	The Drexel Institute, Philadelphia, Pennsylvania	1897	8, 140, 268, 284
PM0799	St. Botolph Club, Boston, Massachusetts	1897	140, 268, 288
MBPI0746	**The Assembly Ball**		**447**
PM0160	The Assembly Ball	February, 1897	44
MBPI0747	**Headpiece with title for The Assembly Ball**		**447**
PM0160	The Assembly Ball	February, 1897	44
MBPI0748	**Illustrated initial I for The Assembly Ball**		**447**
PM0160	The Assembly Ball	February, 1897	44
MBPI0749	**Tailpiece for The Assembly Ball**		**447**
PM0160	The Assembly Ball	February, 1897	44
MBPI0750	**Love and Death**		**447**
PM0161	Love and Death	March, 1897	44
MBPI0751	**Headpiece for Love and Death**		**447**
PM0161	Love and Death	March, 1897	44
MBPI0752	**Tailpiece for Love and Death**		**447**
PM0161	Love and Death	March, 1897	44
MBPI0753	**A Banquet to Genet**		**448**
PM0162	Washington and the French Craze of '93	April, 1897	44
PM0759	A History of the American People	1902	165
PM0795	A History of the American People	1918	166, 170, 273
MBPI0754	**Headpiece, Arrival of Genet at Gray's Ferry**		**448**
PM0162	Washington and the French Craze of '93	April, 1897	44
MBPI0755	**The News of the Execution of Louis XVI**		**448**
PM0162	Washington and the French Craze of '93	April, 1897	44
MBPI0756	**Citizen Genet formally presented to Washington**		**448**
PM0162	Washington and the French Craze of '93	April, 1897	44
PM0759	A History of the American People	1902	165
PM0795	A History of the American People	1918	166, 170, 273
MBPI0757	**Tailpiece for Washington and the French Craze of '93**		**448**
PM0162	Washington and the French Craze of '93	April, 1897	44
PM1534	Memorable Events in American History	March 29, 1914	125
MBPI0758	**Decoration with title for Old Chester Tales**		**448**
PM0163	Old Chester Tales. I	April, 1898	44
PM0164	Old Chester Tales. II	May, 1898	45
PM0165	Old Chester Tales. III	June, 1898	45
PM0166	Old Chester Tales. IV	July, 1898	45
PM0167	Old Chester Tales. V	August, 1898	45
PM0168	Old Chester Tales. VI	September, 1898	45

PM0169	Old Chester Tales. VII	October, 1898	45
PM0170	Old Chester Tales. VIII	November, 1898	45
PM0171	Old Chester Tales. IX	December, 1898	45
MBPI0759	**Headpiece for "The Promises of Dorthea"**		**448**
PM0163	Old Chester Tales. I	April, 1898	44
PM0746	Old Chester Tales	1898	192
PM1392	Advertisements	December, 1898	46
PM1225	Notice of Old Chester Tales	January, 1899	99
PM1003	Dr. Lavendar's People	1903	149
MBPI0760	**"She seemed 'a tall white lily,' he said"**		**448**
PM0163	Old Chester Tales. I	April, 1898	44
PM0746	Old Chester Tales	1898	192
MBPI0761	**"'Change it? My name?' she said"**		**448**
PM0164	Old Chester Tales. II	May, 1898	45
PM0746	Old Chester Tales	1898	192
PM0747	Good for the Soul	1899	157
PM1173	Howard Pyle	January, 1912	61
MBPI0762	**Headpiece for "Good For the Soul"**		**448**
PM0164	Old Chester Tales. II	May, 1898	45
PM0746	Old Chester Tales	1898	192
PM0867	Howard Pyle–An Appreciation	November 18, 1911	74
PM0792	Around Old Chester	1915	131
MBPI0763	**Headpiece for "Miss Maria"**		**448**
PM0165	Old Chester Tales. III	June, 1898	45
MBPI0764	**"'And who's going to support 'em?' demanded Mrs. Barkley"**		**448**
PM0165	Old Chester Tales. III	June, 1898	45
PM0746	Old Chester Tales	1898	192
MBPI0765	**"Judge Morrison read these harmless jingles, chuckling and sneering"**		**448**
PM0166	Old Chester Tales. IV	July, 1898	45
PM0792	Around Old Chester	1915	131
MBPI0766	**Headpiece for "The Thief"**		**448**
PM0166	Old Chester Tales. IV	July, 1898	45
PM0746	Old Chester Tales	1898	192
MBPI0767	**Headpiece for "The Child's Mother"**		**448**
PM0167	Old Chester Tales. V	August, 1898	45
PM0746	Old Chester Tales	1898	192
MBPI0768	**"Mary turned white, then she dropped down at his feet"**		**448**
PM0167	Old Chester Tales. V	August, 1898	45
PM0746	Old Chester Tales	1898	192
MBPI0769	**Headpiece for "Justice and the Judge"**		**449**
PM0168	Old Chester Tales. VI	September, 1898	45
PM0746	Old Chester Tales	1898	192
PM1129	Book Reviews	December, 1898	8
MBPI0770	**"'So you're hanging the locusts?' inquired the Judge, contemptuously"**		**449**
PM0168	Old Chester Tales. VI	September, 1898	45
PM0746	Old Chester Tales	1898	192
MBPI0771	**Headpiece for "Where the Laborers Are Few"**		**449**
PM0169	Old Chester Tales. VII	October, 1898	45
PM0746	Old Chester Tales	1898	192
MBPI0772	**"I had enemies in my line"**		**449**
PM0169	Old Chester Tales. VII	October, 1898	45
PM0746	Old Chester Tales	1898	192
MBPI0773	**Headpiece for "Sally"**		**449**
PM0170	Old Chester Tales. VIII	November, 1898	45
PM0746	Old Chester Tales	1898	192
MBPI0774	**"They told each other about it"**		**449**
PM0170	Old Chester Tales. VIII	November, 1898	45
PM0746	Old Chester Tales	1898	192
MBPI0775	**Headpiece for "The Unexpectedness of Mr. Horace Shields"**		**449**
PM0171	Old Chester Tales. IX	December, 1898	45

PM0746	Old Chester Tales	1898	192
PM0931	Great American Illustrators: Howard Pyle, Illustrator	September, 1907	99, 106
MBPI0776	**"Mr. Horace looked at her with instant sympathy"**		**449**
PM0171	Old Chester Tales. IX	December, 1898	45
PM0746	Old Chester Tales	1898	192
PM1129	Book Reviews	December, 1898	8
MBPI0777	**"And you shall not hinder me"**		**449**
PM0172	Old Captain	December, 1898	45
PM1455	The New Century Club, Wilmington, Delaware	1899	294
PM1482	The Wilmington Society of the Fine Arts, Wilmington, Delaware	1917	316
MBPI0778	**Headpiece for Old Captain**		**449**
PM0172	Old Captain	December, 1898	45
PM1464	Art Institute of Chicago, Chicago, Illinois	1903	130, 297
PM0867	Howard Pyle–An Appreciation	November 18, 1911	74
PM1096	Howard Pyle, Biographical Sketches of American Artists	October, 1915	2
MBPI0779	**Illustration for Old Captain**		**449**
PM0172	Old Captain	December, 1898	45
MBPI0780	**Illustration for Old Captain**		**449**
PM0172	Old Captain	December, 1898	45
PM0931	Great American Illustrators: Howard Pyle, Illustrator	September, 1907	99, 106
PM0867	Howard Pyle–An Appreciation	November 18, 1911	74
MBPI0781	**Illustration for Old Captain**		**449**
PM0172	Old Captain	December, 1898	45
MBPI0782	**Illustration for Old Captain**		**449**
PM0172	Old Captain	December, 1898	45
PM1464	Art Institute of Chicago, Chicago, Illinois	1903	130, 297
MBPI0783	**Illustration for Old Captain**		**449**
PM0172	Old Captain	December, 1898	45
MBPI0784	**Illustration for Old Captain**		**449**
PM0172	Old Captain	December, 1898	45
MBPI0785	**Illustration for Old Captain**		**450**
PM0172	Old Captain	December, 1898	45
MBPI0786	**Illustration for Old Captain**		**450**
PM0172	Old Captain	December, 1898	45
MBPI0787	**Tailpiece for Old Captain**		**450**
PM0172	Old Captain	December, 1898	45
MBPI0788	**Frontispiece for The Body to the Soul**		**450**
PM0173	The Body to the Soul	August, 1899	46
PM1414	The Body Piping to the Soul	1900	333-334
PM1460	Pan-American Exposition, Buffalo, New York	1901	296
PM1464	Art Institute of Chicago, Chicago, Illinois	1903	130, 297
MBPI0789	**Headpiece with title for The Body to the Soul**		**450**
PM0173	The Body to the Soul	August, 1899	46
MBPI0790	**Marginal decoration for The Body to the Soul**		**450**
PM0173	The Body to the Soul	August, 1899	46
PM1415	Piping a Roundelay	1900	333-334
PM1460	Pan-American Exposition, Buffalo, New York	1901	296
MBPI0791	**Decoration for The Body to the Soul**		**450**
PM0173	The Body to the Soul	August, 1899	46
MBPI0792	**Marginal decoration for The Body to the Soul**		**450**
PM0173	The Body to the Soul	August, 1899	46
PM1460	Pan-American Exposition, Buffalo, New York	1901	296
MBPI0793	**Marginal decoration for The Body to the Soul**		**450**
PM0173	The Body to the Soul	August, 1899	46
PM1416	An Earth Child	1900	333-334
PM1460	Pan-American Exposition, Buffalo, New York	1901	296
MBPI0794	**Tailpiece for The Body to the Soul**		**450**
PM0173	The Body to the Soul	August, 1899	46
MBPI0795	**Headpiece with title with illustrated initial T for A Puppet of Fate**		**450**
PM0174	A Puppet of Fate	December, 1899	46

PM1457	Howard Pyle's Studio, Wilmington, Delaware	1900	295
MBPI0796	**Vignette for A Puppet of Fate**		**450**
PM0174	A Puppet of Fate	December, 1899	46
PM1457	Howard Pyle's Studio, Wilmington, Delaware	1900	295
MBPI0797	**Chapter heading with illustrated initial N for A Puppet of Fate**		**450**
PM0174	A Puppet of Fate	December, 1899	46
PM1457	Howard Pyle's Studio, Wilmington, Delaware	1900	295
MBPI0798	**Vignette for A Puppet of Fate**		**450**
PM0174	A Puppet of Fate	December, 1899	46
PM1457	Howard Pyle's Studio, Wilmington, Delaware	1900	295
MBPI0799	**Vignette for A Puppet of Fate**		**450**
PM0174	A Puppet of Fate	December, 1899	46
PM1457	Howard Pyle's Studio, Wilmington, Delaware	1900	295
MBPI0800	**Vignette for A Puppet of Fate**		**450**
PM0174	A Puppet of Fate	December, 1899	46
PM1457	Howard Pyle's Studio, Wilmington, Delaware	1900	295
MBPI0801	**Vignette for A Puppet of Fate**		**451**
PM0174	A Puppet of Fate	December, 1899	46
PM1457	Howard Pyle's Studio, Wilmington, Delaware	1900	295
MBPI0802	**Chapter heading with illustrated initial F for A Puppet of Fate**		**451**
PM0174	A Puppet of Fate	December, 1899	46
PM1457	Howard Pyle's Studio, Wilmington, Delaware	1900	295
MBPI0803	**Vignette for A Puppet of Fate**		**451**
PM0174	A Puppet of Fate	December, 1899	46
PM1457	Howard Pyle's Studio, Wilmington, Delaware	1900	295
MBPI0804	**Illustration for A Puppet of Fate**		**451**
PM0174	A Puppet of Fate	December, 1899	46
PM1457	Howard Pyle's Studio, Wilmington, Delaware	1900	295
PM1464	Art Institute of Chicago, Chicago, Illinois	1903	130, 297
MBPI0805	**Chapter heading with illustrated initial A for A Puppet of Fate**		**451**
PM0174	A Puppet of Fate	December, 1899	46
PM1457	Howard Pyle's Studio, Wilmington, Delaware	1900	295
MBPI0806	**Vignette for A Puppet of Fate**		**451**
PM0174	A Puppet of Fate	December, 1899	46
PM1457	Howard Pyle's Studio, Wilmington, Delaware	1900	295
MBPI0807	**Headpiece with title for A Prelude**		**451**
PM0175	A Prelude	April, 1900	46
MBPI0808	**Illustrated initial T for A Prelude**		**451**
PM0175	A Prelude	April, 1900	46
MBPI0809	**In Springtime**		**451**
PM0175	A Prelude	April, 1900	46
PM1456	Art Students League, New York, New York	1900	295
MBPI0810	**Tailpiece for A Prelude**		**451**
PM0175	A Prelude	April, 1900	46
MBPI0811	**Headpiece for The Yellow of the Leaf**		**451**
PM0177	The Yellow of the Leaf	November, 1900	47
MBPI0812	**Title with decorations for The Yellow of the Leaf**		**451**
PM0177	The Yellow of the Leaf	November, 1900	47
MBPI0813	**Illustrated initial T for The Yellow of the Leaf**		**451**
PM0177	The Yellow of the Leaf	November, 1900	47
MBPI0814	**The falling leaf is at the door; The Autumn Wind is on the Hill**		**451**
PM0177	The Yellow of the Leaf	November, 1900	47
PM1460	Pan-American Exposition, Buffalo, New York	1901	296
PM1461	Cincinnati Art Museum, Cincinnati, Ohio	1902	297
PM1464	Art Institute of Chicago, Chicago, Illinois	1903	130, 297
PM1470	St. Botolph Club, Boston, Massachusetts	1906	303
PM0931	Great American Illustrators: Howard Pyle, Illustrator	September, 1907	99, 106
MBPI0815	**Tailpiece for The Yellow of the Leaf**		**451**
PM0177	The Yellow of the Leaf	November, 1900	47
PM1565	Howard Pyle, Author-Illustrator 1853-1911	February, 1912	2

PM1479	Hotel Dupont, Wilmington, Delaware	1912	141, 310
MBPI0816	**Truth Leaves the Fairies' Wonderland**		**451**
PM0178	The Pilgrimage of Truth	December, 1900	47
PM1460	Pan-American Exposition, Buffalo, New York	1901	296
PM1461	Cincinnati Art Museum, Cincinnati, Ohio	1902	297
PM1464	Art Institute of Chicago, Chicago, Illinois	1903	130, 297
PM1470	St. Botolph Club, Boston, Massachusetts	1906	303
PM1473	Macbeth Gallery, New York	1908	307
PM1479	Hotel Dupont, Wilmington, Delaware	1912	141, 310
MBPI0817	**Truth before the King**		**452**
PM0178	The Pilgrimage of Truth	December, 1900	47
PM1460	Pan-American Exposition, Buffalo, New York	1901	296
PM1461	Cincinnati Art Museum, Cincinnati, Ohio	1902	297
PM1464	Art Institute of Chicago, Chicago, Illinois	1903	130, 297
PM1470	St. Botolph Club, Boston, Massachusetts	1906	303
PM1473	Macbeth Gallery, New York	1908	307
PM1479	Hotel Dupont, Wilmington, Delaware	1912	141, 310
MBPI0818	**Truth in the Temple**		**452**
PM0178	The Pilgrimage of Truth	December, 1900	47
PM1460	Pan-American Exposition, Buffalo, New York	1901	296
PM1461	Cincinnati Art Museum, Cincinnati, Ohio	1902	297
PM1464	Art Institute of Chicago, Chicago, Illinois	1903	130, 297
PM1470	St. Botolph Club, Boston, Massachusetts	1906	303
PM1473	Macbeth Gallery, New York	1908	307
PM1479	Hotel Dupont, Wilmington, Delaware	1912	141, 310
MBPI0819	**Truth before the Seer**		**452**
PM0178	The Pilgrimage of Truth	December, 1900	47
PM1460	Pan-American Exposition, Buffalo, New York	1901	296
PM1461	Cincinnati Art Museum, Cincinnati, Ohio	1902	297
PM1464	Art Institute of Chicago, Chicago, Illinois	1903	130, 297
PM1470	St. Botolph Club, Boston, Massachusetts	1906	303
PM1473	Macbeth Gallery, New York	1908	307
PM1479	Hotel Dupont, Wilmington, Delaware	1912	141, 310
MBPI0820	**Truth Went on Her Way Alone**		**452**
PM0178	The Pilgrimage of Truth	December, 1900	47
PM1460	Pan-American Exposition, Buffalo, New York	1901	296
PM1461	Cincinnati Art Museum, Cincinnati, Ohio	1902	297
PM1464	Art Institute of Chicago, Chicago, Illinois	1903	130, 297
PM1470	St. Botolph Club, Boston, Massachusetts	1906	303
PM1473	Macbeth Gallery, New York	1908	307
PM1479	Hotel Dupont, Wilmington, Delaware	1912	141, 310
MBPI0821	**Truth in the Fool's Lodge**		**452**
PM0178	The Pilgrimage of Truth	December, 1900	47
PM1460	Pan-American Exposition, Buffalo, New York	1901	296
PM1461	Cincinnati Art Museum, Cincinnati, Ohio	1902	297
PM1464	Art Institute of Chicago, Chicago, Illinois	1903	130, 297
PM1470	St. Botolph Club, Boston, Massachusetts	1906	303
PM1473	Macbeth Gallery, New York	1908	307
PM1479	Hotel Dupont, Wilmington, Delaware	1912	141, 310
MBPI0822	**Headpiece with title for The Pilgrimage of Truth**		**452**
PM0178	The Pilgrimage of Truth	December, 1900	47
MBPI0823	**Illustrated initial F for The Pilgrimage of Truth**		**452**
PM0178	The Pilgrimage of Truth	December, 1900	47
MBPI0824	**Tailpiece for The Pilgrimage of Truth**		**452**
PM0178	The Pilgrimage of Truth	December, 1900	47
MBPI0825	**Illustrated initial T for The Pilgrimage of Truth**		**452**
PM0178	The Pilgrimage of Truth	December, 1900	47
MBPI0826	**Tailpiece for The Pilgrimage of Truth**		**452**
PM0178	The Pilgrimage of Truth	December, 1900	47
MBPI0827	**Illustrated initial T for The Pilgrimage of Truth**		**452**

PM0178	The Pilgrimage of Truth	December, 1900	47
MBPI0828	**Headband for The Pilgrimage of Truth**		**452**
PM0178	The Pilgrimage of Truth	December, 1900	47
MBPI0829	**Headband for The Pilgrimage of Truth**		**452**
PM0178	The Pilgrimage of Truth	December, 1900	47
MBPI0830	**Illustrated initial B for The Pilgrimage of Truth**		**452**
PM0178	The Pilgrimage of Truth	December, 1900	47
MBPI0831	**Illustrated initial O for The Pilgrimage of Truth**		**452**
PM0178	The Pilgrimage of Truth	December, 1900	47
MBPI0832	**Illustrated initial H for The Pilgrimage of Truth**		**452**
PM0178	The Pilgrimage of Truth	December, 1900	47
MBPI0833	**Headpiece with decoration and title for Colonies and Nation**		**453**
PM0179	Colonies and Nation	January, 1901	48
PM0759	A History of the American People	1902	165
PM1535	Letters & Lettering: A Treatise with 200 Examples	1902	176
PM0795	A History of the American People	1918	166, 170, 273
MBPI0834	**Landing negroes at Jamestown from Dutch man-of-war, 1619**		**453**
PM1393	Harper's Magazine Advertiser	December, 1900	48
PM0179	Colonies and Nation	January, 1901	48
PM0759	A History of the American People	1902	165
PM0761	Harper's Encyclopaedia of United States History	1902	158
PM1464	Art Institute of Chicago, Chicago, Illinois	1903	130, 297
PM1466	Kellogg Public Library, Green Bay, Wisconsin	1904	301
PM0954	Harper's Encyclopaedia of United States History from 458 A.D. to 1915	1915	161
PM0795	A History of the American People	1918	166, 170, 273
PM1556	A History of The American People	1918	273
MBPI0835	**Anne Hutchinson preaching in her house in Boston**		**453**
PM0180	Colonies and Nation	February, 1901	48
PM0759	A History of the American People	1902	165
PM1464	Art Institute of Chicago, Chicago, Illinois	1903	130, 297
PM1466	Kellogg Public Library, Green Bay, Wisconsin	1904	301
PM0795	A History of the American People	1918	166, 170, 273
MBPI0836	**Arrival of Stuyvesant in New Amsterdam**		**453**
PM0180	Colonies and Nation	February, 1901	48
PM0759	A History of the American People	1902	165
PM1464	Art Institute of Chicago, Chicago, Illinois	1903	130, 297
PM1466	Kellogg Public Library, Green Bay, Wisconsin	1904	301
PM0954	Harper's Encyclopaedia of United States History from 458 A.D. to 1915	1915	161
PM0795	A History of the American People	1918	166, 170, 273
MBPI0837	**The Burning of Jamestown**		**453**
PM0181	Colonies and Nation	March, 1901	48
PM0759	A History of the American People	1902	165
PM0761	Harper's Encyclopaedia of United States History	1902	158
PM1464	Art Institute of Chicago, Chicago, Illinois	1903	130, 297
PM1466	Kellogg Public Library, Green Bay, Wisconsin	1904	301
PM0954	Harper's Encyclopaedia of United States History from 458 A.D. to 1915	1915	161
PM0795	A History of the American People	1918	166, 170, 273
PM1302	If You Could Talk To President Wilson!	1918	170
PM1556	A History of The American People	1918	273
PM1220	Advertisement: History of the American People	March 29, 1919	99
MBPI0838	**Ships loading in Albemarle Sound**		**453**
PM0181	Colonies and Nation	March, 1901	48
PM0759	A History of the American People	1902	165
PM1464	Art Institute of Chicago, Chicago, Illinois	1903	130, 297
PM1466	Kellogg Public Library, Green Bay, Wisconsin	1904	301
PM0795	A History of the American People	1918	166, 170, 273
MBPI0839	**On the War-Path**		**453**
PM0181	Colonies and Nation	March, 1901	48
PM0759	A History of the American People	1902	165
PM0761	Harper's Encyclopaedia of United States History	1902	158

PM1464	Art Institute of Chicago, Chicago, Illinois	1903	130, 297
PM1466	Kellogg Public Library, Green Bay, Wisconsin	1904	301
PM0999	Decisive Battles of America	1909	145
PM0795	A History of the American People	1918	166, 170, 273
PM1556	A History of The American People	1918	273
MBPI0840	**A Pennsylvania Cave-Dwelling XVIIth Century**		**453**
PM0182	Colonies and Nation	April, 1901	48
PM0759	A History of the American People	1902	165
PM1464	Art Institute of Chicago, Chicago, Illinois	1903	130, 297
PM1466	Kellogg Public Library, Green Bay, Wisconsin	1904	301
PM0795	A History of the American People	1918	166, 170, 273
MBPI0841	**An interview between Sir Edmund Andros and James Blair**		**453**
PM0182	Colonies and Nation	April, 1901	48
PM0759	A History of the American People	1902	165
PM1464	Art Institute of Chicago, Chicago, Illinois	1903	130, 297
PM1466	Kellogg Public Library, Green Bay, Wisconsin	1904	301
PM0795	A History of the American People	1918	166, 170, 273
MBPI0842	**Phips recovering the sunken treasure**		**453**
PM0182	Colonies and Nation	April, 1901	48
PM0759	A History of the American People	1902	165
PM1464	Art Institute of Chicago, Chicago, Illinois	1903	130, 297
PM1466	Kellogg Public Library, Green Bay, Wisconsin	1904	301
PM0795	A History of the American People	1918	166, 170, 273
MBPI0843	**Sloughter signing the death warrant of Leisler**		**453**
PM0182	Colonies and Nation	April, 1901	48
PM0759	A History of the American People	1902	165
PM1464	Art Institute of Chicago, Chicago, Illinois	1903	130, 297
PM1466	Kellogg Public Library, Green Bay, Wisconsin	1904	301
PM0795	A History of the American People	1918	166, 170, 273
PM1556	A History of The American People	1918	273
MBPI0844	**Colonel Rhett and Pirate Stede Bonnet**		**453**
PM0183	Colonies and Nation	May, 1901	48
PM0759	A History of the American People	1902	165
PM1464	Art Institute of Chicago, Chicago, Illinois	1903	130, 297
PM1466	Kellogg Public Library, Green Bay, Wisconsin	1904	301
PM0795	A History of the American People	1918	166, 170, 273
PM1556	A History of The American People	1918	273
MBPI0845	**The Capitulation of Louisbourg**		**453**
PM0184	Colonies and Nation	June, 1901	48
PM0759	A History of the American People	1902	165
PM1464	Art Institute of Chicago, Chicago, Illinois	1903	130, 297
PM1466	Kellogg Public Library, Green Bay, Wisconsin	1904	301
PM0795	A History of the American People	1918	166, 170, 273
MBPI0846	**After the Massacre; Samuel Adams demanding of Governor Hutchinson the instant withdrawal of British Troops**		**453**
PM0185	Colonies and Nation	August, 1901	48
PM0759	A History of the American People	1902	165
PM0795	A History of the American People	1918	166, 170, 273
PM1556	A History of The American People	1918	273
MBPI0847	**Burning of the "Gaspee"**		**453**
PM0185	Colonies and Nation	August, 1901	48
PM0759	A History of the American People	1902	165
PM1464	Art Institute of Chicago, Chicago, Illinois	1903	130, 297
PM1466	Kellogg Public Library, Green Bay, Wisconsin	1904	301
PM0795	A History of the American People	1918	166, 170, 273
MBPI0848	**The Boston Tea Party**		**453**
PM0185	Colonies and Nation	August, 1901	48
PM0759	A History of the American People	1902	165
PM1356	A List of Holiday Books	1902	269
PM1464	Art Institute of Chicago, Chicago, Illinois	1903	130, 297

PM1466	Kellogg Public Library, Green Bay, Wisconsin	1904	301
PM0795	A History of the American People	1918	166, 170, 273
MBPI0849	**Viewing the Battle of Bunker's Hill**		**454**
PM0186	Colonies and Nation	October, 1901	49
PM0759	A History of the American People	1902	165
PM0761	Harper's Encyclopaedia of United States History	1902	158
PM1464	Art Institute of Chicago, Chicago, Illinois	1903	130, 297
PM1051	Poems for Young Americans from Will Carleton	1906	203
PM0931	Great American Illustrators: Howard Pyle, Illustrator	September, 1907	99, 106
PM0999	Decisive Battles of America	1909	145
PM1073	The Story of New England	1910	223
PM1173	Howard Pyle	January, 1912	61
PM0982	American Graphic Art	1912	130
PM1096	Howard Pyle, Biographical Sketches of American Artists	October, 1915	2
PM0954	Harper's Encyclopaedia of United States History from 458 A.D. to 1915	1915	161
PM0795	A History of the American People	1918	166, 170, 273
PM1556	A History of The American People	1918	273
PM1304	Crown Ducal Plate	1920	277
MBPI0850	**Fight between "Bonhomme Richard" and "Serapis"**		**454**
PM0186	Colonies and Nation	October, 1901	49
PM0759	A History of the American People	1902	165
PM1464	Art Institute of Chicago, Chicago, Illinois	1903	130, 297
PM1466	Kellogg Public Library, Green Bay, Wisconsin	1904	301
PM0795	A History of the American People	1918	166, 170, 273
MBPI0851	**Washington and Rochambeau before the trenches at Yorktown**		**454**
PM0187	Colonies and Nation	November, 1901	49
PM0759	A History of the American People	1902	165
PM1464	Art Institute of Chicago, Chicago, Illinois	1903	130, 297
PM1466	Kellogg Public Library, Green Bay, Wisconsin	1904	301
PM0954	Harper's Encyclopaedia of United States History from 458 A.D. to 1915	1915	161
PM0795	A History of the American People	1918	166, 170, 273
MBPI0852	**Tory Refugees on their way to Canada**		**454**
PM0188	Colonies and Nation	December, 1901	49
PM0759	A History of the American People	1902	165
PM0761	Harper's Encyclopaedia of United States History	1902	158
PM1464	Art Institute of Chicago, Chicago, Illinois	1903	130, 297
PM0795	A History of the American People	1918	166, 170, 273
MBPI0853	**A Political Discussion**		**454**
PM0188	Colonies and Nation	December, 1901	49
PM0759	A History of the American People	1902	165
PM1464	Art Institute of Chicago, Chicago, Illinois	1903	130, 297
PM1466	Kellogg Public Library, Green Bay, Wisconsin	1904	301
PM0795	A History of the American People	1918	166, 170, 273
PM1556	A History of The American People	1918	273
MBPI0854	**A Dream of Young Summer**		**454**
PM0189	A Dream of Young Summer	June, 1901	48
MBPI0855	**Headpiece for King Custom**		**454**
PM0190	King Custom	October, 1901	49
MBPI0856	**Illustrated initial M for King Custom**		**454**
PM0190	King Custom	October, 1901	49
MBPI0857	**Marginal decoration for King Custom**		**454**
PM0190	King Custom	October, 1901	49
MBPI0858	**Vignette for King Custom**		**454**
PM0190	King Custom	October, 1901	49
MBPI0859	**My Lady of Brede**		**454**
PM0190	King Custom	October, 1901	49
MBPI0860	**Headpiece for Margaret of Cortona**		**454**
PM0191	Margaret of Cortona	November, 1901	49
MBPI0861	**The Sea Man**		**454**
PM0192	The Sea Man	December, 1901	49

MBPI0862	**Frontispiece for North Folk Legends of the Sea**		**454**
PM0193	North Folk Legends of the Sea	January, 1902	49
MBPI0863	**Decoration with title for North Folk Legends of the Sea**		**454**
PM0193	North Folk Legends of the Sea	January, 1902	49
MBPI0864	**Illustrated initial T for North Folk Legends of the Sea**		**454**
PM0193	North Folk Legends of the Sea	January, 1902	49
MBPI0865	**Decoration with title for North Folk Legends of the Sea**		**455**
PM0193	North Folk Legends of the Sea	January, 1902	49
MBPI0866	**The Fishing of Thor and Hymir**		**455**
PM0193	North Folk Legends of the Sea	January, 1902	49
PM1470	St. Botolph Club, Boston, Massachusetts	1906	303
PM1479	Hotel Dupont, Wilmington, Delaware	1912	141, 310
MBPI0867	**Headpiece for North Folk Legends of the Sea**		**455**
PM0193	North Folk Legends of the Sea	January, 1902	49
MBPI0868	**Title with decorations, The Fairy Morgana**		**455**
PM0193	North Folk Legends of the Sea	January, 1902	49
MBPI0869	**The Fairy Morgana**		**455**
PM0193	North Folk Legends of the Sea	January, 1902	49
PM1482	The Wilmington Society of the Fine Arts, Wilmington, Delaware	1917	316
MBPI0870	**Headpiece for North Folk Legends of the Sea**		**455**
PM0193	North Folk Legends of the Sea	January, 1902	49
MBPI0871	**Title with decorations, Saint Brendan's Island**		**455**
PM0193	North Folk Legends of the Sea	January, 1902	49
MBPI0872	**Saint Brendan**		**455**
PM0193	North Folk Legends of the Sea	January, 1902	49
PM1482	The Wilmington Society of the Fine Arts, Wilmington, Delaware	1917	316
MBPI0873	**Headpiece for North Folk Legends of the Sea**		**455**
PM0193	North Folk Legends of the Sea	January, 1902	49
MBPI0874	**Title with decorations, Mother Carey's Chickens**		**455**
PM0193	North Folk Legends of the Sea	January, 1902	49
MBPI0875	**Mother Carey**		**455**
PM0193	North Folk Legends of the Sea	January, 1902	49
MBPI0876	**Headpiece for North Folk Legends of the Sea**		**455**
PM0193	North Folk Legends of the Sea	January, 1902	49
MBPI0877	**Title with decorations, The Flying Dutchman**		**455**
PM0193	North Folk Legends of the Sea	January, 1902	49
PM1464	Art Institute of Chicago, Chicago, Illinois	1903	130, 297
PM1054	Practical Illustration	1920	203
MBPI0878	**Headpiece for The Voice**		**455**
PM0195	The Voice	September, 1902	50
MBPI0879	**An autumn field of which she had dreamed**		**455**
PM0195	The Voice	September, 1902	50
MBPI0880	**She cried out**		**455**
PM0195	The Voice	September, 1902	50
MBPI0881	**She felt her blood tingling in every vein**		**456**
PM0195	The Voice	September, 1902	50
MBPI0882	**Headpiece for The True Captain Kidd**		**456**
PM0196	The True Captain Kidd	December, 1902	50
PM1464	Art Institute of Chicago, Chicago, Illinois	1903	130, 297
PM1470	St. Botolph Club, Boston, Massachusetts	1906	303
MBPI0883	**Title with decoration for The True Captain Kidd**		**456**
PM0196	The True Captain Kidd	December, 1902	50
MBPI0884	**Illustrated initial W for The True Captain Kidd**		**456**
PM0196	The True Captain Kidd	December, 1902	50
MBPI0885	**Kidd on the Deck of the "Adventure Galley"**		**456**
PM0196	The True Captain Kidd	December, 1902	50
PM1464	Art Institute of Chicago, Chicago, Illinois	1903	130, 297
PM1470	St. Botolph Club, Boston, Massachusetts	1906	303
PM1565	Howard Pyle, Author-Illustrator 1853-1911	February, 1912	2
PM0809	Catalogue of Pictures by Howard Pyle	1912	141, 310

PM1479	Hotel Dupont, Wilmington, Delaware	1912	141, 310
PM1481	Panama and Pacific International Exhibition, San Francisco, California	1915	315
MBPI0886	**Burning the Ship**		**456**
PM0196	The True Captain Kidd	December, 1902	50
PM1464	Art Institute of Chicago, Chicago, Illinois	1903	130, 297
PM1470	St. Botolph Club, Boston, Massachusetts	1906	303
MBPI0887	**Buried Treasure**		**456**
PM0196	The True Captain Kidd	December, 1902	50
PM1464	Art Institute of Chicago, Chicago, Illinois	1903	130, 297
PM1470	St. Botolph Club, Boston, Massachusetts	1906	303
PM0660	Stolen Treasure	1907	64, 73, 214
PM0787	The Buccaneers, Rough Verse	1912	138
MBPI0888	**The Chantey-Man**		**456**
PM0197	The Chantey-Man	January, 1903	50
MBPI0889	**"Small heed had we of the fleet, sweet hours"**		**456**
PM1196	Advertisement: Harper's Magazine, August 1903	July 25, 1903	74
PM0198	The Castle of Content	August, 1903	50
PM1282	Harper's Magazine: August Fiction Number	1903	328
PM1464	Art Institute of Chicago, Chicago, Illinois	1903	130, 297
PM1424	The Jester	1904	339
PM1206	A Selection From The Year's Holiday Books	December 14, 1905	96
PM0771	The Line of Love	1905	177
MBPI0890	**"'Twas a strange tale she had ended"**		**456**
PM0198	The Castle of Content	August, 1903	50
PM0771	The Line of Love	1905	177
MBPI0891	**Lady Adeliza came wondering to the balcony**		**456**
PM0198	The Castle of Content	August, 1903	50
PM1105	Book Review	November, 1905	4
PM0771	The Line of Love	1905	177
MBPI0892	**He thought of his love**		**456**
PM0198	The Castle of Content	August, 1903	50
PM1464	Art Institute of Chicago, Chicago, Illinois	1903	130, 297
MBPI0893	**In the night**		**456**
PM0198	The Castle of Content	August, 1903	50
PM1464	Art Institute of Chicago, Chicago, Illinois	1903	130, 297
PM0771	The Line of Love	1905	177
MBPI0894	**"Nothing harms me all the day"**		**456**
PM0199	Peire Vidal, Troubadour	December, 1903	50
PM1466	Kellogg Public Library, Green Bay, Wisconsin	1904	301
PM1470	St. Botolph Club, Boston, Massachusetts	1906	303
MBPI0895	**At the gate of the Castle**		**456**
PM0199	Peire Vidal, Troubadour	December, 1903	50
PM1466	Kellogg Public Library, Green Bay, Wisconsin	1904	301
PM1470	St. Botolph Club, Boston, Massachusetts	1906	303
PM1472	Pratt Institute, Brooklyn, New York	1908	106, 306
PM1473	Macbeth Gallery, New York	1908	307
PM1479	Hotel Dupont, Wilmington, Delaware	1912	141, 310
PM1481	Panama and Pacific International Exhibition, San Francisco, California	1915	315
MBPI0896	**Vidal–Poet and Satirist**		**456**
PM0199	Peire Vidal, Troubadour	December, 1903	50
PM1470	St. Botolph Club, Boston, Massachusetts	1906	303
PM1472	Pratt Institute, Brooklyn, New York	1908	106, 306
PM1473	Macbeth Gallery, New York	1908	307
MBPI0897	**In the train of King Alfonzo**		**457**
PM0199	Peire Vidal, Troubadour	December, 1903	50
PM1466	Kellogg Public Library, Green Bay, Wisconsin	1904	301
PM1470	St. Botolph Club, Boston, Massachusetts	1906	303
PM0789	The Soul of Melicent	1913	213
MBPI0898	**Her whisper was so soft he only guessed the words**		**457**
PM0200	The Stairway of Honor	January, 1904	50

MBPI0899	**This last picture**		**457**
PM0200	The Stairway of Honor	January, 1904	50
PM1470	St. Botolph Club, Boston, Massachusetts	1906	303
PM1472	Pratt Institute, Brooklyn, New York	1908	106, 306
PM1473	Macbeth Gallery, New York	1908	307
PM1479	Hotel Dupont, Wilmington, Delaware	1912	141, 310
PM1481	Panama and Pacific International Exhibition, San Francisco, California	1915	315
MBPI0900	**He stretched out his hand to the curtains**		**457**
PM0200	The Stairway of Honor	January, 1904	50
MBPI0901	**He found Melite alone**		**457**
PM0201	The Story of Adhelmar	April, 1904	50
PM0771	The Line of Love	1905	177
MBPI0902	**He sang for her as they sat in the gardens**		**457**
PM0201	The Story of Adhelmar	April, 1904	50
PM0771	The Line of Love	1905	177
MBPI0903	**He climbed the stairs slowly, for he was growing feeble**		**457**
PM0201	The Story of Adhelmar	April, 1904	50
PM0771	The Line of Love	1905	177
MBPI0904	**Estercel**		**457**
PM0202	The Charming of Estercel	June, 1904	51
PM1423	The Cavalier	1904	339
MBPI0905	**"There is a charm," said the nurse at last**		**457**
PM0202	The Charming of Estercel	June, 1904	51
MBPI0906	**Eileen slipped the ring into the nest**		**457**
PM0202	The Charming of Estercel	June, 1904	51
MBPI0907	**The Battle of the Stairs**		**457**
PM0203	The Sword of Ahab	August, 1904	51
MBPI0908	**The dark folk trooped to meet them on the shore**		**457**
PM0203	The Sword of Ahab	August, 1904	51
PM1470	St. Botolph Club, Boston, Massachusetts	1906	303
PM0789	The Soul of Melicent	1913	213
MBPI0909	**Bertha, the much beloved**		**457**
PM0203	The Sword of Ahab	August, 1904	51
MBPI0910	**The drawing of the sword**		**457**
PM0203	The Sword of Ahab	August, 1904	51
PM1470	St. Botolph Club, Boston, Massachusetts	1906	303
PM0789	The Soul of Melicent	1913	213
MBPI0911	**The rescue of Azilicz**		**457**
PM0204	The Maid of Landevennec	September, 1904	51
MBPI0912	**Her head and shoulders hung over the space without**		**457**
PM0204	The Maid of Landevennec	September, 1904	51
MBPI0913	**"She tricked me, little maid"**		**458**
PM0204	The Maid of Landevennec	September, 1904	51
MBPI0914	**Catherine de Vaucelles, in her garden**		**458**
PM0205	In Necessity's Mortar	October, 1904	51
PM0771	The Line of Love	1905	177
MBPI0915	**"Villon–The singer Fate fashioned to her liking"**		**458**
PM0205	In Necessity's Mortar	October, 1904	51
PM0771	The Line of Love	1905	177
PM1484	Advertisements	December, 1905	53
MBPI0916	**"The King himself hauled me out of gaol"**		**458**
PM0205	In Necessity's Mortar	October, 1904	51
PM0771	The Line of Love	1905	177
PM1470	St. Botolph Club, Boston, Massachusetts	1906	303
PM1054	Practical Illustration	1920	203
MBPI0917	**The charge**		**458**
PM0206	Non-Combatants	November, 1904	51
PM0954	Harper's Encyclopaedia of United States History from 458 A.D. to 1915	1915	161
MBPI0918	**They brought in their dead and wounded on hay wagons**		**458**
PM0206	Non-Combatants	November, 1904	51

MBPI0919	**"I thought of you, when I was falling," he said vaguely**		**458**
PM0206	Non-Combatants	November, 1904	51
MBPI0920	**She believed that she had daily speech with angels**		**458**
PM0207	Saint Joan of Arc	December, 1904	51
PM0796	Saint Joan of Arc	1919	209
MBPI0921	**The triumphal entry into Rheims**		**458**
PM0207	Saint Joan of Arc	December, 1904	51
PM0931	Great American Illustrators: Howard Pyle, Illustrator	September, 1907	99, 106
PM0796	Saint Joan of Arc	1919	209
MBPI0922	**Guarded by rough English soldiers**		**458**
PM0207	Saint Joan of Arc	December, 1904	51
PM0796	Saint Joan of Arc	1919	209
MBPI0923	**A lithe, young, slender figure**		**458**
PM0207	Saint Joan of Arc	December, 1904	51
PM0796	Saint Joan of Arc	1919	209
MBPI0924	**Parson Rawson spoke to her with a pleasant chiding**		**458**
PM0208	The Gold	December, 1904	51
MBPI0925	**Catherine Duke quickened her steps**		**458**
PM0208	The Gold	December, 1904	51
PM1470	St. Botolph Club, Boston, Massachusetts	1906	303
MBPI0926	**Melicent stood motionless like a wild thing at gaze**		**458**
PM0209	Melicent	January, 1905	51
MBPI0927	**A man lay prone there, half turned upon his face**		**458**
PM0209	Melicent	January, 1905	51
MBPI0928	**Sir John shook his spear at the ladies who sneered**		**458**
PM0209	Melicent	January, 1905	51
PM0966	The Founder of an American School of Art	February 23, 1907	106
MBPI0929	**La Salle christening the country "Louisiana"**		**459**
PM0210	The Great La Salle	February, 1905	52
PM0773	History of the United States From 986 to 1905	1905	168
PM0954	Harper's Encyclopaedia of United States History from 458 A.D. to 1915	1915	161
PM0795	A History of the American People	1918	166, 170, 273
PM1302	If You Could Talk To President Wilson!	1918	170
MBPI0930	**La Salle petitions the King for permission to explore the Mississippi**		**459**
PM0210	The Great La Salle	February, 1905	52
PM1479	Hotel Dupont, Wilmington, Delaware	1912	141, 310
PM0954	Harper's Encyclopaedia of United States History from 458 A.D. to 1915	1915	161
PM1481	Panama and Pacific International Exhibition, San Francisco, California	1915	315
MBPI0931	**She drew bridle, listening–there was no sound**		**459**
PM0211	Special Messenger	February, 1905	52
MBPI0932	**"Are you ever lonely here?" he inquired**		**459**
PM0211	Special Messenger	February, 1905	52
MBPI0933	**"Come, come, your Future Majesty! Cheer up!"**		**459**
PM0212	Eden Gates	March, 1905	52
MBPI0934	**I knelt by the whispering, muttering old man**		**459**
PM0212	Eden Gates	March, 1905	52
MBPI0935	**They stood staring at the violent sky**		**459**
PM0213	"An Amazing Belief"	April, 1905	52
MBPI0936	**With a cry, Shallum flung up his arms and jumped**		**459**
PM0213	"An Amazing Belief"	April, 1905	52
MBPI0937	**The Crown-Prince Karl, dead by his own hand**		**459**
PM0214	Carlotta	May, 1905	52
PM1470	St. Botolph Club, Boston, Massachusetts	1906	303
PM1472	Pratt Institute, Brooklyn, New York	1908	106, 306
PM1473	Macbeth Gallery, New York	1908	307
PM1479	Hotel Dupont, Wilmington, Delaware	1912	141, 310
PM1481	Panama and Pacific International Exhibition, San Francisco, California	1915	315
MBPI0938	**Carlotta–tall, white, queenly–a cluster of flowers in her arms**		**459**
PM0214	Carlotta	May, 1905	52
MBPI0939	**Her outstretched arms seemed to close upon something**		**459**

PM0214	Carlotta	May, 1905	52
MBPI0940	**Old Immortality**		**459**
PM0215	Old Immortality	May, 1905	52
PM1470	St. Botolph Club, Boston, Massachusetts	1906	303
MBPI0941	**"I loved the husk of a man"**		**459**
PM0216	The Fox Brush	August, 1905	52
PM1470	St. Botolph Club, Boston, Massachusetts	1906	303
MBPI0942	**Headpiece with title for The Fox Brush**		**459**
PM0216	The Fox Brush	August, 1905	52
MBPI0943	**So for a heart-beat she saw him**		**459**
PM0216	The Fox Brush	August, 1905	52
PM1470	St. Botolph Club, Boston, Massachusetts	1906	303
PM1472	Pratt Institute, Brooklyn, New York	1908	106, 306
PM0778	Chivalry	1909	143
MBPI0944	**He came to her–in his helmet a fox brush spangled with jewels**		**459**
PM0216	The Fox Brush	August, 1905	52
PM1470	St. Botolph Club, Boston, Massachusetts	1906	303
MBPI0945	**Headband for The Fox Brush**		**460**
PM0216	The Fox Brush	August, 1905	52
PM0228	The Ruby of Kishmoor	August, 1907	54, 208
MBPI0946	**Marginal decoration, female with outstretched arm**		**460**
PM0216	The Fox Brush	August, 1905	52
PM0770	The Island of Enchantment	1905	173
MBPI0947	**Marginal decoration, male with sword and shield**		**460**
PM0216	The Fox Brush	August, 1905	52
PM0776	Gallantry, An Eighteenth Century Dizain	1907	153
PM0778	Chivalry	1909	143
PM0265	The Buccaneers	January, 1911	60
PM0787	The Buccaneers, Rough Verse	1912	138
MBPI0948	**The doge sat alone in a great carven chair**		**460**
PM0217	The Island of Enchantment. I	September, 1905	52
PM0770	The Island of Enchantment	1905	173
PM1470	St. Botolph Club, Boston, Massachusetts	1906	303
MBPI0949	**He laid the mantle over the girl's shoulders**		**460**
PM0217	The Island of Enchantment. I	September, 1905	52
PM0770	The Island of Enchantment	1905	173
PM1484	Advertisements	December, 1905	53
PM1470	St. Botolph Club, Boston, Massachusetts	1906	303
MBPI0950	**"He lay awhile conscious of great comfort"**		**460**
PM0218	The Island of Enchantment. II	October, 1905	52
PM0770	The Island of Enchantment	1905	173
MBPI0951	**"She hung drooping in the great chair of state"**		**460**
PM0218	The Island of Enchantment. II	October, 1905	52
PM0770	The Island of Enchantment	1905	173
MBPI0952	**The buccaneer was a picturesque fellow**		**460**
PM0219	The Fate of a Treasure Town	December, 1905	53, 129
PM1470	St. Botolph Club, Boston, Massachusetts	1906	303
PM0663	Adventures of Pirates and Sea-Rovers	1908	53, 129
PM1472	Pratt Institute, Brooklyn, New York	1908	106, 306
PM1473	Macbeth Gallery, New York	1908	307
PM1479	Hotel Dupont, Wilmington, Delaware	1912	141, 310
PM0954	Harper's Encyclopaedia of United States History from 458 A.D. to 1915	1915	161
PM1481	Panama and Pacific International Exhibition, San Francisco, California	1915	315
MBPI0953	**An attack on a galleon**		**460**
PM0219	The Fate of a Treasure Town	December, 1905	53, 129
PM1470	St. Botolph Club, Boston, Massachusetts	1906	303
PM1472	Pratt Institute, Brooklyn, New York	1908	106, 306
PM1473	Macbeth Gallery, New York	1908	307
PM0809	Catalogue of Pictures by Howard Pyle	1912	141, 310
PM1479	Hotel Dupont, Wilmington, Delaware	1912	141, 310

PM0789	The Soul of Melicent	1913	213
PM0954	Harper's Encyclopaedia of United States History from 458 A.D. to 1915	1915	161
PM1481	Panama and Pacific International Exhibition, San Francisco, California	1915	315
MBPI0954	**So the treasure was divided**		**460**
PM0219	The Fate of a Treasure Town	December, 1905	53, 129
PM1470	St. Botolph Club, Boston, Massachusetts	1906	303
PM0931	Great American Illustrators: Howard Pyle, Illustrator	September, 1907	99, 106
PM0663	Adventures of Pirates and Sea-Rovers	1908	53, 129
PM1472	Pratt Institute, Brooklyn, New York	1908	106, 306
PM1473	Macbeth Gallery, New York	1908	307
PM1477	Art Students League, New York	1909	309
PM1061	Art Society of Wilmington	November 11, 1912	15
PM0809	Catalogue of Pictures by Howard Pyle	1912	141, 310
PM1479	Hotel Dupont, Wilmington, Delaware	1912	141, 310
PM1481	Panama and Pacific International Exhibition, San Francisco, California	1915	315
MBPI0955	**Extorting tribute from the citizens**		**460**
PM0219	The Fate of a Treasure Town	December, 1905	53, 129
PM1470	St. Botolph Club, Boston, Massachusetts	1906	303
PM1472	Pratt Institute, Brooklyn, New York	1908	106, 306
PM1473	Macbeth Gallery, New York	1908	307
PM1479	Hotel Dupont, Wilmington, Delaware	1912	141, 310
PM0954	Harper's Encyclopaedia of United States History from 458 A.D. to 1915	1915	161
PM1481	Panama and Pacific International Exhibition, San Francisco, California	1915	315
MBPI0956	**Headband for The Fate of a Treasure Town**		**460**
PM0219	The Fate of a Treasure Town	December, 1905	53, 129
PM0932	The Toy-Shop	December, 1907	55
PM1172	In the Same Boat	December, 1911	61
PM1174	How To Make History Dates Stick	December, 1914	62
PM1176	A Poet and His Child's Friends	December, 1917	62
MBPI0957	**Headpiece for The Fate of a Treasure Town**		**460**
PM0219	The Fate of a Treasure Town	December, 1905	53, 129
PM0265	The Buccaneers	January, 1911	60
PM0787	The Buccaneers, Rough Verse	1912	138
MBPI0958	**Illustrated initial A for The Fate of a Treasure Town**		**460**
PM0219	The Fate of a Treasure Town	December, 1905	53, 129
MBPI0959	**Marginal decoration, female with ship**		**460**
PM0219	The Fate of a Treasure Town	December, 1905	53, 129
MBPI0960	**Marginal decoration, male with tree**		**460**
PM0219	The Fate of a Treasure Town	December, 1905	53, 129
MBPI0961	**A neat and shrivelled gentleman sat at a desk**		**461**
PM0220	The Sestina	January, 1906	53
PM0778	Chivalry	1909	143
PM1211	Howard Pyle, NA, Illustrator, Painter	January, 1912	97
MBPI0962	**They were overtaken by Falmouth himself**		**461**
PM0220	The Sestina	January, 1906	53
PM0778	Chivalry	1909	143
MBPI0963	**Beatrix and Esmond**		**461**
PM0221	Pictures from Thackeray	August, 1906	53
PM0783	The Works of William Makepeace Thackeray	1910	254
MBPI0964	**Becky Sharp and Lord Steyne**		**461**
PM0222	Pictures from Thackeray	December, 1906	53
PM1217	A Revolutionary Force In American Art	March 23, 1907	98
PM0781	The Works of William Makepeace Thackeray	1910	253
MBPI0965	**A figure to provoke tears**		**461**
PM0223	A Sense of Scarlet	February, 1907	53
MBPI0966	**Pendennis**		**461**
PM0224	Pictures from Thackeray	March, 1907	53
PM0782	The Works of William Makepeace Thackeray	1910	253
MBPI0967	**"Who is the lucky miss, my little villain?"**		**461**
PM0225	In the Second April	April, 1907	53

PM0776	Gallantry, An Eighteenth Century Dizain	1907	153
PM1472	Pratt Institute, Brooklyn, New York	1908	106, 306
PM1473	Macbeth Gallery, New York	1908	307
PM0809	Catalogue of Pictures by Howard Pyle	1912	141, 310
PM1479	Hotel Dupont, Wilmington, Delaware	1912	141, 310
PM1481	Panama and Pacific International Exhibition, San Francisco, California	1915	315
MBPI0968	**The duel between John Blumer and Cazaio**		**461**
PM0225	In the Second April	April, 1907	53
PM1207	A Note on American Illustration	November 21, 1907	96
PM0776	Gallantry, An Eighteenth Century Dizain	1907	153
PM1583	Advertisements	December, 1907	55
PM1395	Advertisement: Gallantry	January, 1908	55
PM0809	Catalogue of Pictures by Howard Pyle	1912	141, 310
PM1479	Hotel Dupont, Wilmington, Delaware	1912	141, 310
PM1481	Panama and Pacific International Exhibition, San Francisco, California	1915	315
MBPI0969	**"The Bastille is not a very healthy place"**		**461**
PM0226	In the Second April	May, 1907	53
PM0776	Gallantry, An Eighteenth Century Dizain	1907	153
MBPI0970	**The Death of Cazaio**		**461**
PM0226	In the Second April	May, 1907	53
PM0776	Gallantry, An Eighteenth Century Dizain	1907	153
MBPI0971	**The king glared down at her**		**461**
PM0227	The Nobel Family of Beaupertuys	July, 1907	54
PM1472	Pratt Institute, Brooklyn, New York	1908	106, 306
PM1473	Macbeth Gallery, New York	1908	307
PM1479	Hotel Dupont, Wilmington, Delaware	1912	141, 310
PM1481	Panama and Pacific International Exhibition, San Francisco, California	1915	315
MBPI0972	**Suddenly their comedy turned tragic**		**461**
PM0227	The Nobel Family of Beaupertuys	July, 1907	54
PM1472	Pratt Institute, Brooklyn, New York	1908	106, 306
PM1473	Macbeth Gallery, New York	1908	307
PM1479	Hotel Dupont, Wilmington, Delaware	1912	141, 310
MBPI0973	**"I am the daughter of that unfortunate Captain Keitt!"**		**461**
PM0228	The Ruby of Kishmoor	August, 1907	54, 208
PM0664	The Ruby of Kishmoor	1908	54, 208
PM1479	Hotel Dupont, Wilmington, Delaware	1912	141, 310
PM1481	Panama and Pacific International Exhibition, San Francisco, California	1915	315
MBPI0974	**Tailpiece, Table of Contents for Twilight Land**		**461**
PM0651	Twilight Land	1895	237
MBPI0975	**Illustrated initial T for The Ruby of Kishmoor**		**461**
PM0228	The Ruby of Kishmoor	August, 1907	54, 208
MBPI0976	**Jonathan Rugg**		**461**
PM0228	The Ruby of Kishmoor	August, 1907	54, 208
MBPI0977	**The negress beckoned him to draw nearer**		**462**
PM0228	The Ruby of Kishmoor	August, 1907	54, 208
PM0664	The Ruby of Kishmoor	1908	54, 208
MBPI0978	**The little gentleman with one eye**		**462**
PM0228	The Ruby of Kishmoor	August, 1907	54, 208
PM0664	The Ruby of Kishmoor	1908	54, 208
MBPI0979	**With great amity the two walked off together**		**462**
PM0228	The Ruby of Kishmoor	August, 1907	54, 208
PM0664	The Ruby of Kishmoor	1908	54, 208
MBPI0980	**The little gentleman in black emitted a piercing scream**		**462**
PM0228	The Ruby of Kishmoor	August, 1907	54, 208
PM0664	The Ruby of Kishmoor	1908	54, 208
MBPI0981	**The man with the silver earrings**		**462**
PM0228	The Ruby of Kishmoor	August, 1907	54, 208
MBPI0982	**The stranger threw himself upon Jonathan with the fury of a madman**		**462**
PM0228	The Ruby of Kishmoor	August, 1907	54, 208
PM0664	The Ruby of Kishmoor	1908	54, 208

MBPI0983	**The man with the broken nose**		**462**
PM0228	The Ruby of Kishmoor	August, 1907	54, 208
PM0664	The Ruby of Kishmoor	1908	54, 208
MBPI0984	**The arms of his captor held him as in a vise**		**462**
PM0228	The Ruby of Kishmoor	August, 1907	54, 208
PM0664	The Ruby of Kishmoor	1908	54, 208
MBPI0985	**The lady with the silver veil**		**462**
PM0228	The Ruby of Kishmoor	August, 1907	54, 208
MBPI0986	**Jonathan Rugg was married to Martha Dobbs the following year**		**462**
PM0228	The Ruby of Kishmoor	August, 1907	54, 208
PM0664	The Ruby of Kishmoor	1908	54, 208
MBPI0987	**Captain Keitt**		**462**
PM0228	The Ruby of Kishmoor	August, 1907	54, 208
PM1208	The Year's Holiday Books	December 17, 1908	96
PM0664	The Ruby of Kishmoor	1908	54, 208
PM1396	Advertisement: The Ruby of Kishmoor	December, 1908	57
PM1397	Advertisement: The Ruby of Kishmoor	January, 1909	57
PM1211	Howard Pyle, NA, Illustrator, Painter	January, 1912	97
MBPI0988	**Abraham Lincoln**		**462**
PM0229	Lincoln's Last Day	September, 1907	54
PM1472	Pratt Institute, Brooklyn, New York	1908	106, 306
PM1473	Macbeth Gallery, New York	1908	307
PM1152	An Interesting Showing of Howard Pyle's Work	January, 1909	17
PM1398	Harper's Bookshelf	March, 1909	58
PM0779	Lincoln and the Sleeping Sentinel	1909	177
PM1175	With Lincoln at the White House	January, 1915	62
PM0954	Harper's Encyclopaedia of United States History from 458 A.D. to 1915	1915	161
PM1177	Advertisement: History of the American People	July, 1918	62
MBPI0989	**She became as famous for speed as her short career allowed**		**462**
PM0230	The Cruise of the Caribbee	December, 1907	54
PM1472	Pratt Institute, Brooklyn, New York	1908	106, 306
PM1473	Macbeth Gallery, New York	1908	307
MBPI0990	**Her captain was a Cuban**		**462**
PM0230	The Cruise of the Caribbee	December, 1907	54
MBPI0991	**The cruiser piled on all sail**		**462**
PM0230	The Cruise of the Caribbee	December, 1907	54
MBPI0992	**They have a so-called native king**		**462**
PM0230	The Cruise of the Caribbee	December, 1907	54
MBPI0993	**They carried fruit and vegetables**		**463**
PM0230	The Cruise of the Caribbee	December, 1907	54
MBPI0994	**'Tween decks of the slaver**		**463**
PM0230	The Cruise of the Caribbee	December, 1907	54
MBPI0995	**The rest were shot and thrown overboard**		**463**
PM0230	The Cruise of the Caribbee	December, 1907	54
MBPI0996	**The mate elevated and sighted the gun**		**463**
PM0230	The Cruise of the Caribbee	December, 1907	54
MBPI0997	**The lighters were soon alongside**		**463**
PM0230	The Cruise of the Caribbee	December, 1907	54
MBPI0998	**She was a solid mass of flame**		**463**
PM0230	The Cruise of the Caribbee	December, 1907	54
MBPI0999	**Meregrett, daughter of Philippe the Bold**		**463**
PM0231	The Rat-Trap	December, 1907	54
PM1472	Pratt Institute, Brooklyn, New York	1908	106, 306
PM1473	Macbeth Gallery, New York	1908	307
PM0778	Chivalry	1909	143
PM0809	Catalogue of Pictures by Howard Pyle	1912	141, 310
PM1479	Hotel Dupont, Wilmington, Delaware	1912	141, 310
PM1481	Panama and Pacific International Exhibition, San Francisco, California	1915	315
MBPI1000	**Then sang Sire Edward**		**463**
PM0231	The Rat-Trap	December, 1907	54

PM0778	Chivalry	1909	143
MBPI1001	**"Others have lived through greater woes than ours"**		**463**
PM0232	A Sign from Heaven	January, 1908	55
MBPI1002	**"Take care, my friend, take care"**		**463**
PM0232	A Sign from Heaven	January, 1908	55
PM0809	Catalogue of Pictures by Howard Pyle	1912	141, 310
PM1479	Hotel Dupont, Wilmington, Delaware	1912	141, 310
PM1481	Panama and Pacific International Exhibition, San Francisco, California	1915	315
MBPI1003	**The officers would be waiting until she should appear**		**463**
PM0233	Dona Victoria	February, 1908	55
MBPI1004	**The passing of Dona Victoria**		**463**
PM0233	Dona Victoria	February, 1908	55
MBPI1005	**Rosamund and Sir Gregory**		**463**
PM0234	The Choices	March, 1908	55
MBPI1006	**Queen Ysabeau in her carven chair**		**463**
PM0234	The Choices	March, 1908	55
PM0778	Chivalry	1909	143
MBPI1007	**She arrayed herself in silence**		**463**
PM0235	A Princess of Kent	April, 1908	55
PM1472	Pratt Institute, Brooklyn, New York	1908	106, 306
PM1473	Macbeth Gallery, New York	1908	307
MBPI1008	**Horse and man plunged heavily after her**		**463**
PM0235	A Princess of Kent	April, 1908	55
PM1472	Pratt Institute, Brooklyn, New York	1908	106, 306
MBPI1009	**The coming of Lancaster**		**464**
PM0236	The Scabbard	May, 1908	55
PM1472	Pratt Institute, Brooklyn, New York	1908	106, 306
PM1473	Macbeth Gallery, New York	1908	307
PM1240	Pratt Institute's Howard Pyle exhibition	January, 1909	106
PM0778	Chivalry	1909	143
PM0809	Catalogue of Pictures by Howard Pyle	1912	141, 310
PM1479	Hotel Dupont, Wilmington, Delaware	1912	141, 310
PM1481	Panama and Pacific International Exhibition, San Francisco, California	1915	315
MBPI1010	**Branwen**		**464**
PM0236	The Scabbard	May, 1908	55
MBPI1011	**The Newcomes**		**464**
PM0237	Pictures from Thackeray	June, 1908	55
PM1472	Pratt Institute, Brooklyn, New York	1908	106, 306
PM1473	Macbeth Gallery, New York	1908	307
PM0784	The Works of William Makepeace Thackeray	1910	254
MBPI1012	**The dark, smiling Salim, with his magic pack, was welcome**		**464**
PM0238	The Minstrel	June, 1908	55
PM1005	Every Man For Himself	1908	150
PM1472	Pratt Institute, Brooklyn, New York	1908	106, 306
PM1473	Macbeth Gallery, New York	1908	307
MBPI1013	**Edric the singer**		**464**
PM0239	Edric and Sylvaine	August, 1908	55
PM0809	Catalogue of Pictures by Howard Pyle	1912	141, 310
PM1479	Hotel Dupont, Wilmington, Delaware	1912	141, 310
PM1481	Panama and Pacific International Exhibition, San Francisco, California	1915	315
MBPI1014	**Marginal decoration with title for Edric and Sylvaine**		**464**
PM0239	Edric and Sylvaine	August, 1908	55
MBPI1015	**Marginal decoration for Edric and Sylvaine**		**464**
PM0239	Edric and Sylvaine	August, 1908	55
MBPI1016	**Marginal decoration for Edric and Sylvaine**		**464**
PM0239	Edric and Sylvaine	August, 1908	55
MBPI1017	**Marginal decoration for Edric and Sylvaine**		**464**
PM0239	Edric and Sylvaine	August, 1908	55
MBPI1018	**Marginal decoration for Edric and Sylvaine**		**464**
PM0239	Edric and Sylvaine	August, 1908	55

MBPI1019	Marginal decoration for Edric and Sylvaine		464
PM0239	Edric and Sylvaine	August, 1908	55
MBPI1020	Marginal decoration for Edric and Sylvaine		464
PM0239	Edric and Sylvaine	August, 1908	55
MBPI1021	Marginal decoration for Edric and Sylvaine		464
PM0239	Edric and Sylvaine	August, 1908	55
MBPI1022	Marginal decoration for Edric and Sylvaine		464
PM0239	Edric and Sylvaine	August, 1908	55
MBPI1023	Marginal decoration for Edric and Sylvaine		464
PM0239	Edric and Sylvaine	August, 1908	55
MBPI1024	Marginal decoration for Edric and Sylvaine		464
PM0239	Edric and Sylvaine	August, 1908	55
MBPI1025	Marginal decoration for Edric and Sylvaine		465
PM0239	Edric and Sylvaine	August, 1908	55
MBPI1026	Marginal decoration for Edric and Sylvaine		465
PM0239	Edric and Sylvaine	August, 1908	55
MBPI1027	Marginal decoration for Edric and Sylvaine		465
PM0239	Edric and Sylvaine	August, 1908	55
MBPI1028	Marginal decoration for Edric and Sylvaine		465
PM0239	Edric and Sylvaine	August, 1908	55
MBPI1029	Tailpiece for Edric and Sylvaine		465
PM0239	Edric and Sylvaine	August, 1908	55
MBPI1030	"I will have him between these hands"		465
PM0240	Manasseh	September, 1908	56
MBPI1031	In an instant those long fingers closed on the Governor		465
PM0240	Manasseh	September, 1908	56
MBPI1032	"The American captain with his mate boarded us"		465
PM0241	Pennsylvania's Defiance of the United States	October, 1908	56
PM0954	Harper's Encyclopaedia of United States History from 458 A.D. to 1915	1915	161
MBPI1033	Then the real fight began		465
PM0241	Pennsylvania's Defiance of the United States	October, 1908	56
MBPI1034	Diana Sherley		465
PM0242	The Ultimate Master	November, 1908	56
MBPI1035	"Go, Madam, and leave the Prodigal among his husks"		465
PM0242	The Ultimate Master	November, 1908	56
MBPI1036	Old Jacob Van Kleek had never favored our hero's suit		465
PM0243	The Mysterious Chest	December, 1908	56
MBPI1037	Decorative title with illustrated initial U for The Mysterious Chest		465
PM0243	The Mysterious Chest	December, 1908	56
MBPI1038	The skeletonlike stranger entered		465
PM0243	The Mysterious Chest	December, 1908	56
MBPI1039	It was his belief that the chest was certainly haunted		465
PM0243	The Mysterious Chest	December, 1908	56
MBPI1040	Swinging his lanthorn and followed by his laboring assistants		465
PM0243	The Mysterious Chest	December, 1908	56
MBPI1041	The Reverend Ebenezer Doolittle		466
PM0243	The Mysterious Chest	December, 1908	56
MBPI1042	"D'ye see what the wretches have left?"		466
PM0243	The Mysterious Chest	December, 1908	56
MBPI1043	Gazed down upon the dreadful object		466
PM0243	The Mysterious Chest	December, 1908	56
MBPI1044	He was greatly addicted to little supper parties of his own sex		466
PM0243	The Mysterious Chest	December, 1908	56
MBPI1045	A dreadful spectacle		466
PM0243	The Mysterious Chest	December, 1908	56
MBPI1046	Old Jacob Van Kleek the money-lender		466
PM0243	The Mysterious Chest	December, 1908	56
MBPI1047	Illustration for The Mysterious Chest		466
PM0243	The Mysterious Chest	December, 1908	56
MBPI1048	Our young gentleman of the law		466

PM0243	The Mysterious Chest	December, 1908	56
MBPI1049	**He perused the inscription with great particularity**		**466**
PM0243	The Mysterious Chest	December, 1908	56
MBPI1050	**"If this dreadful thing is not taken away I shall go mad"**		**466**
PM0243	The Mysterious Chest	December, 1908	56
MBPI1051	**Lugged the mysterious chest to the lawyer's house**		**466**
PM0243	The Mysterious Chest	December, 1908	56
MBPI1052	**Tailpiece for The Mysterious Chest**		**466**
PM0243	The Mysterious Chest	December, 1908	56
MBPI1053	**The Shell**		**466**
PM0244	A Child at the Siege of Vicksburg	December, 1908	57
MBPI1054	**"The Dancer"**		**466**
PM1473	Macbeth Gallery, New York	1908	307
PM0245	Lola	January, 1909	57
PM1479	Hotel Dupont, Wilmington, Delaware	1912	141, 310
PM1481	Panama and Pacific International Exhibition, San Francisco, California	1915	315
MBPI1055	**His eyes fell on the dancer in her shimmering scarlet**		**466**
PM0245	Lola	January, 1909	57
MBPI1056	**In place of the apple hung a little gilded skull**		**466**
PM0246	The Apple of Venus	February, 1909	57
PM1479	Hotel Dupont, Wilmington, Delaware	1912	141, 310
MBPI1057	**The precious minutes flew past, but she was silent**		**467**
PM0246	The Apple of Venus	February, 1909	57
MBPI1058	**"He watched me as a cat watches a mouse"**		**467**
PM0247	The Grain Ship	March, 1909	57
PM1479	Hotel Dupont, Wilmington, Delaware	1912	141, 310
MBPI1059	**"He lost his hold and fell, taking me with him"**		**467**
PM0247	The Grain Ship	March, 1909	57
PM1479	Hotel Dupont, Wilmington, Delaware	1912	141, 310
MBPI1060	**The Duke of Gloucester sent for Edward Maudelain**		**467**
PM0248	The Satraps	April, 1909	58
PM0778	Chivalry	1909	143
MBPI1061	**The Queen read the Scriptures in the vulgar tongue**		**467**
PM0248	The Satraps	April, 1909	58
PM0778	Chivalry	1909	143
MBPI1062	**Dim and faded pictures at times came before them**		**467**
PM0249	The Garden of Eden	May, 1909	58
MBPI1063	**Vitia and the Governor**		**467**
PM0249	The Garden of Eden	May, 1909	58
MBPI1064	**Sheridan's first interview with Rowand**		**467**
PM0250	Rowand	June, 1909	58
PM0954	Harper's Encyclopaedia of United States History from 458 A.D. to 1915	1915	161
PM1483	The Wilmington Society of the Fine Arts, Wilmington, Delaware	1920	317
MBPI1065	**A lonely duel in the middle of a great, sunny field**		**467**
PM0250	Rowand	June, 1909	58
PM0786	On Hazardous Service, Scouts and Spies of the North and South	1912	193
MBPI1066	**When All the World Was Young**		**467**
PM1473	Macbeth Gallery, New York	1908	307
PM0251	When All the World Was Young	August, 1909	58
PM0809	Catalogue of Pictures by Howard Pyle	1912	141, 310
PM1479	Hotel Dupont, Wilmington, Delaware	1912	141, 310
MBPI1067	**The Midnight Court Martial**		**467**
PM0252	"Williams, C.S.A."	September, 1909	58
PM0786	On Hazardous Service, Scouts and Spies of the North and South	1912	193
PM0954	Harper's Encyclopaedia of United States History from 458 A.D. to 1915	1915	161
MBPI1068	**She put the silver coronet upon her head**		**467**
PM0253	The Castle on the Dunes	September, 1909	58
MBPI1069	**She saw herself for what he had said, and swooned**		**467**
PM0253	The Castle on the Dunes	September, 1909	58
MBPI1070	**Theirs was a spirited encounter upon the beach of Teviot Bay**		**467**

PM0254	The Second Chance	October, 1909	58
MBPI1071	**"Who are we that Heaven should make of the old sea a fowling net?"**		**467**
PM0254	The Second Chance	October, 1909	58
PM1482	The Wilmington Society of the Fine Arts, Wilmington, Delaware	1917	316
MBPI1072	**It was a comrade from his own regiment**		**467**
PM0255	Landegon	November, 1909	58
PM0786	On Hazardous Service, Scouts and Spies of the North and South	1912	193
MBPI1073	**"They talked it over–with me sitting on the horse"**		**468**
PM0255	Landegon	November, 1909	58
MBPI1074	**A wolf had not been seen at Salem for thirty years**		**468**
PM0256	The Salem Wolf	December, 1909	58
PM0809	Catalogue of Pictures by Howard Pyle	1912	141, 310
PM1479	Hotel Dupont, Wilmington, Delaware	1912	141, 310
MBPI1075	**Decorative title with illustrated initial T for The Salem Wolf**		**468**
PM0256	The Salem Wolf	December, 1909	58
MBPI1076	**Once it chased Dr. Wilkinson into the very town itself**		**468**
PM0256	The Salem Wolf	December, 1909	58
MBPI1077	**Marginal illustration for The Salem Wolf**		**468**
PM0256	The Salem Wolf	December, 1909	58
MBPI1078	**Vignette for The Salem Wolf**		**468**
PM0256	The Salem Wolf	December, 1909	58
MBPI1079	**Vignette for The Salem Wolf**		**468**
PM0256	The Salem Wolf	December, 1909	58
MBPI1080	**Marginal illustration for The Salem Wolf**		**468**
PM0256	The Salem Wolf	December, 1909	58
MBPI1081	**Marginal illustration for The Salem Wolf**		**468**
PM0256	The Salem Wolf	December, 1909	58
MBPI1082	**Vignette for The Salem Wolf**		**468**
PM0256	The Salem Wolf	December, 1909	58
MBPI1083	**Vignette for The Salem Wolf**		**468**
PM0256	The Salem Wolf	December, 1909	58
MBPI1084	**Headpiece for The Salem Wolf**		**468**
PM0256	The Salem Wolf	December, 1909	58
MBPI1085	**Vignette for The Salem Wolf**		**468**
PM0256	The Salem Wolf	December, 1909	58
MBPI1086	**The nation is at war and must have men**		**468**
PM0257	Young	December, 1909	59
MBPI1087	**They awaited the order for the charge**		**468**
PM0257	Young	December, 1909	59
MBPI1088	**"I grow old, having no son but Randver"**		**468**
PM0258	Swanhild	January, 1910	59
PM0809	Catalogue of Pictures by Howard Pyle	1912	141, 310
PM1479	Hotel Dupont, Wilmington, Delaware	1912	141, 310
MBPI1089	**Thereafter she clung about Randver**		**469**
PM0258	Swanhild	January, 1910	59
MBPI1090	**"I found him and he wasn't alone"**		**469**
PM0259	The Wrecker	March, 1910	59
MBPI1091	**"My boy wanted to do the divin', but 'twas me that went down"**		**469**
PM0259	The Wrecker	March, 1910	59
PM1086	Wide Courses	1912	241
MBPI1092	**The whole world goes afield today**		**469**
PM0260	An Initial Letter	April, 1910	59
MBPI1093	**Flaggingly the reed pen went up and down the vellum**		**469**
PM0260	An Initial Letter	April, 1910	59
MBPI1094	**She told him her adventures in a breath**		**469**
PM0261	"Holy Mr. Herbert"	May, 1910	59
MBPI1095	**Writing on some loose sheets of paper that he held on his knee**		**469**
PM0261	"Holy Mr. Herbert"	May, 1910	59
MBPI1096	**"I have broken it," she wailed**		**469**
PM0262	The Black Night	June, 1910	59

MBPI1097	"And see that you watch well," he snarled		469
PM0262	The Black Night	June, 1910	59
MBPI1098	"They questioned him with malevolent persistence"		469
PM0262	The Black Night	June, 1910	59
PM1479	Hotel Dupont, Wilmington, Delaware	1912	141, 310
MBPI1099	The sea boiled over the wreckage in streaky white		469
PM0263	"Page, A. B."	July, 1910	59
MBPI1100	Page was at the wheel, steering		469
PM0263	"Page, A. B."	July, 1910	59
MBPI1101	There stood the Faery Prince		469
PM0264	Ysobel de Corveaux	August, 1910	59
MBPI1102	Decorative title with illustrated initial T for Ysobel de Corveaux		469
PM0264	Ysobel de Corveaux	August, 1910	59
MBPI1103	Marginal illustration for Ysobel de Corveaux		469
PM0264	Ysobel de Corveaux	August, 1910	59
MBPI1104	Marginal illustration for Ysobel de Corveaux		469
PM0264	Ysobel de Corveaux	August, 1910	59
MBPI1105	Marginal illustration for Ysobel de Corveaux		470
PM0264	Ysobel de Corveaux	August, 1910	59
MBPI1106	Marginal illustration for Ysobel de Corveaux		470
PM0264	Ysobel de Corveaux	August, 1910	59
MBPI1107	Marginal illustration for Ysobel de Corveaux		470
PM0264	Ysobel de Corveaux	August, 1910	59
MBPI1108	Marginal illustration for Ysobel de Corveaux		470
PM0264	Ysobel de Corveaux	August, 1910	59
MBPI1109	Marginal illustration for Ysobel de Corveaux		470
PM0264	Ysobel de Corveaux	August, 1910	59
MBPI1110	Marginal illustration for Ysobel de Corveaux		470
PM0264	Ysobel de Corveaux	August, 1910	59
MBPI1111	Marginal illustration for Ysobel de Corveaux		470
PM0264	Ysobel de Corveaux	August, 1910	59
MBPI1112	Marginal illustration for Ysobel de Corveaux		470
PM0264	Ysobel de Corveaux	August, 1910	59
MBPI1113	Headpiece for Ysobel de Coreaux		470
PM0264	Ysobel de Corveaux	August, 1910	59
MBPI1114	Which shall be Captain?		470
PM1473	Macbeth Gallery, New York	1908	307
PM0265	The Buccaneers	January, 1911	60
PM0787	The Buccaneers, Rough Verse	1912	138
MBPI1115	"'Tis an unfair race, O master," cried Ephialtes		470
PM0629	A Cycle of Children	August, 1886	126
PM1560	A Cycle of Children	December, 1886	14
PM0694	Storied Holidays	1887	218
MBPI1116	"Come hither, lads," she said		470
PM0630	A Cycle of Children	September, 1886	126
PM1560	A Cycle of Children	December, 1886	14
PM1110	A Cycle of Historic Red-Letter Days	October, 1887	5
PM0694	Storied Holidays	1887	218
MBPI1117	General Lee on his famous charger "Traveler"		470
PM0266	General Lee as I Knew Him	February, 1911	60
PM0954	Harper's Encyclopaedia of United States History from 458 A.D. to 1915	1915	161
MBPI1118	His army broke up and followed him, weeping and sobbing		470
PM0266	General Lee as I Knew Him	February, 1911	60
MBPI1119	So long as Gann would follow, his Master would lead		470
PM0267	Man and Dog	March, 1911	60
MBPI1120	Man and staff sank into the peat mud		470
PM0267	Man and Dog	March, 1911	60
MBPI1121	Jocelin, with many encomiums, displayed his emeralds		471
PM0268	The Soul of Mervisaunt	April, 1911	60
MBPI1122	"I have loved you for a great while, fair Mervisaunt"		471

PM0268	The Soul of Mervisaunt	April, 1911	60
MBPI1123	**She was continually beset by spies**		**471**
PM0269	Miss Van Lew	June, 1911	60
MBPI1124	**The secret room**		**471**
PM0269	Miss Van Lew	June, 1911	60
PM0786	On Hazardous Service, Scouts and Spies of the North and South	1912	193
PM1540	Ten American Girls From History	1917	235
MBPI1125	**The Virginians**		**471**
PM0785	The Works of William Makepeace Thackeray	1910	254
PM0270	Pictures from Thackeray	July, 1911	60
PM1054	Practical Illustration	1920	203
MBPI1126	**"Everything you wish for shall be yours"**		**471**
PM0271	The Dead Finger	September, 1911	61
MBPI1127	**Decorative title for The Dead Finger**		**471**
PM0271	The Dead Finger	September, 1911	61
MBPI1128	**So Beppo's first wish was fulfilled**		**471**
PM0271	The Dead Finger	September, 1911	61
MBPI1129	**The two rode away together**		**471**
PM0271	The Dead Finger	September, 1911	61
MBPI1130	**Beppo sat in the Notary's house talking about the will**		**471**
PM0271	The Dead Finger	September, 1911	61
MBPI1131	**He saw a great coach approaching**		**471**
PM0271	The Dead Finger	September, 1911	61
MBPI1132	**The grand duke gave him a golden chain**		**471**
PM0271	The Dead Finger	September, 1911	61
MBPI1133	**He thrust the cobbler back against the door**		**471**
PM0271	The Dead Finger	September, 1911	61
MBPI1134	**He was poor as ever**		**471**
PM0271	The Dead Finger	September, 1911	61
MBPI1135	**The last of the "Naronic"**		**471**
PM0272	Sea Tolls	September, 1911	61
MBPI1136	**Stefano and Serafina at the well**		**471**
PM0273	The Painted Pitcher	November, 1911	61
MBPI1137	**Decorative title for The Painted Pitcher**		**472**
PM0273	The Painted Pitcher	November, 1911	61
MBPI1138	**Montofacini, the Magician**		**472**
PM0273	The Painted Pitcher	November, 1911	61
MBPI1139	**The shopman**		**472**
PM0273	The Painted Pitcher	November, 1911	61
MBPI1140	**The bear would stand upon his hind legs and dance**		**472**
PM0273	The Painted Pitcher	November, 1911	61
MBPI1141	**Nicolo, the tallow chandler**		**472**
PM0273	The Painted Pitcher	November, 1911	61
MBPI1142	**Serafina was leaning from the window**		**472**
PM0273	The Painted Pitcher	November, 1911	61
MBPI1143	**Cassacinci and the runaway horse**		**472**
PM0273	The Painted Pitcher	November, 1911	61
MBPI1144	**Decorative title for The Evil Eye**		**472**
PM0274	The Evil Eye	February, 1912	61
MBPI1145	**He was engaged to Caterina**		**472**
PM0274	The Evil Eye	February, 1912	61
MBPI1146	**She pointed her finger at Caterina**		**472**
PM0274	The Evil Eye	February, 1912	61
MBPI1147	**One of the horses fell dead in the field**		**472**
PM0274	The Evil Eye	February, 1912	61
MBPI1148	**While she stood looking the cow died**		**472**
PM0274	The Evil Eye	February, 1912	61
MBPI1149	**The vines were dying**		**472**
PM0274	The Evil Eye	February, 1912	61
MBPI1150	**"The Evil Eye," he said**		**472**

PM0274	The Evil Eye	February, 1912	61
MBPI1151	**Montofacini, the Magician**		**472**
PM0274	The Evil Eye	February, 1912	61
MBPI1152	**"I am a ruined man"**		**472**
PM0274	The Evil Eye	February, 1912	61
MBPI1153	**That night his straw stack caught fire**		**473**
PM0274	The Evil Eye	February, 1912	61
MBPI1154	**He knew not what ailed her or what to do**		**473**
PM0274	The Evil Eye	February, 1912	61
MBPI1155	**He was lying on the library floor in the morning**		**473**
PM0275	The Crime in Jedidiah Peeble's House	March, 1912	62
MBPI1156	**The traveller found the stone behind the hedge a resting-place**		**473**
PM0275	The Crime in Jedidiah Peeble's House	March, 1912	62
MBPI1157	**Nicolo and the Robber**		**473**
PM0276	The Die of Fate	May, 1912	62
MBPI1158	**Herr Vollmer quietly stepped out into the street**		**473**
PM0277	Huntford's Fair Nihilist	June, 1913	62
MBPI1159	**She began to talk to Huntford about himself**		**473**
PM0277	Huntford's Fair Nihilist	June, 1913	62
MBPI1160	**The little man raced down the stairs and out into the street**		**473**
PM0277	Huntford's Fair Nihilist	June, 1913	62
MBPI1161	**Headband with title for Tom Chist and the Treasure Box**		**473**
PM0278	Tom Chist and the Treasure Box	March 24, 1896	63, 214
PM1650	Harper's Round Table for 1898	1898	268
MBPI1162	**Such a wreck was a Godsend to the poor and needy settlers**		**473**
PM0278	Tom Chist and the Treasure Box	March 24, 1896	63, 214
MBPI1163	**"And twenty one and twenty two"**		**473**
PM0278	Tom Chist and the Treasure Box	March 24, 1896	63, 214
PM0660	Stolen Treasure	1907	64, 73, 214
MBPI1164	**The pirate captain looked impassively on**		**473**
PM0278	Tom Chist and the Treasure Box	March 24, 1896	63, 214
MBPI1165	**Over the next rise he ran, and so on over the sliding, shifting ground, panting and gasping**		**473**
PM0278	Tom Chist and the Treasure Box	March 24, 1896	63, 214
MBPI1166	**"'Tis enough to make us both rich men"**		**473**
PM0278	Tom Chist and the Treasure Box	March 24, 1896	63, 214
PM0660	Stolen Treasure	1907	64, 73, 214
MBPI1167	**"I knew it, I knew it," exclaimed the great man**		**473**
PM0278	Tom Chist and the Treasure Box	March 24, 1896	63, 214
MBPI1168	**Headpiece with title for The Buccaneers**		**473**
PM0279	The Buccaneers	June 29, 1897	64, 214
MBPI1169	**He asked this figure of war to step aside for him**		**474**
PM0279	The Buccaneers	June 29, 1897	64, 214
PM0660	Stolen Treasure	1907	64, 73, 214
MBPI1170	**The crowd scattered**		**474**
PM0279	The Buccaneers	June 29, 1897	64, 214
MBPI1171	**He leaped to the wheel**		**474**
PM0279	The Buccaneers	June 29, 1897	64, 214
PM0660	Stolen Treasure	1907	64, 73, 214
MBPI1172	**They would stand hours together**		**474**
PM0279	The Buccaneers	June 29, 1897	64, 214
PM0660	Stolen Treasure	1907	64, 73, 214
MBPI1173	**Decoration with title for The Man with the Hoe**		**474**
PM0750	The Man with the Hoe and Other Poems	1900	179
MBPI1174	**St. Valentine's Day in Merrie Old England**		**474**
PM0280	St. Valentine	February 24, 1877	64
PM1365	The Pictorial Album	1880	265
MBPI1175	**Queen of the May–Unpropitious Skies**		**474**
PM0281	Queen of the May–Unpropitious Skies	May 12, 1877	65
MBPI1176	**"One of Those City Fellows"–A Hundred Years Ago**		**474**
PM0282	"One of Those City Fellows"–A Hundred Years Ago	September 8, 1877	65

MBPI1177	**Entangled**		**474**
PM0283	Entangled	January 19, 1878	65
MBPI1178	**"Wreck in the Offing!"**		**474**
PM0284	"Wreck in the Offing!"–Scene in a Lifesaving Station	March 9, 1878	65
PM0931	Great American Illustrators: Howard Pyle, Illustrator	September, 1907	99, 106
MBPI1179	**Lost in the Snow**		**474**
PM0285	Lost in the Snow–A Canadian Sketch	March 16, 1878	65
MBPI1180	**A Matrimonial Difficulty–Legal Intervention**		**474**
PM0286	A Matrimonial Difficulty–Legal Intervention	April 6, 1878	65
MBPI1181	**The Robin's Vesper, with title and poem inserted**		**474**
PM0287	The Robin's Vesper	June 7, 1879	65
MBPI1182	**A Love Affair of the Olden Time–Consulting the Wise Woman**		**474**
PM0288	A Love Affair of the Olden Time–Consulting the Wise Woman	July 12, 1879	65
MBPI1183	**The Milkmaid's Song, with title and poem inserted**		**474**
PM0289	The Milkmaid's Song	July 19, 1879	65
MBPI1184	**The Dance of the Veterans**		**474**
PM0290	The Dance of the Veterans	July 26, 1879	65
MBPI1185	**"Breaking the News"**		**475**
PM0291	"Breaking the News"	August 16, 1879	65
MBPI1186	**The Outcast's Return**		**475**
PM0292	The Outcast's Return	January 10, 1880	65
MBPI1187	**The Song of the Whip-poor-Will, with title and poem inserted**		**475**
PM0293	The Song of the Whip-poor-Will	June 12, 1880	66
PM1203	The Song of The Whippoorwill	October 16, 1880	96
MBPI1188	**Illustrated initial E for The Song of The Whip-poor-Will**		**475**
PM0293	The Song of the Whip-poor-Will	June 12, 1880	66
PM1203	The Song of The Whippoorwill	October 16, 1880	96
MBPI1189	**Illustrated initial B for The Song of The Whip-poor-Will**		**475**
PM0293	The Song of the Whip-poor-Will	June 12, 1880	66
PM1203	The Song of The Whippoorwill	October 16, 1880	96
MBPI1190	**The First Public Reading of the Declaration of Independence**		**475**
PM0294	The First Public Reading of the Declaration of Independence–The Members of Congress Leaving Independence Hall	July 10, 1880	66
MBPI1191	**An Interrupted Performance**		**475**
PM1436	Art Students League, New York, New York	1878	104, 281
PM0295	The Circus–An Interrupted Performance	July 31, 1880	66
MBPI1192	**Women at the Polls in New Jersey in the Good Old Times**		**475**
PM0296	Women at the Polls	November 13, 1880	66
MBPI1193	**Christmas Morning in Old New York**		**475**
PM0297	Christmas Morning in Old New York	December 25, 1880	66
MBPI1194	**New Year's Day Seventy Years Ago–The Last Evening Caller**		**475**
PM0298	New Year's Day Seventy Years Ago–The Last Evening Caller	January 8, 1881	66
MBPI1195	**St. Valentine's Day in the Morning**		**475**
PM0299	St. Valentine's Day in the Morning	February 26, 1881	66
MBPI1196	**Politics in the Olden Times–General Jackson, President-elect, on his way to Washington**		**475**
PM0300	A Presidential Progress	March 12, 1881	67
MBPI1197	**Shad-Fishing on the Lower Delaware at Night–The Last Haul Before Dawn**		**475**
PM0301	Shad-Fishing on the Delaware	April 30, 1881	67
MBPI1198	**The Surrender of Cornwallis**		**475**
PM0302	The Surrender of Cornwallis	October 22, 1881	67
PM0761	Harper's Encyclopaedia of United States History	1902	158
PM0954	Harper's Encyclopaedia of United States History from 458 A.D. to 1915	1915	161
PM0795	A History of the American People	1918	166, 170, 273
PM1433	The Surrender of Cornwallis	1920	341
MBPI1199	**"He was doubtless a tramp"**		**475**
PM0303	John Paul	November 5, 1881	67
MBPI1200	**"Suppose you let me take care of this young lady in future?"**		**475**
PM0303	John Paul	November 5, 1881	67
MBPI1201	**"'Thee hasn't killed him?' timidly inquired the girl"**		**476**
PM0303	John Paul	November 5, 1881	67

MBPI1202	**The Christmas Tree, title inserted**		**476**
PM0304	The Christmas Tree	December 24, 1881	67
PM0676	Farm Ballads	1882	150
PM1164	Yuletide Stories and Pictures	December, 1888	21
PM1006	Farm Ballads	1905	151
PM1051	Poems for Young Americans from Will Carleton	1906	203
MBPI1203	**"Holding forth the missive, he stood by, breathless and speechless"**		**476**
PM0305	Exchange No Robbery	February 18, 1882	67
MBPI1204	**"Heart of gold! kindest of men!"**		**476**
PM0306	Exchange No Robbery	February 25, 1882	67
MBPI1205	**"Hilda, airily mounting a high pair of steps, proceeded to catalogue the various articles that she now dropped one by one into Grettel's wide-spread apron"**		**476**
PM0307	Exchange No Robbery	March 4, 1882	67
MBPI1206	**"Glancing at the white-robed girlish figure before him, with evident admiration, he made a becoming obeisance"**		**476**
PM0308	Exchange No Robbery	March 11, 1882	67
MBPI1207	**"They sat down and chatted in an easy, friendly fashion"**		**476**
PM0309	Exchange No Robbery	March 18, 1882	68
MBPI1208	**"Then the Hofrath emerged from the balcony, and etiquette forbade a longer interview"**		**476**
PM0310	Exchange No Robbery	March 25, 1882	68
MBPI1209	**Washington's Birth-Day, with title and verses inserted**		**476**
PM0311	Washington's Birth-Day	March 4, 1882	67
MBPI1210	**"The old man's face changed suddenly, and he pressed his hand hard upon the arm of the hair-cloth sofa"**		**476**
PM0312	A Modern Puritan	April 15, 1882	68
MBPI1211	**"Breaking from her companions with an excited exclamation, Mlle. Bland grasped the old woman by the wrists"**		**476**
PM0312	A Modern Puritan	April 15, 1882	68
MBPI1212	**The Dead Stowaway**		**476**
PM0314	The Dead Stowaway	June 3, 1882	68
PM0688	City Ballads	1886	143
MBPI1213	**The Sea-Gull's Song**		**476**
PM0315	The Sea-Gull's Song	November 25, 1882	68
MBPI1214	**Headpiece with initial D for Christmas Time Two Hundred Years Ago**		**476**
PM0316	Christmas Time Two Hundred Years Ago	December 9, 1882	68
MBPI1215	**Christmas presents for the Squire**		**476**
PM0316	Christmas Time Two Hundred Years Ago	December 9, 1882	68
MBPI1216	**The Arrival at the Blue Boar Inn**		**476**
PM0316	Christmas Time Two Hundred Years Ago	December 9, 1882	68
MBPI1217	**The stirrup-cup**		**477**
PM0316	Christmas Time Two Hundred Years Ago	December 9, 1882	68
MBPI1218	**The Mummers**		**477**
PM0316	Christmas Time Two Hundred Years Ago	December 9, 1882	68
MBPI1219	**The Snapdragon**		**477**
PM0316	Christmas Time Two Hundred Years Ago	December 9, 1882	68
MBPI1220	**Bringing in the Yule-Log**		**477**
PM0316	Christmas Time Two Hundred Years Ago	December 9, 1882	68
MBPI1221	**The Glee Singers**		**477**
PM0316	Christmas Time Two Hundred Years Ago	December 9, 1882	68
MBPI1222	**The Return from Church, Christmas Morning**		**477**
PM0316	Christmas Time Two Hundred Years Ago	December 9, 1882	68
MBPI1223	**Christmas Pudding**		**477**
PM0316	Christmas Time Two Hundred Years Ago	December 9, 1882	68
MBPI1224	**The Contra-Dance**		**477**
PM0316	Christmas Time Two Hundred Years Ago	December 9, 1882	68
MBPI1225	**The Duel**		**477**
PM0316	Christmas Time Two Hundred Years Ago	December 9, 1882	68
MBPI1226	**The Elopement**		**477**
PM0316	Christmas Time Two Hundred Years Ago	December 9, 1882	68
MBPI1227	**A Valentine to Phillis**		**477**

PM0317	A Valentine to Phillis	February 17, 1883	68
MBPI1228	**A Love Feast Among the Dunkers**		**477**
PM0318	A Love Feast Among the Dunkers	March 17, 1883	68
MBPI1229	**Scene in a Tavern on the Old Albany Post Road**		**477**
PM0319	The Mysterious Guest–Scene in a Tavern on the Old Albany Post Road	March 24, 1883	68
MBPI1230	**A Conference with the Colonists**		**477**
PM0320	The First Visit of William Penn to America	March 31, 1883	69, 169
PM1166	The First Visit of William Penn to America	April 14, 1883	21
PM1019	The History of the United States	1906	169
MBPI1231	**"Autumn Leaves"**		**477**
PM0321	"Autumn Leaves"	November 24, 1883	69
MBPI1232	**Evacuation Day One Hundred Years Ago–The Continental Army Marching Down the Old Bowery, New York, November 25, 1783**		**477**
PM0322	The Evacuation 1783	November 24, 1883	69
PM1400	Specimen Book of Engravings	1885	265
MBPI1233	**Headpiece with title for Ye True Story of Granny Greene of Salem Town**		**478**
PM0323	Ye True Story of Granny Greene of Salem Town	December 1, 1883	69
MBPI1234	**Illustrated initial S for Ye True Story of Granny Greene of Salem Town**		**478**
PM0323	Ye True Story of Granny Greene of Salem Town	December 1, 1883	69
MBPI1235	**Vignette for Ye True Story of Granny Greene of Salem Town**		**478**
PM0323	Ye True Story of Granny Greene of Salem Town	December 1, 1883	69
MBPI1236	**Granny Greene seeketh the Life of ye Hen**		**478**
PM0323	Ye True Story of Granny Greene of Salem Town	December 1, 1883	69
MBPI1237	**Dame Charity Greene meeteth Ye Strange Little Man**		**478**
PM0323	Ye True Story of Granny Greene of Salem Town	December 1, 1883	69
MBPI1238	**Granny Greene Falleth Into Ill Repute**		**478**
PM0323	Ye True Story of Granny Greene of Salem Town	December 1, 1883	69
MBPI1239	**The Arrest**		**478**
PM0323	Ye True Story of Granny Greene of Salem Town	December 1, 1883	69
MBPI1240	**Ye End for Ye True Story of Granny Greene of Salem Town**		**478**
PM0323	Ye True Story of Granny Greene of Salem Town	December 1, 1883	69
MBPI1241	**Washington Taking Leave of His Officers, Dec. 4, 1783**		**478**
PM0324	Washington Taking Leave of His Officers, Dec. 4, 1783	December 1, 1883	69
MBPI1242	**"The Ant and the Grasshopper"**		**478**
PM0325	The Ant and the Grasshopper	December 29, 1883	69
MBPI1243	**"He seized and held the treasure near the light"**		**478**
PM0326	Mr. Merridew's Goldpiece	December 13, 1884	69
MBPI1244	**Vignette with illustrated initial C for The Strange Adventures of Carl Spich**		**478**
PM0327	The Strange Adventures of Carl Spich	January 3, 1885	69
MBPI1245	**"Maybe the snow deadened his footsteps, maybe it was the Devil"**		**478**
PM0327	The Strange Adventures of Carl Spich	January 3, 1885	69
MBPI1246	**"The tall stranger with the club-foot stood before her"**		**478**
PM0327	The Strange Adventures of Carl Spich	January 3, 1885	69
MBPI1247	**"He stopped when he had come close to Carl"**		**478**
PM0327	The Strange Adventures of Carl Spich	January 3, 1885	69
MBPI1248	**"I am going to run away with you"**		**478**
PM0328	Markham's Bays	February 28, 1885	70
MBPI1249	**"She came close to him and laid her hand lovingly on his arm"**		**479**
PM0329	Squire Tripp's Old Arm Chair	December 12, 1885	70
MBPI1250	**"The Squire went on as though he had not heard"**		**479**
PM0329	Squire Tripp's Old Arm Chair	December 12, 1885	70
MBPI1251	**"He held his hammer poised for a moment"**		**479**
PM0329	Squire Tripp's Old Arm Chair	December 12, 1885	70
MBPI1252	**"The fingers of the hand were clutched like a claw"**		**479**
PM0329	Squire Tripp's Old Arm Chair	December 12, 1885	70
MBPI1253	**"Mr. Longways looked up under his brows at me with a very curious leer"**		**479**
PM0330	The Rose of Paradise	June 11, 1887	70, 208
PM1193	Advertisement: Books for Holiday Gifts	November 26, 1887	71
PM0643	The Rose of Paradise	1888	70-71, 207

PM1249	The Rose of Paradise	February, 1894	62, 208
MBPI1254	**"'Boat ahoy!' I cried out, and then levelled my pistol and fired"**		**479**
PM0331	The Rose of Paradise	June 18, 1887	70, 208
PM0643	The Rose of Paradise	1888	70-71, 207
PM1249	The Rose of Paradise	February, 1894	62, 208
MBPI1255	**"'Captain Mackra,' said he, coldly, 'you were pleased to put upon me last night a gross and uncalled for insult.'"**		**479**
PM0332	The Rose of Paradise	June 25, 1887	70, 208
PM0643	The Rose of Paradise	1888	70-71, 207
PM1249	The Rose of Paradise	February, 1894	62, 208
MBPI1256	**"So soon as they saw me they fell to screaming and clung to one another"**		**479**
PM0333	The Rose of Paradise	July 2, 1887	70, 208
PM0643	The Rose of Paradise	1888	70-71, 207
PM1249	The Rose of Paradise	February, 1894	62, 208
MBPI1257	**"'I am Captain John Mackra,' said I, and I sat down upon the gunwale of the boat"**		**479**
PM0334	The Rose of Paradise	July 9, 1887	70, 208
PM0643	The Rose of Paradise	1888	70-71, 207
PM1249	The Rose of Paradise	February, 1894	62, 208
MBPI1258	**"I rose slowly from my chair, and stood with my hand leaning upon the table"**		**479**
PM0335	The Rose of Paradise	July 16, 1887	71, 208
PM0643	The Rose of Paradise	1888	70-71, 207
PM1249	The Rose of Paradise	February, 1894	62, 208
MBPI1259	**"The three fellows were brought aft to the quarterdeck, where Captain Croker stood, just below the rail of the deck above"**		**479**
PM0336	The Rose of Paradise	July 23, 1887	71, 208
PM0643	The Rose of Paradise	1888	70-71, 207
PM1249	The Rose of Paradise	February, 1894	62, 208
MBPI1260	**"There, in the corner, I beheld the famous pirate, Captain Edward England"**		**479**
PM0337	The Rose of Paradise	July 30, 1887	71, 208
PM0643	The Rose of Paradise	1888	70-71, 207
PM1249	The Rose of Paradise	February, 1894	62, 208
MBPI1261	**Headpiece for The Two Cornets of Monmouth**		**479**
PM0339	The Two Cornets of Monmouth	September 12, 1891	71
MBPI1262	**"On sped the light chestnut, with the little officer bending almost to the saddle-bow"**		**479**
PM0339	The Two Cornets of Monmouth	September 12, 1891	71
MBPI1263	**Headpiece for A Thread Without a Knot**		**479**
PM0341	A Thread Without a Knot–A Sketch in Outline	September 3, 1892	71
MBPI1264	**Stopping the Christmas Stage**		**479**
PM0342	Stopping the Christmas Stage	December 10, 1892	71
MBPI1265	**Illustration for Stamford's Soprano**		**480**
PM0343	Stamford's Soprano–A Sketch in Outline	June 24, 1893	72
MBPI1266	**Scene in the Town Jail**		**480**
PM0344	The Pirate's Christmas	December 16, 1893	72
PM0798	The Drexel Institute, Philadelphia, Pennsylvania	1897	8, 140, 268, 284
PM0799	St. Botolph Club, Boston, Massachusetts	1897	140, 268, 288
PM1458	Paris Exposition, Paris, France	1900	296
MBPI1267	**"'Austin,' she said, 'I have come to tell you our engagement is at an end'"**		**480**
PM0345	The Parasite	November 10, 1894	72
PM0724	The Parasite, A Story	1895	199
MBPI1268	**"I was conscious only of her own eyes looking down at me, gray, deep, inscrutable"**		**480**
PM0346	The Parasite	November 17, 1894	72
PM0724	The Parasite, A Story	1895	199
MBPI1269	**"I stopped, for the woman's head had fallen back–she had fainted"**		**480**
PM0347	The Parasite	November 24, 1894	72
PM0724	The Parasite, A Story	1895	199
MBPI1270	**Illustration for The Parasite**		**480**
PM0348	The Parasite	December 1, 1894	72
PM0724	The Parasite, A Story	1895	199
MBPI1271	**Headpiece with title for Sailors and Landsmen, A Story of 1812**		**480**
PM0349	Sailors and Landsmen, A Story of 1812	December 15, 1894	72

PM1500	A Ballad of The Constitution	October 8, 1895	63
MBPI1272	**Vignette for Sailors and Landsmen, A Story of 1812**		**480**
PM0349	Sailors and Landsmen, A Story of 1812	December 15, 1894	72
MBPI1273	**Vignette for Sailors and Landsmen, A Story of 1812**		**480**
PM0349	Sailors and Landsmen, A Story of 1812	December 15, 1894	72
MBPI1274	**Vignette for Sailors and Landsmen, A Story of 1812**		**480**
PM0349	Sailors and Landsmen, A Story of 1812	December 15, 1894	72
MBPI1275	**Vignette for Sailors and Landsmen, A Story of 1812**		**480**
PM0349	Sailors and Landsmen, A Story of 1812	December 15, 1894	72
MBPI1276	**Vignette for Sailors and Landsmen, A Story of 1812**		**480**
PM0349	Sailors and Landsmen, A Story of 1812	December 15, 1894	72
MBPI1277	**Vignette for Sailors and Landsmen, A Story of 1812**		**480**
PM0349	Sailors and Landsmen, A Story of 1812	December 15, 1894	72
PM1500	A Ballad of The Constitution	October 8, 1895	63
MBPI1278	**Vignette for Sailors and Landsmen, A Story of 1812**		**480**
PM0349	Sailors and Landsmen, A Story of 1812	December 15, 1894	72
MBPI1279	**Vignette for Sailors and Landsmen, A Story of 1812**		**480**
PM0349	Sailors and Landsmen, A Story of 1812	December 15, 1894	72
MBPI1280	**Vignette for Sailors and Landsmen, A Story of 1812**		**480**
PM0349	Sailors and Landsmen, A Story of 1812	December 15, 1894	72
MBPI1281	**An Unwelcome Toast**		**481**
PM0350	An Unwelcome Toast	December 14, 1895	72
MBPI1282	**"Captain Malyoe shot Captain Brand through the head"**		**481**
PM0351	The Ghost of Captain Brand	December 19, 1896	72, 156, 214
PM0652	The Ghost of Captain Brand	1896	73, 156
PM0798	The Drexel Institute, Philadelphia, Pennsylvania	1897	8, 140, 268, 284
PM0799	St. Botolph Club, Boston, Massachusetts	1897	140, 268, 288
PM0660	Stolen Treasure	1907	64, 73, 214
MBPI1283	**Headpiece with title for The Ghost of Captain Brand**		**481**
PM0351	The Ghost of Captain Brand	December 19, 1896	72, 156, 214
PM0652	The Ghost of Captain Brand	1896	73, 156
PM0798	The Drexel Institute, Philadelphia, Pennsylvania	1897	8, 140, 268, 284
PM0799	St. Botolph Club, Boston, Massachusetts	1897	140, 268, 288
PM1188	An Early Free-Trader	January, 1899	64
PM0768	How to Draw: A Practical Book of Instruction in the Art of Illustration	1904	169
MBPI1284	**Illustrated initial B for The Ghost of Captain Brand**		**481**
PM0351	The Ghost of Captain Brand	December 19, 1896	72, 156, 214
MBPI1285	**Headpiece for The Ghost of Captain Brand**		**481**
PM0351	The Ghost of Captain Brand	December 19, 1896	72, 156, 214
PM0652	The Ghost of Captain Brand	1896	73, 156
PM0798	The Drexel Institute, Philadelphia, Pennsylvania	1897	8, 140, 268, 284
PM0799	St. Botolph Club, Boston, Massachusetts	1897	140, 268, 288
MBPI1286	**Headpiece for The Ghost of Captain Brand**		**481**
PM0351	The Ghost of Captain Brand	December 19, 1896	72, 156, 214
PM0652	The Ghost of Captain Brand	1896	73, 156
PM0798	The Drexel Institute, Philadelphia, Pennsylvania	1897	8, 140, 268, 284
PM0799	St. Botolph Club, Boston, Massachusetts	1897	140, 268, 288
MBPI1287	**Headpiece for The Ghost of Captain Brand**		**481**
PM0351	The Ghost of Captain Brand	December 19, 1896	72, 156, 214
PM0652	The Ghost of Captain Brand	1896	73, 156
PM0798	The Drexel Institute, Philadelphia, Pennsylvania	1897	8, 140, 268, 284
PM0799	St. Botolph Club, Boston, Massachusetts	1897	140, 268, 288
PM0768	How to Draw: A Practical Book of Instruction in the Art of Illustration	1904	169
MBPI1288	**"She would sit quite still, permitting Barnaby to gaze"**		**481**
PM0351	The Ghost of Captain Brand	December 19, 1896	72, 156, 214
PM0652	The Ghost of Captain Brand	1896	73, 156
PM0798	The Drexel Institute, Philadelphia, Pennsylvania	1897	8, 140, 268, 284
PM0799	St. Botolph Club, Boston, Massachusetts	1897	140, 268, 288

MBPI1289	**Headpiece for The Ghost of Captain Brand**		**481**
PM0351	The Ghost of Captain Brand	December 19, 1896	72, 156, 214
PM0652	The Ghost of Captain Brand	1896	73, 156
PM0798	The Drexel Institute, Philadelphia, Pennsylvania	1897	8, 140, 268, 284
PM0799	St. Botolph Club, Boston, Massachusetts	1897	140, 268, 288
MBPI1290	**"I've kept my ears open to all your doings"**		**481**
PM0353	A True History of the Devil at New Hope	December 18, 1897	73, 214
PM0660	Stolen Treasure	1907	64, 73, 214
MBPI1291	**How the Devil Haunted the Meeting-House, Part I.**		**481**
PM0353	A True History of the Devil at New Hope	December 18, 1897	73, 214
PM0660	Stolen Treasure	1907	64, 73, 214
MBPI1292	**How the Devil Stole the Collector's Snuff Box, Part II.**		**481**
PM0353	A True History of the Devil at New Hope	December 18, 1897	73, 214
MBPI1293	**The Strange Adventures of a Young Gentleman of Quality, Part III.**		**481**
PM0353	A True History of the Devil at New Hope	December 18, 1897	73, 214
MBPI1294	**A Romantic Episode in the Life of a Young Lady, Part IV.**		**481**
PM0353	A True History of the Devil at New Hope	December 18, 1897	73, 214
MBPI1295	**How the Devil Was Cast Out of the Meeting-House, Part V.**		**481**
PM0353	A True History of the Devil at New Hope	December 18, 1897	73, 214
MBPI1296	**Tailpiece for A True History of the Devil at New Hope**		**481**
PM0353	A True History of the Devil at New Hope	December 18, 1897	73, 214
MBPI1297	**Small Game Better Than None**		**482**
PM0355	Small Game Better Than None	December 17, 1898	73
PM1279	Christmas Number Harper's Weekly For Sale Here	1898	327
PM1403	A List of Holiday Books	1904	51, 53, 270
PM1426	Small Game Better Than None	1904	340
PM1582	Advertisement: Harper's "Prints"	December, 1904	51
PM1484	Advertisements	December, 1905	53
MBPI1298	**How the Buccaneers Kept Christmas**		**482**
PM0356	How the Buccaneers Kept Christmas	December 16, 1899	73
PM1457	Howard Pyle's Studio, Wilmington, Delaware	1900	295
PM1425	How the Buccaneers Kept Christmas	1904	339
MBPI1299	**"Here is all I have to give thee–It is the King's Jewel"**		**482**
PM0357	The King's Jewel	December 10, 1904	74
MBPI1300	**"I know thy heart, that thou dost love me well"**		**482**
PM0357	The King's Jewel	December 10, 1904	74
MBPI1301	**"Not for myself do I seek this vengeance"**		**482**
PM0357	The King's Jewel	December 10, 1904	74
MBPI1302	**So may the future bring its wreath of roses and of bay to you.**		**482**
PM0358	Henry Mills Alden's 70th Birthday	December 15, 1906	74
MBPI1303	**Preliminary study for MBPI3240 The Landing of Carteret**		**482**
PM0834	Mural preliminary study for MBPI3240 The Landing of Carteret	1906	257
MBPI1304	**Miss Nancy takes leave of the officers**		**482**
PM0360	Nancy Hansen's Project	April 13, 1880	74
MBPI1305	**Early settlers going to meeting**		**482**
PM0361	Old Times in the Colonies	August 3, 1880	75
PM1577	Selections from Holiday Books	December 11, 1880	103
PM1191	Guarding Against the Dangers of the Wilderness (1681) and of Civilization (1881)	January 8, 1881	66
PM0671	Old Times in the Colonies	1881	193
PM0761	Harper's Encyclopaedia of United States History	1902	158
PM0954	Harper's Encyclopaedia of United States History from 458 A.D. to 1915	1915	161
MBPI1306	**Isaac Bradley carrying Joseph into the settlement**		**482**
PM0361	Old Times in the Colonies	August 3, 1880	75
PM0671	Old Times in the Colonies	1881	193
MBPI1307	**The escape of Hannah Dustin**		**482**
PM0362	Old Times in the Colonies	August 17, 1880	75
PM0671	Old Times in the Colonies	1881	193
PM0761	Harper's Encyclopaedia of United States History	1902	158
PM0954	Harper's Encyclopaedia of United States History from 458 A.D. to 1915	1915	161

MBPI1308	**"Lieutenant Wyman, creeping up, put a bullet through him"**		**482**
PM0363	Old Times in the Colonies	September 21, 1880	75
PM0671	Old Times in the Colonies	1881	193
MBPI1309	**"Crack! Crack! went the guns of the Indians"**		**482**
PM0364	Old Times in the Colonies	October 5, 1880	75
PM0671	Old Times in the Colonies	1881	193
PM0686	Indian History For Young Folks	1885	172
PM0698	Library of Universal Adventure by Sea and Land	1888	177
PM0929	Indian History For Young Folks	1919	172
MBPI1310	**Cutting off a queue to bind a wound**		**482**
PM0365	Old Times in the Colonies	October 19, 1880	75
MBPI1311	**Franklin on his way to France**		**482**
PM0366	The Story of the American Navy	July 13, 1880	75
PM0938	The Story of the United States Navy for Boys	1881	233
PM0761	Harper's Encyclopaedia of United States History	1902	158
PM0954	Harper's Encyclopaedia of United States History from 458 A.D. to 1915	1915	161
MBPI1312	**Battle between the "Bon Homme Richard" and the "Serapis"**		**482**
PM0367	The Story of the American Navy	July 20, 1880	75
MBPI1313	**Decatur and his men boarding the gun-boat**		**483**
PM0368	The Story of the American Navy	August 3, 1880	75
MBPI1314	**A Christmas Carol, with title, illustrations, and verse**		**483**
PM0369	A Christmas Carol	December 21, 1880	75
PM1266	Santa Claus Up To Date	1880	209
MBPI1315	**"There's something in there"**		**483**
PM0370	The Magic Wand	March 29, 1881	75
MBPI1316	**Paul Revere at Lexington**		**483**
PM0371	Hours with the Octogenarians	May 10, 1881	75
PM0761	Harper's Encyclopaedia of United States History	1902	158
PM0954	Harper's Encyclopaedia of United States History from 458 A.D. to 1915	1915	161
MBPI1317	**"And blew as he'd not blown since he was born"**		**483**
PM0372	Jeremy Black's Fourth of July	July 5, 1881	75
MBPI1318	**"What a racket they made at the gate"**		**483**
PM0373	A Perfect Christmas	December 20, 1881	75
MBPI1319	**"It seemed to lie sound asleep, with a snow blanket all over its roof"**		**483**
PM0373	A Perfect Christmas	December 20, 1881	75
MBPI1320	**"I'm Bijah"**		**483**
PM0373	A Perfect Christmas	December 20, 1881	75
MBPI1321	**"Do you live with Santa Claus in his own house?"**		**483**
PM0373	A Perfect Christmas	December 20, 1881	75
MBPI1322	**"With a plate of mince-pie in his lap, and Bush, the big house-dog, sitting beside him"**		**483**
PM0373	A Perfect Christmas	December 20, 1881	75
PM1412	Waiting for his Share	1900	333
MBPI1323	**"Grandfather came in with a back-load of sleds"**		**483**
PM0373	A Perfect Christmas	December 20, 1881	75
MBPI1324	**"He crawled forward, and looked down through the scuttle hole"**		**483**
PM0373	A Perfect Christmas	December 20, 1881	75
MBPI1325	**"Then Uncle Tom lifted her in his big, strong arms"**		**483**
PM0374	Willie's Christmas	December 12, 1882	76
MBPI1326	**Robin on his way to Nottingham**		**483**
PM0375	Merry Adventures of Robin Hood	January 9, 1883	76
MBPI1327	**Robin meets a fair lady**		**483**
PM0376	Merry Adventures of Robin Hood	January 16, 1883	76
MBPI1328	**Robin encounters John Little**		**483**
PM0376	Merry Adventures of Robin Hood	January 16, 1883	76
MBPI1329	**Ye Romantic Adventures of Three Tailors, with title, illustrations and verse**		**484**
PM0377	Ye Romantic Adventures of Three Tailors	August 28, 1883	76, 202
PM0641	Pepper & Salt	1886	76-82, 200
MBPI1330	**Two Opinions, with title, illustrations and verse**		**484**
PM0378	Two Opinions	October 9, 1883	76, 202
PM0641	Pepper & Salt	1886	76-82, 200

MBPI1331	**A Victim to Science, with title, illustrations and verse**		**484**
PM0379	A Victim to Science	November 20, 1883	76, 202
PM0641	Pepper & Salt	1886	76-82, 200
MBPI1332	**Headpiece with title for The Revolt of the Holidays**		**484**
PM0380	The Revolt of the Holidays	December 18, 1883	76
PM0780	Harper's Book of Little Plays	1910	158
MBPI1333	**Fred**		**484**
PM0380	The Revolt of the Holidays	December 18, 1883	76
PM0780	Harper's Book of Little Plays	1910	158
MBPI1334	**Dora–Dorothy**		**484**
PM0380	The Revolt of the Holidays	December 18, 1883	76
PM0780	Harper's Book of Little Plays	1910	158
MBPI1335	**Thanksgiving Day (entering politely)**		**484**
PM0380	The Revolt of the Holidays	December 18, 1883	76
PM0780	Harper's Book of Little Plays	1910	158
MBPI1336	**Enter Fourth of July bowing and followed by Washington's Birthday**		**484**
PM0380	The Revolt of the Holidays	December 18, 1883	76
PM0780	Harper's Book of Little Plays	1910	158
MBPI1337	**The Chorus of the Six Jolly Feeders**		**484**
PM0380	The Revolt of the Holidays	December 18, 1883	76
PM0780	Harper's Book of Little Plays	1910	158
MBPI1338	**The Military Ballet dance**		**484**
PM0380	The Revolt of the Holidays	December 18, 1883	76
MBPI1339	**Easter & Saturday**		**484**
PM0380	The Revolt of the Holidays	December 18, 1883	76
PM0780	Harper's Book of Little Plays	1910	158
MBPI1340	**Four Pages armed with spears attendant**		**484**
PM0380	The Revolt of the Holidays	December 18, 1883	76
PM0780	Harper's Book of Little Plays	1910	158
MBPI1341	**Enter New Years Day saluting**		**484**
PM0380	The Revolt of the Holidays	December 18, 1883	76
PM0780	Harper's Book of Little Plays	1910	158
MBPI1342	**Santa Claus bursts into the room from the chimney followed by the Elves & Fairies. Tableau**		**484**
PM0380	The Revolt of the Holidays	December 18, 1883	76
MBPI1343	**A Disappointment, with title, illustrations and verse**		**484**
PM0381	A Disappointment	December 25, 1883	77, 202
PM0641	Pepper & Salt	1886	76-82, 200
MBPI1344	**The Accident of Birth, with title, illustrations and verse**		**484**
PM0382	The Accident of Birth	January 29, 1884	77, 202
PM0641	Pepper & Salt	1886	76-82, 200
PM1479	Hotel Dupont, Wilmington, Delaware	1912	141, 310
MBPI1345	**A Verse with a Moral but No Name, with title, illustrations and verse**		**485**
PM0383	A Verse with a Moral but No Name	March 11, 1884	77, 202
PM0641	Pepper & Salt	1886	76-82, 200
MBPI1346	**"I am the Grand Duke"**		**485**
PM0384	Facing a Giant	March 11, 1884	77
PM1479	Hotel Dupont, Wilmington, Delaware	1912	141, 310
MBPI1347	**A Tale of a Tub, with title, illustrations and verse**		**485**
PM0385	A Tale of a Tub	April 8, 1884	77, 202
PM0641	Pepper & Salt	1886	76-82, 200
MBPI1348	**Pride in Distress, with title, illustrations and verse**		**485**
PM0386	Pride in Distress	May 6, 1884	77, 202
PM1170	Advertisement: Pepper & Salt	January, 1886	30
PM0641	Pepper & Salt	1886	76-82, 200
MBPI1349	**Moral Blindness, with title, illustrations and verse**		**485**
PM0387	Moral Blindness	June 3, 1884	77, 202
PM0641	Pepper & Salt	1886	76-82, 200
MBPI1350	**Serious Advice, with title, illustrations and verse**		**485**
PM0388	Serious Advice	June 24, 1884	77
MBPI1351	**Three Fortunes, with title, illustrations and verse**		**485**

PM0389	Three Fortunes	July 15, 1884	78, 202
PM0641	Pepper & Salt	1886	76-82, 200
MBPI1352	**The Young Baron leaves his Home**		**485**
PM0390	The Accommodating Circumstance I	July 15, 1884	78
MBPI1353	**An old woman & a young girl coming towards the Castle**		**485**
PM0390	The Accommodating Circumstance I	July 15, 1884	78
MBPI1354	**Instantly there appeared before her a strange being**		**485**
PM0390	The Accommodating Circumstance I	July 15, 1884	78
MBPI1355	**Blow ye horn for ye ferry man**		**485**
PM0390	The Accommodating Circumstance I	July 15, 1884	78
MBPI1356	**Ye School for Men**		**485**
PM0391	The Accommodating Circumstance II	July 22, 1884	78
MBPI1357	**Then they began to pull**		**485**
PM0391	The Accommodating Circumstance II	July 22, 1884	78
MBPI1358	**Instantly there stood by her side a School Trustee**		**485**
PM0391	The Accommodating Circumstance II	July 22, 1884	78
MBPI1359	**Fitting a long arrow to his bow he sent it directly through the foremost horseman**		**485**
PM0391	The Accommodating Circumstance II	July 22, 1884	78
MBPI1360	**They sat down under a tree in a quiet corner of the palace grounds**		**485**
PM0392	The Accommodating Circumstance III	July 29, 1884	78
MBPI1361	**To Zisk, I**		**486**
PM0392	The Accommodating Circumstance III	July 29, 1884	78
MBPI1362	**To Zisk, II**		**486**
PM0392	The Accommodating Circumstance III	July 29, 1884	78
MBPI1363	**Ye Song of Ye Gossips, with title, illustrations and verse**		**486**
PM0393	Ye Song of Ye Gossips	August 5, 1884	78, 202
PM0641	Pepper & Salt	1886	76-82, 200
MBPI1364	**Venturesome Boldness, with title, illustrations and verse**		**486**
PM0394	Venturesome Boldness	August 26, 1884	78, 202
PM1197	Advertisement: Pepper & Salt	January 19, 1886	83
PM0641	Pepper & Salt	1886	76-82, 200
MBPI1365	**Ye Song of Ye Foolish Old Woman, with title, illustrations and verse**		**486**
PM0395	Ye Song of Ye Foolish Old Woman	September 16, 1884	78, 202
PM0641	Pepper & Salt	1886	76-82, 200
MBPI1366	**Ye Song of Ye Rajah & Ye Fly, with title, illustrations and verse**		**486**
PM0396	Ye Song of Ye Rajah and Ye Fly	October 21, 1884	78, 202
PM0641	Pepper & Salt	1886	76-82, 200
MBPI1367	**Ye Two Wishes, with title, illustrations and verse**		**486**
PM0397	Ye Two Wishes	November 4, 1884	79, 202
PM0641	Pepper & Salt	1886	76-82, 200
MBPI1368	**Superficial Culture, with title, illustrations and verse**		**486**
PM0398	Superficial Culture	November 18, 1884	79, 202
PM0641	Pepper & Salt	1886	76-82, 200
MBPI1369	**Play & Earnest, with title, illustrations and verse**		**486**
PM0399	Play and Earnest	December 2, 1884	79, 202
PM1192	Advertisement: Harper & Brothers Holiday Books	November 28, 1885	70
PM0641	Pepper & Salt	1886	76-82, 200
MBPI1370	**Headpiece with initial T for The Sword of Hildebrand**		**486**
PM0400	The Sword of Hildebrand	December 16, 1884	79
PM0469	Men of Iron	March 24, 1891	93, 183
PM1485	An Army of Giants	May 5, 1891	93
PM1183	"The Sailing of Jean-Paul"	March 23, 1897	64
PM1184	How Tom Rodman Got To West Point	January, 1898	64
MBPI1371	**Vignette for The Sword of Hildebrand**		**486**
PM0400	The Sword of Hildebrand	December 16, 1884	79
MBPI1372	**Vignette for The Sword of Hildebrand**		**486**
PM0400	The Sword of Hildebrand	December 16, 1884	79
MBPI1373	**Vignette for The Sword of Hildebrand**		**486**
PM0400	The Sword of Hildebrand	December 16, 1884	79
MBPI1374	**Vignette for The Sword of Hildebrand**		**486**

Index–Publication and Exhibition History of Pyle's Art

PM0400	The Sword of Hildebrand	December 16, 1884	79
MBPI1375	**Vignette for The Sword of Hildebrand**		**486**
PM0400	The Sword of Hildebrand	December 16, 1884	79
MBPI1376	**The Force of Need, with title, illustrations and verse**		**486**
PM0401	The Force of Need	December 30, 1884	79, 202
PM0049	A Quaker Wedding	December 12, 1885	22
PM0641	Pepper & Salt	1886	76-82, 200
MBPI1377	**Ye Story of a Blue China Plate, with title, illustrations and verse**		**487**
PM0402	Ye Story of a Blue China Plate	January 20, 1885	79, 202
PM0641	Pepper & Salt	1886	76-82, 200
MBPI1378	**Ye sad story concerning one innocent little Lamb and four wicked Wolves, with title, illustrations and verse**		**487**
PM0403	"Ye Sad Story Concerning One Innocent Little Lamb and Four Wicked Wolves"	November 27, 1885	83, 202
PM0641	Pepper & Salt	1886	76-82, 200
MBPI1379	**Overconfidence, with title, illustrations and verse**		**487**
PM0404	Overconfidence	February 10, 1885	79, 202
PM0641	Pepper & Salt	1886	76-82, 200
MBPI1380	**Title and illustrated initial H for Hans Hecklemann's Luck**		**487**
PM0405	Hans Hecklemann's Luck	February 24, 1885	80, 202
PM0641	Pepper & Salt	1886	76-82, 200
MBPI1381	**Hans Hecklemann**		**487**
PM0405	Hans Hecklemann's Luck	February 24, 1885	80, 202
PM1198	Beautiful Books for the Holiday Season (Supplement Section)	November 23, 1886	85
PM0641	Pepper & Salt	1886	76-82, 200
MBPI1382	**Catherine**		**487**
PM0405	Hans Hecklemann's Luck	February 24, 1885	80, 202
PM0641	Pepper & Salt	1886	76-82, 200
MBPI1383	**Hans Hecklemann goes to the cottage of the Old Wise-Woman in search of his Luck**		**487**
PM0405	Hans Hecklemann's Luck	February 24, 1885	80, 202
PM0641	Pepper & Salt	1886	76-82, 200
MBPI1384	**Hans Hecklemann and the Old Wise-Woman**		**487**
PM0405	Hans Hecklemann's Luck	February 24, 1885	80, 202
PM0641	Pepper & Salt	1886	76-82, 200
MBPI1385	**Hans finds his Luck**		**487**
PM0405	Hans Hecklemann's Luck	February 24, 1885	80, 202
PM0641	Pepper & Salt	1886	76-82, 200
MBPI1386	**Hans Hecklemann ploughs for Gold**		**487**
PM0405	Hans Hecklemann's Luck	February 24, 1885	80, 202
PM0641	Pepper & Salt	1886	76-82, 200
MBPI1387	**Profession & Practice, with title, illustrations and verse**		**487**
PM0406	Profession and Practice	March 10, 1885	80, 202
PM0641	Pepper & Salt	1886	76-82, 200
PM1479	Hotel Dupont, Wilmington, Delaware	1912	141, 310
MBPI1388	**Title and illustrated initial H for How Dame Margery Twist saw more than was good for her**		**487**
PM0407	How Dame Margery Twist Saw More than was Good for Her	March 17, 1885	80, 202
PM0641	Pepper & Salt	1886	76-82, 200
MBPI1389	**Dame Twist drinketh tea**		**487**
PM0407	How Dame Margery Twist Saw More than was Good for Her	March 17, 1885	80, 202
PM0641	Pepper & Salt	1886	76-82, 200
MBPI1390	**The Little Man and the Great Horse**		**487**
PM0407	How Dame Margery Twist Saw More than was Good for Her	March 17, 1885	80, 202
PM0641	Pepper & Salt	1886	76-82, 200
MBPI1391	**Dame Twist visits a Strange Patient**		**487**
PM0407	How Dame Margery Twist Saw More than was Good for Her	March 17, 1885	80, 202
PM0641	Pepper & Salt	1886	76-82, 200
MBPI1392	**Dame Margery Twist goeth to see the merry doings at the Fair**		**487**
PM0407	How Dame Margery Twist Saw More than was Good for Her	March 17, 1885	80, 202
PM0641	Pepper & Salt	1886	76-82, 200

MBPI1393	**Dame Twist drives away the Little Folks**		**488**
PM0407	How Dame Margery Twist Saw More than was Good for Her	March 17, 1885	80, 202
PM0641	Pepper & Salt	1886	76-82, 200
MBPI1394	**Dame Twist sees the Little Man in Green for the last time**		**488**
PM0407	How Dame Margery Twist Saw More than was Good for Her	March 17, 1885	80, 202
PM0641	Pepper & Salt	1886	76-82, 200
MBPI1395	**A Newspaper Puff, with title, illustrations and verse**		**488**
PM0408	A Newspaper Puff	March 24, 1885	80, 202
PM0641	Pepper & Salt	1886	76-82, 200
MBPI1396	**Headpiece with title for Clever Peter & the Two Bottles**		**488**
PM0409	Clever Peter and the Two Bottles	April 7, 1885	80, 202
PM0641	Pepper & Salt	1886	76-82, 200
MBPI1397	**Clever Peter & the Little Gentleman in Black**		**488**
PM0409	Clever Peter and the Two Bottles	April 7, 1885	80, 202
PM0641	Pepper & Salt	1886	76-82, 200
MBPI1398	**Clever Peter rides to the King's Palace upon his fine Horse**		**488**
PM0409	Clever Peter and the Two Bottles	April 7, 1885	80, 202
PM0641	Pepper & Salt	1886	76-82, 200
MBPI1399	**Peter Eats With the King and Princess**		**488**
PM0409	Clever Peter and the Two Bottles	April 7, 1885	80, 202
PM0641	Pepper & Salt	1886	76-82, 200
MBPI1400	**Clever Peter and the Unlucky Bottle**		**488**
PM0409	Clever Peter and the Two Bottles	April 7, 1885	80, 202
PM0641	Pepper & Salt	1886	76-82, 200
MBPI1401	**Clever Peter opens the Unlucky Bottle for the King and Princess**		**488**
PM0409	Clever Peter and the Two Bottles	April 7, 1885	80, 202
PM0641	Pepper & Salt	1886	76-82, 200
MBPI1402	**Fancy and Fact, with title, illustrations and verse**		**488**
PM0410	Fancy and Fact	April 21, 1885	81, 202
PM1579	Selections from Holiday Books	December 16, 1885	103
PM0641	Pepper & Salt	1886	76-82, 200
MBPI1403	**Headpiece with title and initial F for Farmer Griggs's Boggart**		**488**
PM0411	Farmer Grigg's Boggart	April 28, 1885	81, 202
PM0641	Pepper & Salt	1886	76-82, 200
MBPI1404	**Farmer Georgie Griggs**		**488**
PM0411	Farmer Grigg's Boggart	April 28, 1885	81, 202
PM0641	Pepper & Salt	1886	76-82, 200
MBPI1405	**Dame Mally Griggs**		**488**
PM0411	Farmer Grigg's Boggart	April 28, 1885	81, 202
PM0641	Pepper & Salt	1886	76-82, 200
MBPI1406	**Farmer Griggs and the Boggart**		**488**
PM0411	Farmer Grigg's Boggart	April 28, 1885	81, 202
PM0641	Pepper & Salt	1886	76-82, 200
MBPI1407	**The Departure**		**488**
PM0411	Farmer Grigg's Boggart	April 28, 1885	81, 202
PM0641	Pepper & Salt	1886	76-82, 200
MBPI1408	**Farmer Griggs and the Wise Man**		**488**
PM0411	Farmer Grigg's Boggart	April 28, 1885	81, 202
PM0641	Pepper & Salt	1886	76-82, 200
MBPI1409	**The Boggart Rejoices**		**489**
PM0411	Farmer Grigg's Boggart	April 28, 1885	81, 202
PM0641	Pepper & Salt	1886	76-82, 200
MBPI1410	**Headpiece with title and illustrated initial O–The Skillful Huntsman**		**489**
PM0412	The Skillful Huntsman	May 19, 1885	81, 202
PM0641	Pepper & Salt	1886	76-82, 200
MBPI1411	**Jacob's Mother & the Herr Mayor**		**489**
PM0412	The Skillful Huntsman	May 19, 1885	81, 202
PM0641	Pepper & Salt	1886	76-82, 200
MBPI1412	**Jacob and The Red One**		**489**
PM0412	The Skillful Huntsman	May 19, 1885	81, 202

PM0641	Pepper & Salt	1886	76-82, 200
MBPI1413	**Jacob shoots at–**		**489**
PM0412	The Skillful Huntsman	May 19, 1885	81, 202
PM1107	Book Reviews	December, 1885	4
PM0641	Pepper & Salt	1886	76-82, 200
MBPI1414	**–the Magpie**		**489**
PM0412	The Skillful Huntsman	May 19, 1885	81, 202
PM1107	Book Reviews	December, 1885	4
PM0641	Pepper & Salt	1886	76-82, 200
MBPI1415	**Jacob and the Magic Plough**		**489**
PM0412	The Skillful Huntsman	May 19, 1885	81, 202
PM0641	Pepper & Salt	1886	76-82, 200
MBPI1416	**Jacob and the Red One go hunting together**		**489**
PM0412	The Skillful Huntsman	May 19, 1885	81, 202
PM0641	Pepper & Salt	1886	76-82, 200
MBPI1417	**Jacob and Gretchen get the best of the Red One and go home together happily**		**489**
PM0412	The Skillful Huntsman	May 19, 1885	81, 202
PM0641	Pepper & Salt	1886	76-82, 200
MBPI1418	**Headpiece with title for Claus & His Wonderful Staff**		**489**
PM0413	Claus and His Wonderful Staff	July 14, 1885	81, 202
PM0641	Pepper & Salt	1886	76-82, 200
MBPI1419	**Claus and the White Snake**		**489**
PM0413	Claus and His Wonderful Staff	July 14, 1885	81, 202
PM0641	Pepper & Salt	1886	76-82, 200
MBPI1420	**Claus and the Master of Black-Arts**		**489**
PM0413	Claus and His Wonderful Staff	July 14, 1885	81, 202
PM0641	Pepper & Salt	1886	76-82, 200
MBPI1421	**The Master is Angry**		**489**
PM0413	Claus and His Wonderful Staff	July 14, 1885	81, 202
PM0641	Pepper & Salt	1886	76-82, 200
MBPI1422	**Claus listens to the talk of the two ravens**		**489**
PM0413	Claus and His Wonderful Staff	July 14, 1885	81, 202
PM0641	Pepper & Salt	1886	76-82, 200
MBPI1423	**Claus and the Manikin**		**489**
PM0413	Claus and His Wonderful Staff	July 14, 1885	81, 202
PM0641	Pepper & Salt	1886	76-82, 200
MBPI1424	**Hans discovers Claus's Luck**		**489**
PM0413	Claus and His Wonderful Staff	July 14, 1885	81, 202
PM0641	Pepper & Salt	1886	76-82, 200
MBPI1425	**Headpiece with title and initial T for The Apple of Contentment**		**490**
PM0414	The Apple of Contentment	August 18, 1885	81, 202
PM0641	Pepper & Salt	1886	76-82, 200
MBPI1426	**The little man asks for his cap**		**490**
PM0414	The Apple of Contentment	August 18, 1885	81, 202
PM0641	Pepper & Salt	1886	76-82, 200
MBPI1427	**Christine's Mother and Sisters wish for the Apple**		**490**
PM0414	The Apple of Contentment	August 18, 1885	81, 202
PM0641	Pepper & Salt	1886	76-82, 200
MBPI1428	**Christine and the Apple**		**490**
PM0414	The Apple of Contentment	August 18, 1885	81, 202
PM0641	Pepper & Salt	1886	76-82, 200
MBPI1429	**The King talks with the Wise Man**		**490**
PM0414	The Apple of Contentment	August 18, 1885	81, 202
PM0641	Pepper & Salt	1886	76-82, 200
MBPI1430	**The King reaches for the Apple**		**490**
PM0414	The Apple of Contentment	August 18, 1885	81, 202
PM0641	Pepper & Salt	1886	76-82, 200
MBPI1431	**The King's Steward and Christine**		**490**
PM0414	The Apple of Contentment	August 18, 1885	81, 202
PM0641	Pepper & Salt	1886	76-82, 200

MBPI1432	**Christine gives the Apple to the King**		**490**
PM0414	The Apple of Contentment	August 18, 1885	81, 202
PM0641	Pepper & Salt	1886	76-82, 200
MBPI1433	**Headpiece with title for The Bird in the Linden Tree**		**490**
PM0415	The Bird in the Linden Tree	September 15, 1885	82, 202
PM0641	Pepper & Salt	1886	76-82, 200
MBPI1434	**Ye King**		**490**
PM0415	The Bird in the Linden Tree	September 15, 1885	82, 202
PM0641	Pepper & Salt	1886	76-82, 200
MBPI1435	**Prince John**		**490**
PM0415	The Bird in the Linden Tree	September 15, 1885	82, 202
PM0641	Pepper & Salt	1886	76-82, 200
MBPI1436	**The Prince aids the Old Woman**		**490**
PM0415	The Bird in the Linden Tree	September 15, 1885	82, 202
PM0641	Pepper & Salt	1886	76-82, 200
MBPI1437	**The Great Ugly Troll finds the Prince by the Fire**		**490**
PM0415	The Bird in the Linden Tree	September 15, 1885	82, 202
PM0641	Pepper & Salt	1886	76-82, 200
MBPI1438	**The Gooseherd & her Daughter meet the Princess at the Roadside**		**490**
PM0415	The Bird in the Linden Tree	September 15, 1885	82, 202
PM0641	Pepper & Salt	1886	76-82, 200
MBPI1439	**The Prince looks through the Magic Key**		**490**
PM0415	The Bird in the Linden Tree	September 15, 1885	82, 202
PM0641	Pepper & Salt	1886	76-82, 200
MBPI1440	**The Old King Rejoices at His New Daughter-in-Law**		**490**
PM0415	The Bird in the Linden Tree	September 15, 1885	82, 202
PM0641	Pepper & Salt	1886	76-82, 200
MBPI1441	**Headpiece with title for The Swan Maiden**		**491**
PM0416	The Swan Maiden	October 13, 1885	82, 251
PM0642	The Wonder Clock	1888	82-88, 242
MBPI1442	**The Swan carries the Prince away**		**491**
PM0416	The Swan Maiden	October 13, 1885	82, 251
PM0642	The Wonder Clock	1888	82-88, 242
MBPI1443	**The Prince and the Old Witch with three eyes**		**491**
PM0416	The Swan Maiden	October 13, 1885	82, 251
PM0642	The Wonder Clock	1888	82-88, 242
MBPI1444	**Ye Prince & Ye Swan Maiden**		**491**
PM0416	The Swan Maiden	October 13, 1885	82, 251
PM0642	The Wonder Clock	1888	82-88, 242
PM1211	Howard Pyle, NA, Illustrator, Painter	January, 1912	97
MBPI1445	**The Witch & the woman of honey & barley meal**		**491**
PM0416	The Swan Maiden	October 13, 1885	82, 251
PM0642	The Wonder Clock	1888	82-88, 242
MBPI1446	**Headpiece with illustrated initial K for The Book of Balbo**		**491**
PM0417	"The Book of Balbo"	November 3, 1885	82
MBPI1447	**The Children are sent to the Asylum**		**491**
PM0417	"The Book of Balbo"	November 3, 1885	82
MBPI1448	**The jolly red-faced Man comes to Town**		**491**
PM0417	"The Book of Balbo"	November 3, 1885	82
MBPI1449	**Rambustius reads the Book of Balbo**		**491**
PM0417	"The Book of Balbo"	November 3, 1885	82
MBPI1450	**The King finds his children**		**491**
PM0417	"The Book of Balbo"	November 3, 1885	82
MBPI1451	**Headpiece with title for How One Turned His Trouble to Some Account**		**491**
PM0418	How One Turned His Trouble to Some Account	November 10, 1885	82, 251
PM0642	The Wonder Clock	1888	82-88, 242
MBPI1452	**The Soldier and his Trouble**		**491**
PM0418	How One Turned His Trouble to Some Account	November 10, 1885	82, 251
PM0642	The Wonder Clock	1888	82-88, 242
MBPI1453	**The Soldier brings his Trouble before the King**		**491**

PM0418	How One Turned His Trouble to Some Account	November 10, 1885	82, 251
PM1199	New Books for the Young (Supplement Section)	November 29, 1887	88
PM0642	The Wonder Clock	1888	82-88, 242
PM0998	De Vlaamse School	1898	145
MBPI1454	**The three giants come to blows**		**491**
PM0418	How One Turned His Trouble to Some Account	November 10, 1885	82, 251
PM0642	The Wonder Clock	1888	82-88, 242
MBPI1455	**The Rich Man finds Money and Trouble**		**491**
PM0418	How One Turned His Trouble to Some Account	November 10, 1885	82, 251
PM0642	The Wonder Clock	1888	82-88, 242
MBPI1456	**Headpiece with title for How Boots Befooled the King**		**491**
PM0419	How Boots Befooled the King	December 1, 1885	83, 251
PM0642	The Wonder Clock	1888	82-88, 242
MBPI1457	**Peter goes to befool the King**		**492**
PM0419	How Boots Befooled the King	December 1, 1885	83, 251
PM0642	The Wonder Clock	1888	82-88, 242
MBPI1458	**Paul goes Home again**		**492**
PM0419	How Boots Befooled the King	December 1, 1885	83, 251
PM0642	The Wonder Clock	1888	82-88, 242
MBPI1459	**The Old Woman breaks things**		**492**
PM0419	How Boots Befooled the King	December 1, 1885	83, 251
PM0642	The Wonder Clock	1888	82-88, 242
MBPI1460	**The Councilor finds the Wisdom Sack**		**492**
PM0419	How Boots Befooled the King	December 1, 1885	83, 251
PM0642	The Wonder Clock	1888	82-88, 242
MBPI1461	**Boots tricks the Princess into showing herself**		**492**
PM0419	How Boots Befooled the King	December 1, 1885	83, 251
MBPI1462	**Headpiece with title for How Three Went Out into the Wide World**		**492**
PM0420	How Three Went Out into Ye Wide World	December 29, 1885	83, 251
PM0642	The Wonder Clock	1888	82-88, 242
MBPI1463	**The Gray Goose meets the Sausage**		**492**
PM0420	How Three Went Out into Ye Wide World	December 29, 1885	83, 251
PM0642	The Wonder Clock	1888	82-88, 242
PM1209	Children's Books and Their Illustrators	December, 1897	97
MBPI1464	**The Fox calls on the Cock**		**492**
PM0420	How Three Went Out into Ye Wide World	December 29, 1885	83, 251
PM0642	The Wonder Clock	1888	82-88, 242
MBPI1465	**The Fox calls on the Sausage**		**492**
PM0420	How Three Went Out into Ye Wide World	December 29, 1885	83, 251
PM0642	The Wonder Clock	1888	82-88, 242
PM1353	Books For The Young	1899	269
MBPI1466	**The Fox's Wife makes his bed**		**492**
PM0420	How Three Went Out into Ye Wide World	December 29, 1885	83, 251
PM0642	The Wonder Clock	1888	82-88, 242
PM1353	Books For The Young	1899	269
MBPI1467	**Headpiece with title for The Princess Golden-Hair and the Great Black Raven**		**492**
PM0421	The Princess Golden Hair and the Great Black Raven	January 26, 1886	83, 251
PM0642	The Wonder Clock	1888	82-88, 242
MBPI1468	**The King meets the Great Black Raven in the Forest**		**492**
PM0421	The Princess Golden Hair and the Great Black Raven	January 26, 1886	83, 251
PM0642	The Wonder Clock	1888	82-88, 242
MBPI1469	**The Princess drinks from the Golden Cup**		**492**
PM0421	The Princess Golden Hair and the Great Black Raven	January 26, 1886	83, 251
PM0642	The Wonder Clock	1888	82-88, 242
MBPI1470	**The Princess comes to Gruff's Door**		**492**
PM0421	The Princess Golden Hair and the Great Black Raven	January 26, 1886	83, 251
PM0642	The Wonder Clock	1888	82-88, 242
MBPI1471	**The Princess finds her dear Prince again**		**492**
PM0421	The Princess Golden Hair and the Great Black Raven	January 26, 1886	83, 251
PM1339	Harper's Catalogue of Books For Boys & Girls	1887	266

PM0642	The Wonder Clock	1888	82-88, 242
MBPI1472	**Headpiece with title for The Clever Student and the Master of Black Arts**		**492**
PM0422	The Clever Student and the Master of Black Arts	February 23, 1886	83, 251
PM0642	The Wonder Clock	1888	82-88, 242
MBPI1473	**The Princess walking beside the Sea**		**493**
PM0422	The Clever Student and the Master of Black Arts	February 23, 1886	83, 251
PM1493	Book Reviews	December, 1887	5
PM0642	The Wonder Clock	1888	82-88, 242
MBPI1474	**The Student and the Princess**		**493**
PM0422	The Clever Student and the Master of Black Arts	February 23, 1886	83, 251
PM0642	The Wonder Clock	1888	82-88, 242
MBPI1475	**The Master of Black Arts with a Hen**		**493**
PM0422	The Clever Student and the Master of Black Arts	February 23, 1886	83, 251
PM0642	The Wonder Clock	1888	82-88, 242
MBPI1476	**What happened to the Master**		**493**
PM0422	The Clever Student and the Master of Black Arts	February 23, 1886	83, 251
PM0642	The Wonder Clock	1888	82-88, 242
MBPI1477	**Headpiece with title for Peterkin and the Little Gray Hare**		**493**
PM0423	Peterkin and the Little Gray Hare	March 23, 1886	84, 251
PM0642	The Wonder Clock	1888	82-88, 242
MBPI1478	**Peterkin's brothers marvel at his fine trappings**		**493**
PM0423	Peterkin and the Little Gray Hare	March 23, 1886	84, 251
PM0642	The Wonder Clock	1888	82-88, 242
MBPI1479	**Peterkin makes off with the Giant's Goose**		**493**
PM0423	Peterkin and the Little Gray Hare	March 23, 1886	84, 251
PM0642	The Wonder Clock	1888	82-88, 242
PM1200	Advertisement: The Wonder Clock	January 29, 1889	88
PM1209	Children's Books and Their Illustrators	December, 1897	97
MBPI1480	**Peterkin brings the Silver Bell to the King**		**493**
PM0423	Peterkin and the Little Gray Hare	March 23, 1886	84, 251
PM0642	The Wonder Clock	1888	82-88, 242
MBPI1481	**Peterkin dressed as a lass, and the Giant**		**493**
PM0423	Peterkin and the Little Gray Hare	March 23, 1886	84, 251
PM0642	The Wonder Clock	1888	82-88, 242
MBPI1482	**Headpiece with title for How the Good Gifts were Used by Two**		**493**
PM0424	How the Good Gifts were Used by Two	April 27, 1886	84, 251
PM0642	The Wonder Clock	1888	82-88, 242
MBPI1483	**Saint Nicholas at the Rich Man's Door**		**493**
PM0424	How the Good Gifts were Used by Two	April 27, 1886	84, 251
PM0642	The Wonder Clock	1888	82-88, 242
MBPI1484	**Saint Nicholas at the Poor Man's House**		**493**
PM0424	How the Good Gifts were Used by Two	April 27, 1886	84, 251
PM0642	The Wonder Clock	1888	82-88, 242
MBPI1485	**The Poor Man and St. Christopher**		**493**
PM0424	How the Good Gifts were Used by Two	April 27, 1886	84, 251
PM0642	The Wonder Clock	1888	82-88, 242
MBPI1486	**The Rich Man and the Two Saints**		**493**
PM0424	How the Good Gifts were Used by Two	April 27, 1886	84, 251
PM0642	The Wonder Clock	1888	82-88, 242
MBPI1487	**Headpiece with title for Mother Hildegarde**		**493**
PM0425	Mother Hildegarde	May 25, 1886	84, 251
PM0642	The Wonder Clock	1888	82-88, 242
MBPI1488	**Mother Hildegarde and the Princess**		**493**
PM0425	Mother Hildegarde	May 25, 1886	84, 251
PM1193	Advertisement: Books for Holiday Gifts	November 26, 1887	71
PM0642	The Wonder Clock	1888	82-88, 242
MBPI1489	**The Princess peeped into the Jar**		**494**
PM0425	Mother Hildegarde	May 25, 1886	84, 251
PM0642	The Wonder Clock	1888	82-88, 242
MBPI1490	**The Princess and the Pigeons**		**494**

PM0425	Mother Hildegarde	May 25, 1886	84, 251
PM0642	The Wonder Clock	1888	82-88, 242
MBPI1491	**Mother Hildegarde carries away the Baby**		**494**
PM0425	Mother Hildegarde	May 25, 1886	84, 251
PM0642	The Wonder Clock	1888	82-88, 242
MBPI1492	**Headpiece with title for Master Jacob**		**494**
PM0426	Master Jacob	June 29, 1886	84, 251
PM0642	The Wonder Clock	1888	82-88, 242
MBPI1493	**Master Jacob brings his Pig to Market**		**494**
PM0426	Master Jacob	June 29, 1886	84, 251
PM0642	The Wonder Clock	1888	82-88, 242
MBPI1494	**Master Jacob goes to Town with his Goat**		**494**
PM0426	Master Jacob	June 29, 1886	84, 251
PM0642	The Wonder Clock	1888	82-88, 242
MBPI1495	**The little tin horn has no effect**		**494**
PM0426	Master Jacob	June 29, 1886	84, 251
PM0642	The Wonder Clock	1888	82-88, 242
MBPI1496	**Master Jacob and the three Cronies meet in the Woods**		**494**
PM0426	Master Jacob	June 29, 1886	84, 251
PM0642	The Wonder Clock	1888	82-88, 242
MBPI1497	**Headpiece with title for How Three Little Pigs Had the Best of the Great Wicked Ogre**		**494**
PM0427	How Three Little Pigs Had the Best of the Great Wicked Ogre	July 27, 1886	84, 173, 251
PM0642	The Wonder Clock	1888	82-88, 242
MBPI1498	**"Have you a roasted apple to put in my mouth?"**		**494**
PM0427	How Three Little Pigs Had the Best of the Great Wicked Ogre	July 27, 1886	84, 173, 251
PM0642	The Wonder Clock	1888	82-88, 242
MBPI1499	**"Do you find the hole?" asked the Little Pig**		**494**
PM0427	How Three Little Pigs Had the Best of the Great Wicked Ogre	July 27, 1886	84, 173, 251
PM0642	The Wonder Clock	1888	82-88, 242
MBPI1500	**"The Ogre shut his eyes and began to count"**		**494**
PM0427	How Three Little Pigs Had the Best of the Great Wicked Ogre	July 27, 1886	84, 173, 251
PM0642	The Wonder Clock	1888	82-88, 242
MBPI1501	**"Here comes the farmer and his men to see what all the stir is about"**		**494**
PM0427	How Three Little Pigs Had the Best of the Great Wicked Ogre	July 27, 1886	84, 173, 251
PM0642	The Wonder Clock	1888	82-88, 242
MBPI1502	**Headpiece with title for The Staff and the Fiddle**		**494**
PM0428	The Staff and the Fiddle	August 31, 1886	85, 251
PM0642	The Wonder Clock	1888	82-88, 242
MBPI1503	**"Give the poor old Woman a penny or two"**		**494**
PM0428	The Staff and the Fiddle	August 31, 1886	85, 251
PM0642	The Wonder Clock	1888	82-88, 242
MBPI1504	**"'Rub-a-dub-dub!' says the Fiddler"**		**494**
PM0428	The Staff and the Fiddle	August 31, 1886	85, 251
PM0642	The Wonder Clock	1888	82-88, 242
MBPI1505	**A Princess as pretty as a ripe Apple**		**495**
PM0428	The Staff and the Fiddle	August 31, 1886	85, 251
PM0642	The Wonder Clock	1888	82-88, 242
PM1209	Children's Books and Their Illustrators	December, 1897	97
MBPI1506	**"What do you want, Master?"**		**495**
PM0428	The Staff and the Fiddle	August 31, 1886	85, 251
PM0642	The Wonder Clock	1888	82-88, 242
MBPI1507	**Headpiece with title for The Simpleton and his Little Black Hen**		**495**
PM0429	The Simpleton and His Little Black Hen	November 2, 1886	85, 251
PM0642	The Wonder Clock	1888	82-88, 242
MBPI1508	**Caspar and the cunning Landlord**		**495**
PM0429	The Simpleton and His Little Black Hen	November 2, 1886	85, 251
PM0642	The Wonder Clock	1888	82-88, 242
PM0998	De Vlaamse School	1898	145
MBPI1509	**Caspar finds the Gold in the Willow-Tree**		**495**
PM0429	The Simpleton and His Little Black Hen	November 2, 1886	85, 251

PM0642	The Wonder Clock	1888	82-88, 242
MBPI1510	**The Two Brothers and the Landlord divide the money**		**495**
PM0429	The Simpleton and His Little Black Hen	November 2, 1886	85, 251
PM0642	The Wonder Clock	1888	82-88, 242
MBPI1511	**Caspar and the Three rascals go to see the King**		**495**
PM0429	The Simpleton and His Little Black Hen	November 2, 1886	85, 251
PM0642	The Wonder Clock	1888	82-88, 242
MBPI1512	**Headpiece with title for King Stork**		**495**
PM0430	King Stork	November 30, 1886	85, 251
PM0642	The Wonder Clock	1888	82-88, 242
MBPI1513	**The Drummer carries the Old Man across the River**		**495**
PM0430	King Stork	November 30, 1886	85, 251
PM0642	The Wonder Clock	1888	82-88, 242
MBPI1514	**The Princess starts for the Witch's House**		**495**
PM0430	King Stork	November 30, 1886	85, 251
PM0642	The Wonder Clock	1888	82-88, 242
MBPI1515	**The Drummer with his Cap of Darkness in the Witch's House**		**495**
PM0430	King Stork	November 30, 1886	85, 251
PM0642	The Wonder Clock	1888	82-88, 242
MBPI1516	**The Drummer captures the one-eyed Raven**		**495**
PM0430	King Stork	November 30, 1886	85, 251
PM0642	The Wonder Clock	1888	82-88, 242
MBPI1517	**Headpiece with title for How the Princess's Pride was Broken**		**495**
PM0431	How the Princess's Pride was Broken	December 28, 1886	85, 251
PM0642	The Wonder Clock	1888	82-88, 242
MBPI1518	**The Gooseherd plays with a Golden Ball**		**495**
PM0431	How the Princess's Pride was Broken	December 28, 1886	85, 251
PM0642	The Wonder Clock	1888	82-88, 242
MBPI1519	**The King peeps over the hedge**		**495**
PM0431	How the Princess's Pride was Broken	December 28, 1886	85, 251
PM0642	The Wonder Clock	1888	82-88, 242
MBPI1520	**The Princess goes to Market with her Eggs**		**495**
PM0431	How the Princess's Pride was Broken	December 28, 1886	85, 251
PM0642	The Wonder Clock	1888	82-88, 242
MBPI1521	**King Florimel greets the Princess**		**496**
PM0431	How the Princess's Pride was Broken	December 28, 1886	85, 251
PM0642	The Wonder Clock	1888	82-88, 242
MBPI1522	**Dame Bridget's Prophecy**		**496**
PM0432	Dame Bridget's Prophecy	January 4, 1887	86, 251
MBPI1523	**Headpiece with title for How Two Went into Partnership**		**496**
PM0433	How Two Went into Partnership	January 25, 1887	86, 251
PM0642	The Wonder Clock	1888	82-88, 242
MBPI1524	**The Great Red Fox at the Store-house**		**496**
PM0433	How Two Went into Partnership	January 25, 1887	86, 251
PM0642	The Wonder Clock	1888	82-88, 242
MBPI1525	**"What are you doing here, Father Goat?"**		**496**
PM0433	How Two Went into Partnership	January 25, 1887	86, 251
PM0642	The Wonder Clock	1888	82-88, 242
MBPI1526	**"Which shall it be first–Sausages or Pudding?"**		**496**
PM0433	How Two Went into Partnership	January 25, 1887	86, 251
PM0642	The Wonder Clock	1888	82-88, 242
MBPI1527	**Uncle Bear and the Great Red Fox after Farmer John's Apples**		**496**
PM0433	How Two Went into Partnership	January 25, 1887	86, 251
PM0642	The Wonder Clock	1888	82-88, 242
MBPI1528	**Headpiece with title for Bearskin**		**496**
PM0434	Bearskin	March 1, 1887	86, 251
PM0642	The Wonder Clock	1888	82-88, 242
MBPI1529	**The basket with the baby in it drifted down the river**		**496**
PM0434	Bearskin	March 1, 1887	86, 251
PM0642	The Wonder Clock	1888	82-88, 242

MBPI1530	**Bearskin and the Princess**		**496**
PM0434	Bearskin	March 1, 1887	86, 251
PM0642	The Wonder Clock	1888	82-88, 242
MBPI1531	**The Princess wept and wept**		**496**
PM0434	Bearskin	March 1, 1887	86, 251
PM0642	The Wonder Clock	1888	82-88, 242
MBPI1532	**Bearskin and the Swineherd had a fine feast together**		**496**
PM0434	Bearskin	March 1, 1887	86, 251
PM0642	The Wonder Clock	1888	82-88, 242
MBPI1533	**Illustration for Hugo Grotius and His Book Chest**		**496**
PM0435	Hugo Grotius and His Book Chest	March 15, 1887	86
MBPI1534	**Headpiece with title for Cousin Greylegs, Ye Great Red Fox and Grandfather Mole**		**496**
PM0436	Cousin Greylegs, Ye Great Red Fox and Grandfather Mole	March 22, 1887	86, 251
PM0642	The Wonder Clock	1888	82-88, 242
MBPI1535	**"The Great Red Fox and Cousin Greylegs were great cronies"**		**496**
PM0436	Cousin Greylegs, Ye Great Red Fox and Grandfather Mole	March 22, 1887	86, 251
PM0642	The Wonder Clock	1888	82-88, 242
MBPI1536	**Cousin Greylegs steals away with the bag of nails**		**496**
PM0436	Cousin Greylegs, Ye Great Red Fox and Grandfather Mole	March 22, 1887	86, 251
PM0642	The Wonder Clock	1888	82-88, 242
MBPI1537	**Brother Fox comes near tramping on the Mole's House**		**497**
PM0436	Cousin Greylegs, Ye Great Red Fox and Grandfather Mole	March 22, 1887	86, 251
PM0642	The Wonder Clock	1888	82-88, 242
MBPI1538	**The Great Red Fox shut his teeth and grinned**		**497**
PM0436	Cousin Greylegs, Ye Great Red Fox and Grandfather Mole	March 22, 1887	86, 251
PM0642	The Wonder Clock	1888	82-88, 242
MBPI1539	**Headpiece and title for Which is Best?**		**497**
PM0437	Which is Best?	April 19, 1887	86, 251
PM0642	The Wonder Clock	1888	82-88, 242
PM1385	Advertisement: Books for Holiday Gifts	December, 1890	35
MBPI1540	**So the Rich Man left him in his blindness**		**497**
PM0437	Which is Best?	April 19, 1887	86, 251
PM0642	The Wonder Clock	1888	82-88, 242
MBPI1541	**He touched the lock with the little black stone**		**497**
PM0437	Which is Best?	April 19, 1887	86, 251
PM0642	The Wonder Clock	1888	82-88, 242
MBPI1542	**The Poor Brother opens the chest**		**497**
PM0437	Which is Best?	April 19, 1887	86, 251
PM0642	The Wonder Clock	1888	82-88, 242
MBPI1543	**The Rich Brother takes the diamond from the statue's hand**		**497**
PM0437	Which is Best?	April 19, 1887	86, 251
PM0642	The Wonder Clock	1888	82-88, 242
MBPI1544	**Headpiece with title for The Best that Life Has to Give**		**497**
PM0438	The Best that Life Has to Give	May 17, 1887	87, 251
PM0642	The Wonder Clock	1888	82-88, 242
MBPI1545	**"'So you are stealing my pine cones,' said he"**		**497**
PM0438	The Best that Life Has to Give	May 17, 1887	87, 251
PM0642	The Wonder Clock	1888	82-88, 242
MBPI1546	**He snatched it and ran**		**497**
PM0438	The Best that Life Has to Give	May 17, 1887	87, 251
PM0642	The Wonder Clock	1888	82-88, 242
MBPI1547	**The Blacksmith carries the Golden Tree to the Queen**		**497**
PM0438	The Best that Life Has to Give	May 17, 1887	87, 251
PM0642	The Wonder Clock	1888	82-88, 242
MBPI1548	**And that was the end of the Dwarf**		**497**
PM0438	The Best that Life Has to Give	May 17, 1887	87, 251
PM0642	The Wonder Clock	1888	82-88, 242
MBPI1549	**Headpiece with title for The Water of Life**		**497**
PM0439	The Water of Life	June 14, 1887	87, 251
PM0642	The Wonder Clock	1888	82-88, 242

MBPI1550	**A Stranger shows the King the portrait of a beautiful Princess**		**497**
PM0439	The Water of Life	June 14, 1887	87, 251
PM0642	The Wonder Clock	1888	82-88, 242
MBPI1551	**The Faithful Servant is borne on the wings of the North Wind**		**497**
PM0439	The Water of Life	June 14, 1887	87, 251
PM0642	The Wonder Clock	1888	82-88, 242
MBPI1552	**The King gives the Water of Life to the beautiful Princess**		**497**
PM0439	The Water of Life	June 14, 1887	87, 251
PM0642	The Wonder Clock	1888	82-88, 242
MBPI1553	**The King goes to cut off the Faithful Servant's arm**		**498**
PM0439	The Water of Life	June 14, 1887	87, 251
PM0642	The Wonder Clock	1888	82-88, 242
MBPI1554	**Headpiece with title for The Step-mother**		**498**
PM0440	The Stepmother	August 2, 1887	87, 251
PM0642	The Wonder Clock	1888	82-88, 242
MBPI1555	**The Step-daughter follows the Golden Ball**		**498**
PM0440	The Stepmother	August 2, 1887	87, 251
PM0642	The Wonder Clock	1888	82-88, 242
PM1209	Children's Books and Their Illustrators	December, 1897	97
PM1565	Howard Pyle, Author-Illustrator 1853-1911	February, 1912	2
MBPI1556	**The King rescues the Maiden from a deep pit**		**498**
PM0440	The Stepmother	August 2, 1887	87, 251
PM0642	The Wonder Clock	1888	82-88, 242
MBPI1557	**The Step-mother changes the Queen into a White Dove**		**498**
PM0440	The Stepmother	August 2, 1887	87, 251
PM0642	The Wonder Clock	1888	82-88, 242
MBPI1558	**The King caresses the White Dove**		**498**
PM0440	The Stepmother	August 2, 1887	87, 251
PM0642	The Wonder Clock	1888	82-88, 242
MBPI1559	**Headpiece with title for The White Bird**		**498**
PM0441	The White Bird	September 6, 1887	87, 251
PM0642	The Wonder Clock	1888	82-88, 242
MBPI1560	**The door was opened by a poor man**		**498**
PM0441	The White Bird	September 6, 1887	87, 251
PM0642	The Wonder Clock	1888	82-88, 242
MBPI1561	**There sat three terrible giants**		**498**
PM0441	The White Bird	September 6, 1887	87, 251
PM0642	The Wonder Clock	1888	82-88, 242
MBPI1562	**The Prince takes the Sword of Brightness**		**498**
PM0441	The White Bird	September 6, 1887	87, 251
PM0642	The Wonder Clock	1888	82-88, 242
MBPI1563	**The White Bird recognizes the Prince**		**498**
PM0441	The White Bird	September 6, 1887	87, 251
PM0642	The Wonder Clock	1888	82-88, 242
MBPI1564	**Headpiece with title for One Good Turn Deserves Another**		**498**
PM0442	One Good Turn Deserves Another	October 11, 1887	87, 251
PM0642	The Wonder Clock	1888	82-88, 242
MBPI1565	**The Fisher Lad catches a strange fish**		**498**
PM0442	One Good Turn Deserves Another	October 11, 1887	87, 251
PM0642	The Wonder Clock	1888	82-88, 242
PM0998	De Vlaamse School	1898	145
MBPI1566	**The Fisher Lad comes to the Gray Master's house**		**498**
PM0442	One Good Turn Deserves Another	October 11, 1887	87, 251
PM0642	The Wonder Clock	1888	82-88, 242
MBPI1567	**The Gray Master is caught in the stream and is swept away**		**498**
PM0442	One Good Turn Deserves Another	October 11, 1887	87, 251
PM0642	The Wonder Clock	1888	82-88, 242
MBPI1568	**The Princess finds the Fisher Lad with the key of Wish-House**		**498**
PM0442	One Good Turn Deserves Another	October 11, 1887	87, 251
PM0642	The Wonder Clock	1888	82-88, 242

MBPI1569	**Headpiece with title for The Three Fortunes**		**499**
PM0443	The Three Fortunes	June 26, 1888	88
MBPI1570	**He was an old man no longer, but a Blessed Angel**		**499**
PM0443	The Three Fortunes	June 26, 1888	88
MBPI1571	**The Angel and the Youngest Brother said "Good-bye" and trudged away**		**499**
PM0443	The Three Fortunes	June 26, 1888	88
MBPI1572	**A great, ugly, poisonous snake crept out of a hole in the wall**		**499**
PM0443	The Three Fortunes	June 26, 1888	88
MBPI1573	**They set before him a loaf of bread and a bowl of milk**		**499**
PM0443	The Three Fortunes	June 26, 1888	88
MBPI1574	**Headpiece with illustrated initial T for The Princess on the Glass Hill**		**499**
PM0444	The Princess on the Glass Hill	July 24, 1888	88
PM1479	Hotel Dupont, Wilmington, Delaware	1912	141, 310
MBPI1575	**The Prince pours water into the barrel**		**499**
PM0444	The Princess on the Glass Hill	July 24, 1888	88
MBPI1576	**The Prince bathes in the fountain**		**499**
PM0444	The Princess on the Glass Hill	July 24, 1888	88
PM1479	Hotel Dupont, Wilmington, Delaware	1912	141, 310
MBPI1577	**The Prince kills the Dragon**		**499**
PM0444	The Princess on the Glass Hill	July 24, 1888	88
MBPI1578	**The Prince wins the Golden Apple and the Silver Pear**		**499**
PM0444	The Princess on the Glass Hill	July 24, 1888	88
MBPI1579	**Headpiece with title and illustrated initial T for That Which is Done Never Dies**		**499**
PM0445	That Which is Done Never Dies	August 27, 1889	88
MBPI1580	**"A golden swan leaped into the air"**		**499**
PM0445	That Which is Done Never Dies	August 27, 1889	88
MBPI1581	**"As it sang it sang so sweetly and so sadly"**		**499**
PM0445	That Which is Done Never Dies	August 27, 1889	88
MBPI1582	**"The Princess sits in the window and sings"**		**499**
PM0445	That Which is Done Never Dies	August 27, 1889	88
MBPI1583	**"The King opened the closet door and brought forth the true bride"**		**499**
PM0445	That Which is Done Never Dies	August 27, 1889	88
MBPI1584	**"There sprang from the midst of the smoke a beautiful bird"**		**499**
PM0445	That Which is Done Never Dies	August 27, 1889	88
MBPI1585	**Headpiece with title for Ill-Luck and the Fiddler**		**500**
PM0446	Ill-Luck and the Fiddler	October 15, 1889	88
PM0651	Twilight Land	1895	237
MBPI1586	**Vignette for Ill-Luck and the Fiddler**		**500**
PM0446	Ill-Luck and the Fiddler	October 15, 1889	88
PM0651	Twilight Land	1895	237
MBPI1587	**Vignette for Ill-Luck and the Fiddler**		**500**
PM0446	Ill-Luck and the Fiddler	October 15, 1889	88
PM0651	Twilight Land	1895	237
MBPI1588	**Vignette for Ill-Luck and the Fiddler**		**500**
PM0446	Ill-Luck and the Fiddler	October 15, 1889	88
PM0651	Twilight Land	1895	237
MBPI1589	**Vignette for Ill-Luck and the Fiddler**		**500**
PM0446	Ill-Luck and the Fiddler	October 15, 1889	88
PM0651	Twilight Land	1895	237
MBPI1590	**Vignette for Ill-Luck and the Fiddler**		**500**
PM0446	Ill-Luck and the Fiddler	October 15, 1889	88
PM0651	Twilight Land	1895	237
MBPI1591	**Vignette for Ill-Luck and the Fiddler**		**500**
PM0446	Ill-Luck and the Fiddler	October 15, 1889	88
MBPI1592	**Headpiece with title for Wisdom's Wages and Folly's Pay**		**500**
PM0447	Wisdom's Wages and Folly's Pay	November 5, 1889	89
PM0651	Twilight Land	1895	237
MBPI1593	**Vignette for Wisdom's Wages and Folly's Pay**		**500**
PM0447	Wisdom's Wages and Folly's Pay	November 5, 1889	89
PM0651	Twilight Land	1895	237

MBPI1594	**Vignette for Wisdom's Wages and Folly's Pay**		**500**
PM0447	Wisdom's Wages and Folly's Pay	November 5, 1889	89
MBPI1595	**Vignette for Wisdom's Wages and Folly's Pay**		**500**
PM0447	Wisdom's Wages and Folly's Pay	November 5, 1889	89
PM0651	Twilight Land	1895	237
MBPI1596	**Vignette for Wisdom's Wages and Folly's Pay**		**500**
PM0447	Wisdom's Wages and Folly's Pay	November 5, 1889	89
PM0651	Twilight Land	1895	237
MBPI1597	**Vignette for Wisdom's Wages and Folly's Pay**		**500**
PM0447	Wisdom's Wages and Folly's Pay	November 5, 1889	89
PM0651	Twilight Land	1895	237
MBPI1598	**Vignette for Wisdom's Wages and Folly's Pay**		**500**
PM0447	Wisdom's Wages and Folly's Pay	November 5, 1889	89
PM0651	Twilight Land	1895	237
MBPI1599	**Vignette for Wisdom's Wages and Folly's Pay**		**500**
PM0447	Wisdom's Wages and Folly's Pay	November 5, 1889	89
PM0651	Twilight Land	1895	237
MBPI1600	**Headpiece with title for The Salt of Life**		**500**
PM0448	The Salt of Life I	January 7, 1890	89
PM0449	The Salt of Life II	January 14, 1890	89
PM1201	Advertisement: Harper's Young People	July 22, 1890	90
PM1202	Advertisement: Harper's Young People	August 26, 1890	90
PM0651	Twilight Land	1895	237
MBPI1601	**"Away with you, and never let me see your face again"**		**501**
PM0448	The Salt of Life I	January 7, 1890	89
PM0651	Twilight Land	1895	237
MBPI1602	**"An old man looked down into the water"**		**501**
PM0448	The Salt of Life I	January 7, 1890	89
PM0651	Twilight Land	1895	237
MBPI1603	**"The Queen raised the veil and looked at the Prince"**		**501**
PM0448	The Salt of Life I	January 7, 1890	89
PM0651	Twilight Land	1895	237
MBPI1604	**"Away the boat went, swifter than the wind"**		**501**
PM0448	The Salt of Life I	January 7, 1890	89
PM0651	Twilight Land	1895	237
MBPI1605	**"Beat the statue with her steel-tipped whip"**		**501**
PM0449	The Salt of Life II	January 14, 1890	89
PM0651	Twilight Land	1895	237
MBPI1606	**"The raven spread his wings and flew"**		**501**
PM0449	The Salt of Life II	January 14, 1890	89
PM0651	Twilight Land	1895	237
MBPI1607	**"At last they dashed against one another"**		**501**
PM0449	The Salt of Life II	January 14, 1890	89
PM0651	Twilight Land	1895	237
MBPI1608	**"The statue became flesh and blood"**		**501**
PM0449	The Salt of Life II	January 14, 1890	89
PM0651	Twilight Land	1895	237
MBPI1609	**"He had a noble feast set for them"**		**501**
PM0449	The Salt of Life II	January 14, 1890	89
PM0651	Twilight Land	1895	237
MBPI1610	**Headpiece with title for Empty Bottles**		**501**
PM0450	Empty Bottles	February 18, 1890	89
PM0651	Twilight Land	1895	237
MBPI1611	**"Making strange figures upon the table"**		**501**
PM0450	Empty Bottles	February 18, 1890	89
PM0651	Twilight Land	1895	237
MBPI11612	**"'Now,' said the Master, 'take me by the belt'"**		**501**
PM0450	Empty Bottles	February 18, 1890	89
PM0651	Twilight Land	1895	237
MBPI1613	**"He gazed and gazed until his heart melted within him"**		**501**

PM0450	Empty Bottles	February 18, 1890	89
PM0651	Twilight Land	1895	237
MBPI1614	**"The dragon leaped into the air"**		**501**
PM0450	Empty Bottles	February 18, 1890	89
PM0651	Twilight Land	1895	237
MBPI1615	**"He raised the dagger to strike"**		**501**
PM0450	Empty Bottles	February 18, 1890	89
PM0651	Twilight Land	1895	237
MBPI1616	**Headpiece with title for Where to Lay the Blame**		**501**
PM0451	Where to Lay the Blame	March 25, 1890	90
PM0651	Twilight Land	1895	237
PM1189	Emilio's Trick	July, 1899	64
MBPI1617	**"The old man began to utter strange spells"**		**502**
PM0451	Where to Lay the Blame	March 25, 1890	90
PM0651	Twilight Land	1895	237
MBPI1618	**"He caught something that weighed heavily as lead"**		**502**
PM0451	Where to Lay the Blame	March 25, 1890	90
PM0651	Twilight Land	1895	237
MBPI1619	**"They kissed one another"**		**502**
PM0451	Where to Lay the Blame	March 25, 1890	90
PM0651	Twilight Land	1895	237
MBPI1620	**"The chief treasurer emptied a bag of money into the fur cap"**		**502**
PM0451	Where to Lay the Blame	March 25, 1890	90
PM0651	Twilight Land	1895	237
MBPI1621	**"Down fell the fisherman"**		**502**
PM0451	Where to Lay the Blame	March 25, 1890	90
PM0651	Twilight Land	1895	237
MBPI1622	**Headpiece with title for Not a Pin to Choose**		**502**
PM0452	Not a Pin to Choose I	June 10, 1890	90
PM0651	Twilight Land	1895	237
MBPI1623	**"He was like one bereft of wits"**		**502**
PM0452	Not a Pin to Choose I	June 10, 1890	90
PM0651	Twilight Land	1895	237
MBPI1624	**"A wise man stopped to enquire the cause of his sorrow"**		**502**
PM0452	Not a Pin to Choose I	June 10, 1890	90
PM0651	Twilight Land	1895	237
MBPI1625	**"A great crowd of horses laden with balls and bundles of rich stuffs"**		**502**
PM0452	Not a Pin to Choose I	June 10, 1890	90
PM0651	Twilight Land	1895	237
MBPI1626	**"There was a passageway yawning before him"**		**502**
PM0452	Not a Pin to Choose I	June 10, 1890	90
PM0651	Twilight Land	1895	237
MBPI1627	**"Out leaped a great hideous Genie"**		**502**
PM0453	Not a Pin to Choose II	June 17, 1890	90
PM0651	Twilight Land	1895	237
MBPI1628	**"Bread as white as snow, and a piece of cheese"**		**502**
PM0453	Not a Pin to Choose II	June 17, 1890	90
PM0651	Twilight Land	1895	237
MBPI1629	**"Blazing with diamonds and rubies and emeralds"**		**502**
PM0453	Not a Pin to Choose II	June 17, 1890	90
PM0651	Twilight Land	1895	237
MBPI1630	**"The Princess looked over the edge of the balcony"**		**502**
PM0453	Not a Pin to Choose II	June 17, 1890	90
PM0651	Twilight Land	1895	237
MBPI1631	**"'Sire,' said the Ambassador, 'I will answer now for my master'"**		**502**
PM0453	Not a Pin to Choose II	June 17, 1890	90
PM0651	Twilight Land	1895	237
MBPI1632	**Headpiece with title for Woman's Wit**		**502**
PM0454	Woman's Wit	July 29, 1890	90
PM0651	Twilight Land	1895	237

MBPI1633	"A box of adamant"		**503**
PM0454	Woman's Wit	July 29, 1890	90
PM0651	Twilight Land	1895	237
MBPI1634	**"The little man set him to work on the bench"**		**503**
PM0454	Woman's Wit	July 29, 1890	90
PM0651	Twilight Land	1895	237
MBPI1635	**"It was the King's daughter passing by"**		**503**
PM0454	Woman's Wit	July 29, 1890	90
PM0651	Twilight Land	1895	237
MBPI1636	**"The young man prostrated himself in the dust"**		**503**
PM0454	Woman's Wit	July 29, 1890	90
PM0651	Twilight Land	1895	237
MBPI1637	**"Then prepare to die"**		**503**
PM0454	Woman's Wit	July 29, 1890	90
PM0651	Twilight Land	1895	237
MBPI1638	**Tailpiece for Woman's Wit**		**503**
PM0454	Woman's Wit	July 29, 1890	90
PM0651	Twilight Land	1895	237
MBPI1639	**Headpiece with title for Good Gifts and a Fool's Folly**		**503**
PM0455	Good Gifts and a Fool's Folly	September 9, 1890	90
PM0651	Twilight Land	1895	237
MBPI1640	**"An old man with a beard as white as snow"**		**503**
PM0455	Good Gifts and a Fool's Folly	September 9, 1890	90
PM0651	Twilight Land	1895	237
MBPI1641	**"Away flew the carpet swifter than the wind"**		**503**
PM0455	Good Gifts and a Fool's Folly	September 9, 1890	90
PM0651	Twilight Land	1895	237
MBPI1642	**"Every day there was feasting and dancing and singing"**		**503**
PM0455	Good Gifts and a Fool's Folly	September 9, 1890	90
PM0651	Twilight Land	1895	237
MBPI1643	**"He balanced the earthen jar on his head"**		**503**
PM0455	Good Gifts and a Fool's Folly	September 9, 1890	90
PM0651	Twilight Land	1895	237
MBPI1644	**"Around and around they spun and whirled"**		**503**
PM0455	Good Gifts and a Fool's Folly	September 9, 1890	90
PM0651	Twilight Land	1895	237
MBPI1645	**"He lay there sighing and groaning"**		**503**
PM0455	Good Gifts and a Fool's Folly	September 9, 1890	90
PM0651	Twilight Land	1895	237
MBPI1646	**Headpiece with title for All Things Are as Fate Wills**		**503**
PM0456	All Things are as Fate Wills	October 14, 1890	91
PM0651	Twilight Land	1895	237
PM1185	A True Ghost Story	July, 1898	64
MBPI1647	**"Three men seized him"**		**503**
PM0456	All Things are as Fate Wills	October 14, 1890	91
PM0651	Twilight Land	1895	237
MBPI1648	**"The King and the beggar feasted"**		**503**
PM0456	All Things are as Fate Wills	October 14, 1890	91
PM0651	Twilight Land	1895	237
MBPI1649	**"He knocked upon the brazen gate"**		**504**
PM0456	All Things are as Fate Wills	October 14, 1890	91
PM0651	Twilight Land	1895	237
MBPI1650	**"The beggar crawled out"**		**504**
PM0456	All Things are as Fate Wills	October 14, 1890	91
PM0651	Twilight Land	1895	237
MBPI1651	**"He was seated upon a throne"**		**504**
PM0456	All Things are as Fate Wills	October 14, 1890	91
PM0651	Twilight Land	1895	237
MBPI1652	**Headpiece with title for Much Shall Have More and Little Shall Have Less**		**504**
PM0457	Much Shall Have More and Little Shall Have Less	November 11, 1890	91

PM0651	Twilight Land	1895	237
PM1182	"Funny How-Do-You-Do's"	March 9, 1897	64
MBPI1653	**"He spread the money out on the table"**		**504**
PM0457	Much Shall Have More and Little Shall Have Less	November 11, 1890	91
PM0651	Twilight Land	1895	237
MBPI1654	**"Sat down by the road-side to eat his pie"**		**504**
PM0457	Much Shall Have More and Little Shall Have Less	November 11, 1890	91
PM0651	Twilight Land	1895	237
MBPI1655	**"He met a poor woman coming home from market"**		**504**
PM0457	Much Shall Have More and Little Shall Have Less	November 11, 1890	91
PM0651	Twilight Land	1895	237
MBPI1656	**"'Keep the bag of money for yourself,' said the King"**		**504**
PM0457	Much Shall Have More and Little Shall Have Less	November 11, 1890	91
PM0651	Twilight Land	1895	237
MBPI1657	**Headpiece with title for The Stool of Fortune**		**504**
PM0458	The Stool of Fortune	December 23, 1890	91
PM0651	Twilight Land	1895	237
MBPI1658	**"If the shot had cracked the sky he could not have been more frightened"**		**504**
PM0458	The Stool of Fortune	December 23, 1890	91
PM0651	Twilight Land	1895	237
MBPI1659	**"Away flew the stool"**		**504**
PM0458	The Stool of Fortune	December 23, 1890	91
PM0651	Twilight Land	1895	237
MBPI1660	**"The prettiest princess the sun ever shone upon"**		**504**
PM0458	The Stool of Fortune	December 23, 1890	91
PM0651	Twilight Land	1895	237
MBPI1661	**"Riding in his gilded coach"**		**504**
PM0458	The Stool of Fortune	December 23, 1890	91
PM1572	Advertisement on white mailing cover	October 2, 1894	96
PM0651	Twilight Land	1895	237
MBPI1662	**"What are my lord's commands?"**		**504**
PM0458	The Stool of Fortune	December 23, 1890	91
PM0651	Twilight Land	1895	237
MBPI1663	**Tailpiece for The Stool of Fortune**		**504**
PM0458	The Stool of Fortune	December 23, 1890	91
PM0651	Twilight Land	1895	237
MBPI1664	**Headpiece with title for The Fruit of Happiness**		**504**
PM0459	The Fruit of Happiness	January 13, 1891	91
PM0651	Twilight Land	1895	237
MBPI1665	**"He came to the cross-roads and the stone cross"**		**505**
PM0459	The Fruit of Happiness	January 13, 1891	91
PM0651	Twilight Land	1895	237
MBPI1666	**"He drew out his pipe, and began to play"**		**505**
PM0459	The Fruit of Happiness	January 13, 1891	91
PM0651	Twilight Land	1895	237
MBPI1667	**"In came the gang of thieves"**		**505**
PM0459	The Fruit of Happiness	January 13, 1891	91
PM0651	Twilight Land	1895	237
MBPI1668	**"All was a red blaze behind them"**		**505**
PM0459	The Fruit of Happiness	January 13, 1891	91
PM0651	Twilight Land	1895	237
MBPI1669	**"Went whirling over rocks and waterfalls"**		**505**
PM0459	The Fruit of Happiness	January 13, 1891	91
PM0651	Twilight Land	1895	237
MBPI1670	**The Flight from Falworth Castle**		**505**
PM0460	Men of Iron	January 20, 1891	92, 183
PM0647	Men of Iron	1892	92-94, 182
MBPI1671	**"Myles as in a dream kneeled, and presented the letter"**		**505**
PM0461	Men of Iron	January 27, 1891	92, 183
PM0647	Men of Iron	1892	92-94, 182

MBPI1672	**Illustration for Men of Iron**		**505**
PM0462	Men of Iron	February 3, 1891	92, 183
PM0924	Book Review	December, 1891	9
PM1118	Book Reviews	December, 1891	6
PM1134	"An Author-Artist's Book"	December, 1891	9
PM1386	A Selection of Books Suitable for Holiday Gifts	December, 1891	36
PM0647	Men of Iron	1892	92-94, 182
MBPI1673	**"At last they had the poor boy down"**		**505**
PM0463	Men of Iron	February 10, 1891	92, 183
PM0647	Men of Iron	1892	92-94, 182
MBPI1674	**"Myles pushed the door further open"**		**505**
PM0464	Men of Iron	February 17, 1891	92, 183
PM0647	Men of Iron	1892	92-94, 182
MBPI1675	**In the "Eyry"**		**505**
PM0465	Men of Iron	February 24, 1891	92, 183
PM0647	Men of Iron	1892	92-94, 182
MBPI1676	**"They bore him away to a bench at the far end of the room"**		**505**
PM0466	Men of Iron	March 3, 1891	92, 183
PM0647	Men of Iron	1892	92-94, 182
MBPI1677	**"But tell me, Robin Ingoldsby, dost know aught more of this matter?"**		**505**
PM0467	Men of Iron	March 10, 1891	92, 183
PM0647	Men of Iron	1892	92-94, 182
MBPI1678	**"'Belike thou sought to take this lad's life,' said Sir James"**		**505**
PM0468	Men of Iron	March 17, 1891	92, 183
PM0647	Men of Iron	1892	92-94, 182
MBPI1679	**"Stories and jests recited by some strolling mummer or minstrel"**		**505**
PM0469	Men of Iron	March 24, 1891	93, 183
PM0647	Men of Iron	1892	92-94, 182
MBPI1680	**Myles entertains the Lady Anne and the Lady Alice with his adventures**		**505**
PM0470	Men of Iron	March 31, 1891	93, 183
PM0647	Men of Iron	1892	92-94, 182
PM1413	The Entertaining Story Teller	1900	333
MBPI1681	**"Myles found himself standing beside the bed"**		**506**
PM0471	Men of Iron	April 7, 1891	93, 183
PM0647	Men of Iron	1892	92-94, 182
MBPI1682	**The Earl of Mackworth receives King Henry IV**		**506**
PM0472	Men of Iron	April 14, 1891	93, 183
PM0647	Men of Iron	1892	92-94, 182
MBPI1683	**"Lord George led him to where the King stood"**		**506**
PM0473	Men of Iron	April 21, 1891	93, 183
PM0647	Men of Iron	1892	92-94, 182
MBPI1684	**"There he watched and guarded while the others slept"**		**506**
PM0474	Men of Iron	April 28, 1891	93, 183
PM0647	Men of Iron	1892	92-94, 182
MBPI1685	**Illustration for Men of Iron**		**506**
PM0475	Men of Iron	May 5, 1891	93, 183
PM0647	Men of Iron	1892	92-94, 182
MBPI1686	**Illustration for Men of Iron**		**506**
PM0476	Men of Iron	May 12, 1891	93, 183
PM0647	Men of Iron	1892	92-94, 182
MBPI1687	**Prior Edward and Myles in the Priory Garden**		**506**
PM0477	Men of Iron	May 19, 1891	94, 183
PM0647	Men of Iron	1892	92-94, 182
MBPI1688	**The Challenge**		**506**
PM0478	Men of Iron	May 26, 1891	94, 183
PM0647	Men of Iron	1892	92-94, 182
MBPI1689	**Illustration for Men of Iron**		**506**
PM0479	Men of Iron	June 2, 1891	94, 183
PM0647	Men of Iron	1892	92-94, 182
MBPI1690	**"He held tightly to the saddle-bow of the fallen man's horse"**		**506**

PM0480	Men of Iron	June 9, 1891	94, 183
PM0647	Men of Iron	1892	92-94, 182
MBPI1691	**Headpiece with title for The Enchanted Island**		**506**
PM0481	The Enchanted Island I	December 15, 1891	94
PM0482	The Enchanted Island II	December 22, 1891	94
PM0651	Twilight Land	1895	237
MBPI1692	**"Selim the Fisherman finds a leaden box"**		**506**
PM0481	The Enchanted Island I	December 15, 1891	94
PM0651	Twilight Land	1895	237
MBPI1693	**"The old man rapped on the door three times"**		**506**
PM0481	The Enchanted Island I	December 15, 1891	94
PM0651	Twilight Land	1895	237
MBPI1694	**"There was feasting and merrymaking"**		**506**
PM0481	The Enchanted Island I	December 15, 1891	94
PM1121	More Holiday Books	January, 1893	7
PM0651	Twilight Land	1895	237
MBPI1695	**"The men brought Selim up in front of the statue"**		**506**
PM0651	Twilight Land	1895	237
MBPI1696	**"Selim the Baker lands on the desert island"**		**506**
PM0482	The Enchanted Island II	December 22, 1891	94
PM0651	Twilight Land	1895	237
MBPI1697	**"'Come with me,' said the little old man"**		**507**
PM0482	The Enchanted Island II	December 22, 1891	94
PM0651	Twilight Land	1895	237
MBPI1698	**"He called the wisest men of the island to him"**		**507**
PM0482	The Enchanted Island II	December 22, 1891	94
PM0651	Twilight Land	1895	237
MBPI1699	**"Down she came from the pedestal where she stood"**		**507**
PM0482	The Enchanted Island II	December 22, 1891	94
PM0651	Twilight Land	1895	237
MBPI1700	**Tailpiece for The Enchanted Island**		**507**
PM0482	The Enchanted Island II	December 22, 1891	94
PM0651	Twilight Land	1895	237
MBPI1701	**"Zadok and his master"**		**507**
PM0483	The Talisman of Solomon I	March 29, 1892	94
PM0651	Twilight Land	1895	237
MBPI1702	**"An old man who had a curious necklace for sale"**		**507**
PM0483	The Talisman of Solomon I	March 29, 1892	94
PM0651	Twilight Land	1895	237
MBPI1703	**"A vessel of brass full of money"**		**507**
PM0483	The Talisman of Solomon I	March 29, 1892	94
PM0651	Twilight Land	1895	237
MBPI1704	**"A great tall Demon"**		**507**
PM0483	The Talisman of Solomon I	March 29, 1892	94
PM0651	Twilight Land	1895	237
MBPI1705	**"He fell on his face and kissed the ground"**		**507**
PM0483	The Talisman of Solomon I	March 29, 1892	94
PM0651	Twilight Land	1895	237
MBPI1706	**"The Demon leaped from the earth"**		**507**
PM0483	The Talisman of Solomon I	March 29, 1892	94
PM0651	Twilight Land	1895	237
MBPI1707	**"A basin filled with jewels"**		**507**
PM0484	The Talisman of Solomon II	April 5, 1892	94
PM0651	Twilight Land	1895	237
MBPI1708	**"A palace of marble and gold"**		**507**
PM0484	The Talisman of Solomon II	April 5, 1892	94
PM0651	Twilight Land	1895	237
MBPI1709	**"'I think everybody has gone mad,' said the young man"**		**507**
PM0484	The Talisman of Solomon II	April 5, 1892	94
PM0651	Twilight Land	1895	237

MBPI1710	**"They entered the vestibule of the palace"**		**507**
PM0484	The Talisman of Solomon II	April 5, 1892	94
PM0651	Twilight Land	1895	237
MBPI1711	**"The young man fell upon his knees"**		**507**
PM0484	The Talisman of Solomon II	April 5, 1892	94
PM0651	Twilight Land	1895	237
MBPI1712	**"Drew a circle upon the ground with his finger-tip"**		**507**
PM0484	The Talisman of Solomon II	April 5, 1892	94
PM0651	Twilight Land	1895	237
MBPI1713	**"'This is my daughter,' said the merchant"**		**508**
PM0485	So It Is with Them All	November 1, 1892	95
MBPI1714	**"There sat an old woman at a wheel spinning"**		**508**
PM0485	So It Is with Them All	November 1, 1892	95
MBPI1715	**"Thou art a wonder of wonders"**		**508**
PM0485	So It Is with Them All	November 1, 1892	95
MBPI1716	**"A dense cloud of blue smoke rose in the air"**		**508**
PM0485	So It Is with Them All	November 1, 1892	95
MBPI1717	**"'I am ready,' said the young man steadily"**		**508**
PM0485	So It Is with Them All	November 1, 1892	95
MBPI1718	**"Flew away swifter than the wind"**		**508**
PM0485	So It Is with Them All	November 1, 1892	95
MBPI1719	**Headpiece with title for A Piece of Good Luck**		**508**
PM0486	A Piece of Good Luck I	April 10, 1894	95
PM0651	Twilight Land	1895	237
MBPI1720	**"They danced around and around the chest"**		**508**
PM0486	A Piece of Good Luck I	April 10, 1894	95
PM1608	Final Notes	December, 1894	7
PM0651	Twilight Land	1895	237
MBPI1721	**"'What will you have?' said the Genie"**		**508**
PM0486	A Piece of Good Luck I	April 10, 1894	95
PM0651	Twilight Land	1895	237
MBPI1722	**"Close your doors! close your doors! her Highness the Princess comes to ride"**		**508**
PM1486	Harper's Young People Annual	November 7, 1893	95
PM0486	A Piece of Good Luck I	April 10, 1894	95
PM0651	Twilight Land	1895	237
MBPI1723	**"The Genie had flown with her through the air"**		**508**
PM0486	A Piece of Good Luck I	April 10, 1894	95
PM0651	Twilight Land	1895	237
MBPI1724	**"Next morning the Prime Minister looked like a shorn sheep"**		**508**
PM0487	A Piece of Good Luck II	April 17, 1894	95
PM0651	Twilight Land	1895	237
MBPI1725	**"Jacob's magnificent court suit"**		**508**
PM0487	A Piece of Good Luck II	April 17, 1894	95
PM0651	Twilight Land	1895	237
MBPI1726	**"As for the King, he could not believe his eyes when he saw it"**		**508**
PM0487	A Piece of Good Luck II	April 17, 1894	95
PM0651	Twilight Land	1895	237
MBPI1727	**"Jacob and the King left in the desert by the Genie"**		**508**
PM0487	A Piece of Good Luck II	April 17, 1894	95
PM0651	Twilight Land	1895	237
MBPI1728	**"The Genie snatched the Minister up and flew away with him"**		**508**
PM0487	A Piece of Good Luck II	April 17, 1894	95
PM0651	Twilight Land	1895	237
MBPI1729	**Headpiece with title for The Good of a Few Words**		**509**
PM0488	The Good of a Few Words I	July 17, 1894	95
PM0651	Twilight Land	1895	237
MBPI1730	**"Feasting and drinking and junketing and merry-making"**		**509**
PM0488	The Good of a Few Words I	July 17, 1894	95
PM0651	Twilight Land	1895	237
MBPI1731	**"'Look at yonder poor man,' said she to her nurse"**		**509**

PM0488	The Good of a Few Words I	July 17, 1894	95
PM0651	Twilight Land	1895	237
MBPI1732	**"The tall man in black knocked upon the gate"**		**509**
PM0488	The Good of a Few Words I	July 17, 1894	95
PM0651	Twilight Land	1895	237
MBPI1733	**"'Now,' said the King, 'now you are married'"**		**509**
PM0488	The Good of a Few Words I	July 17, 1894	95
PM0651	Twilight Land	1895	237
MBPI1734	**"Then Beppo carried the Princess ashore"**		**509**
PM0488	The Good of a Few Words I	July 17, 1894	95
PM0651	Twilight Land	1895	237
MBPI1735	**"Again Sebastian served a feast"**		**509**
PM0489	The Good of a Few Words II	July 24, 1894	96
PM0651	Twilight Land	1895	237
MBPI1736	**"Beppo offers the King milk"**		**509**
PM0489	The Good of a Few Words II	July 24, 1894	96
PM0651	Twilight Land	1895	237
MBPI1737	**"'Alas, my poor friend!' said he"**		**509**
PM0489	The Good of a Few Words II	July 24, 1894	96
PM0651	Twilight Land	1895	237
MBPI1738	**"The King laid his hands on Beppo's shoulders"**		**509**
PM0489	The Good of a Few Words II	July 24, 1894	96
PM0651	Twilight Land	1895	237
MBPI1739	**"'Do you not know me?' said she; 'I am the Queen'"**		**509**
PM0489	The Good of a Few Words II	July 24, 1894	96
PM0651	Twilight Land	1895	237
MBPI1740	**"The werewolf…skulked for a moment in the shadow of the yews, and…Yseult plucked old Siegfried's spear from her girdle"**		**509**
PM0490	The Werewolf	March, 1896	98
PM1407	Ladies Home Journal Prints	1896	267
PM1410	The Werewolf	1896	331
PM1448	Auditorium Hotel, Chicago, Illinois	1896	284
PM0798	The Drexel Institute, Philadelphia, Pennsylvania	1897	8, 140, 268, 284
PM0799	St. Botolph Club, Boston, Massachusetts	1897	140, 268, 288
PM1553	Gilbert's Studio, Washington, D. C.	1898	293
MBPI1741	**"My dear," said General Washington, "Captain Prescott's behavior was inexcusable"**		**509**
PM0491	Love at Valley Forge	December, 1896	98
PM1448	Auditorium Hotel, Chicago, Illinois	1896	284
PM0798	The Drexel Institute, Philadelphia, Pennsylvania	1897	8, 140, 268, 284
PM0799	St. Botolph Club, Boston, Massachusetts	1897	140, 268, 288
PM1553	Gilbert's Studio, Washington, D. C.	1898	293
MBPI1742	**Spirit of Spring**		**509**
PM0492	Cover Design	May, 1897	98
MBPI1743	**George and Martha Washington entertaining their friends on the lawn at Mount Vernon**		**509**
PM0493	The Last Years of Washington's Life	October, 1899	98
MBPI1744	**"He called on Franklin and received the necessary recognition"**		**509**
PM0494	The Man for the Hour	December, 1899	101
MBPI1745	**"The good, aged Doctor, the appearance of whose rotund figure on the streets was the signal for the Parisians to doff their hats"**		**510**
PM0494	The Man for the Hour	December, 1899	101
MBPI1746	**"At the same time he extended toward King Louis the precious Memorial"**		**510**
PM0494	The Man for the Hour	December, 1899	101
MBPI1747	**The Death of Colonel John Laurens**		**510**
PM0494	The Man for the Hour	December, 1899	101
MBPI1748	**Cover design for McClure's Magazine**		**510**
PM0495	Cover Design	January, 1900	101
MBPI1749	**Headband for At the Turn of the Glass**		**510**
PM0496	At the Turn of the Glass	December, 1900	101
MBPI1750	**At the Turn of the Glass**		**510**
PM0496	At the Turn of the Glass	December, 1900	101

MBPI1751	**Marginal decoration for At the Turn of the Glass**		**510**
PM0496	At the Turn of the Glass	December, 1900	101
MBPI1752	**Uncle Sammy and Joe**		**510**
PM0497	The Chase of the Tide	August, 1901	101
MBPI1753	**Headpiece with title and initial T for The Chase of the Tide**		**510**
PM0497	The Chase of the Tide	August, 1901	101
MBPI1754	**Marginal illustration for The Chase of the Tide**		**510**
PM0497	The Chase of the Tide	August, 1901	101
MBPI1755	**Vignette for The Chase of the Tide**		**510**
PM0497	The Chase of the Tide	August, 1901	101
MBPI1756	**Illustration for The Chase of the Tide**		**510**
PM0497	The Chase of the Tide	August, 1901	101
MBPI1757	**"The Sea–He've cotched us!"**		**510**
PM0497	The Chase of the Tide	August, 1901	101
PM1085	The Way of The Sea	1903	241
MBPI1758	**"The tall man was lying at his feet, huddled hideously on the floor"**		**510**
PM0498	The Second-Class Passenger	October, 1906	101
PM1479	Hotel Dupont, Wilmington, Delaware	1912	141, 310
PM1481	Panama and Pacific International Exhibition, San Francisco, California	1915	315
MBPI1759	**Headband for The Second-Class Passenger**		**510**
PM0498	The Second-Class Passenger	October, 1906	101
MBPI1760	**"I have been reserved for this–to free the land from spiritual tyranny"**		**510**
PM0499	The Hanging of Mary Dyer	November, 1906	101
PM0777	Dulcibel, A Tale of Old Salem	1907	149
MBPI1761	**"The Lord hath sent me here to die like Stephen at the feet of Saul"**		**511**
PM0499	The Hanging of Mary Dyer	November, 1906	101
PM0777	Dulcibel, A Tale of Old Salem	1907	149
MBPI1762	**"At her appearing the multitude was hushed, awed by that air she wore"**		**511**
PM0499	The Hanging of Mary Dyer	November, 1906	101
PM1283	McClure's Magazine November	1906	328
PM1427	The Execution of Mary Dyer	1906	340
PM0777	Dulcibel, A Tale of Old Salem	1907	149
MBPI1763	**Headpiece with title for The Captain's Well**		**511**
PM0500	The Captain's Well	January 11, 1890	104
PM0703	The Captain's Well	1890	139
PM1340	The New York Ledger Announcement for 1890	1890	266
MBPI1764	**Illustration for The Captain's Well**		**511**
PM0500	The Captain's Well	January 11, 1890	104
PM1580	Advertisement: The Captain's Well	March 1, 1890	104
PM0703	The Captain's Well	1890	139
PM1340	The New York Ledger Announcement for 1890	1890	266
MBPI1765	**Illustration for The Captain's Well**		**511**
PM0500	The Captain's Well	January 11, 1890	104
PM0703	The Captain's Well	1890	139
MBPI1766	**Illustration for The Captain's Well**		**511**
PM0500	The Captain's Well	January 11, 1890	104
PM0703	The Captain's Well	1890	139
MBPI1767	**Illustration for The Captain's Well**		**511**
PM0500	The Captain's Well	January 11, 1890	104
PM0703	The Captain's Well	1890	139
MBPI1768	**"He lay silent and still, with his face half buried in the sand"**		**511**
PM0501	Blueskin the Pirate	December, 1890	105
PM1101	Blueskin the Pirate III	September 3, 1910	3
PM1104	Tenth Anniversary Issue	July 1, 1916	3
PM1033	The Miller's Holiday	1920	185
MBPI1769	**"He struck once and again at the bald, narrow forehead beneath him"**		**511**
PM0502	Captain Scarfield	December, 1900	105
PM1103	Captain Scarfield II	December 2, 1911	3
MBPI1770	**"A child, sunburned, and with many fluttering shreds of raiment"**		**511**
PM0503	Under Green Apple Boughs	February 15, 1882	105

PM0679	Under Green Apple Boughs	1882	105, 240
MBPI1771	**"She hadn't on anything but a little nightgown, the same as if they'd snatched her out o' the berth, with no time to dress her"**		**511**
PM0504	Under Green Apple Boughs	February 22, 1882	105
PM0679	Under Green Apple Boughs	1882	105, 240
MBPI1772	**"Then turned to the table where master and pupil sat absorbed"**		**511**
PM0505	Under Green Apple Boughs	March 1, 1882	105
PM0679	Under Green Apple Boughs	1882	105, 240
MBPI1773	**Sylvia's troubles**		**511**
PM0506	Under Green Apple Boughs	March 8, 1882	105
PM0679	Under Green Apple Boughs	1882	105, 240
MBPI1774	**"She wasn't no kin when I marr'ed her, but we've lived together over thirty year"**		**511**
PM0507	Under Green Apple Boughs	March 15, 1882	105
MBPI1775	**The fight in the fog**		**511**
PM0508	Under Green Apple Boughs	March 22, 1882	105
PM0679	Under Green Apple Boughs	1882	105, 240
MBPI1776	**The Gosling states his opinion of the Cock**		**511**
PM0509	The Crafty Fox	February, 1877	116
MBPI1777	**The Gosling is punished**		**512**
PM0509	The Crafty Fox	February, 1877	116
MBPI1778	**The Fox and the Tablet**		**512**
PM0510	The Fox and the Tablet	April, 1877	116
MBPI1779	**The Swineherd who knew curious things**		**512**
PM0511	Hans Gottenlieb, the Fiddler	April, 1877	116
MBPI1780	**Gottenlieb's music works a charm**		**512**
PM0511	Hans Gottenlieb, the Fiddler	April, 1877	116
PM1059	St. Nicholas Songs	1885	214
MBPI1781	**Pictorial Puzzle**		**512**
PM0512	The Riddle-Box	July, 1877	116
MBPI1782	**The King and his Prime Minister**		**512**
PM0513	Drummer Fritz and His Exploits	September, 1877	116
MBPI1783	**Fritz guides the Baron**		**512**
PM0513	Drummer Fritz and His Exploits	September, 1877	116
PM1252	An Abbreviation of "The History of St. Nicholas"	November, 1878	117
MBPI1784	**"I have brought you the Baron's head"**		**512**
PM0513	Drummer Fritz and His Exploits	September, 1877	116
MBPI1785	**The Princess and her Pigs**		**512**
PM0513	Drummer Fritz and His Exploits	September, 1877	116
MBPI1786	**"Poor Piggy led the way"**		**512**
PM0513	Drummer Fritz and His Exploits	September, 1877	116
MBPI1787	**The Royal Bodyguard**		**512**
PM0513	Drummer Fritz and His Exploits	September, 1877	116
MBPI1788	**Tailpiece for Drummer Fritz and His Exploits**		**512**
PM0513	Drummer Fritz and His Exploits	September, 1877	116
MBPI1789	**Kitty and Turkish Merchant**		**512**
PM0515	How Kitty was Lost in a Turkish Bazaar	April, 1878	116
MBPI1790	**"A very little old man seated in a very large chair"**		**512**
PM0516	Wise Catherine and the Kaboutermanneken	April, 1878	117
MBPI1791	**"He examined with astonishment and delight"**		**512**
PM0516	Wise Catherine and the Kaboutermanneken	April, 1878	117
MBPI1792	**"A page was appointed to escort it"**		**512**
PM0516	Wise Catherine and the Kaboutermanneken	April, 1878	117
MBPI1793	**"The king sat upon a chair of state, with a learned judge at each side"**		**513**
PM0516	Wise Catherine and the Kaboutermanneken	April, 1878	117
MBPI1794	**An Old-time May-Day in "Merrie England"**		**513**
PM1295	The Illustrated Magazines for May	April 20, 1878	103
PM0517	The Story of May-Day	May, 1878	117
MBPI1795	**Illustration for How Willy-Wolly Went A-Fishing**		**513**
PM0518	How Willy-Wolly Went A-Fishing	June, 1878	117
MBPI1796	**Illustration for How Willy-Wolly Went A-Fishing**		**513**

PM0518	How Willy-Wolly Went A-Fishing	June, 1878	117
MBPI1797	**Illustration for How Willy-Wolly Went A-Fishing**		**513**
PM1296	The Illustrated Magazines for June	May 22, 1878	103
PM0518	How Willy-Wolly Went A-Fishing	June, 1878	117
MBPI1798	**The Fox, the Monkey, and the Pig**		**513**
PM0519	The Fox, the Monkey, and the Pig	September, 1878	117
MBPI1799	**"As good as new"**		**513**
PM0520	About Violins	February, 1879	117
MBPI1800	**Tailpiece for The Origin of the Jumping-Jack**		**513**
PM0521	The Origin of the Jumping-Jack	February, 1879	117
MBPI1801	**The Gourd and the Oak**		**513**
PM0522	The Gourd and the Oak	May, 1879	117
MBPI1802	**Front cover design for The Price of Blood**		**513**
PM0653	The Price of Blood	1899	15, 204
MBPI1803	**Bluetree declines Lord Diddledaddle's offer**		**513**
PM0524	Robin Goodfellow and His Friend Bluetree	June, 1879	117
MBPI1804	**A Bowl of Milk for Robin Goodfellow**		**513**
PM0524	Robin Goodfellow and His Friend Bluetree	June, 1879	117
MBPI1805	**A Great Black Bear came out of the Woods**		**513**
PM0524	Robin Goodfellow and His Friend Bluetree	June, 1879	117
MBPI1806	**Gretelein and the Elf King**		**513**
PM0525	Gretelein and Her Queer Stove	September, 1879	117
MBPI1807	**Back cover design for The Price of Blood**		**513**
PM0653	The Price of Blood	1899	15, 204
MBPI1808	**"A Person of Consequence, carefully fed and attended to"**		**513**
PM0526	Fables	December, 1879	118
MBPI1809	**"Edmund Burton, you are a genius!"**		**514**
PM0527	Phaeton Rogers	January, 1881	118
MBPI1810	**The Boys consult Jack-in-the-Box**		**514**
PM0527	Phaeton Rogers	January, 1881	118
PM0673	Phaeton Rogers	1881	202
MBPI1811	**Jupiter and the Philosopher**		**514**
PM0528	A Fable from Deacon Green	February, 1881	118
MBPI1812	**"One of the policemen produced a bull's-eye lantern"**		**514**
PM0529	Phaeton Rogers	March, 1881	118
MBPI1813	**"The clown counted the money"**		**514**
PM0529	Phaeton Rogers	March, 1881	118
MBPI1814	**"They used to drill every evening"**		**514**
PM0530	The Soldiering of Beniah Stidham	December, 1892	118
PM1447	World's Columbian Exposition, Chicago, Illinois	1893	283
PM1524	Boys and Girls Bookshelf: True Stories from Every Land	1920	137
MBPI1815	**Headpiece with title and initial W for The Soldiering of Beniah Stidham**		**514**
PM0530	The Soldiering of Beniah Stidham	December, 1892	118
MBPI1816	**Vignette for The Soldiering of Beniah Stidham**		**514**
PM0530	The Soldiering of Beniah Stidham	December, 1892	118
MBPI1817	**Vignette for The Soldiering of Beniah Stidham**		**514**
PM0530	The Soldiering of Beniah Stidham	December, 1892	118
MBPI1818	**Vignette for The Soldiering of Beniah Stidham**		**514**
PM0530	The Soldiering of Beniah Stidham	December, 1892	118
PM0936	Howard Pyle–Maker of Pictures and Stories	May, 1915	124
MBPI1819	**Vignette for The Soldiering of Beniah Stidham**		**514**
PM0530	The Soldiering of Beniah Stidham	December, 1892	118
PM0936	Howard Pyle–Maker of Pictures and Stories	May, 1915	124
MBPI1820	**Vignette for The Soldiering of Beniah Stidham**		**514**
PM0530	The Soldiering of Beniah Stidham	December, 1892	118
MBPI1821	**Vignette for The Soldiering of Beniah Stidham**		**514**
PM0530	The Soldiering of Beniah Stidham	December, 1892	118
MBPI1822	**Vignette for The Soldiering of Beniah Stidham**		**514**
PM0530	The Soldiering of Beniah Stidham	December, 1892	118
MBPI1823	**Vignette for The Soldiering of Beniah Stidham**		**514**

PM0530	The Soldiering of Beniah Stidham	December, 1892	118
MBPI1824	**Uncle and Nephew–"Well, Jacky, you shall have that hundred pounds, you shall"**		**514**
PM0531	Jack Ballister's Fortunes	April, 1894	118, 219
PM1405	St. Nicholas	1894	326
PM1344	Catalogue of the Century Company's Posters	1896	267
MBPI1825	**"'He'll come to by and by; he's only stunned a trifle,' said the Captain"**		**515**
PM0532	Jack Ballister's Fortunes	May, 1894	119, 219
PM0649	The Story of Jack Ballister's Fortunes	1895	119-120, 219
MBPI1826	**"'Now then, Gentlemen, how much do you bid for this boy?' said the auctioneer"**		**515**
PM0533	Jack Ballister's Fortunes	June, 1894	119, 219
PM1148	Advertisement: Century Co's publications	November, 1895	12
PM0649	The Story of Jack Ballister's Fortunes	1895	119-120, 219
MBPI1827	**"'Speak up, boy,–speak up,' said the gentleman"**		**515**
PM0534	Jack Ballister's Fortunes	July, 1894	119, 219
PM0649	The Story of Jack Ballister's Fortunes	1895	119-120, 219
MBPI1828	**"Mr. Parker stood looking at his visitor with his usual calm reserve"**		**515**
PM0535	Jack Ballister's Fortunes	August, 1894	119, 219
PM0649	The Story of Jack Ballister's Fortunes	1895	119-120, 219
PM0984	Barnes's School History of the United States	1903	134
MBPI1829	**"I don't want to be anybody's servant, lady, and wouldn't if I could help it"**		**515**
PM0536	Jack Ballister's Fortunes	September, 1894	119, 219
PM0649	The Story of Jack Ballister's Fortunes	1895	119-120, 219
PM1125	Book Reviews	December, 1895	7
MBPI1830	**"He picked up the bird and held it out at arm's length"**		**515**
PM0537	Jack Ballister's Fortunes	October, 1894	119, 219
PM0649	The Story of Jack Ballister's Fortunes	1895	119-120, 219
MBPI1831	**"He led Jack up to a man who sat on a barrel"**		**515**
PM0538	Jack Ballister's Fortunes	November, 1894	119, 219
PM0649	The Story of Jack Ballister's Fortunes	1895	119-120, 219
MBPI1832	**"Jack followed the Captain and the young lady up the crooked path to the house"**		**515**
PM0539	Jack Ballister's Fortunes	December, 1894	119, 219
PM0649	The Story of Jack Ballister's Fortunes	1895	119-120, 219
MBPI1833	**"They found her still sitting in the same place"**		**515**
PM0540	Jack Ballister's Fortunes	January, 1895	120, 219
PM0649	The Story of Jack Ballister's Fortunes	1895	119-120, 219
MBPI1834	**Governor Spottiswood visits Colonel Parker**		**515**
PM0541	Jack Ballister's Fortunes	February, 1895	120, 219
MBPI1835	**Jack and Dred rescue Eleanor–The Start**		**515**
PM0542	Jack Ballister's Fortunes	March, 1895	120, 219
PM0649	The Story of Jack Ballister's Fortunes	1895	119-120, 219
MBPI1836	**The pirates fire upon the fugitives**		**515**
PM0543	Jack Ballister's Fortunes	April, 1895	120, 219
PM0649	The Story of Jack Ballister's Fortunes	1895	119-120, 219
MBPI1837	**"Colonel Parker reached out and laid his hand upon Jack's shoulder; 'Ay,' said he, 'tis a good, honest face'"**		**515**
PM0545	Jack Ballister's Fortunes	June, 1895	120, 219
PM0649	The Story of Jack Ballister's Fortunes	1895	119-120, 219
MBPI1838	**Blackbeard's last fight**		**515**
PM0546	Jack Ballister's Fortunes	July, 1895	120, 219
PM0649	The Story of Jack Ballister's Fortunes	1895	119-120, 219
PM0995	The Century Book of the American Colonies	1900	142
MBPI1839	**"'Then I will come,' said he"**		**515**
PM0548	Jack Ballister's Fortunes	September, 1895	120, 219
PM0649	The Story of Jack Ballister's Fortunes	1895	119-120, 219
MBPI1840	**Title with illustrated initial T for The Story of King Arthur and His Knights**		**515**
PM0549	The Story of King Arthur and His Knights	November, 1902	121, 223
PM0657	The Story of King Arthur and His Knights	1903	121-124, 220
MBPI1841	**The Enchanter Merlin**		**516**
PM0549	The Story of King Arthur and His Knights	November, 1902	121, 223
PM0657	The Story of King Arthur and His Knights	1903	121-124, 220

PM1464	Art Institute of Chicago, Chicago, Illinois	1903	130, 297
PM1470	St. Botolph Club, Boston, Massachusetts	1906	303
PM1479	Hotel Dupont, Wilmington, Delaware	1912	141, 310
MBPI1842	**Headpiece for The Story of King Arthur and His Knights**		**516**
PM0549	The Story of King Arthur and His Knights	November, 1902	121, 223
PM0657	The Story of King Arthur and His Knights	1903	121-124, 220
PM1464	Art Institute of Chicago, Chicago, Illinois	1903	130, 297
MBPI1843	**Illustrated initial A for The Story of King Arthur and His Knights**		**516**
PM0549	The Story of King Arthur and His Knights	November, 1902	121, 223
MBPI1844	**Title with illustrated initial H for The Story of King Arthur and His Knights**		**516**
PM0549	The Story of King Arthur and His Knights	November, 1902	121, 223
MBPI1845	**How one clad all in black did a wonder before King Leodegrance of Camilard**		**516**
PM0549	The Story of King Arthur and His Knights	November, 1902	121, 223
MBPI1846	**Sir Kay overthroweth his Enemies**		**516**
PM1257	Advertisement: The Story of King Arthur And His Knights	October, 1902	121
PM0549	The Story of King Arthur and His Knights	November, 1902	121, 223
PM1536	Advertisement: The Story of King Arthur And His Knights	November, 1902	121
PM0657	The Story of King Arthur and His Knights	1903	121-124, 220
PM1472	Pratt Institute, Brooklyn, New York	1908	106, 306
PM1479	Hotel Dupont, Wilmington, Delaware	1912	141, 310
MBPI1847	**Illustrated initial I for The Story of King Arthur and His Knights**		**516**
PM0549	The Story of King Arthur and His Knights	November, 1902	121, 223
MBPI1848	**Title with illustrated initial S for The Story of King Arthur and His Knights**		**516**
PM0549	The Story of King Arthur and His Knights	November, 1902	121, 223
PM0657	The Story of King Arthur and His Knights	1903	121-124, 220
MBPI1849	**Sir Kay breaketh his sword at ye Tournament**		**516**
PM0549	The Story of King Arthur and His Knights	November, 1902	121, 223
PM0657	The Story of King Arthur and His Knights	1903	121-124, 220
PM1464	Art Institute of Chicago, Chicago, Illinois	1903	130, 297
MBPI1850	**Headpiece for The Story of King Arthur and His Knights**		**516**
PM0550	The Story of King Arthur and His Knights	December, 1902	121, 223
PM0657	The Story of King Arthur and His Knights	1903	121-124, 220
PM1464	Art Institute of Chicago, Chicago, Illinois	1903	130, 297
MBPI1851	**Title with illustrated initial S for The Story of King Arthur and His Knights**		**516**
PM0550	The Story of King Arthur and His Knights	December, 1902	121, 223
PM0657	The Story of King Arthur and His Knights	1903	121-124, 220
MBPI1852	**Sir Kay showeth the mystic Sword unto Sir Ector**		**516**
PM0550	The Story of King Arthur and His Knights	December, 1902	121, 223
PM0657	The Story of King Arthur and His Knights	1903	121-124, 220
PM1464	Art Institute of Chicago, Chicago, Illinois	1903	130, 297
MBPI1853	**Title with illustrated initial K for The Story of King Arthur and His Knights**		**516**
PM0550	The Story of King Arthur and His Knights	December, 1902	121, 223
MBPI1854	**King Leodegrance cometh to the assay of the Sword**		**516**
PM0550	The Story of King Arthur and His Knights	December, 1902	121, 223
MBPI1855	**Title with illustrated initial K for The Story of King Arthur and His Knights**		**516**
PM0551	The Story of King Arthur and His Knights	January, 1903	121, 223
PM0657	The Story of King Arthur and His Knights	1903	121-124, 220
MBPI1856	**How Arthur drew forth Ye Sword**		**516**
PM0551	The Story of King Arthur and His Knights	January, 1903	121, 223
PM0657	The Story of King Arthur and His Knights	1903	121-124, 220
PM1464	Art Institute of Chicago, Chicago, Illinois	1903	130, 297
PM1470	St. Botolph Club, Boston, Massachusetts	1906	303
MBPI1857	**Headpiece for The Story of King Arthur and His Knights**		**517**
PM0551	The Story of King Arthur and His Knights	January, 1903	121, 223
PM0657	The Story of King Arthur and His Knights	1903	121-124, 220
PM1464	Art Institute of Chicago, Chicago, Illinois	1903	130, 297
MBPI1858	**Title with illustrated initial K for The Story of King Arthur and His Knights**		**517**
PM0551	The Story of King Arthur and His Knights	January, 1903	121, 223
PM0657	The Story of King Arthur and His Knights	1903	121-124, 220
MBPI1859	**King Arthur of Britain**		**517**

PM0551	The Story of King Arthur and His Knights	January, 1903	121, 223
PM0657	The Story of King Arthur and His Knights	1903	121-124, 220
PM1464	Art Institute of Chicago, Chicago, Illinois	1903	130, 297
MBPI1860	**Illustrated initial S for The Story of King Arthur and His Knights**		**517**
PM0552	The Story of King Arthur and His Knights	February, 1903	122, 223
MBPI1861	**Title with illustrated initial I for The Story of King Arthur and His Knights**		**517**
PM0552	The Story of King Arthur and His Knights	February, 1903	122, 223
PM0657	The Story of King Arthur and His Knights	1903	121-124, 220
MBPI1862	**In the Valley of Delight**		**517**
PM0552	The Story of King Arthur and His Knights	February, 1903	122, 223
PM0657	The Story of King Arthur and His Knights	1903	121-124, 220
PM1464	Art Institute of Chicago, Chicago, Illinois	1903	130, 297
MBPI1863	**Title with illustrated initial T for The Story of King Arthur and His Knights**		**517**
PM0552	The Story of King Arthur and His Knights	February, 1903	122, 223
PM0657	The Story of King Arthur and His Knights	1903	121-124, 220
MBPI1864	**The Battle with the Sable Knight**		**517**
PM0552	The Story of King Arthur and His Knights	February, 1903	122, 223
PM0657	The Story of King Arthur and His Knights	1903	121-124, 220
PM1464	Art Institute of Chicago, Chicago, Illinois	1903	130, 297
MBPI1865	**The Winning of a Sword and a Queen**		**517**
PM0553	The Story of King Arthur and His Knights	March, 1903	122, 223
PM0657	The Story of King Arthur and His Knights	1903	121-124, 220
MBPI1866	**Title with illustrated initial E for The Story of King Arthur and His Knights**		**517**
PM0553	The Story of King Arthur and His Knights	March, 1903	122, 223
PM0657	The Story of King Arthur and His Knights	1903	121-124, 220
MBPI1867	**Excalibur the Sword**		**517**
PM0553	The Story of King Arthur and His Knights	March, 1903	122, 223
PM0657	The Story of King Arthur and His Knights	1903	121-124, 220
PM1464	Art Institute of Chicago, Chicago, Illinois	1903	130, 297
PM0930	Art in Illustration	July, 1905	10
MBPI1868	**Title with illustrated initial T for The Story of King Arthur and His Knights**		**517**
PM0553	The Story of King Arthur and His Knights	March, 1903	122, 223
PM0657	The Story of King Arthur and His Knights	1903	121-124, 220
MBPI1869	**The Lady Guinevere**		**517**
PM0553	The Story of King Arthur and His Knights	March, 1903	122, 223
PM0657	The Story of King Arthur and His Knights	1903	121-124, 220
PM1464	Art Institute of Chicago, Chicago, Illinois	1903	130, 297
PM1470	St. Botolph Club, Boston, Massachusetts	1906	303
MBPI1870	**Title with illustrated initial T for The Story of King Arthur and His Knights**		**517**
PM0553	The Story of King Arthur and His Knights	March, 1903	122, 223
PM0657	The Story of King Arthur and His Knights	1903	121-124, 220
PM1479	Hotel Dupont, Wilmington, Delaware	1912	141, 310
MBPI1871	**Two Knights do Battle before Cameliard**		**517**
PM0553	The Story of King Arthur and His Knights	March, 1903	122, 223
PM0657	The Story of King Arthur and His Knights	1903	121-124, 220
PM1464	Art Institute of Chicago, Chicago, Illinois	1903	130, 297
PM1470	St. Botolph Club, Boston, Massachusetts	1906	303
PM1479	Hotel Dupont, Wilmington, Delaware	1912	141, 310
PM1259	King Arthur's Round Table	February, 1915	124
MBPI1872	**Headpiece for The Story of King Arthur and His Knights**		**517**
PM0554	The Story of King Arthur and His Knights	April, 1903	122, 223
PM0657	The Story of King Arthur and His Knights	1903	121-124, 220
PM1464	Art Institute of Chicago, Chicago, Illinois	1903	130, 297
MBPI1873	**Title with illustrated initial T for The Story of King Arthur and His Knights**		**518**
PM0554	The Story of King Arthur and His Knights	April, 1903	122, 223
PM0657	The Story of King Arthur and His Knights	1903	121-124, 220
MBPI1874	**The White Champion meets two Knights at the Mill**		**518**
PM0554	The Story of King Arthur and His Knights	April, 1903	122, 223
PM0657	The Story of King Arthur and His Knights	1903	121-124, 220
PM1214	Book Review: The Story of King Arthur And His Knights	December, 1903	98

PM1357	Books For Young People	1903	269
PM1464	Art Institute of Chicago, Chicago, Illinois	1903	130, 297
MBPI1875	**Title with illustrated initial F for The Story of King Arthur and His Knights**		**518**
PM0554	The Story of King Arthur and His Knights	April, 1903	122, 223
PM0657	The Story of King Arthur and His Knights	1903	121-124, 220
MBPI1876	**Four Knights serve the Gardener Lad**		**518**
PM0554	The Story of King Arthur and His Knights	April, 1903	122, 223
PM0657	The Story of King Arthur and His Knights	1903	121-124, 220
PM1464	Art Institute of Chicago, Chicago, Illinois	1903	130, 297
MBPI1877	**Headpiece for The Story of King Arthur and His Knights**		**518**
PM0555	The Story of King Arthur and His Knights	May, 1903	122, 223
PM0657	The Story of King Arthur and His Knights	1903	121-124, 220
PM1464	Art Institute of Chicago, Chicago, Illinois	1903	130, 297
MBPI1878	**Title with illustrated initial T for The Story of King Arthur and His Knights**		**518**
PM0555	The Story of King Arthur and His Knights	May, 1903	122, 223
PM0657	The Story of King Arthur and His Knights	1903	121-124, 220
PM1479	Hotel Dupont, Wilmington, Delaware	1912	141, 310
MBPI1879	**The Gardener Lad takes off his Cap**		**518**
PM0555	The Story of King Arthur and His Knights	May, 1903	122, 223
PM0657	The Story of King Arthur and His Knights	1903	121-124, 220
PM1464	Art Institute of Chicago, Chicago, Illinois	1903	130, 297
PM1479	Hotel Dupont, Wilmington, Delaware	1912	141, 310
MBPI1880	**Title with illustrated initial K for The Story of King Arthur and His Knights**		**518**
PM0555	The Story of King Arthur and His Knights	May, 1903	122, 223
PM0657	The Story of King Arthur and His Knights	1903	121-124, 220
MBPI1881	**King Arthur meets the Lady Guinevere**		**518**
PM0555	The Story of King Arthur and His Knights	May, 1903	122, 223
PM0657	The Story of King Arthur and His Knights	1903	121-124, 220
PM1464	Art Institute of Chicago, Chicago, Illinois	1903	130, 297
PM1470	St. Botolph Club, Boston, Massachusetts	1906	303
MBPI1882	**Headpiece for The Story of King Arthur and His Knights**		**518**
PM0556	The Story of King Arthur and His Knights	June, 1903	123, 223
PM0657	The Story of King Arthur and His Knights	1903	121-124, 220
PM1464	Art Institute of Chicago, Chicago, Illinois	1903	130, 297
MBPI1883	**Title with illustrated initial S for The Story of King Arthur and His Knights**		**518**
PM0556	The Story of King Arthur and His Knights	June, 1903	123, 223
PM0657	The Story of King Arthur and His Knights	1903	121-124, 220
MBPI1884	**Sir Pellias encounters the Sorrowful Lady in Arroy**		**518**
PM0556	The Story of King Arthur and His Knights	June, 1903	123, 223
PM0657	The Story of King Arthur and His Knights	1903	121-124, 220
PM1464	Art Institute of Chicago, Chicago, Illinois	1903	130, 297
MBPI1885	**Title with illustrated initial S for The Story of King Arthur and His Knights**		**518**
PM0556	The Story of King Arthur and His Knights	June, 1903	123, 223
PM0657	The Story of King Arthur and His Knights	1903	121-124, 220
PM1464	Art Institute of Chicago, Chicago, Illinois	1903	130, 297
PM1479	Hotel Dupont, Wilmington, Delaware	1912	141, 310
MBPI1886	**Sir Pellias, the Gentle Knight**		**518**
PM0556	The Story of King Arthur and His Knights	June, 1903	123, 223
PM0657	The Story of King Arthur and His Knights	1903	121-124, 220
PM1464	Art Institute of Chicago, Chicago, Illinois	1903	130, 297
PM1470	St. Botolph Club, Boston, Massachusetts	1906	303
PM1479	Hotel Dupont, Wilmington, Delaware	1912	141, 310
MBPI1887	**Headpiece for The Story of King Arthur and His Knights**		**518**
PM0557	The Story of King Arthur and His Knights	July, 1903	123, 223
PM0657	The Story of King Arthur and His Knights	1903	121-124, 220
PM1464	Art Institute of Chicago, Chicago, Illinois	1903	130, 297
MBPI1888	**Title with illustrated initial P for The Story of King Arthur and His Knights**		**518**
PM0557	The Story of King Arthur and His Knights	July, 1903	123, 223
PM0657	The Story of King Arthur and His Knights	1903	121-124, 220
MBPI11889	**Parcenet covers Sir Pellias with a cloak**		**519**

PM0557	The Story of King Arthur and His Knights	July, 1903	123, 223
PM0657	The Story of King Arthur and His Knights	1903	121-124, 220
PM1464	Art Institute of Chicago, Chicago, Illinois	1903	130, 297
MBPI1890	**Title with illustrated initial T for The Story of King Arthur and His Knights**		**519**
PM0557	The Story of King Arthur and His Knights	July, 1903	123, 223
PM0657	The Story of King Arthur and His Knights	1903	121-124, 220
MBPI1891	**The Lady of the Lake sits by the Fountain in Arroy**		**519**
PM0557	The Story of King Arthur and His Knights	July, 1903	123, 223
PM1204	The Year's Juvenile Books	December 17, 1903	96
PM0657	The Story of King Arthur and His Knights	1903	121-124, 220
PM1214	Book Review: The Story of King Arthur And His Knights	December, 1903	98
PM1464	Art Institute of Chicago, Chicago, Illinois	1903	130, 297
PM1470	St. Botolph Club, Boston, Massachusetts	1906	303
MBPI1892	**Headpiece for The Story of King Arthur and His Knights**		**519**
PM0558	The Story of King Arthur and His Knights	August, 1903	123, 223
PM0657	The Story of King Arthur and His Knights	1903	121-124, 220
PM1464	Art Institute of Chicago, Chicago, Illinois	1903	130, 297
MBPI1893	**Title with illustrated initial S for The Story of King Arthur and His Knights**		**519**
PM0558	The Story of King Arthur and His Knights	August, 1903	123, 223
PM0657	The Story of King Arthur and His Knights	1903	121-124, 220
MBPI1894	**Sir Gawaine sups with ye Lady Ettard**		**519**
PM0558	The Story of King Arthur and His Knights	August, 1903	123, 223
PM0657	The Story of King Arthur and His Knights	1903	121-124, 220
PM1464	Art Institute of Chicago, Chicago, Illinois	1903	130, 297
MBPI1895	**Title with illustrated initial T for The Story of King Arthur and His Knights**		**519**
PM0558	The Story of King Arthur and His Knights	August, 1903	123, 223
PM0657	The Story of King Arthur and His Knights	1903	121-124, 220
PM1479	Hotel Dupont, Wilmington, Delaware	1912	141, 310
MBPI1896	**The Lady of the Lake finds Sir Pellias wounded**		**519**
PM0558	The Story of King Arthur and His Knights	August, 1903	123, 223
PM0657	The Story of King Arthur and His Knights	1903	121-124, 220
PM1479	Hotel Dupont, Wilmington, Delaware	1912	141, 310
MBPI1897	**Headpiece for The Story of King Arthur and His Knights**		**519**
PM0559	The Story of King Arthur and His Knights	September, 1903	123, 223
PM0658	The Story of the Champions of the Round Table	1905	226
PM1359	The Scribner's Holiday Books	1905	270
MBPI1898	**Title with illustrated initial S for The Story of King Arthur and His Knights**		**519**
PM0559	The Story of King Arthur and His Knights	September, 1903	123, 223
PM0658	The Story of the Champions of the Round Table	1905	226
MBPI1899	**Sir Percival of Gales**		**519**
PM0559	The Story of King Arthur and His Knights	September, 1903	123, 223
PM0658	The Story of the Champions of the Round Table	1905	226
MBPI1900	**Title with illustrated initial S for The Story of King Arthur and His Knights**		**519**
PM0559	The Story of King Arthur and His Knights	September, 1903	123, 223
PM0658	The Story of the Champions of the Round Table	1905	226
MBPI1901	**Sir Percival and Sir Pellinore ride together**		**519**
PM0559	The Story of King Arthur and His Knights	September, 1903	123, 223
PM0658	The Story of the Champions of the Round Table	1905	226
MBPI1902	**Headpiece, Vivien for The Story of King Arthur and His Knights**		**519**
PM0560	The Story of King Arthur and His Knights	October, 1903	124, 223
PM0657	The Story of King Arthur and His Knights	1903	121-124, 220
MBPI1903	**Title with illustrated initial S for The Story of King Arthur and His Knights**		**519**
PM0560	The Story of King Arthur and His Knights	October, 1903	124, 223
PM0658	The Story of the Champions of the Round Table	1905	226
MBPI1904	**Sir Percival overcometh ye Enchantress Vivien**		**519**
PM0560	The Story of King Arthur and His Knights	October, 1903	124, 223
PM0658	The Story of the Champions of the Round Table	1905	226
MBPI1905	**Title with illustrated initial S for The Story of King Arthur and His Knights**		**520**
PM0560	The Story of King Arthur and His Knights	October, 1903	124, 223
PM0658	The Story of the Champions of the Round Table	1905	226

PM1479	Hotel Dupont, Wilmington, Delaware	1912	141, 310
MBPI1906	**Sir Kay interrupts ye meditations of Sir Percival**		**520**
PM0560	The Story of King Arthur and His Knights	October, 1903	124, 223
PM0658	The Story of the Champions of the Round Table	1905	226
PM1479	Hotel Dupont, Wilmington, Delaware	1912	141, 310
MBPI1907	**Title with illustrated initial T for The Story of King Arthur and His Knights**		**520**
PM0560	The Story of King Arthur and His Knights	October, 1903	124, 223
PM0658	The Story of the Champions of the Round Table	1905	226
MBPI1908	**The Lady Yvette the Fair**		**520**
PM0560	The Story of King Arthur and His Knights	October, 1903	124, 223
PM0658	The Story of the Champions of the Round Table	1905	226
MBPI1909	**Gambetta Proclaiming the Republic of France**		**520**
PM0561	The Siege and Commune of Paris	January, 1887	107
PM0700	Recollections of a Minister to France	1887	205
PM1447	World's Columbian Exposition, Chicago, Illinois	1893	283
PM1548	A Short History of France	1907	211
PM1250	Twenty-five years of Scribner's magazine	January, 1912	114
MBPI1910	**Looking into the Prussian Lines from the Chateau de la Muette**		**520**
PM0562	The Siege and Commune of Paris	February, 1887	107
MBPI1911	**"Then faced her the leonine chief"**		**520**
PM0563	Tarpeia	December, 1887	108
MBPI1912	**"A moment later there was a great hammering on the oak door"**		**520**
PM0564	In the Valley	September, 1889	108
PM1447	World's Columbian Exposition, Chicago, Illinois	1893	283
PM0718	The Art of the American Wood Engraver	1894	131, 329-330
PM0881	"A moment later there was a great hammering on the oak door"	1894	131, 329-330
MBPI1913	**"Five red-coated soldiers on horse-back, with another cloaked to the eyes... Clustering about these, a motley score of poor people, young and old"**		**520**
PM0564	In the Valley	September, 1889	108
PM0702	In the Valley	1890	171
MBPI1914	**Within sound of the shouting waters**		**520**
PM0565	In the Valley	October, 1889	108
PM1221	Notice of In The Valley	November, 1890	99
PM0702	In the Valley	1890	171
PM1459	Detroit Museum of Art, Detroit, Michigan	1901	296
MBPI1915	**"We men-folk thought the music as sweet as that of the Cherubim"**		**520**
PM0565	In the Valley	October, 1889	108
PM0702	In the Valley	1890	171
MBPI1916	**"This is Enoch Wade, gentlemen," said the baronet**		**520**
PM0566	In the Valley	November, 1889	108
PM0702	In the Valley	1890	171
MBPI1917	**"Good-by, big brother," she said softly**		**520**
PM0566	In the Valley	November, 1889	108
PM0702	In the Valley	1890	171
MBPI1918	**"He told them, when we chanced to sit around the fires of an evening, most remarkable stories of field and forest"**		**520**
PM0567	In the Valley	December, 1889	108
PM0702	In the Valley	1890	171
MBPI1919	**"At sight of me the good soul gave a guttural exclamation, and stared at me open-mouthed"**		**520**
PM0567	In the Valley	December, 1889	108
MBPI1920	**"The negro boy, arms whirling wide in air, shot over the side of the cliff"**		**520**
PM0568	In the Valley	January, 1890	108
PM0702	In the Valley	1890	171
MBPI1921	**"The blow–the whole crushing series of blows–had fallen!"**		**521**
PM0568	In the Valley	January, 1890	108
PM0702	In the Valley	1890	171
MBPI1922	**"She was silent for a moment, her eyes seeking the floor"**		**521**
PM0569	In the Valley	February, 1890	108
PM1453	Trans-Mississippi and International Exposition, Omaha, Nebraska	1898	293
PM1565	Howard Pyle, Author-Illustrator 1853-1911	February, 1912	2

MBPI1923	"The dignified sober figure of Abraham Ten Broeck appeared in our wrathful circle"		**521**
PM0569	In the Valley	February, 1890	108
PM0702	In the Valley	1890	171
MBPI1924	"While his eyes still glowed fiery wrath, the trembling lips became piteous in their inability to form words"		**521**
PM0570	In the Valley	March, 1890	109
PM0702	In the Valley	1890	171
PM1459	Detroit Museum of Art, Detroit, Michigan	1901	296
MBPI1925	"Then a great mashing blow on my face ended my fight"		**521**
PM0570	In the Valley	March, 1890	109
MBPI1926	"'Who are you? and off with your hat!' I said to the man, sharply"		**521**
PM0571	In the Valley	April, 1890	109
PM0702	In the Valley	1890	171
MBPI1927	"Is your hanging-party ready?" he said		**521**
PM0571	In the Valley	April, 1890	109
PM0702	In the Valley	1890	171
MBPI1928	"I turned the sheet over and over in my hands, re-reading lines here and there"		**521**
PM0572	In the Valley	May, 1890	109
PM0702	In the Valley	1890	171
MBPI1929	"'I wish to God we were well out of this all,' he said, almost gloomily"		**521**
PM0572	In the Valley	May, 1890	109
PM0702	In the Valley	1890	171
MBPI1930	"There, half stretched on the wet blood-stained grass, lay Philip Cross"		**521**
PM0573	In the Valley	June, 1890	109
PM1115	Recent Fiction	October, 1890	6
PM0702	In the Valley	1890	171
MBPI1931	"My hatred of him seemed suddenly to have taken to itself wings"		**521**
PM0574	In the Valley	July, 1890	109
PM0702	In the Valley	1890	171
PM1116	Book Reviews	December, 1890	6
PM0801	American Illustrators	1892	130
PM1453	Trans-Mississippi and International Exposition, Omaha, Nebraska	1898	293
MBPI1932	Breton Peasants at a Wayside Cross		**521**
PM0575	The Pardon of Ste. Anne d'Auray	December, 1889	108
MBPI1933	Decorative title for A Pastoral Without Words		**521**
PM0576	A Pastoral Without Words	December, 1890	109
PM0798	The Drexel Institute, Philadelphia, Pennsylvania	1897	8, 140, 268, 284
PM0799	St. Botolph Club, Boston, Massachusetts	1897	140, 268, 288
PM1479	Hotel Dupont, Wilmington, Delaware	1912	141, 310
MBPI1934	Subtitle, A Pastoral Without Words		**521**
PM0576	A Pastoral Without Words	December, 1890	109
PM0718	The Art of the American Wood Engraver	1894	131, 329-330
PM0882	Sub-title, A Pastoral Without Words	1894	131, 329-330
PM0889	Pictures From Scribner's	1898	325, 331-332
PM0890	A Pastoral Without Words, No. 1	1898	325, 331-333
PM1479	Hotel Dupont, Wilmington, Delaware	1912	141, 310
MBPI1935	Decorative title, Verse I for A Pastoral Without Words		**521**
PM0576	A Pastoral Without Words	December, 1890	109
PM0798	The Drexel Institute, Philadelphia, Pennsylvania	1897	8, 140, 268, 284
PM0799	St. Botolph Club, Boston, Massachusetts	1897	140, 268, 288
PM1479	Hotel Dupont, Wilmington, Delaware	1912	141, 310
MBPI1936	Verse I, A Pastoral Without Words		**521**
PM0576	A Pastoral Without Words	December, 1890	109
PM0718	The Art of the American Wood Engraver	1894	131, 329-330
PM0883	Verse I, A Pastoral Without Words	1894	131, 329-330
PM0889	Pictures From Scribner's	1898	325, 331-332
PM0891	A Pastoral Without Words, No. 2	1898	325, 331-333
PM1479	Hotel Dupont, Wilmington, Delaware	1912	141, 310
MBPI1937	Decorative title, Verse II for A Pastoral Without Words		**522**
PM0576	A Pastoral Without Words	December, 1890	109

PM0798	The Drexel Institute, Philadelphia, Pennsylvania	1897	8, 140, 268, 284
PM0799	St. Botolph Club, Boston, Massachusetts	1897	140, 268, 288
PM1479	Hotel Dupont, Wilmington, Delaware	1912	141, 310
MBPI1938	**Verse II, A Pastoral Without Words**		**522**
PM0576	A Pastoral Without Words	December, 1890	109
PM0718	The Art of the American Wood Engraver	1894	131, 329-330
PM0884	Verse II, A Pastoral Without Words	1894	131, 329-330
PM0889	Pictures From Scribner's	1898	325, 331-332
PM0892	A Pastoral Without Words, No. 3	1898	325, 331-333
PM1479	Hotel Dupont, Wilmington, Delaware	1912	141, 310
MBPI1939	**Decorative title, Verse III for A Pastoral Without Words**		**522**
PM0576	A Pastoral Without Words	December, 1890	109
PM0798	The Drexel Institute, Philadelphia, Pennsylvania	1897	8, 140, 268, 284
PM0799	St. Botolph Club, Boston, Massachusetts	1897	140, 268, 288
PM1479	Hotel Dupont, Wilmington, Delaware	1912	141, 310
MBPI1940	**Verse III, A Pastoral Without Words**		**522**
PM0576	A Pastoral Without Words	December, 1890	109
PM0718	The Art of the American Wood Engraver	1894	131, 329-330
PM0885	Verse III, A Pastoral Without Words	1894	131, 329-330
PM0889	Pictures From Scribner's	1898	325, 331-332
PM0893	A Pastoral Without Words, No. 4	1898	325, 331-333
PM1479	Hotel Dupont, Wilmington, Delaware	1912	141, 310
MBPI1941	**Decorative title, Verse IV for A Pastoral Without Words**		**522**
PM0576	A Pastoral Without Words	December, 1890	109
PM0798	The Drexel Institute, Philadelphia, Pennsylvania	1897	8, 140, 268, 284
PM0799	St. Botolph Club, Boston, Massachusetts	1897	140, 268, 288
PM1479	Hotel Dupont, Wilmington, Delaware	1912	141, 310
MBPI1942	**Verse IV, A Pastoral Without Words**		**522**
PM0576	A Pastoral Without Words	December, 1890	109
PM0801	American Illustrators	1892	130
PM0718	The Art of the American Wood Engraver	1894	131, 329-330
PM0886	Verse IV, A Pastoral Without Words	1894	131, 329-330
PM0889	Pictures From Scribner's	1898	325, 331-332
PM0894	A Pastoral Without Words, No. 5	1898	325, 331-333
PM1479	Hotel Dupont, Wilmington, Delaware	1912	141, 310
MBPI1943	**Decorative title, L'Envoy for A Pastoral Without Words**		**522**
PM0576	A Pastoral Without Words	December, 1890	109
PM0798	The Drexel Institute, Philadelphia, Pennsylvania	1897	8, 140, 268, 284
PM0799	St. Botolph Club, Boston, Massachusetts	1897	140, 268, 288
PM1479	Hotel Dupont, Wilmington, Delaware	1912	141, 310
MBPI1944	**L'Envoy, A Pastoral Without Words**		**522**
PM0576	A Pastoral Without Words	December, 1890	109
PM0718	The Art of the American Wood Engraver	1894	131, 329-330
PM0887	L'Envoy, A Pastoral Without Words	1894	131, 329-330
PM0889	Pictures From Scribner's	1898	325, 331-332
PM0895	A Pastoral Without Words, No. 6	1898	325, 331-333
MBPI1945	**The First Christmas Tree**		**522**
PM0577	The Oak of Geismar	December, 1891	109
PM1447	World's Columbian Exposition, Chicago, Illinois	1893	283
PM0739	The First Christmas Tree	1897	151
PM1609	Book Reviews	December, 1897	8
PM0889	Pictures From Scribner's	1898	325, 331-332
PM0896	The First Christmas Tree	1898	325, 331-333
PM1008	The First Christmas Tree	1906	152
MBPI1946	**"It poised for an instant above the child's fair head–death cruel and imminent"**		**522**
PM0577	The Oak of Geismar	December, 1891	109
PM1238	The Illustrators of Books	December 4, 1897	106
PM0739	The First Christmas Tree	1897	151
PM0762	The Blue Flower	1902	135
PM1538	His Voice is Like The Wind in the Tree-Tops	1920	273

MBPI1947	**Headpiece with title for Peter Rugg Ye Bostonian**		**522**
PM0578	Peter Rugg Ye Bostonian	December, 1891	110
MBPI1948	**Vignette for Peter Rugg Ye Bostonian**		**522**
PM0578	Peter Rugg Ye Bostonian	December, 1891	110
MBPI1949	**Vignette for Peter Rugg Ye Bostonian**		**522**
PM0578	Peter Rugg Ye Bostonian	December, 1891	110
MBPI1950	**Vignette for Peter Rugg Ye Bostonian**		**522**
PM0578	Peter Rugg Ye Bostonian	December, 1891	110
PM0801	American Illustrators	1892	130
MBPI1951	**Vignette for Peter Rugg Ye Bostonian**		**522**
PM0578	Peter Rugg Ye Bostonian	December, 1891	110
MBPI1952	**Vignette for Peter Rugg Ye Bostonian**		**522**
PM0578	Peter Rugg Ye Bostonian	December, 1891	110
MBPI1953	**Vignette for Peter Rugg Ye Bostonian**		**523**
PM0578	Peter Rugg Ye Bostonian	December, 1891	110
MBPI1954	**Vignette for Peter Rugg Ye Bostonian**		**523**
PM0578	Peter Rugg Ye Bostonian	December, 1891	110
PM0801	American Illustrators	1892	130
MBPI1955	**Vignette for Peter Rugg Ye Bostonian**		**523**
PM0578	Peter Rugg Ye Bostonian	December, 1891	110
MBPI1956	**Vignette for Peter Rugg Ye Bostonian**		**523**
PM0578	Peter Rugg Ye Bostonian	December, 1891	110
MBPI1957	**Vignette for Peter Rugg Ye Bostonian**		**523**
PM0578	Peter Rugg Ye Bostonian	December, 1891	110
PM1118	Book Reviews	December, 1891	6
PM0801	American Illustrators	1892	130
MBPI1958	**Vignette for Peter Rugg Ye Bostonian**		**523**
PM0578	Peter Rugg Ye Bostonian	December, 1891	110
MBPI1959	**"Seeing no enemy, and themselves falling every moment from the fire"**		**523**
PM0579	An Unpublished Autograph Narrative by Washington	May, 1893	110
PM0725	History of the United States	1895	168
PM0769	A History of the United States	1904	168
PM1018	History of the United States	1915	168
MBPI1960	**The Death of Braddock**		**523**
PM0579	An Unpublished Autograph Narrative by Washington	May, 1893	110
PM0718	The Art of the American Wood Engraver	1894	131, 329-330
PM0888	The Death of Braddock	1894	131, 329-330
PM0725	History of the United States	1895	168
PM1018	History of the United States	1915	168
MBPI1961	**"For a while no one said a word"**		**523**
PM0580	Beneath the Mask	August, 1893	110
MBPI1962	**January and May**		**523**
PM0581	January and May	December, 1893	110
MBPI1963	**Decorative border with title for January and May**		**523**
PM0581	January and May	December, 1893	110
MBPI1964	**Illustration with illustrated initial M for McAndrew's Hymn**		**523**
PM0582	McAndrew's Hymn	December, 1894	110
PM1355	Scribner's Magazine Miniature Copy	1901	269
MBPI1965	**Illustration for McAndrew's Hymn**		**523**
PM0582	McAndrew's Hymn	December, 1894	110
MBPI1966	**Headpiece for McAndrew's Hymn**		**523**
PM0582	McAndrew's Hymn	December, 1894	110
PM1355	Scribner's Magazine Miniature Copy	1901	269
MBPI1967	**Illustrated initial L for McAndrew's Hymn**		**523**
PM0582	McAndrew's Hymn	December, 1894	110
MBPI1968	**"I heard a land-breeze ca'"**		**523**
PM0582	McAndrew's Hymn	December, 1894	110
PM1453	Trans-Mississippi and International Exposition, Omaha, Nebraska	1898	293
PM1355	Scribner's Magazine Miniature Copy	1901	269
MBPI1969	**Headpiece for McAndrew's Hymn**		**524**

PM0582	McAndrew's Hymn	December, 1894	110
MBPI1970	**Tailpiece for McAndrew's Hymn**		**524**
PM0582	McAndrew's Hymn	December, 1894	110
MBPI1971	**Illustration for A Forgotten Tale**		**524**
PM0583	A Forgotten Tale	January, 1895	111
MBPI1972	**Illustration for A Forgotten Tale**		**524**
PM0583	A Forgotten Tale	January, 1895	111
MBPI1973	**The Brooks Forces evacuating the State House at Little Rock**		**524**
PM0584	A History of the Last Quarter-Century in the United States	May, 1895	111
PM0731	The History of the Last Quarter-Century in the United States, 1870–1895	1896	168
PM1459	Detroit Museum of Art, Detroit, Michigan	1901	296
MBPI1974	**The rush from the New York Stock Exchange on September 18, 1873**		**524**
PM0585	A History of the Last Quarter-Century in the United States	July, 1895	111
PM0731	The History of the Last Quarter-Century in the United States, 1870–1895	1896	168
MBPI1975	**Dennis Kearney being drawn through the streets of San Francisco after his release from the House of Correction**		**524**
PM0586	A History of the Last Quarter-Century in the United States	October, 1895	111
PM0731	The History of the Last Quarter-Century in the United States, 1870–1895	1896	168
MBPI1976	**November, 1776**		**524**
PM0587	Some Thanksgiving-Time Fancies	November, 1895	111
MBPI1977	**The Enemy at the Door**		**524**
PM0587	Some Thanksgiving-Time Fancies	November, 1895	111
PM1124	Book Reviews	November, 1895	7
PM1316	Scribner's Magazine for November 1895	1895	271
MBPI1978	**Esmond and the Prince**		**524**
PM0588	Scenes from the Great Novels III	March, 1897	111
MBPI1979	**Undergraduate Life in 1679**		**524**
PM0589	Undergraduate Life at Harvard	May, 1897	111
MBPI1980	**"Bringing fire and terror to roof tree and bed"**		**524**
PM0590	The Birds of Cirencester	January, 1898	111
MBPI1981	**Headpiece with title and illustrated initial T for The Birds of Cirencester**		**524**
PM0590	The Birds of Cirencester	January, 1898	111
MBPI1982	**Illustrated initial D for The Birds of Cirencester**		**524**
PM0590	The Birds of Cirencester	January, 1898	111
MBPI1983	**Illustrated initial A for The Birds of Cirencester**		**524**
PM0590	The Birds of Cirencester	January, 1898	111
MBPI1984	**Illustrated initial A for The Birds of Cirencester**		**524**
PM0590	The Birds of Cirencester	January, 1898	111
MBPI1985	**Illustrated initial F for The Birds of Cirencester**		**525**
PM0590	The Birds of Cirencester	January, 1898	111
MBPI1986	**Illustrated initial S for The Birds of Cirencester**		**525**
PM0590	The Birds of Cirencester	January, 1898	111
MBPI1987	**Illustrated initial H for The Birds of Cirencester**		**525**
PM0590	The Birds of Cirencester	January, 1898	111
MBPI1988	**Illustrated initial S for The Birds of Cirencester**		**525**
PM0590	The Birds of Cirencester	January, 1898	111
MBPI1989	**Illustrated initial F for The Birds of Cirencester**		**525**
PM0590	The Birds of Cirencester	January, 1898	111
MBPI1990	**Illustrated initial Y for The Birds of Cirencester**		**525**
PM0590	The Birds of Cirencester	January, 1898	111
MBPI1991	**The Fight on Lexington Common, April 19, 1775**		**525**
PM0591	The Story of the Revolution	January, 1898	111
PM0743	The Story of the Revolution	1898	232-233
PM1351	Scribner's Magazine for 1898	1898	268
PM1452	New Haven, Connecticut and other cities	1898	292
PM1303	Wedgewood Plate	1899	277

PM1455	The New Century Club, Wilmington, Delaware	1899	294
PM1550	Pictures by Popular American Artists	1900	326, 337
PM1551	The Fight on Lexington Common, April 19, 1775	1900	326, 337
PM1355	Scribner's Magazine Miniature Copy	1901	269
PM1074	The Story of The Revolution	1903	233
PM0769	A History of the United States	1904	168
PM1479	Hotel Dupont, Wilmington, Delaware	1912	141, 310
PM1052	Poems of American Patriotism	1914	203
PM1481	Panama and Pacific International Exhibition, San Francisco, California	1915	315
MBPI1992	**The Battle of Bunker Hill**		**525**
PM0592	The Story of the Revolution	February, 1898	111
PM0743	The Story of the Revolution	1898	232-233
PM0889	Pictures From Scribner's	1898	325, 331-332
PM0898	The Battle of Bunker Hill	1898	325, 331-333
PM1452	New Haven, Connecticut and other cities	1898	292
PM1455	The New Century Club, Wilmington, Delaware	1899	294
PM1074	The Story of The Revolution	1903	233
PM0769	A History of the United States	1904	168
PM1479	Hotel Dupont, Wilmington, Delaware	1912	141, 310
PM1052	Poems of American Patriotism	1914	203
PM1481	Panama and Pacific International Exhibition, San Francisco, California	1915	315
MBPI1993	**Thomas Jefferson Writing the Declaration of Independence**		**525**
PM0593	The Story of the Revolution	March, 1898	112
PM0743	The Story of the Revolution	1898	232-233
PM1452	New Haven, Connecticut and other cities	1898	292
PM1455	The New Century Club, Wilmington, Delaware	1899	294
PM1550	Pictures by Popular American Artists	1900	326, 337
PM1552	Thomas Jefferson Writing the Declaration of Independence	1900	326, 337
PM1074	The Story of The Revolution	1903	233
PM1479	Hotel Dupont, Wilmington, Delaware	1912	141, 310
PM0793	Stories of Later American History	1915	218
PM1481	Panama and Pacific International Exhibition, San Francisco, California	1915	315
MBPI1994	**The Retreat Through the Jerseys**		**525**
PM0594	The Story of the Revolution	April, 1898	112
PM0743	The Story of the Revolution	1898	232-233
PM1452	New Haven, Connecticut and other cities	1898	292
PM1455	The New Century Club, Wilmington, Delaware	1899	294
PM1074	The Story of The Revolution	1903	233
PM1479	Hotel Dupont, Wilmington, Delaware	1912	141, 310
PM1481	Panama and Pacific International Exhibition, San Francisco, California	1915	315
MBPI1995	**The Burial of General Fraser**		**525**
PM0595	The Story of the Revolution	May, 1898	112
PM0743	The Story of the Revolution	1898	232-233
PM1074	The Story of The Revolution	1903	233
MBPI1996	**The Attack Upon the Chew House**		**525**
PM0596	The Story of the Revolution	June, 1898	112
PM0743	The Story of the Revolution	1898	232-233
PM0889	Pictures From Scribner's	1898	325, 331-332
PM0897	The Attack Upon the Chew House	1898	325, 331-333
PM1074	The Story of The Revolution	1903	233
PM0769	A History of the United States	1904	168
PM1479	Hotel Dupont, Wilmington, Delaware	1912	141, 310
PM1212	A Tribute to Howard Pyle	January, 1915	97
PM1481	Panama and Pacific International Exhibition, San Francisco, California	1915	315
MBPI1997	**Clark on his way to Kaskaskia**		**525**
PM0597	The Story of the Revolution	July, 1898	112
PM0743	The Story of the Revolution	1898	232-233
PM1074	The Story of The Revolution	1903	233
PM0769	A History of the United States	1904	168
PM1232	Advertisement: Important Scribner's Books	April, 1911	102

PM1079	Trails of the Pathfinder	1911	236
PM0793	Stories of Later American History	1915	218
MBPI1998	**The Meeting of Greene and Gates at Charlotte, N.C.**		**525**
PM0598	The Story of the Revolution	August, 1898	112
PM0743	The Story of the Revolution	1898	232-233
PM1074	The Story of The Revolution	1903	233
PM1479	Hotel Dupont, Wilmington, Delaware	1912	141, 310
PM0793	Stories of Later American History	1915	218
PM1481	Panama and Pacific International Exhibition, San Francisco, California	1915	315
PM1088	Young People's History of North Carolina	1916	255
MBPI1999	**The Evacuation of Charleston by the British December 14, 1782**		**525**
PM0599	The Story of the Revolution	September, 1898	112
PM0743	The Story of the Revolution	1898	232-233
PM1074	The Story of The Revolution	1903	233
PM1479	Hotel Dupont, Wilmington, Delaware	1912	141, 310
PM1481	Panama and Pacific International Exhibition, San Francisco, California	1915	315
MBPI2000	**Arnold Tells his Wife of the Discovery of his Treason**		**525**
PM0600	The Story of the Revolution	October, 1898	112
PM0743	The Story of the Revolution	1898	232-233
PM1074	The Story of The Revolution	1903	233
PM1482	The Wilmington Society of the Fine Arts, Wilmington, Delaware	1917	316
MBPI2001	**Washington Firing the First Gun at the Siege of Yorktown**		**526**
PM0601	The Story of the Revolution	November, 1898	112
PM0743	The Story of the Revolution	1898	232-233
PM1074	The Story of The Revolution	1903	233
PM0769	A History of the United States	1904	168
MBPI2002	**Benjamin Franklin and Richard Oswald Discussing the Treaty of Peace at Paris**		**526**
PM0602	The Story of the Revolution	December, 1898	112
PM0743	The Story of the Revolution	1898	232-233
PM1074	The Story of The Revolution	1903	233
MBPI2003	**His niece had found him lying dead**		**526**
PM0603	A Life for a Life	January, 1900	112
MBPI2004	**Another rush of breakers pitching the boat, cork-like, into the air**		**526**
PM0603	A Life for a Life	January, 1900	112
MBPI2005	**He looked down and sang out, "Lower away!"**		**526**
PM0603	A Life for a Life	January, 1900	112
PM1459	Detroit Museum of Art, Detroit, Michigan	1901	296
MBPI2006	**General Wayne endeavoring to quell the mutiny of the Pennsylvania Regiments at Morristown, N.J.**		**526**
PM0604	The United States Army	September, 1901	112
MBPI2007	**General Andrew Jackson receiving the plaudits of his motley army after the victory of New Orleans**		**526**
PM0605	The United States Army	October, 1901	113
MBPI2008	**Queen Esther inciting the Indians to attack the settlers at Wyoming**		**526**
PM0606	A Story of Three States	April, 1902	113
PM1041	Ohio and Her Western Reserve, With a Story of Three States	1902	192
PM1417	Queen Esther	1902	338
PM1464	Art Institute of Chicago, Chicago, Illinois	1903	130, 297
PM1483	The Wilmington Society of the Fine Arts, Wilmington, Delaware	1920	317
MBPI2009	**The Connecticut Settlers entering the Western Reserve**		**526**
PM0607	A Story of Three States	May, 1902	113
PM1041	Ohio and Her Western Reserve, With a Story of Three States	1902	192
PM0769	A History of the United States	1904	168
MBPI2010	**We started to run back to the raft for our lives**		**526**
PM0608	Sindbad on Burrator	August, 1902	113
PM1464	Art Institute of Chicago, Chicago, Illinois	1903	130, 297
PM1470	St. Botolph Club, Boston, Massachusetts	1906	303
PM1479	Hotel Dupont, Wilmington, Delaware	1912	141, 310
PM1481	Panama and Pacific International Exhibition, San Francisco, California	1915	315
MBPI2011	**The boat and I went by him with a rush**		**526**

PM0608	Sindbad on Burrator	August, 1902	113
PM1464	Art Institute of Chicago, Chicago, Illinois	1903	130, 297
PM1470	St. Botolph Club, Boston, Massachusetts	1906	303
PM1479	Hotel Dupont, Wilmington, Delaware	1912	141, 310
PM1481	Panama and Pacific International Exhibition, San Francisco, California	1915	315
MBPI2012	**Decorative title with illustrated initial S for Sindbad on Burrator**		**526**
PM0608	Sindbad on Burrator	August, 1902	113
PM1464	Art Institute of Chicago, Chicago, Illinois	1903	130, 297
PM1470	St. Botolph Club, Boston, Massachusetts	1906	303
MBPI2013	**I began to play**		**526**
PM0608	Sindbad on Burrator	August, 1902	113
PM1464	Art Institute of Chicago, Chicago, Illinois	1903	130, 297
PM1470	St. Botolph Club, Boston, Massachusetts	1906	303
PM1479	Hotel Dupont, Wilmington, Delaware	1912	141, 310
PM1481	Panama and Pacific International Exhibition, San Francisco, California	1915	315
MBPI2014	**I sat at her feet while she drilled the island language into me**		**526**
PM0608	Sindbad on Burrator	August, 1902	113
PM1464	Art Institute of Chicago, Chicago, Illinois	1903	130, 297
PM1470	St. Botolph Club, Boston, Massachusetts	1906	303
PM1479	Hotel Dupont, Wilmington, Delaware	1912	141, 310
PM1481	Panama and Pacific International Exhibition, San Francisco, California	1915	315
MBPI2015	**"If I catch you here again you'll need someone to sew you up"**		**526**
PM0608	Sindbad on Burrator	August, 1902	113
PM1464	Art Institute of Chicago, Chicago, Illinois	1903	130, 297
PM1470	St. Botolph Club, Boston, Massachusetts	1906	303
PM1479	Hotel Dupont, Wilmington, Delaware	1912	141, 310
PM1481	Panama and Pacific International Exhibition, San Francisco, California	1915	315
MBPI2016	**I clutched at his ankle**		**526**
PM0608	Sindbad on Burrator	August, 1902	113
PM1464	Art Institute of Chicago, Chicago, Illinois	1903	130, 297
PM1470	St. Botolph Club, Boston, Massachusetts	1906	303
PM1479	Hotel Dupont, Wilmington, Delaware	1912	141, 310
PM1481	Panama and Pacific International Exhibition, San Francisco, California	1915	315
MBPI2017	**"There is a time to fight and that time has now come"**		**527**
PM1248	Scribner's Magazine for January 1903	December, 1902	113
PM0609	The Story of a Great Grandfather	January, 1903	113
PM1464	Art Institute of Chicago, Chicago, Illinois	1903	130, 297
MBPI2018	**"Humbility is the fountain of all wirtue"**		**527**
PM0610	The Natural-Born Preacher	April, 1903	113
PM1422	The Natural-Born Preacher	1903	339
PM1070	Six Stars	1906	212
MBPI2019	**"'Ah me!' said the Parson, 'I wish I were young'"**		**527**
PM0611	The Magic Pill	July, 1876	114, 127
PM0931	Great American Illustrators: Howard Pyle, Illustrator	September, 1907	99, 106
MBPI2020	**"Alas! he had turned to a terrible boy"**		**527**
PM0611	The Magic Pill	July, 1876	114, 127
PM0931	Great American Illustrators: Howard Pyle, Illustrator	September, 1907	99, 106
MBPI2021	**Peter asks the fatal question**		**527**
PM0612	Papa Hoorn's Tulip	January, 1877	114
MBPI2022	**Grief and indignation**		**527**
PM0612	Papa Hoorn's Tulip	January, 1877	114
MBPI2023	**"I'll do it!"**		**527**
PM0612	Papa Hoorn's Tulip	January, 1877	114
MBPI2024	**"Do you see this knife?"**		**527**
PM0612	Papa Hoorn's Tulip	January, 1877	114
MBPI2025	**The Notary beckons**		**527**
PM0612	Papa Hoorn's Tulip	January, 1877	114
MBPI2026	**"She's yours"**		**527**
PM0612	Papa Hoorn's Tulip	January, 1877	114
MBPI2027	**"Why don't you show him?"**		**527**

PM0612	Papa Hoorn's Tulip	January, 1877	114
MBPI2028	**The reconciliation**		**527**
PM0612	Papa Hoorn's Tulip	January, 1877	114
MBPI2029	**The Sailor from Constantinople**		**527**
PM0612	Papa Hoorn's Tulip	January, 1877	114
MBPI2030	**"Horror! Devastation! Agony!"**		**527**
PM0612	Papa Hoorn's Tulip	January, 1877	114
MBPI2031	**The Sailor is saved**		**527**
PM0612	Papa Hoorn's Tulip	January, 1877	114
MBPI2032	**The End**		**527**
PM0612	Papa Hoorn's Tulip	January, 1877	114
MBPI2033	**Catching a pony**		**528**
PM0613	Chincoteague, the Island of Ponies	April, 1877	114, 127
MBPI2034	**A son of the soil**		**528**
PM0613	Chincoteague, the Island of Ponies	April, 1877	114, 127
MBPI2035	**The lady of the house**		**528**
PM0613	Chincoteague, the Island of Ponies	April, 1877	114, 127
MBPI2036	**Uncle Ken**		**528**
PM0613	Chincoteague, the Island of Ponies	April, 1877	114, 127
MBPI2037	**Old Dan Tucker**		**528**
PM0613	Chincoteague, the Island of Ponies	April, 1877	114, 127
MBPI2038	**The majesty of the law**		**528**
PM0613	Chincoteague, the Island of Ponies	April, 1877	114, 127
MBPI2039	**Crossing to Assateague**		**528**
PM0613	Chincoteague, the Island of Ponies	April, 1877	114, 127
MBPI2040	**Uncle Benny**		**528**
PM0613	Chincoteague, the Island of Ponies	April, 1877	114, 127
MBPI2041	**The pony pen**		**528**
PM0613	Chincoteague, the Island of Ponies	April, 1877	114, 127
MBPI2042	**J. A. M. Whealton**		**528**
PM0613	Chincoteague, the Island of Ponies	April, 1877	114, 127
MBPI2043	**Family Cares**		**528**
PM0614	Family Cares	April, 1877	114
MBPI2044	**Bliss**		**528**
PM0615	Bliss	May, 1877	115
MBPI2045	**In the Park**		**528**
PM0616	In the Park	July, 1877	115
MBPI2046	**A Quotation from "King Lear"**		**528**
PM0617	A Quotation from "King Lear"	July, 1877	115
MBPI2047	**Spearing Eels in Eel Bay**		**528**
PM0618	Among the Thousand Islands	April, 1878	115
PM0639	Sport with Gun and Rod in American Woods and Waters	1883	213
MBPI2048	**French Canadian**		**528**
PM0618	Among the Thousand Islands	April, 1878	115
MBPI2049	**Ruins of Old Fort, Carleton's Island**		**529**
PM0618	Among the Thousand Islands	April, 1878	115
PM0639	Sport with Gun and Rod in American Woods and Waters	1883	213
MBPI2050	**Catching Muskallonge**		**529**
PM0618	Among the Thousand Islands	April, 1878	115
PM0639	Sport with Gun and Rod in American Woods and Waters	1883	213
PM0950	The Boys' Book of Sports and Outdoor Life	1886	137
PM1135	With The New Books	December, 1891	9
MBPI2051	**Camping Out**		**529**
PM0618	Among the Thousand Islands	April, 1878	115
PM0639	Sport with Gun and Rod in American Woods and Waters	1883	213
MBPI2052	**Billy Patterson**		**529**
PM0618	Among the Thousand Islands	April, 1878	115
MBPI2053	**Joseph Gladd**		**529**
PM0618	Among the Thousand Islands	April, 1878	115
MBPI2054	**McCue**		**529**

PM0618	Among the Thousand Islands	April, 1878	115
PM1030	Lyrics of Home-Land	1882	179
MBPI2055	**Cooking a Camp Dinner**		**529**
PM0618	Among the Thousand Islands	April, 1878	115
PM0639	Sport with Gun and Rod in American Woods and Waters	1883	213
MBPI2056	**George Campbell**		**529**
PM1294	The Illustrated Magazines for April	March 21, 1878	102
PM0618	Among the Thousand Islands	April, 1878	115
MBPI2057	**Young De Lesken**		**529**
PM0619	The Story of Lesken	June, 1878	115
PM1027	Kitwyk Stories	1895	174
MBPI2058	**Mistress Betty**		**529**
PM0619	The Story of Lesken	June, 1878	115
PM1027	Kitwyk Stories	1895	174
PM1125	Book Reviews	December, 1895	7
MBPI2059	**Dietrich examines the disaster from a distance**		**529**
PM0619	The Story of Lesken	June, 1878	115
PM1027	Kitwyk Stories	1895	174
MBPI2060	**"He kissed the little hand"**		**529**
PM0619	The Story of Lesken	June, 1878	115
PM1027	Kitwyk Stories	1895	174
MBPI2061	**Kobus and his pupil**		**529**
PM0619	The Story of Lesken	June, 1878	115
PM1027	Kitwyk Stories	1895	174
MBPI2062	**Jan's courtship**		**529**
PM0619	The Story of Lesken	June, 1878	115
PM1027	Kitwyk Stories	1895	174
MBPI2063	**De Lesken entertaining**		**529**
PM0619	The Story of Lesken	June, 1878	115
PM1027	Kitwyk Stories	1895	174
MBPI2064	**Kobus brings news of Mynheer Jan**		**529**
PM0619	The Story of Lesken	June, 1878	115
PM1027	Kitwyk Stories	1895	174
PM1364	Original Drawings by Howard Pyle and Other Well–Known Artists and Illustrators	1917	276
MBPI2065	**Jan returns**		**530**
PM0619	The Story of Lesken	June, 1878	115
PM1027	Kitwyk Stories	1895	174
MBPI2066	**Tailpiece for The Story of Lesken**		**530**
PM0619	The Story of Lesken	June, 1878	115
PM1027	Kitwyk Stories	1895	174
MBPI2067	**Anthony Von Corlear, The Trumpeter of New Amsterdam**		**530**
PM0797	Stained Glass Window, Colonial Club	1896	347
PM0620	"A Beautiful Window"	March, 1899	125, 347
PM1231	Window Making as an Art	December, 1901	102
MBPI2068	**Prince Charles sprang to his side: "If he goes, so do I!"**		**530**
PM0621	A Cycle of Children	December, 1885	126
PM1560	A Cycle of Children	December, 1886	14
PM0694	Storied Holidays	1887	218
MBPI2069	**Was this...King Henry's self? Margery dropped to her knee**		**530**
PM0622	A Cycle of Children	January, 1886	126
PM1560	A Cycle of Children	December, 1886	14
PM0694	Storied Holidays	1887	218
MBPI2070	**Young William Penn meets the disapproval of his Father, the Admiral**		**530**
PM0623	A Cycle of Children	February, 1886	126
PM1560	A Cycle of Children	December, 1886	14
PM0694	Storied Holidays	1887	218
PM0705	The Story of the United States of America	1891	233
MBPI2071	**On the great terrace of Donegal Castle**		**530**
PM0624	A Cycle of Children	March, 1886	126

PM1560	A Cycle of Children	December, 1886	14
PM1110	A Cycle of Historic Red-Letter Days	October, 1887	5
PM0694	Storied Holidays	1887	218
MBPI2072	**"To sea in a bowl!" exclaimed the puzzled Pembroke**		**530**
PM0625	A Cycle of Children	April, 1886	126
PM1560	A Cycle of Children	December, 1886	14
PM0694	Storied Holidays	1887	218
PM1009	For Children All	1887	152
MBPI2073	**The Young Emperor's Entrance to the Circus Maximus**		**530**
PM0626	A Cycle of Children	May, 1886	126
PM1023	Idyls & Pastorals	1886	170
PM1560	A Cycle of Children	December, 1886	14
PM0694	Storied Holidays	1887	218
PM1024	Verses	1891	241
PM1545	Chit Chat for Boys and Girls	1893	143
PM0721	Great Men's Sons	1895	157
PM1139	Great Men's Sons	January, 1896	9
MBPI2074	**"The dark and shadowy outline of a man"**		**530**
PM0627	A Cycle of Children	June, 1886	126
PM1560	A Cycle of Children	December, 1886	14
PM0694	Storied Holidays	1887	218
MBPI2075	**"A great day this, my young friend," said Mr. John Adams of Massachusetts**		**530**
PM0628	A Cycle of Children	July, 1886	126
PM1560	A Cycle of Children	December, 1886	14
PM0694	Storied Holidays	1887	218
PM0705	The Story of the United States of America	1891	233
PM0996	The Childrens' History Book: Tales of the History of our Native Land	1901	143
MBPI2076	**Headpiece for The Little Maid at the Door**		**530**
PM0131	The Little Maid at the Door	February, 1892	36
MBPI2077	**Illustrated initial J for The Little Maid at the Door**		**530**
PM0131	The Little Maid at the Door	February, 1892	36
MBPI2078	**"I see naught but a little maid at the door"**		**530**
PM0131	The Little Maid at the Door	February, 1892	36
PM1391	Advertisement: Silence and Other Stories	April, 1898	45
PM0745	Silence and Other Stories	1898	211
MBPI2079	**Surprised by the Hero of Seventy Fights–The Good Lord James of Douglas**		**530**
PM0631	A Cycle of Children	October, 1886	126
PM1560	A Cycle of Children	December, 1886	14
PM0694	Storied Holidays	1887	218
MBPI2080	**Washington refuses the Colt**		**530**
PM0632	George Washington's Boyhood	July, 1887	127
PM0722	The True Story of George Washington	1895	236
PM1087	Winter Tales for Fireside Reading	1902	242
MBPI2081	**The Star Bearer**		**531**
PM0633	The Star Bearer	December, 1887	127
PM0695	The Star Bearer	1888	214
MBPI2082	**Marginal decoration with title for The Star Bearer**		**531**
PM0633	The Star Bearer	December, 1887	127
PM0695	The Star Bearer	1888	214
MBPI2083	**Marginal decoration for The Star Bearer**		**531**
PM0633	The Star Bearer	December, 1887	127
PM0695	The Star Bearer	1888	214
MBPI2084	**Marginal decoration for The Star Bearer**		**531**
PM0633	The Star Bearer	December, 1887	127
PM0695	The Star Bearer	1888	214
MBPI2085	**The Saving of King Ingé**		**531**
PM0634	Ingé, the Boy-King	December, 1888	127
PM1645	Ingé, the Boy-King	January, 1889	2
PM1029	Lothrop's Annual	1898	178
MBPI2086	**Half-title decoration for The Merry Adventures of Robin Hood**		**531**

PM0638	The Merry Adventures of Robin Hood	1883	183
PM1106	Book Reviews	December, 1884	4
MBPI2087	**The Merry Friar carrieth Robin across the Water**		**531**
PM0638	The Merry Adventures of Robin Hood	1883	183
PM0655	Some Merry Adventures of Robin Hood	1902	212
PM1011	The Graphic Arts	1920	157
MBPI2088	**Title page decoration for The Merry Adventures of Robin Hood**		**531**
PM0638	The Merry Adventures of Robin Hood	1883	183
PM1011	The Graphic Arts	1920	157
MBPI2089	**Headpiece, Preface for The Merry Adventures of Robin Hood**		**531**
PM0638	The Merry Adventures of Robin Hood	1883	183
MBPI2090	**Tailpiece, Preface for The Merry Adventures of Robin Hood**		**531**
PM0638	The Merry Adventures of Robin Hood	1883	183
MBPI2091	**Headpiece, Table of Contents for The Merry Adventures of Robin Hood**		**531**
PM0638	The Merry Adventures of Robin Hood	1883	183
MBPI2092	**Headpiece, List of Illustrations for The Merry Adventures of Robin Hood**		**531**
PM0638	The Merry Adventures of Robin Hood	1883	183
PM1493	Book Reviews	December, 1887	5
PM1111	List of Fiction	June, 1888	5
PM1112	Book Reviews	December, 1888	5
PM1113	The Holiday Books	December, 1889	6
PM1116	Book Reviews	December, 1890	6
PM1118	Book Reviews	December, 1891	6
PM1120	Book Reviews	December, 1892	6
MBPI2093	**Tailpiece, List of Illustrations for The Merry Adventures of Robin Hood**		**531**
PM0638	The Merry Adventures of Robin Hood	1883	183
MBPI2094	**Robin Hood meeteth the tall Stranger on the Bridge**		**531**
PM0638	The Merry Adventures of Robin Hood	1883	183
PM0655	Some Merry Adventures of Robin Hood	1902	212
PM1211	Howard Pyle, NA, Illustrator, Painter	January, 1912	97
MBPI2095	**Young Robin goes to the Shooting Match**		**531**
PM1237	Robin Hood	December 19, 1883	16
PM0638	The Merry Adventures of Robin Hood	1883	183
PM0644	Otto of the Silver Hand	1888	197
MBPI2096	**Illustrated initial I for The Merry Adventures of Robin Hood**		**531**
PM0638	The Merry Adventures of Robin Hood	1883	183
PM1106	Book Reviews	December, 1884	4
MBPI2097	**Tailpiece, Prologue for The Merry Adventures of Robin Hood**		**532**
PM0638	The Merry Adventures of Robin Hood	1883	183
MBPI2098	**Robin and the Tinker at the Blue Boar Inn**		**532**
PM0638	The Merry Adventures of Robin Hood	1883	183
PM1106	Book Reviews	December, 1884	4
PM1109	Book Reviews	December, 1886	5
MBPI2099	**The Sheriff of Nottingham plotting against Robin sends a messenger to Lincoln**		**532**
PM1254	Advertisement: Robin Hood	October, 1883	118
PM1237	Robin Hood	December 19, 1883	16
PM0638	The Merry Adventures of Robin Hood	1883	183
MBPI2100	**Illustrated initial N for The Merry Adventures of Robin Hood**		**532**
PM0638	The Merry Adventures of Robin Hood	1883	183
PM1107	Book Reviews	December, 1885	4
MBPI2101	**The Sheriff of Nottingham cometh before the King at London**		**532**
PM0638	The Merry Adventures of Robin Hood	1883	183
PM1106	Book Reviews	December, 1884	4
PM1107	Book Reviews	December, 1885	4
MBPI2102	**The Aged Palmer gives Young David of Doncaster news of Will Stutely**		**532**
PM0638	The Merry Adventures of Robin Hood	1883	183
MBPI2103	**Tailpiece, Part I for The Merry Adventures of Robin Hood**		**532**
PM0638	The Merry Adventures of Robin Hood	1883	183
MBPI2104	**Robin turns butcher and sells his meat in Nottingham**		**532**
PM1237	Robin Hood	December 19, 1883	16

PM0638	The Merry Adventures of Robin Hood	1883	183
MBPI2105	**Robin buys the Butcher's Meat**		**532**
PM0638	The Merry Adventures of Robin Hood	1883	183
MBPI2106	**Illustrated initial N for The Merry Adventures of Robin Hood**		**532**
PM0638	The Merry Adventures of Robin Hood	1883	183
MBPI2107	**Little John overcomes Eric o' Lincoln**		**532**
PM0638	The Merry Adventures of Robin Hood	1883	183
PM0655	Some Merry Adventures of Robin Hood	1902	212
MBPI2108	**The Mighty Fight betwixt Little John and the Cook**		**532**
PM1237	Robin Hood	December 19, 1883	16
PM0638	The Merry Adventures of Robin Hood	1883	183
MBPI2109	**The stout bout between Little John and Arthur a Bland**		**532**
PM0638	The Merry Adventures of Robin Hood	1883	183
PM1247	American Illustration of Today. Third Paper	March, 1892	110
MBPI2110	**Little John knoweth not which road to take**		**532**
PM0638	The Merry Adventures of Robin Hood	1883	183
PM1091	Illustrated Books for the Holidays	December, 1883	1
PM1106	Book Reviews	December, 1884	4
PM0644	Otto of the Silver Hand	1888	197
MBPI2111	**Illustrated initial I for The Merry Adventures of Robin Hood**		**532**
PM0638	The Merry Adventures of Robin Hood	1883	183
MBPI2112	**Merry Robin stops a Stranger in Scarlet**		**532**
PM1237	Robin Hood	December 19, 1883	16
PM0638	The Merry Adventures of Robin Hood	1883	183
PM0655	Some Merry Adventures of Robin Hood	1902	212
MBPI2113	**The Four Yeomen have Merry Sport with a Stout Miller**		**533**
PM0638	The Merry Adventures of Robin Hood	1883	183
MBPI2114	**Tailpiece, Part III for The Merry Adventures of Robin Hood**		**533**
PM0638	The Merry Adventures of Robin Hood	1883	183
MBPI2115	**Allan a Dale lieth beside the Fountain**		**533**
PM0638	The Merry Adventures of Robin Hood	1883	183
MBPI2116	**Allan a Dale tells his Story**		**533**
PM0638	The Merry Adventures of Robin Hood	1883	183
MBPI2117	**Illustrated initial I for The Merry Adventures of Robin Hood**		**533**
PM0638	The Merry Adventures of Robin Hood	1883	183
MBPI2118	**The Merry Friar sings a goodly song**		**533**
PM0638	The Merry Adventures of Robin Hood	1883	183
MBPI2119	**Robin Hood steps betwixt Sir Stephen and his Bride**		**533**
PM0638	The Merry Adventures of Robin Hood	1883	183
MBPI2120	**Tailpiece, Part IV for The Merry Adventures of Robin Hood**		**533**
PM0638	The Merry Adventures of Robin Hood	1883	183
PM1116	Book Reviews	December, 1890	6
MBPI2121	**Merry Robin stops a Sorrowful Knight**		**533**
PM0638	The Merry Adventures of Robin Hood	1883	183
MBPI2122	**The young Knight of the Lea overcomes the Knight of Lancaster**		**533**
PM0638	The Merry Adventures of Robin Hood	1883	183
MBPI2123	**Illustrated initial S for The Merry Adventures of Robin Hood**		**533**
PM0638	The Merry Adventures of Robin Hood	1883	183
PM1106	Book Reviews	December, 1884	4
MBPI2124	**Sir Richard pleadeth before the Prior of Emmet**		**533**
PM0638	The Merry Adventures of Robin Hood	1883	183
MBPI2125	**Tailpiece, Part V for The Merry Adventures of Robin Hood**		**533**
PM0638	The Merry Adventures of Robin Hood	1883	183
MBPI2126	**Little John in ye guise of a Friar stops three Lasses**		**533**
PM1237	Robin Hood	December 19, 1883	16
PM0638	The Merry Adventures of Robin Hood	1883	183
MBPI2127	**Little John journeys in Holy Company**		**533**
PM0638	The Merry Adventures of Robin Hood	1883	183
PM0644	Otto of the Silver Hand	1888	197
PM1546	Sara Crewe; or, What Happened at Miss Minchin's	1888	209

MBPI2128	**Illustrated initial C for The Merry Adventures of Robin Hood**		**533**
PM0638	The Merry Adventures of Robin Hood	1883	183
PM1106	Book Reviews	December, 1884	4
PM1107	Book Reviews	December, 1885	4
MBPI2129	**Merry Robin clad as a Beggar stops the Corn Engrosser by the Cross nigh Ollerton**		**534**
PM0638	The Merry Adventures of Robin Hood	1883	183
MBPI2130	**Tailpiece, Part VI for The Merry Adventures of Robin Hood**		**534**
PM0638	The Merry Adventures of Robin Hood	1883	183
PM1106	Book Reviews	December, 1884	4
MBPI2131	**Allan a Dale Singeth Before Our Good Queen Eleanor**		**534**
PM0638	The Merry Adventures of Robin Hood	1883	183
PM1106	Book Reviews	December, 1884	4
PM1107	Book Reviews	December, 1885	4
MBPI2132	**Young Richard Partington cometh to seek Merry Robin Hood**		**534**
PM0638	The Merry Adventures of Robin Hood	1883	183
PM1091	Illustrated Books for the Holidays	December, 1883	1
PM0644	Otto of the Silver Hand	1888	197
PM1546	Sara Crewe; or, What Happened at Miss Minchin's	1888	209
PM1317	A New Illustrated Book by Howard Pyle	1895	271
MBPI2133	**Illustrated initial T for The Merry Adventures of Robin Hood**		**534**
PM0638	The Merry Adventures of Robin Hood	1883	183
PM1106	Book Reviews	December, 1884	4
PM1107	Book Reviews	December, 1885	4
MBPI2134	**Stout Robin hath a narrow escape**		**534**
PM0638	The Merry Adventures of Robin Hood	1883	183
MBPI2135	**Tailpiece, Part VII for The Merry Adventures of Robin Hood**		**534**
PM0638	The Merry Adventures of Robin Hood	1883	183
MBPI2136	**Robin Hood slayeth Guy of Gisbourne**		**534**
PM0638	The Merry Adventures of Robin Hood	1883	183
PM1106	Book Reviews	December, 1884	4
PM1107	Book Reviews	December, 1885	4
PM1108	The Tribute to George Fuller	March, 1886	5
PM1109	Book Reviews	December, 1886	5
MBPI2137	**Robin and Little John go their ways in search of Adventure**		**534**
PM1237	Robin Hood	December 19, 1883	16
PM0638	The Merry Adventures of Robin Hood	1883	183
MBPI2138	**Illustrated initial A for The Merry Adventures of Robin Hood**		**534**
PM0638	The Merry Adventures of Robin Hood	1883	183
MBPI2139	**Merry Robin hath the worst of a Bargain**		**534**
PM1237	Robin Hood	December 19, 1883	16
PM0638	The Merry Adventures of Robin Hood	1883	183
PM1106	Book Reviews	December, 1884	4
MBPI2140	**Tailpiece, Part VIII for The Merry Adventures of Robin Hood**		**534**
PM0638	The Merry Adventures of Robin Hood	1883	183
MBPI2141	**Robin shooteth his Last Shaft**		**534**
PM0638	The Merry Adventures of Robin Hood	1883	183
PM1091	Illustrated Books for the Holidays	December, 1883	1
MBPI2142	**So Ye Great Reaper reapeth among the Flowers**		**534**
PM0638	The Merry Adventures of Robin Hood	1883	183
MBPI2143	**Illustrated initial A for The Merry Adventures of Robin Hood**		**534**
PM0638	The Merry Adventures of Robin Hood	1883	183
PM1107	Book Reviews	December, 1885	4
MBPI2144	**Finis for The Merry Adventures of Robin Hood**		**534**
PM0638	The Merry Adventures of Robin Hood	1883	183
MBPI2145	**Cover design for The Merry Adventures of Robin Hood**		**535**
PM0638	The Merry Adventures of Robin Hood	1883	183
PM1151	Commercial Bookbinding	October, 1894	11
PM1130	The Grolier Club, New York	1894	284
PM0987	Bookbindings, Old And New	1896	136
PM1349	Scribner's New Books For the Young	1897	268

MBPI2146	**Spine design for The Merry Adventures of Robin Hood**		**535**
PM0638	The Merry Adventures of Robin Hood	1883	183
MBPI2147	**Front cover design for Pepper & Salt**		**535**
PM0641	Pepper & Salt	1886	76-82, 200
PM1080	Twentieth Century Cover Designs	1902	236
MBPI2148	**Back cover design for Pepper & Salt**		**535**
PM0641	Pepper & Salt	1886	76-82, 200
MBPI2149	**Half-title decoration for Pepper & Salt**		**535**
PM0641	Pepper & Salt	1886	76-82, 200
MBPI2150	**This is the way that one in Cap and Motley stops for awhile along the stony Path of Life to make you laugh**		**535**
PM1610	Book Reviews	December, 1885	9
PM0641	Pepper & Salt	1886	76-82, 200
MBPI2151	**Title page decoration for Pepper & Salt**		**535**
PM0641	Pepper & Salt	1886	76-82, 200
MBPI2152	**Headpiece, Preface for Pepper & Salt**		**535**
PM0641	Pepper & Salt	1886	76-82, 200
MBPI2153	**Tailpiece, Preface for Pepper & Salt**		**535**
PM0641	Pepper & Salt	1886	76-82, 200
MBPI2154	**Headpiece, Table of Contents for Pepper & Salt**		**535**
PM0641	Pepper & Salt	1886	76-82, 200
MBPI2155	**Tailpiece, Table of Contents for Pepper & Salt**		**535**
PM0641	Pepper & Salt	1886	76-82, 200
MBPI2156	**Headpiece, List of Illustrations for Pepper & Salt**		**535**
PM0641	Pepper & Salt	1886	76-82, 200
MBPI2157	**Tailpiece, List of Illustrations for Pepper & Salt**		**535**
PM0641	Pepper & Salt	1886	76-82, 200
MBPI2158	**How Hans was caught**		**535**
PM0641	Pepper & Salt	1886	76-82, 200
MBPI2159	**Decoration for Pepper & Salt**		**535**
PM0641	Pepper & Salt	1886	76-82, 200
MBPI2160	**Decoration for Pepper & Salt**		**535**
PM0641	Pepper & Salt	1886	76-82, 200
MBPI2161	**Decoration for Pepper & Salt**		**536**
PM0641	Pepper & Salt	1886	76-82, 200
MBPI2162	**Decoration for Pepper & Salt**		**536**
PM0641	Pepper & Salt	1886	76-82, 200
MBPI2163	**Cover design for The Wonder Clock**		**536**
PM0642	The Wonder Clock	1888	82-88, 242
MBPI2164	**Half-title decoration for The Wonder Clock**		**536**
PM0642	The Wonder Clock	1888	82-88, 242
MBPI2165	**Frontispiece for The Wonder Clock**		**536**
PM0642	The Wonder Clock	1888	82-88, 242
PM0699	Pen Drawing and Pen Draughtsmen	1889	199
PM1209	Children's Books and Their Illustrators	December, 1897	97
MBPI2166	**Title page decoration for The Wonder Clock**		**536**
PM0642	The Wonder Clock	1888	82-88, 242
MBPI2167	**Headpiece, Preface for The Wonder Clock**		**536**
PM0642	The Wonder Clock	1888	82-88, 242
MBPI2168	**Illustrated initial I, Preface for The Wonder Clock**		**536**
PM0642	The Wonder Clock	1888	82-88, 242
MBPI2169	**Headpiece, Table of Contents for The Wonder Clock**		**536**
PM0642	The Wonder Clock	1888	82-88, 242
PM1353	Books For The Young	1899	269
MBPI2170	**Tailpiece, Table of Contents for The Wonder Clock**		**536**
PM0642	The Wonder Clock	1888	82-88, 242
MBPI2171	**Headpiece, List of Illustrations for The Wonder Clock**		**536**
PM0642	The Wonder Clock	1888	82-88, 242
MBPI2172	**Tailpiece, List of Illustrations for The Wonder Clock**		**536**
PM0642	The Wonder Clock	1888	82-88, 242

MBPI2173	**Illustrated initial T for Bearskin**		**536**
PM0642	The Wonder Clock	1888	82-88, 242
MBPI2174	**Illustrated initial T with heading for Bearskin**		**536**
PM0642	The Wonder Clock	1888	82-88, 242
MBPI2175	**Illustrated initial B with heading for Bearskin**		**536**
PM0642	The Wonder Clock	1888	82-88, 242
MBPI2176	**Illustrated initial O for The Water of Life**		**536**
PM0642	The Wonder Clock	1888	82-88, 242
MBPI2177	**Illustrated initial T with heading for The Water of Life**		**537**
PM0642	The Wonder Clock	1888	82-88, 242
MBPI2178	**Illustrated initial T with heading for The Water of Life**		**537**
PM0642	The Wonder Clock	1888	82-88, 242
MBPI2179	**Illustrated initial T with heading for The Water of Life**		**537**
PM0642	The Wonder Clock	1888	82-88, 242
MBPI2180	**Illustrated initial T for How One Turned His Trouble to Some Account**		**537**
PM0642	The Wonder Clock	1888	82-88, 242
MBPI2181	**Illustrated initial T with heading for How One Turned His Trouble to Some Account**		**537**
PM0642	The Wonder Clock	1888	82-88, 242
MBPI2182	**Illustrated initial H with heading for How One Turned His Trouble to Some Account**		**537**
PM0642	The Wonder Clock	1888	82-88, 242
MBPI2183	**Illustrated initial T for How Three Went Out into the Wide World**		**537**
PM0642	The Wonder Clock	1888	82-88, 242
MBPI2184	**Illustrated initial T with heading for How Three Went Out into the Wide World**		**537**
PM0642	The Wonder Clock	1888	82-88, 242
MBPI2185	**Illustrated initial T with heading for How Three Went Out into the Wide World**		**537**
PM0642	The Wonder Clock	1888	82-88, 242
MBPI2186	**Illustrated initial T for The Clever Student and the Master of Black Arts**		**537**
PM0642	The Wonder Clock	1888	82-88, 242
MBPI2187	**Illustrated initial A with heading for The Clever Student and the Master of Black Arts**		**537**
PM0642	The Wonder Clock	1888	82-88, 242
MBPI2188	**Illustrated initial T with heading for The Clever Student and the Master of Black Arts**		**537**
PM0642	The Wonder Clock	1888	82-88, 242
MBPI2189	**Illustrated initial T with heading for The Clever Student and the Master of Black Arts**		**537**
PM0642	The Wonder Clock	1888	82-88, 242
MBPI2190	**Illustrated initial W with heading for The Wonder Clock**		**537**
PM0642	The Wonder Clock	1888	82-88, 242
MBPI2191	**Decoration for The Wonder Clock**		**537**
PM0642	The Wonder Clock	1888	82-88, 242
MBPI2192	**Illustrated initial O for The Princess Golden-Hair and the Great Black Raven**		**537**
PM0642	The Wonder Clock	1888	82-88, 242
MBPI2193	**Illustrated initial T with heading for The Princess Golden-Hair and the Great Black Raven**		**538**
PM0642	The Wonder Clock	1888	82-88, 242
MBPI2194	**Illustrated initial P with heading for The Princess Golden-Hair and the Great Black Raven**		**538**
PM0642	The Wonder Clock	1888	82-88, 242
MBPI2195	**Illustrated initial P with heading for The Princess Golden-Hair and the Great Black Raven**		**538**
PM0642	The Wonder Clock	1888	82-88, 242
MBPI2196	**Illustrated initial T with heading for The Princess Golden-Hair and the Great Black Raven**		**538**
PM0642	The Wonder Clock	1888	82-88, 242
MBPI2197	**Illustrated initial I for Cousin Greylegs, Ye Great Red Fox and Grandfather Mole**		**538**
PM0642	The Wonder Clock	1888	82-88, 242
MBPI2198	**Illustrated initial C with heading for Cousin Greylegs, Ye Great Red Fox and Grandfather Mole**		**538**
PM0642	The Wonder Clock	1888	82-88, 242
MBPI2199	**Illustrated initial C with heading for Cousin Greylegs, Ye Great Red Fox and Grandfather Mole**		**538**
PM0642	The Wonder Clock	1888	82-88, 242
MBPI2200	**Illustrated initial O for One Good Turn Deserves Another**		**538**
PM0642	The Wonder Clock	1888	82-88, 242
MBPI2201	**Illustrated initial F with heading for One Good Turn Deserves Another**		**538**
PM0642	The Wonder Clock	1888	82-88, 242
MBPI2202	**Illustrated initial T with heading for One Good Turn Deserves Another**		**538**
PM0642	The Wonder Clock	1888	82-88, 242

MBPI2203 **Illustrated initial T with heading for One Good Turn Deserves Another** **538**
PM0642 The Wonder Clock 1888 82-88, 242
MBPI2204 **Illustrated initial T with heading for One Good Turn Deserves Another** **538**
PM0642 The Wonder Clock 1888 82-88, 242
MBPI2205 **Illustrated initial O for The White Bird** **538**
PM0642 The Wonder Clock 1888 82-88, 242
MBPI2206 **Illustrated initial T with heading for The White Bird** **538**
PM0642 The Wonder Clock 1888 82-88, 242
MBPI2207 **Illustrated initial T with heading for The White Bird** **538**
PM0642 The Wonder Clock 1888 82-88, 242
MBPI2208 **Illustrated initial T with heading for The White Bird** **538**
PM0642 The Wonder Clock 1888 82-88, 242
MBPI2209 **Illustrated initial T with heading for The White Bird** **539**
PM0642 The Wonder Clock 1888 82-88, 242
MBPI2210 **Illustrated initial T for How the Good Gifts were Used by Two** **539**
PM0642 The Wonder Clock 1888 82-88, 242
MBPI2211 **Illustrated initial S with heading for How the Good Gifts were Used by Two** **539**
PM0642 The Wonder Clock 1888 82-88, 242
MBPI2212 **Illustrated initial S with heading for How the Good Gifts were Used by Two** **539**
PM0642 The Wonder Clock 1888 82-88, 242
MBPI2213 **Illustrated initial T with heading for How the Good Gifts were Used by Two** **539**
PM0642 The Wonder Clock 1888 82-88, 242
MBPI2214 **Decoration for The Wonder Clock** **539**
PM0642 The Wonder Clock 1888 82-88, 242
MBPI2215 **Illustrated initial O for How Boots Befooled the King** **539**
PM0642 The Wonder Clock 1888 82-88, 242
MBPI2216 **Illustrated initial P with heading for How Boots Befooled the King** **539**
PM0642 The Wonder Clock 1888 82-88, 242
MBPI2217 **Illustrated initial P with heading for How Boots Befooled the King** **539**
PM0642 The Wonder Clock 1888 82-88, 242
MBPI2218 **Illustrated initial T with heading for How Boots Befooled the King** **539**
PM0642 The Wonder Clock 1888 82-88, 242
MBPI2219 **Illustrated initial T with heading for How Boots Befooled the King** **539**
PM0642 The Wonder Clock 1888 82-88, 242
MBPI2220 **Decoration for The Wonder Clock** **539**
PM0642 The Wonder Clock 1888 82-88, 242
MBPI2221 **Illustrated initial O for The Step-mother** **539**
PM0642 The Wonder Clock 1888 82-88, 242
MBPI2222 **Illustrated initial T with heading for The Step-mother** **539**
PM0642 The Wonder Clock 1888 82-88, 242
MBPI2223 **Illustrated initial T with heading for The Step-mother** **539**
PM0642 The Wonder Clock 1888 82-88, 242
MBPI2224 **Illustrated initial T with heading for The Step-mother** **539**
PM0642 The Wonder Clock 1888 82-88, 242
MBPI2225 **Illustrated initial O for Master Jacob** **540**
PM0642 The Wonder Clock 1888 82-88, 242
MBPI2226 **Illustrated initial M with heading for Master Jacob** **540**
PM0642 The Wonder Clock 1888 82-88, 242
MBPI2227 **Illustrated initial T with heading for Master Jacob** **540**
PM0642 The Wonder Clock 1888 82-88, 242
MBPI2228 **Illustrated initial M with heading for Master Jacob** **540**
PM0642 The Wonder Clock 1888 82-88, 242
MBPI2229 **Illustrated initial T for Peterkin and the Little Grey Hare** **540**
PM0642 The Wonder Clock 1888 82-88, 242
MBPI2230 **Illustrated initial P with heading for Peterkin and the Little Grey Hare** **540**
PM0642 The Wonder Clock 1888 82-88, 242
MBPI2231 **Illustrated initial P with heading for Peterkin and the Little Grey Hare** **540**
PM0642 The Wonder Clock 1888 82-88, 242
MBPI2232 **Illustrated initial P with heading for Peterkin and the Little Grey Hare** **540**
PM0642 The Wonder Clock 1888 82-88, 242

MBPI2233	**Illustrated initial O for Mother Hildegarde**		**540**
PM0642	The Wonder Clock	1888	82-88, 242
MBPI2234	**Illustrated initial T with heading for Mother Hildegarde**		**540**
PM0642	The Wonder Clock	1888	82-88, 242
MBPI2235	**Illustrated initial T with heading for Mother Hildegarde**		**540**
PM0642	The Wonder Clock	1888	82-88, 242
MBPI2236	**Illustrated initial T with heading for Mother Hildegarde**		**540**
PM0642	The Wonder Clock	1888	82-88, 242
MBPI2237	**Illustrated initial M with heading for Mother Hildegarde**		**540**
PM0642	The Wonder Clock	1888	82-88, 242
MBPI2238	**Illustrated initial T for Which is Best?**		**540**
PM0642	The Wonder Clock	1888	82-88, 242
MBPI2239	**Illustrated initial H with heading for Which is Best?**		**540**
PM0642	The Wonder Clock	1888	82-88, 242
MBPI2240	**Illustrated initial T with heading for Which is Best?**		**540**
PM0642	The Wonder Clock	1888	82-88, 242
MBPI2241	**Illustrated initial T with heading for Which is Best?**		**541**
PM0642	The Wonder Clock	1888	82-88, 242
MBPI2242	**Decoration for The Wonder Clock**		**541**
PM0642	The Wonder Clock	1888	82-88, 242
MBPI2243	**Illustrated initial T for The Simpleton and his Little Black Hen**		**541**
PM0642	The Wonder Clock	1888	82-88, 242
MBPI2244	**Illustrated initial T with heading for The Simpleton and his Little Black Hen**		**541**
PM0642	The Wonder Clock	1888	82-88, 242
MBPI2245	**Illustrated initial T with heading for The Simpleton and his Little Black Hen**		**541**
PM0642	The Wonder Clock	1888	82-88, 242
MBPI2246	**Illustrated initial O for The Swan Maiden**		**541**
PM0642	The Wonder Clock	1888	82-88, 242
MBPI2247	**Illustrated initial T with heading for The Swan Maiden**		**541**
PM0642	The Wonder Clock	1888	82-88, 242
MBPI2248	**Illustrated initial T with heading for The Swan Maiden**		**541**
PM0642	The Wonder Clock	1888	82-88, 242
MBPI2249	**Illustrated initial T with heading for The Swan Maiden**		**541**
PM0642	The Wonder Clock	1888	82-88, 242
MBPI2250	**Illustrated initial T for The Three Little Pigs and the Ogre**		**541**
PM0642	The Wonder Clock	1888	82-88, 242
MBPI2251	**Illustrated initial T with heading for The Three Little Pigs and the Ogre**		**541**
PM0642	The Wonder Clock	1888	82-88, 242
MBPI2252	**Illustrated initial T with heading for The Three Little Pigs and the Ogre**		**541**
PM0642	The Wonder Clock	1888	82-88, 242
MBPI2253	**Decoration for The Wonder Clock**		**541**
PM0642	The Wonder Clock	1888	82-88, 242
MBPI2254	**Illustrated initial T for The Staff and the Fiddle**		**541**
PM0642	The Wonder Clock	1888	82-88, 242
MBPI2255	**Illustrated initial T with heading for The Staff and the Fiddle**		**541**
PM0642	The Wonder Clock	1888	82-88, 242
MBPI2256	**Illustrated initial T with heading for The Staff and the Fiddle**		**541**
PM0642	The Wonder Clock	1888	82-88, 242
MBPI2257	**Illustrated initial T with heading for The Staff and the Fiddle**		**542**
PM0642	The Wonder Clock	1888	82-88, 242
MBPI2258	**Illustrated initial T for How the Princess's Pride was broken**		**542**
PM0642	The Wonder Clock	1888	82-88, 242
MBPI2259	**Illustrated initial T with heading for How the Princess's Pride was broken**		**542**
PM0642	The Wonder Clock	1888	82-88, 242
MBPI2260	**Illustrated initial T with heading for How the Princess's Pride was broken**		**542**
PM0642	The Wonder Clock	1888	82-88, 242
MBPI2261	**Illustrated initial T for How Two went into Partnership**		**542**
PM0642	The Wonder Clock	1888	82-88, 242
MBPI2262	**Illustrated initial T with heading for How Two went into Partnership**		**542**
PM0642	The Wonder Clock	1888	82-88, 242

MBPI2263	**Illustrated initial U with heading for for How Two went into Partnership**		**542**
PM0642	The Wonder Clock	1888	82-88, 242
MBPI2264	**Illustrated initial T for King Stork**		**542**
PM0642	The Wonder Clock	1888	82-88, 242
MBPI2265	**Illustrated initial T with heading for King Stork**		**542**
PM0642	The Wonder Clock	1888	82-88, 242
MBPI2266	**Illustrated initial T with heading for King Stork**		**542**
PM0642	The Wonder Clock	1888	82-88, 242
MBPI2267	**Illustrated initial T with heading for King Stork**		**542**
PM0642	The Wonder Clock	1888	82-88, 242
MBPI2268	**Illustrated initial T for The Best that Life has to give**		**542**
PM0642	The Wonder Clock	1888	82-88, 242
MBPI2269	**Illustrated initial T with heading for The Best that Life has to give**		**542**
PM0642	The Wonder Clock	1888	82-88, 242
MBPI2270	**Illustrated initial T with heading for The Best that Life has to give**		**542**
PM0642	The Wonder Clock	1888	82-88, 242
MBPI2271	**Illustrated initial T with heading for The Best that Life has to give**		**542**
PM0642	The Wonder Clock	1888	82-88, 242
MBPI2272	**Tailpiece, The End for The Wonder Clock**		**542**
PM0642	The Wonder Clock	1888	82-88, 242
MBPI2273	**Cover design for Otto of the Silver Hand**		**543**
PM0644	Otto of the Silver Hand	1888	197
MBPI2274	**Half-title decoration for Otto of the Silver Hand**		**543**
PM0644	Otto of the Silver Hand	1888	197
MBPI2275	**In the Belfry**		**543**
PM0644	Otto of the Silver Hand	1888	197
MBPI2276	**Headpiece, Contents for Otto of the Silver Hand**		**543**
PM0644	Otto of the Silver Hand	1888	197
MBPI2277	**Tailpiece, Contents for Otto of the Silver Hand**		**543**
PM0644	Otto of the Silver Hand	1888	197
MBPI2278	**Headpiece, List of Illustrations for Otto of the Silver Hand**		**543**
PM0644	Otto of the Silver Hand	1888	197
MBPI2279	**Tailpiece, List of Illustrations for Otto of the Silver Hand**		**543**
PM0644	Otto of the Silver Hand	1888	197
MBPI2280	**Headpiece, Foreword for Otto of the Silver Hand**		**543**
PM0644	Otto of the Silver Hand	1888	197
PM1000	Decorative Illustrations of Books Old and New	1896	145
MBPI2281	**Illustrated initial B, Foreword for Otto of the Silver Hand**		**543**
PM0644	Otto of the Silver Hand	1888	197
MBPI2282	**Tailpiece, Foreword for Otto of the Silver Hand**		**543**
PM0644	Otto of the Silver Hand	1888	197
MBPI2283	**Headpiece, Chapter I for Otto of the Silver Hand**		**543**
PM0644	Otto of the Silver Hand	1888	197
MBPI2284	**Illustrated initial U for Otto of the Silver Hand**		**543**
PM0644	Otto of the Silver Hand	1888	197
MBPI2285	**There they sat, just as little children of the town might sit upon their father's doorstep**		**543**
PM0644	Otto of the Silver Hand	1888	197
PM1211	Howard Pyle, NA, Illustrator, Painter	January, 1912	97
MBPI2286	**Tailpiece, Chapter I for Otto of the Silver Hand**		**543**
PM0644	Otto of the Silver Hand	1888	197
MBPI2287	**Headpiece, Chapter II for Otto of the Silver Hand**		**543**
PM0644	Otto of the Silver Hand	1888	197
MBPI2288	**Illustrated initial B for Otto of the Silver Hand**		**543**
PM0644	Otto of the Silver Hand	1888	197
MBPI2289	**Away they rode with clashing hoofs and ringing armor**		**544**
PM0644	Otto of the Silver Hand	1888	197
MBPI2290	**Tailpiece, Chapter II for Otto of the Silver Hand**		**544**
PM0644	Otto of the Silver Hand	1888	197
MBPI2291	**Headpiece, Chapter III for Otto of the Silver Hand**		**544**
PM0644	Otto of the Silver Hand	1888	197

MBPI2292	Illustrated initial B for Otto of the Silver Hand		544
PM0644	Otto of the Silver Hand	1888	197
MBPI2293	No one was within but old Ursela, who sat crooning over a fire		544
PM0644	Otto of the Silver Hand	1888	197
MBPI2294	Tailpiece, Chapter III for Otto of the Silver Hand		544
PM0644	Otto of the Silver Hand	1888	197
MBPI2295	Headpiece, Chapter IV for Otto of the Silver Hand		544
PM0644	Otto of the Silver Hand	1888	197
MBPI2296	Illustrated initial W for Otto of the Silver Hand		544
PM0644	Otto of the Silver Hand	1888	197
MBPI2297	Abbot Otto of St. Michaelsburg was a gentle, patient, pale-faced old man		544
PM0644	Otto of the Silver Hand	1888	197
PM1000	Decorative Illustrations of Books Old and New	1896	145
PM1049	Pen Drawing: An Illustrated Treatise	1899	199
PM1287	Eben C. Hill, Baltimore, Maryland	1900	275
PM1565	Howard Pyle, Author-Illustrator 1853-1911	February, 1912	2
MBPI2298	"While I lay there with my horse upon me, Baron Frederick ran me down with his lance"		544
PM0644	Otto of the Silver Hand	1888	197
MBPI2299	Tailpiece, Chapter IV for Otto of the Silver Hand		544
PM0644	Otto of the Silver Hand	1888	197
PM1112	Book Reviews	December, 1888	5
MBPI2300	Headpiece, Chapter V for Otto of the Silver Hand		544
PM0644	Otto of the Silver Hand	1888	197
PM1112	Book Reviews	December, 1888	5
MBPI2301	Illustrated initial S for Otto of the Silver Hand		544
PM0644	Otto of the Silver Hand	1888	197
MBPI2302	The poor simple Brother sitting under the pear tree close to the bee-hives, rocking the little baby in his arms		544
PM0644	Otto of the Silver Hand	1888	197
MBPI2303	Always it was one picture that little Otto sought		544
PM0644	Otto of the Silver Hand	1888	197
MBPI2304	Tailpiece, Chapter V for Otto of the Silver Hand		544
PM0644	Otto of the Silver Hand	1888	197
MBPI2305	Headpiece, Chapter VI for Otto of the Silver Hand		545
PM0644	Otto of the Silver Hand	1888	197
MBPI2306	Illustrated initial T for Otto of the Silver Hand		545
PM0644	Otto of the Silver Hand	1888	197
MBPI2307	Poor Brother John came forward and took the boy's hand		545
PM0644	Otto of the Silver Hand	1888	197
MBPI2308	Otto lay close to her feet upon a bear-skin		545
PM0644	Otto of the Silver Hand	1888	197
MBPI2309	Tailpiece, Chapter VI for Otto of the Silver Hand		545
PM0644	Otto of the Silver Hand	1888	197
PM1112	Book Reviews	December, 1888	5
MBPI2310	Headpiece, Chapter VII for Otto of the Silver Hand		545
PM0644	Otto of the Silver Hand	1888	197
MBPI2311	Illustrated initial T for Otto of the Silver Hand		545
PM0644	Otto of the Silver Hand	1888	197
MBPI2312	The grim Baron sat silent with his chin resting upon his clenched fist		545
PM0644	Otto of the Silver Hand	1888	197
MBPI2313	Slowly raising himself upon the narrow foot-hold, he peeped cautiously within		545
PM0644	Otto of the Silver Hand	1888	197
PM1341	Scribner's New List of Books For the Young	1892	266
MBPI2314	Schwartz Carl, holding his arbelast in his hand, stood silently watching		545
PM0644	Otto of the Silver Hand	1888	197
MBPI2315	He strode forward into the room and laid his hand heavily on the boy's shoulder		545
PM0644	Otto of the Silver Hand	1888	197
PM1112	Book Reviews	December, 1888	5
MBPI2316	Tailpiece, Chapter VII for Otto of the Silver Hand		545
PM0644	Otto of the Silver Hand	1888	197

MBPI2317	Headpiece, Chapter VIII for Otto of the Silver Hand		545
PM1245	Advertisement: "Otto of the Silver Hand"	November, 1888	108
PM0644	Otto of the Silver Hand	1888	197
MBPI2318	Illustrated initial A for Otto of the Silver Hand		545
PM0644	Otto of the Silver Hand	1888	197
MBPI2319	"Then dost thou not know why I am here?" said the Baron		545
PM0644	Otto of the Silver Hand	1888	197
MBPI2320	Headpiece, Chapter IX for Otto of the Silver Hand		545
PM0644	Otto of the Silver Hand	1888	197
MBPI2321	Illustrated initial F for Otto of the Silver Hand		546
PM0644	Otto of the Silver Hand	1888	197
MBPI2322	Fritz, the swineherd, sat eating his late supper of porridge		546
PM0644	Otto of the Silver Hand	1888	197
MBPI2323	Hans held up a necklace of blue and white beads		546
PM0644	Otto of the Silver Hand	1888	197
MBPI2324	Tailpiece, Chapter IX for Otto of the Silver Hand		546
PM0644	Otto of the Silver Hand	1888	197
MBPI2325	Headpiece, Chapter X for Otto of the Silver Hand		546
PM0644	Otto of the Silver Hand	1888	197
MBPI2326	Illustrated initial H for Otto of the Silver Hand		546
PM0644	Otto of the Silver Hand	1888	197
MBPI2327	"Thou ugly toad," said the woman		546
PM0644	Otto of the Silver Hand	1888	197
MBPI2328	The man was Long Jacob, the bowman		546
PM0644	Otto of the Silver Hand	1888	197
MBPI2329	In an instant he was flung back and down		546
PM0644	Otto of the Silver Hand	1888	197
PM1480	California Pacific International Exposition, San Diego, California	1915	314
MBPI2330	Tailpiece, Chapter X for Otto of the Silver Hand		546
PM0644	Otto of the Silver Hand	1888	197
MBPI2331	Headpiece, Chapter XI for Otto of the Silver Hand		546
PM0644	Otto of the Silver Hand	1888	197
MBPI2332	Illustrated initial L for Otto of the Silver Hand		546
PM0644	Otto of the Silver Hand	1888	197
MBPI2333	The next moment they were hanging in mid-air		546
PM0644	Otto of the Silver Hand	1888	197
PM1317	A New Illustrated Book by Howard Pyle	1895	271
PM1343	Scribner's New List of Books for the Young	1895	266
PM1349	Scribner's New Books For the Young	1897	268
MBPI2334	Tailpiece, Chapter XI for Otto of the Silver Hand		546
PM0644	Otto of the Silver Hand	1888	197
MBPI2335	Headpiece, Chapter XII for Otto of the Silver Hand		546
PM0644	Otto of the Silver Hand	1888	197
MBPI2336	Illustrated initial B for Otto of the Silver Hand		546
PM0644	Otto of the Silver Hand	1888	197
MBPI2337	He was gazing straight before him with a set and stony face		547
PM0644	Otto of the Silver Hand	1888	197
PM0922	Book Review	December, 1888	9
MBPI2338	Tailpiece, Chapter XII for Otto of the Silver Hand		547
PM0644	Otto of the Silver Hand	1888	197
MBPI2339	Headpiece, Chapter XIII for Otto of the Silver Hand		547
PM0644	Otto of the Silver Hand	1888	197
MBPI2340	Illustrated initial A for Otto of the Silver Hand		547
PM0644	Otto of the Silver Hand	1888	197
MBPI2341	In the middle of the narrow way stood the motionless, steel-clad figure		547
PM0644	Otto of the Silver Hand	1888	197
MBPI2342	For a moment they stood swaying backward and forward		547
PM0644	Otto of the Silver Hand	1888	197
MBPI2343	Tailpiece, Chapter XIII for Otto of the Silver Hand		547
PM0644	Otto of the Silver Hand	1888	197

MBPI2344	**Headpiece, Chapter XIV for Otto of the Silver Hand**		**547**
PM0644	Otto of the Silver Hand	1888	197
MBPI2345	**Illustrated initial T for Otto of the Silver Hand**		**547**
PM0644	Otto of the Silver Hand	1888	197
PM1112	Book Reviews	December, 1888	5
MBPI2346	**It was the great Emperor Rudolph**		**547**
PM0644	Otto of the Silver Hand	1888	197
MBPI2347	**Tailpiece, Chapter XIV for Otto of the Silver Hand**		**547**
PM0644	Otto of the Silver Hand	1888	197
MBPI2348	**He took her hand and set it to his lips**		**547**
PM0644	Otto of the Silver Hand	1888	197
PM1112	Book Reviews	December, 1888	5
PM1246	Advertisement: "Otto of the Silver Hand"	December, 1888	108
MBPI2349	**Headpiece, Afterword for Otto of the Silver Hand**		**547**
PM0644	Otto of the Silver Hand	1888	197
MBPI2350	**Illustrated initial T for Otto of the Silver Hand**		**547**
PM0644	Otto of the Silver Hand	1888	197
MBPI2351	**Cover design for Men of Iron**		**547**
PM0647	Men of Iron	1892	92-94, 182
MBPI2352	**"Enter Oliver and Mademoiselle Celeste"**		**547**
PM0648	A Modern Aladdin	1892	22-24, 185
MBPI2353	**Cover design for The Garden Behind the Moon**		**548**
PM0650	The Garden Behind the Moon	1895	154
MBPI2354	**In the garden behind the moon**		**548**
PM0650	The Garden Behind the Moon	1895	154
MBPI2355	**Headband for The Garden Behind the Moon**		**548**
PM0650	The Garden Behind the Moon	1895	154
PM1317	A New Illustrated Book by Howard Pyle	1895	271
MBPI2356	**Headband, Illustrations for The Garden Behind the Moon**		**548**
PM0650	The Garden Behind the Moon	1895	154
MBPI2357	**Headpiece, Foreword for The Garden Behind the Moon**		**548**
PM0650	The Garden Behind the Moon	1895	154
MBPI2358	**Tailpiece, Foreword for The Garden Behind the Moon**		**548**
PM0650	The Garden Behind the Moon	1895	154
MBPI2359	**Headpiece, Chapter I for The Garden Behind the Moon**		**548**
PM0650	The Garden Behind the Moon	1895	154
PM1125	Book Reviews	December, 1895	7
PM1317	A New Illustrated Book by Howard Pyle	1895	271
MBPI2360	**Headband, Chapter II for The Garden Behind the Moon**		**548**
PM0650	The Garden Behind the Moon	1895	154
MBPI2361	**Headband, Chapter III for The Garden Behind the Moon**		**548**
PM0650	The Garden Behind the Moon	1895	154
MBPI2362	**Headband, Chapter IV for The Garden Behind the Moon**		**548**
PM0650	The Garden Behind the Moon	1895	154
MBPI2363	**David looked up into Hans Krout's face**		**548**
PM0650	The Garden Behind the Moon	1895	154
MBPI2364	**Headband, Chapter V for The Garden Behind the Moon**		**548**
PM0650	The Garden Behind the Moon	1895	154
MBPI2365	**Suddenly a half-door opened and there stood a little man**		**548**
PM0650	The Garden Behind the Moon	1895	154
MBPI2366	**Headband, Chapter VI for The Garden Behind the Moon**		**548**
PM0650	The Garden Behind the Moon	1895	154
MBPI2367	**David sat down on the wooden bench and took up a big blue star**		**548**
PM0650	The Garden Behind the Moon	1895	154
MBPI2368	**Headband, Chapter VII for The Garden Behind the Moon**		**548**
PM0650	The Garden Behind the Moon	1895	154
MBPI2369	**He was standing at an open window**		**549**
PM0650	The Garden Behind the Moon	1895	154
MBPI2370	**"Where did you come from, little boy?" she said**		**549**
PM1124	Book Reviews	November, 1895	7

PM0650	The Garden Behind the Moon	1895	154
MBPI2371	**Headband, Chapter VIII for The Garden Behind the Moon**		**549**
PM0650	The Garden Behind the Moon	1895	154
MBPI2372	**Headband, Chapter IX for The Garden Behind the Moon**		**549**
PM0650	The Garden Behind the Moon	1895	154
MBPI2373	**Headband, Chapter X for The Garden Behind the Moon**		**549**
PM0650	The Garden Behind the Moon	1895	154
MBPI2374	**Headband, Chapter XI for The Garden Behind the Moon**		**549**
PM0650	The Garden Behind the Moon	1895	154
MBPI2375	**Headband, Chapter XII for The Garden Behind the Moon**		**549**
PM0650	The Garden Behind the Moon	1895	154
MBPI2376	**Quick as a flash, David leaped out and upon it**		**549**
PM0650	The Garden Behind the Moon	1895	154
PM1317	A New Illustrated Book by Howard Pyle	1895	271
MBPI2377	**Headband, Chapter XIII for The Garden Behind the Moon**		**549**
PM0650	The Garden Behind the Moon	1895	154
MBPI2378	**Headband, Chapter XIV for The Garden Behind the Moon**		**549**
PM0650	The Garden Behind the Moon	1895	154
MBPI2379	**Headband, Chapter XV for The Garden Behind the Moon**		**549**
PM0650	The Garden Behind the Moon	1895	154
MBPI2380	**Fast flew the black winged horse**		**549**
PM0650	The Garden Behind the Moon	1895	154
PM1125	Book Reviews	December, 1895	7
PM1343	Scribner's New List of Books for the Young	1895	266
PM1349	Scribner's New Books For the Young	1897	268
MBPI2381	**Headband, Chapter XVI for The Garden Behind the Moon**		**549**
PM0650	The Garden Behind the Moon	1895	154
MBPI2382	**The giant fell crashing upon the stones**		**549**
PM0650	The Garden Behind the Moon	1895	154
MBPI2383	**Cover design for Stops of Various Quills**		**549**
PM0723	Stops of Various Quills	1895	215
MBPI2384	**Headband, Chapter XVIII for The Garden Behind the Moon**		**549**
PM0650	The Garden Behind the Moon	1895	154
PM1317	A New Illustrated Book by Howard Pyle	1895	271
MBPI2385	**Headband, Chapter XIX for The Garden Behind the Moon**		**550**
PM0650	The Garden Behind the Moon	1895	154
MBPI2386	**She placed her hands on his shoulders**		**550**
PM0650	The Garden Behind the Moon	1895	154
MBPI2387	**Cover design for Twilight Land**		**550**
PM0651	Twilight Land	1895	237
MBPI2388	**Ita Primo Ita Semper**		**550**
PM0651	Twilight Land	1895	237
MBPI2389	**Dedication for Twilight Land**		**550**
PM0651	Twilight Land	1895	237
MBPI2390	**Headpiece, Table of Contents for Twilight Land**		**550**
PM0651	Twilight Land	1895	237
MBPI2391	**Headpiece with illustrated initial I, Introduction for Twilight Land**		**550**
PM0651	Twilight Land	1895	237
MBPI2392	**Title page decoration for First Year Book of The Bibliophile Society**		**550**
PM0654	First Year Book	1902	152
MBPI2393	**The Bibliophile**		**550**
PM0654	First Year Book	1902	152
PM0810	Portfolio of Etchings by W. H. W. Bicknell	1913	326
PM0825	Willard S. Morse, Seaford, Delaware	1916	276
MBPI2394	**Cover design for The Story of King Arthur and His Knights**		**550**
PM0657	The Story of King Arthur and His Knights	1903	121-124, 220
MBPI2395	**Spine design for The Story of King Arthur and His Knights**		**550**
PM0657	The Story of King Arthur and His Knights	1903	121-124, 220
MBPI2396	**Title page decoration for The Story of King Arthur and His Knights**		**550**
PM0657	The Story of King Arthur and His Knights	1903	121-124, 220

PM0658	The Story of the Champions of the Round Table	1905	226
PM0662	The Story of Sir Launcelot and his Companions	1907	223
PM0665	The Story of the Grail and the Passing of Arthur	1910	230
MBPI2397	**Tailpiece, Foreword for The Story of King Arthur and His Knights**		**550**
PM0657	The Story of King Arthur and His Knights	1903	121-124, 220
MBPI2398	**Tailpiece, Contents for The Story of King Arthur and His Knights**		**550**
PM0657	The Story of King Arthur and His Knights	1903	121-124, 220
MBPI2399	**Tailpiece, List of Illustrations for The Story of King Arthur and His Knights**		**550**
PM0657	The Story of King Arthur and His Knights	1903	121-124, 220
MBPI2400	**Subtitle page decoration for The Story of King Arthur and His Knights**		**550**
PM0657	The Story of King Arthur and His Knights	1903	121-124, 220
PM1479	Hotel Dupont, Wilmington, Delaware	1912	141, 310
MBPI2401	**Illustrated initial U with heading for The Story of King Arthur and His Knights**		**551**
PM0657	The Story of King Arthur and His Knights	1903	121-124, 220
MBPI2402	**Uther-Pendragon**		**551**
PM0657	The Story of King Arthur and His Knights	1903	121-124, 220
MBPI2403	**Tailpiece, Prologue for The Story of King Arthur and His Knights**		**551**
PM0657	The Story of King Arthur and His Knights	1903	121-124, 220
MBPI2404	**Tailpiece for The Story of King Arthur and His Knights**		**551**
PM0657	The Story of King Arthur and His Knights	1903	121-124, 220
MBPI2405	**Tailpiece for The Story of King Arthur and His Knights**		**551**
PM0657	The Story of King Arthur and His Knights	1903	121-124, 220
MBPI2406	**Tailpiece for The Story of King Arthur and His Knights**		**551**
PM0657	The Story of King Arthur and His Knights	1903	121-124, 220
MBPI2407	**Tailpiece for The Story of King Arthur and His Knights**		**551**
PM0657	The Story of King Arthur and His Knights	1903	121-124, 220
MBPI2408	**Illustrated initial T with heading for The Story of King Arthur and His Knights**		**551**
PM0657	The Story of King Arthur and His Knights	1903	121-124, 220
PM1479	Hotel Dupont, Wilmington, Delaware	1912	141, 310
MBPI2409	**The Lady of Ye Lake**		**551**
PM0657	The Story of King Arthur and His Knights	1903	121-124, 220
PM1470	St. Botolph Club, Boston, Massachusetts	1906	303
PM1479	Hotel Dupont, Wilmington, Delaware	1912	141, 310
MBPI2410	**Tailpiece for The Story of King Arthur and His Knights**		**551**
PM0657	The Story of King Arthur and His Knights	1903	121-124, 220
MBPI2411	**Illustrated initial T with heading for The Story of King Arthur and His Knights**		**551**
PM0657	The Story of King Arthur and His Knights	1903	121-124, 220
MBPI2412	**The Enchantress Vivien**		**551**
PM0657	The Story of King Arthur and His Knights	1903	121-124, 220
PM1470	St. Botolph Club, Boston, Massachusetts	1906	303
MBPI2413	**Illustrated initial V with heading for The Story of King Arthur and His Knights**		**551**
PM0657	The Story of King Arthur and His Knights	1903	121-124, 220
MBPI2414	**Vivien bewitches Merlin**		**551**
PM0657	The Story of King Arthur and His Knights	1903	121-124, 220
MBPI2415	**Illustrated initial Q with heading for The Story of King Arthur and His Knights**		**551**
PM0657	The Story of King Arthur and His Knights	1903	121-124, 220
MBPI2416	**Queen Morgana le Fay**		**551**
PM0657	The Story of King Arthur and His Knights	1903	121-124, 220
MBPI2417	**Illustrated initial Q with heading for The Story of King Arthur and His Knights**		**552**
PM0657	The Story of King Arthur and His Knights	1903	121-124, 220
PM1479	Hotel Dupont, Wilmington, Delaware	1912	141, 310
MBPI2418	**Queen Morgana loses Excalibur his sheath**		**552**
PM0657	The Story of King Arthur and His Knights	1903	121-124, 220
PM1470	St. Botolph Club, Boston, Massachusetts	1906	303
PM1479	Hotel Dupont, Wilmington, Delaware	1912	141, 310
MBPI2419	**Tailpiece for The Story of King Arthur and His Knights**		**552**
PM0657	The Story of King Arthur and His Knights	1903	121-124, 220
MBPI2420	**Tailpiece for The Story of King Arthur and His Knights**		**552**
PM0657	The Story of King Arthur and His Knights	1903	121-124, 220
MBPI2421	**Illustrated initial S with heading for The Story of King Arthur and His Knights**		**552**

PM0657	The Story of King Arthur and His Knights	1903	121-124, 220
MBPI2422	**Sir Gawaine the Son of Lot, King of Orkney**		**552**
PM0657	The Story of King Arthur and His Knights	1903	121-124, 220
MBPI2423	**Headpiece for The Story of King Arthur and His Knights**		**552**
PM0657	The Story of King Arthur and His Knights	1903	121-124, 220
MBPI2424	**Illustrated initial K with heading for The Story of King Arthur and His Knights**		**552**
PM0657	The Story of King Arthur and His Knights	1903	121-124, 220
MBPI2425	**King Arthur findeth ye old woman in ye hut**		**552**
PM0657	The Story of King Arthur and His Knights	1903	121-124, 220
MBPI2426	**Illustrated initial S with heading for The Story of King Arthur and His Knights**		**552**
PM0657	The Story of King Arthur and His Knights	1903	121-124, 220
MBPI2427	**Sir Gawaine finds the beautiful Lady**		**552**
PM0657	The Story of King Arthur and His Knights	1903	121-124, 220
MBPI2428	**Tailpiece for The Story of King Arthur and His Knights**		**552**
PM0657	The Story of King Arthur and His Knights	1903	121-124, 220
MBPI2429	**Cover design for The Story of Champions of the Round Table**		**552**
PM0658	The Story of the Champions of the Round Table	1905	226
MBPI2430	**Spine design for The Story of the Champions of the Round Table**		**552**
PM0658	The Story of the Champions of the Round Table	1905	226
MBPI2431	**Illustrated initial S with heading for The Story of the Champions of the Round Table**		**552**
PM0658	The Story of the Champions of the Round Table	1905	226
MBPI2432	**Sir Launcelot of the Lake**		**552**
PM0658	The Story of the Champions of the Round Table	1905	226
MBPI2433	**Headpiece, Foreword for The Story of the Champions of the Round Table**		**553**
PM0658	The Story of the Champions of the Round Table	1905	226
MBPI2434	**Tailpiece, Foreword for The Story of the Champions of the Round Table**		**553**
PM0658	The Story of the Champions of the Round Table	1905	226
MBPI2435	**Headpiece, Contents for The Story of the Champions of the Round Table**		**553**
PM0658	The Story of the Champions of the Round Table	1905	226
MBPI2436	**Tailpiece, Contents for The Story of the Champions of the Round Table**		**553**
PM0658	The Story of the Champions of the Round Table	1905	226
MBPI2437	**Headpiece, List of Illustrations for The Story of the Champions of the Round Table**		**553**
PM0658	The Story of the Champions of the Round Table	1905	226
MBPI2438	**Tailpiece, List of Illustrations for The Story of the Champions of the Round Table**		**553**
PM0658	The Story of the Champions of the Round Table	1905	226
MBPI2439	**Illustrated initial T with heading for The Story of the Champions of the Round Table**		**553**
PM0658	The Story of the Champions of the Round Table	1905	226
MBPI2440	**The Lady Nymue beareth away Launcelot into the Lake**		**553**
PM0658	The Story of the Champions of the Round Table	1905	226
MBPI2441	**Headpiece for The Story of the Champions of the Round Table**		**553**
PM0658	The Story of the Champions of the Round Table	1905	226
MBPI2442	**Tailpiece for The Story of the Champions of the Round Table**		**553**
PM0658	The Story of the Champions of the Round Table	1905	226
MBPI2443	**Illustrated initial S with heading for The Story of the Champions of the Round Table**		**553**
PM0658	The Story of the Champions of the Round Table	1905	226
MBPI2444	**Sir Launcelot greets Queen Guinevere**		**553**
PM0658	The Story of the Champions of the Round Table	1905	226
MBPI2445	**Headpiece for The Story of the Champions of the Round Table**		**553**
PM0658	The Story of the Champions of the Round Table	1905	226
MBPI2446	**Illustrated initial S with heading for The Story of the Champions of the Round Table**		**553**
PM0658	The Story of the Champions of the Round Table	1905	226
MBPI2447	**Sir Lionel of Britain**		**553**
PM0658	The Story of the Champions of the Round Table	1905	226
MBPI2448	**Illustrated initial Q with heading for The Story of the Champions of the Round Table**		**553**
PM0658	The Story of the Champions of the Round Table	1905	226
MBPI2449	**Queen Morgana appears unto Sir Launcelot**		**554**
PM0658	The Story of the Champions of the Round Table	1905	226
PM1483	The Wilmington Society of the Fine Arts, Wilmington, Delaware	1920	317
MBPI2450	**Illustrated initial S with heading for The Story of the Champions of the Round Table**		**554**
PM0658	The Story of the Champions of the Round Table	1905	226

MBPI2451	**Sir Launcelot doeth battle with Sir Turquine**		**554**
PM0658	The Story of the Champions of the Round Table	1905	226
MBPI2452	**Illustrated initial S with heading for The Story of the Champions of the Round Table**		**554**
PM0658	The Story of the Champions of the Round Table	1905	226
MBPI2453	**Sir Launcelot sits with Sir Hilaire and Croisette**		**554**
PM0658	The Story of the Champions of the Round Table	1905	226
PM1483	The Wilmington Society of the Fine Arts, Wilmington, Delaware	1920	317
MBPI2454	**Illustrated initial S with heading for The Story of the Champions of the Round Table**		**554**
PM0658	The Story of the Champions of the Round Table	1905	226
MBPI2455	**Sir Launcelot and Elouise the Fair**		**554**
PM0658	The Story of the Champions of the Round Table	1905	226
MBPI2456	**Illustrated initial S with heading for The Story of the Champions of the Round Table**		**554**
PM0658	The Story of the Champions of the Round Table	1905	226
PM1479	Hotel Dupont, Wilmington, Delaware	1912	141, 310
MBPI2457	**Sir Launcelot climbs to catch the lady's falcon**		**554**
PM0658	The Story of the Champions of the Round Table	1905	226
PM1479	Hotel Dupont, Wilmington, Delaware	1912	141, 310
MBPI2458	**Illustrated initial S with heading for The Story of the Champions of the Round Table**		**554**
PM0658	The Story of the Champions of the Round Table	1905	226
MBPI2459	**Sir Launcelot takes the armor of Sir Kay**		**554**
PM0658	The Story of the Champions of the Round Table	1905	226
MBPI2460	**Tailpiece for The Story of the Champions of the Round Table**		**554**
PM0658	The Story of the Champions of the Round Table	1905	226
MBPI2461	**Illustrated initial S with heading for The Story of the Champions of the Round Table**		**554**
PM0658	The Story of the Champions of the Round Table	1905	226
MBPI2462	**Sir Tristram of Lyonesse**		**554**
PM0658	The Story of the Champions of the Round Table	1905	226
PM1483	The Wilmington Society of the Fine Arts, Wilmington, Delaware	1920	317
MBPI2463	**Headpiece for The Story of the Champions of the Round Table**		**554**
PM0658	The Story of the Champions of the Round Table	1905	226
MBPI2464	**Tailpiece for The Story of the Champions of the Round Table**		**554**
PM0658	The Story of the Champions of the Round Table	1905	226
MBPI2465	**Illustrated initial T with heading for The Story of the Champions of the Round Table**		**555**
PM0658	The Story of the Champions of the Round Table	1905	226
MBPI2466	**Tristram succors the Lady Moeya**		**555**
PM0658	The Story of the Champions of the Round Table	1905	226
MBPI2467	**Headpiece for The Story of the Champions of the Round Table**		**555**
PM0658	The Story of the Champions of the Round Table	1905	226
PM1479	Hotel Dupont, Wilmington, Delaware	1912	141, 310
MBPI2468	**Illustrated initial K with heading for The Story of the Champions of the Round Table**		**555**
PM0658	The Story of the Champions of the Round Table	1905	226
MBPI2469	**King Mark of Cornwall**		**555**
PM0658	The Story of the Champions of the Round Table	1905	226
MBPI2470	**Illustrated initial T with heading for The Story of the Champions of the Round Table**		**555**
PM0658	The Story of the Champions of the Round Table	1905	226
MBPI2471	**The Lady Belle Isoult**		**555**
PM0658	The Story of the Champions of the Round Table	1905	226
MBPI2472	**Illustrated initial T with heading for The Story of the Champions of the Round Table**		**555**
PM0658	The Story of the Champions of the Round Table	1905	226
MBPI2473	**The Queen of Ireland seeks to slay Sir Tristram**		**555**
PM0658	The Story of the Champions of the Round Table	1905	226
MBPI2474	**Illustrated initial S with heading for The Story of the Champions of the Round Table**		**555**
PM0658	The Story of the Champions of the Round Table	1905	226
MBPI2475	**Sir Tristram harpeth before King Mark**		**555**
PM0658	The Story of the Champions of the Round Table	1905	226
MBPI2476	**Illustrated initial S with heading for The Story of the Champions of the Round Table**		**555**
PM0658	The Story of the Champions of the Round Table	1905	226
MBPI2477	**Sir Tristram sits with Sir Launcelot**		**555**
PM0658	The Story of the Champions of the Round Table	1905	226
PM1483	The Wilmington Society of the Fine Arts, Wilmington, Delaware	1920	317

MBPI2478	**Tailpiece for The Story of the Champions of the Round Table**		**555**
PM0658	The Story of the Champions of the Round Table	1905	226
MBPI2479	**Illustrated initial B with heading for The Story of the Champions of the Round Table**		**555**
PM0658	The Story of the Champions of the Round Table	1905	226
MBPI2480	**Belle Isoult and Sir Tristram drink the love draught**		**555**
PM0658	The Story of the Champions of the Round Table	1905	226
MBPI2481	**Tailpiece for The Story of the Champions of the Round Table**		**556**
PM0658	The Story of the Champions of the Round Table	1905	226
MBPI2482	**Illustrated initial S with heading for The Story of the Champions of the Round Table**		**556**
PM0658	The Story of the Champions of the Round Table	1905	226
MBPI2483	**Sir Lamorack of Gales**		**556**
PM0658	The Story of the Champions of the Round Table	1905	226
PM1483	The Wilmington Society of the Fine Arts, Wilmington, Delaware	1920	317
MBPI2484	**Headpiece for The Story of the Champions of the Round Table**		**556**
PM0658	The Story of the Champions of the Round Table	1905	226
MBPI2485	**Illustrated initial S with heading for The Story of the Champions of the Round Table**		**556**
PM0658	The Story of the Champions of the Round Table	1905	226
MBPI2486	**Sir Tristram cometh to ye castle of Sir Nabon**		**556**
PM0658	The Story of the Champions of the Round Table	1905	226
MBPI2487	**Illustrated initial S with heading for The Story of the Champions of the Round Table**		**556**
PM0658	The Story of the Champions of the Round Table	1905	226
MBPI2488	**Sir Lamorack herds the swine of Sir Nabon**		**556**
PM0658	The Story of the Champions of the Round Table	1905	226
MBPI2489	**Tailpiece for The Story of the Champions of the Round Table**		**556**
PM0658	The Story of the Champions of the Round Table	1905	226
PM1479	Hotel Dupont, Wilmington, Delaware	1912	141, 310
MBPI2490	**Illustrated initial S with heading for The Story of the Champions of the Round Table**		**556**
PM0658	The Story of the Champions of the Round Table	1905	226
MBPI2491	**Sir Tristram assaults King Mark**		**556**
PM0658	The Story of the Champions of the Round Table	1905	226
MBPI2492	**Headpiece for The Story of the Champions of the Round Table**		**556**
PM0658	The Story of the Champions of the Round Table	1905	226
MBPI2493	**Illustrated initial S with heading for The Story of the Champions of the Round Table**		**556**
PM0658	The Story of the Champions of the Round Table	1905	226
PM1479	Hotel Dupont, Wilmington, Delaware	1912	141, 310
MBPI2494	**Sir Kay and the Forest Madman**		**556**
PM0658	The Story of the Champions of the Round Table	1905	226
PM1479	Hotel Dupont, Wilmington, Delaware	1912	141, 310
MBPI2495	**Illustrated initial S with heading for The Story of the Champions of the Round Table**		**556**
PM0658	The Story of the Champions of the Round Table	1905	226
MBPI2496	**Sir Tristram leaps into ye Sea**		**556**
PM0658	The Story of the Champions of the Round Table	1905	226
MBPI2497	**Illustrated initial K with heading for The Story of the Champions of the Round Table**		**557**
PM0658	The Story of the Champions of the Round Table	1905	226
PM1479	Hotel Dupont, Wilmington, Delaware	1912	141, 310
MBPI2498	**King Mark broods mischief**		**557**
PM0658	The Story of the Champions of the Round Table	1905	226
PM1479	Hotel Dupont, Wilmington, Delaware	1912	141, 310
MBPI2499	**Tailpiece for The Story of the Champions of the Round Table**		**557**
PM0658	The Story of the Champions of the Round Table	1905	226
MBPI2500	**Hendryk Hudson and the Half-Moon**		**557**
PM0831	Mural paintings–Hudson County Court House, Jersey City, New Jersey	1910	258
MBPI2501	**Peter Stuyvesant and the English Fleet**		**557**
PM0831	Mural paintings–Hudson County Court House, Jersey City, New Jersey	1910	258
MBPI2502	**Life in an Old Dutch Town**		**557**
PM0831	Mural paintings–Hudson County Court House, Jersey City, New Jersey	1910	258
MBPI2503	**Dutch Soldier**		**557**
PM0831	Mural paintings–Hudson County Court House, Jersey City, New Jersey	1910	258
MBPI2504	**English Soldier**		**557**
PM0831	Mural paintings–Hudson County Court House, Jersey City, New Jersey	1910	258

MBPI2505	**Spring**		**557**
PM0832	Spring	1901	
MBPI2506	**The Garden of Youth**		**557**
PM0833	The Garden of Youth	1903	
MBPI2507	**The Midsummer Moon**		**557**
PM0835	The Midsummer Moon	1908	
MBPI2508	**The Enchanted Seas**		**557**
PM0836	The Enchanted Seas	1909	
MBPI2509	**Illustrated initial T with heading for The Story of the Champions of the Round Table**		**557**
PM0658	The Story of the Champions of the Round Table	1905	226
MBPI2510	**The Demoiselle Blanchefleur**		**557**
PM0658	The Story of the Champions of the Round Table	1905	226
PM1483	The Wilmington Society of the Fine Arts, Wilmington, Delaware	1920	317
MBPI2511	**Marooned**		**557**
PM0837	Marooned	1909	
PM1530	Marooned	June, 1912	21
PM1479	Hotel Dupont, Wilmington, Delaware	1912	141, 310
MBPI2512	**The Mermaid**		**557**
PM0838	The Mermaid	1910	
PM1482	The Wilmington Society of the Fine Arts, Wilmington, Delaware	1917	316
MBPI2513	**Tailpiece for The Story of the Champions of the Round Table**		**558**
PM0658	The Story of the Champions of the Round Table	1905	226
MBPI2514	**Cover design for The Story of Sir Launcelot and his Companions**		**558**
PM0662	The Story of Sir Launcelot and his Companions	1907	223
MBPI2515	**Spine design for The Story of Sir Launcelot and his Companions**		**558**
PM0662	The Story of Sir Launcelot and his Companions	1907	223
MBPI2516	**Illustrated initial T with heading for The Story of Sir Launcelot and his Companions**		**558**
PM0662	The Story of Sir Launcelot and his Companions	1907	223
MBPI2517	**The Lady Elaine the Fair**		**558**
PM0662	The Story of Sir Launcelot and his Companions	1907	223
MBPI2518	**Headpiece, Foreword for The Story of Sir Launcelot and his Companions**		**558**
PM0662	The Story of Sir Launcelot and his Companions	1907	223
MBPI2519	**Tailpiece, Foreword for The Story of Sir Launcelot and his Companions**		**558**
PM0662	The Story of Sir Launcelot and his Companions	1907	223
MBPI2520	**Headpiece, Contents for The Story of Sir Launcelot and his Companions**		**558**
PM0662	The Story of Sir Launcelot and his Companions	1907	223
MBPI2521	**Tailpiece, Contents for The Story of Sir Launcelot and his Companions**		**558**
PM0662	The Story of Sir Launcelot and his Companions	1907	223
MBPI2522	**Headpiece, List of Illustrations for The Story of Sir Launcelot and his Companions**		**558**
PM0662	The Story of Sir Launcelot and his Companions	1907	223
MBPI2523	**Tailpiece, List of Illustrations for The Story of Sir Launcelot and his Companions**		**558**
PM0662	The Story of Sir Launcelot and his Companions	1907	223
MBPI2524	**Illustrated initial S with heading for The Story of Sir Launcelot and his Companions**		**558**
PM0662	The Story of Sir Launcelot and his Companions	1907	223
MBPI2525	**Sir Mellegrans interrupts the sport of the Queen**		**558**
PM0662	The Story of Sir Launcelot and his Companions	1907	223
MBPI2526	**Headpiece for The Story of Sir Launcelot and his Companions**		**558**
PM0662	The Story of Sir Launcelot and his Companions	1907	223
MBPI2527	**Tailpiece for The Story of Sir Launcelot and his Companions**		**558**
PM0662	The Story of Sir Launcelot and his Companions	1907	223
MBPI2528	**Illustrated initial D with heading for The Story of Sir Launcelot and his Companions**		**558**
PM0662	The Story of Sir Launcelot and his Companions	1907	223
MBPI2529	**Denneys and the Hermit help Sir Launcelot to his armor**		**559**
PM0662	The Story of Sir Launcelot and his Companions	1907	223
MBPI2530	**Headpiece for The Story of Sir Launcelot and his Companions**		**559**
PM0662	The Story of Sir Launcelot and his Companions	1907	223
MBPI2531	**Illustrated initial H with heading for The Story of Sir Launcelot and his Companions**		**559**
PM0662	The Story of Sir Launcelot and his Companions	1907	223
MBPI2532	**How Sir Launcelot rode errant in a cart**		**559**
PM0662	The Story of Sir Launcelot and his Companions	1907	223

MBPI2533	**Illustrated initial T with heading for The Story of Sir Launcelot and his Companions**		**559**
PM0662	The Story of Sir Launcelot and his Companions	1907	223
MBPI2534	**The Damsel Elose the Fair rescues Sir Launcelot**		**559**
PM0662	The Story of Sir Launcelot and his Companions	1907	223
MBPI2535	**Illustrated initial S with heading for The Story of Sir Launcelot and his Companions**		**559**
PM0662	The Story of Sir Launcelot and his Companions	1907	223
MBPI2536	**Sir Gareth of Orkney**		**559**
PM0662	The Story of Sir Launcelot and his Companions	1907	223
MBPI2537	**Headpiece for The Story of Sir Launcelot and his Companions**		**559**
PM0662	The Story of Sir Launcelot and his Companions	1907	223
MBPI2538	**Illustrated initial T with heading for The Story of Sir Launcelot and his Companions**		**559**
PM0662	The Story of Sir Launcelot and his Companions	1907	223
MBPI2539	**The Damsel Lynette**		**559**
PM0662	The Story of Sir Launcelot and his Companions	1907	223
MBPI2540	**Illustrated initial S with heading for The Story of Sir Launcelot and his Companions**		**559**
PM0662	The Story of Sir Launcelot and his Companions	1907	223
MBPI2541	**Sir Gareth doeth Battle with the Knight of the River Ford**		**559**
PM0662	The Story of Sir Launcelot and his Companions	1907	223
MBPI2542	**Illustrated initial T with heading for The Story of Sir Launcelot and his Companions**		**559**
PM0662	The Story of Sir Launcelot and his Companions	1907	223
MBPI2543	**The Lady Layonnesse**		**559**
PM0662	The Story of Sir Launcelot and his Companions	1907	223
MBPI2544	**Illustrated initial T with heading for The Story of Sir Launcelot and his Companions**		**559**
PM0662	The Story of Sir Launcelot and his Companions	1907	223
MBPI2545	**The Lady Layonnesse cometh to the Pavilion of Sir Gareth**		**560**
PM0662	The Story of Sir Launcelot and his Companions	1907	223
MBPI2546	**Tailpiece for The Story of Sir Launcelot and his Companions**		**560**
PM0662	The Story of Sir Launcelot and his Companions	1907	223
MBPI2547	**Illustrated initial H with heading for The Story of Sir Launcelot and his Companions**		**560**
PM0662	The Story of Sir Launcelot and his Companions	1907	223
MBPI2548	**How Sir Launcelot held discourse with ye merry Minstrels**		**560**
PM1093	Advertisement: The Story of Sir Launcelot	November, 1907	113
PM0662	The Story of Sir Launcelot and his Companions	1907	223
PM1583	Advertisements	December, 1907	55
MBPI2549	**Headpiece for The Story of Sir Launcelot and his Companions**		**560**
PM0662	The Story of Sir Launcelot and his Companions	1907	223
MBPI2550	**Illustrated initial S with heading for The Story of Sir Launcelot and his Companions**		**560**
PM0662	The Story of Sir Launcelot and his Companions	1907	223
MBPI2551	**Sir Launcelot slayeth the Worm of Corbin**		**560**
PM0662	The Story of Sir Launcelot and his Companions	1907	223
MBPI2552	**Illustrated initial S with heading for The Story of Sir Launcelot and his Companions**		**560**
PM0662	The Story of Sir Launcelot and his Companions	1907	223
MBPI2553	**Sir Launcelot confideth his Shield to Elaine the Fair**		**560**
PM0662	The Story of Sir Launcelot and his Companions	1907	223
MBPI2554	**Illustrated initial S with heading for The Story of Sir Launcelot and his Companions**		**560**
PM0662	The Story of Sir Launcelot and his Companions	1907	223
MBPI2555	**Sir Launcelot and Sir Lavaine overlook the Field of Astolat**		**560**
PM0662	The Story of Sir Launcelot and his Companions	1907	223
MBPI2556	**Illustrated initial S with heading for The Story of Sir Launcelot and his Companions**		**560**
PM0662	The Story of Sir Launcelot and his Companions	1907	223
MBPI2557	**Sir Gawaine knoweth the shield of Sir Launcelot**		**560**
PM0662	The Story of Sir Launcelot and his Companions	1907	223
PM1483	The Wilmington Society of the Fine Arts, Wilmington, Delaware	1920	317
MBPI2558	**Illustrated initial S with heading for The Story of Sir Launcelot and his Companions**		**560**
PM0662	The Story of Sir Launcelot and his Companions	1907	223
MBPI2559	**Sir Launcelot leapeth from the window**		**560**
PM0662	The Story of Sir Launcelot and his Companions	1907	223
MBPI2560	**Tailpiece for The Story of Sir Launcelot and his Companions**		**560**
PM0662	The Story of Sir Launcelot and his Companions	1907	223
MBPI2561	**Illustrated initial T with heading for The Story of Sir Launcelot and his Companions**		**561**

PM0662	The Story of Sir Launcelot and his Companions	1907	223
MBPI2562	**The Madman of the Forest who was Sir Launcelot**		**561**
PM0662	The Story of Sir Launcelot and his Companions	1907	223
MBPI2563	**Headpiece for The Story of Sir Launcelot and his Companions**		**561**
PM0662	The Story of Sir Launcelot and his Companions	1907	223
MBPI2564	**Illustrated initial T with heading for The Story of Sir Launcelot and his Companions**		**561**
PM0662	The Story of Sir Launcelot and his Companions	1907	223
MBPI2565	**The Forest Madman saveth ye Life of King Arthur**		**561**
PM0662	The Story of Sir Launcelot and his Companions	1907	223
MBPI2566	**Illustrated initial T with heading for The Story of Sir Launcelot and his Companions**		**561**
PM0662	The Story of Sir Launcelot and his Companions	1907	223
MBPI2567	**The Lady Elaine the Fair Knoweth Sir Launcelot**		**561**
PM0662	The Story of Sir Launcelot and his Companions	1907	223
PM1483	The Wilmington Society of the Fine Arts, Wilmington, Delaware	1920	317
MBPI2568	**Tailpiece for The Story of Sir Launcelot and his Companions**		**561**
PM0662	The Story of Sir Launcelot and his Companions	1907	223
MBPI2569	**Illustrated initial S with heading for The Story of Sir Launcelot and his Companions**		**561**
PM0662	The Story of Sir Launcelot and his Companions	1907	223
MBPI2570	**Sir Gawaine, Knight of the Fountain**		**561**
PM0662	The Story of Sir Launcelot and his Companions	1907	223
MBPI2571	**Headpiece for The Story of Sir Launcelot and his Companions**		**561**
PM0662	The Story of Sir Launcelot and his Companions	1907	223
MBPI2572	**Illustrated initial S with heading for The Story of Sir Launcelot and his Companions**		**561**
PM0662	The Story of Sir Launcelot and his Companions	1907	223
MBPI2573	**Sir Ewaine poureth water on the slab**		**561**
PM0662	The Story of Sir Launcelot and his Companions	1907	223
MBPI2574	**Illustrated initial T with heading for The Story of Sir Launcelot and his Companions**		**561**
PM0662	The Story of Sir Launcelot and his Companions	1907	223
MBPI2575	**The Damsel Elose giveth a ring to Sir Ewaine**		**561**
PM0662	The Story of Sir Launcelot and his Companions	1907	223
MBPI2576	**Illustrated initial T with heading for The Story of Sir Launcelot and his Companions**		**561**
PM0662	The Story of Sir Launcelot and his Companions	1907	223
MBPI2577	**The Lady of the Fountain**		**562**
PM0662	The Story of Sir Launcelot and his Companions	1907	223
PM1483	The Wilmington Society of the Fine Arts, Wilmington, Delaware	1920	317
MBPI2578	**Illustrated initial A with heading for The Story of Sir Launcelot and his Companions**		**562**
PM0662	The Story of Sir Launcelot and his Companions	1907	223
MBPI2579	**A Damsel bringeth aid unto Sir Ewaine**		**562**
PM0662	The Story of Sir Launcelot and his Companions	1907	223
PM1483	The Wilmington Society of the Fine Arts, Wilmington, Delaware	1920	317
MBPI2580	**Tailpiece for The Story of Sir Launcelot and his Companions**		**562**
PM0662	The Story of Sir Launcelot and his Companions	1907	223
MBPI2581	**Illustrated initial S with heading for The Story of Sir Launcelot and his Companions**		**562**
PM0662	The Story of Sir Launcelot and his Companions	1907	223
MBPI2582	**Sir Lamorack and Sir Percival receive their Mother's Blessing**		**562**
PM0662	The Story of Sir Launcelot and his Companions	1907	223
PM1483	The Wilmington Society of the Fine Arts, Wilmington, Delaware	1920	317
MBPI2583	**Headpiece for The Story of Sir Launcelot and his Companions**		**562**
PM0662	The Story of Sir Launcelot and his Companions	1907	223
MBPI2584	**Illustrated initial S with heading for The Story of Sir Launcelot and his Companions**		**562**
PM0662	The Story of Sir Launcelot and his Companions	1907	223
MBPI2585	**Sir Percival and Sir Ector look upon the Isle of Joy**		**562**
PM0662	The Story of Sir Launcelot and his Companions	1907	223
MBPI2586	**Illustrated initial S with heading for The Story of Sir Launcelot and his Companions**		**562**
PM0662	The Story of Sir Launcelot and his Companions	1907	223
MBPI2587	**Sir Lavaine the Son of Pelles**		**562**
PM0662	The Story of Sir Launcelot and his Companions	1907	223
MBPI2588	**Illustrated initial M with heading for The Story of Sir Launcelot and his Companions**		**562**
PM0662	The Story of Sir Launcelot and his Companions	1907	223
MBPI2589	**Merlin Prophesieth from a Cloud of Mist**		**562**

PM0662	The Story of Sir Launcelot and his Companions	1907	223
PM1483	The Wilmington Society of the Fine Arts, Wilmington, Delaware	1920	317
MBPI2590	**Headpiece for The Story of Sir Launcelot and his Companions**		**562**
PM0662	The Story of Sir Launcelot and his Companions	1907	223
MBPI2591	**Illustrated initial S with heading for The Story of Sir Launcelot and his Companions**		**562**
PM0662	The Story of Sir Launcelot and his Companions	1907	223
MBPI2592	**Sir Bors de Ganis, the good**		**562**
PM0662	The Story of Sir Launcelot and his Companions	1907	223
MBPI2593	**Illustrated initial T with heading for The Story of Sir Launcelot and his Companions**		**563**
PM0662	The Story of Sir Launcelot and his Companions	1907	223
MBPI2594	**The Barge of the Dead**		**563**
PM0662	The Story of Sir Launcelot and his Companions	1907	223
MBPI2595	**Cover design for The Story of the Grail and the Passing of Arthur**		**563**
PM0665	The Story of the Grail and the Passing of Arthur	1910	230
MBPI2596	**Spine design for The Story of the Grail and the Passing of Arthur**		**563**
PM0665	The Story of the Grail and the Passing of Arthur	1910	230
MBPI2597	**Illustrated initial S with heading for The Story of the Grail and the Passing of Arthur**		**563**
PM0665	The Story of the Grail and the Passing of Arthur	1910	230
MBPI2598	**Sir Galahad of the Grail**		**563**
PM0665	The Story of the Grail and the Passing of Arthur	1910	230
MBPI2599	**Headpiece, Foreword for The Story of the Grail and the Passing of Arthur**		**563**
PM0665	The Story of the Grail and the Passing of Arthur	1910	230
MBPI2600	**Tailpiece for The Story of the Grail and the Passing of Arthur**		**563**
PM0665	The Story of the Grail and the Passing of Arthur	1910	230
MBPI2601	**Headpiece, Contents for The Story of the Grail and the Passing of Arthur**		**563**
PM0665	The Story of the Grail and the Passing of Arthur	1910	230
MBPI2602	**Tailpiece, Contents for The Story of the Grail and the Passing of Arthur**		**563**
PM0665	The Story of the Grail and the Passing of Arthur	1910	230
MBPI2603	**Headpiece, List of Illustrations for The Story of the Grail and the Passing of Arthur**		**563**
PM0665	The Story of the Grail and the Passing of Arthur	1910	230
MBPI2604	**Tailpiece, List of Illustrations for The Story of the Grail and the Passing of Arthur**		**563**
PM0665	The Story of the Grail and the Passing of Arthur	1910	230
MBPI2605	**Illustrated initial S with heading for The Story of the Grail and the Passing of Arthur**		**563**
PM0665	The Story of the Grail and the Passing of Arthur	1910	230
MBPI2606	**Sir Geraint, Son of Erbin**		**563**
PM0665	The Story of the Grail and the Passing of Arthur	1910	230
PM1483	The Wilmington Society of the Fine Arts, Wilmington, Delaware	1920	317
MBPI2607	**Headpiece for The Story of the Grail and the Passing of Arthur**		**563**
PM0665	The Story of the Grail and the Passing of Arthur	1910	230
MBPI2608	**Tailpiece for The Story of the Grail and the Passing of Arthur**		**563**
PM0665	The Story of the Grail and the Passing of Arthur	1910	230
MBPI2609	**Illustrated initial E with heading for The Story of the Grail and the Passing of Arthur**		**564**
PM0665	The Story of the Grail and the Passing of Arthur	1910	230
MBPI2610	**Enid and Geraint in the garden**		**564**
PM0665	The Story of the Grail and the Passing of Arthur	1910	230
MBPI2611	**Headpiece for The Story of the Grail and the Passing of Arthur**		**564**
PM0665	The Story of the Grail and the Passing of Arthur	1910	230
MBPI2612	**Illustrated initial S with heading for The Story of the Grail and the Passing of Arthur**		**564**
PM0665	The Story of the Grail and the Passing of Arthur	1910	230
MBPI2613	**Sir Geraint and the Knight of the Sparrowhawk**		**564**
PM0665	The Story of the Grail and the Passing of Arthur	1910	230
PM1483	The Wilmington Society of the Fine Arts, Wilmington, Delaware	1920	317
MBPI2614	**Illustrated initial S with heading for The Story of the Grail and the Passing of Arthur**		**564**
PM0665	The Story of the Grail and the Passing of Arthur	1910	230
MBPI2615	**Sir Geraint lies asleep**		**564**
PM0665	The Story of the Grail and the Passing of Arthur	1910	230
MBPI2616	**Illustrated initial E with heading for The Story of the Grail and the Passing of Arthur**		**564**
PM0665	The Story of the Grail and the Passing of Arthur	1910	230
MBPI2617	**Enid talks with the Earl**		**564**
PM0665	The Story of the Grail and the Passing of Arthur	1910	230

MBPI2618	**Illustrated initial E with heading for The Story of the Grail and the Passing of Arthur**		**564**
PM0665	The Story of the Grail and the Passing of Arthur	1910	230
MBPI2619	**Enid and Geraint ride past the Town bridge**		**564**
PM0665	The Story of the Grail and the Passing of Arthur	1910	230
MBPI2620	**Illustrated initial T with heading for The Story of the Grail and the Passing of Arthur**		**564**
PM0665	The Story of the Grail and the Passing of Arthur	1910	230
MBPI2621	**The King's Physicians attend Sir Geraint**		**564**
PM0665	The Story of the Grail and the Passing of Arthur	1910	230
MBPI2622	**Spine design for Stops of Various Quills**		**564**
PM0723	Stops of Various Quills	1895	215
MBPI2623	**Illustrated initial S with heading for The Story of the Grail and the Passing of Arthur**		**564**
PM0665	The Story of the Grail and the Passing of Arthur	1910	230
MBPI2624	**Sir Galahad cometh with the Hermit of the Forest**		**564**
PM0665	The Story of the Grail and the Passing of Arthur	1910	230
MBPI2625	**Headpiece for The Story of the Grail and the Passing of Arthur**		**565**
PM0665	The Story of the Grail and the Passing of Arthur	1910	230
MBPI2626	**Illustrated initial T with heading for The Story of the Grail and the Passing of Arthur**		**565**
PM0665	The Story of the Grail and the Passing of Arthur	1910	230
MBPI2627	**The Lady of the Lake and Sir Galahad**		**565**
PM0665	The Story of the Grail and the Passing of Arthur	1910	230
MBPI2628	**Illustrated initial S with heading for The Story of the Grail and the Passing of Arthur**		**565**
PM0665	The Story of the Grail and the Passing of Arthur	1910	230
PM1479	Hotel Dupont, Wilmington, Delaware	1912	141, 310
MBPI2629	**Sir Galahad meets Sir Melyas**		**565**
PM0665	The Story of the Grail and the Passing of Arthur	1910	230
PM1479	Hotel Dupont, Wilmington, Delaware	1912	141, 310
MBPI2630	**Illustrated initial T with heading for The Story of the Grail and the Passing of Arthur**		**565**
PM0665	The Story of the Grail and the Passing of Arthur	1910	230
MBPI2631	**The Grail is manifested, and Sir Launcelot sleepeth**		**565**
PM0665	The Story of the Grail and the Passing of Arthur	1910	230
MBPI2632	**Illustrated initial S with heading for The Story of the Grail and the Passing of Arthur**		**565**
PM0665	The Story of the Grail and the Passing of Arthur	1910	230
PM1479	Hotel Dupont, Wilmington, Delaware	1912	141, 310
MBPI2633	**Sir Percival rideth the black horse**		**565**
PM0665	The Story of the Grail and the Passing of Arthur	1910	230
PM1479	Hotel Dupont, Wilmington, Delaware	1912	141, 310
MBPI2634	**Illustrated initial S with heading for The Story of the Grail and the Passing of Arthur**		**565**
PM0665	The Story of the Grail and the Passing of Arthur	1910	230
MBPI2635	**Sir Bors rides with the white knight**		**565**
PM0665	The Story of the Grail and the Passing of Arthur	1910	230
MBPI2636	**Illustrated initial S with heading for The Story of the Grail and the Passing of Arthur**		**565**
PM0665	The Story of the Grail and the Passing of Arthur	1910	230
MBPI2637	**Sir Galahad rides with the Lady**		**565**
PM0665	The Story of the Grail and the Passing of Arthur	1910	230
PM1483	The Wilmington Society of the Fine Arts, Wilmington, Delaware	1920	317
MBPI2638	**Illustrated initial T with heading for The Story of the Grail and the Passing of Arthur**		**565**
PM0665	The Story of the Grail and the Passing of Arthur	1910	230
MBPI2639	**The Queen's pages clothe Sir Launcelot**		**565**
PM0665	The Story of the Grail and the Passing of Arthur	1910	230
MBPI2640	**Headpiece for The Story of the Grail and the Passing of Arthur**		**565**
PM0665	The Story of the Grail and the Passing of Arthur	1910	230
MBPI2641	**Illustrated initial S with heading for The Story of the Grail and the Passing of Arthur**		**566**
PM0665	The Story of the Grail and the Passing of Arthur	1910	230
MBPI2642	**Sir Mador de la Porte**		**566**
PM0665	The Story of the Grail and the Passing of Arthur	1910	230
PM1483	The Wilmington Society of the Fine Arts, Wilmington, Delaware	1920	317
MBPI2643	**Illustrated initial S with heading for The Story of the Grail and the Passing of Arthur**		**566**
PM0665	The Story of the Grail and the Passing of Arthur	1910	230
MBPI2644	**Sir Mador begs for his Life**		**566**
PM0665	The Story of the Grail and the Passing of Arthur	1910	230

PM0860	Advertisement: The Story of the Grail and the Passing of Arthur	January, 1911	113
MBPI2645	**Illustrated initial S with heading for The Story of the Grail and the Passing of Arthur**		**566**
PM0665	The Story of the Grail and the Passing of Arthur	1910	230
MBPI2646	**Sir Launcelot defends the door**		**566**
PM0665	The Story of the Grail and the Passing of Arthur	1910	230
MBPI2647	**Illustrated initial T with heading for The Story of the Grail and the Passing of Arthur**		**566**
PM0665	The Story of the Grail and the Passing of Arthur	1910	230
MBPI2648	**The Bishop of Rochester and the King**		**566**
PM0665	The Story of the Grail and the Passing of Arthur	1910	230
PM1483	The Wilmington Society of the Fine Arts, Wilmington, Delaware	1920	317
MBPI2649	**Illustrated initial S with heading for The Story of the Grail and the Passing of Arthur**		**566**
PM0665	The Story of the Grail and the Passing of Arthur	1910	230
MBPI2650	**Sir Gawaine challenges Sir Launcelot**		**566**
PM0665	The Story of the Grail and the Passing of Arthur	1910	230
MBPI2651	**Illustrated initial T with heading for The Story of the Grail and the Passing of Arthur**		**566**
PM0665	The Story of the Grail and the Passing of Arthur	1910	230
MBPI2652	**The Passing of Sir Gawaine**		**566**
PM0665	The Story of the Grail and the Passing of Arthur	1910	230
PM1483	The Wilmington Society of the Fine Arts, Wilmington, Delaware	1920	317
MBPI2653	**Illustrated initial S with heading for The Story of the Grail and the Passing of Arthur**		**566**
PM0665	The Story of the Grail and the Passing of Arthur	1910	230
MBPI2654	**Sir Mordred the traitor**		**566**
PM0665	The Story of the Grail and the Passing of Arthur	1910	230
MBPI2655	**Illustrated initial T with heading for The Story of the Grail and the Passing of Arthur**		**566**
PM0665	The Story of the Grail and the Passing of Arthur	1910	230
MBPI2656	**The Passing of Arthur**		**566**
PM0665	The Story of the Grail and the Passing of Arthur	1910	230
MBPI2657	**Illustrated initial T with heading for The Story of the Grail and the Passing of Arthur**		**567**
PM0665	The Story of the Grail and the Passing of Arthur	1910	230
MBPI2658	**The Passing of Guinevere**		**567**
PM0665	The Story of the Grail and the Passing of Arthur	1910	230
MBPI2659	**Tailpiece for The Story of the Grail and the Passing of Arthur**		**567**
PM0665	The Story of the Grail and the Passing of Arthur	1910	230
MBPI2660	**Illustration for McGuffey's Fifth Eclectic Reader**		**567**
PM0668	McGuffey's Fifth Eclectic Reader	1879	181
MBPI2661	**Illustration for McGuffey's Fifth Eclectic Reader**		**567**
PM0668	McGuffey's Fifth Eclectic Reader	1879	181
MBPI2662	**The Quack**		**567**
PM0669	McGuffey's Sixth Eclectic Reader	1879	181
MBPI2663	**Front cover design for Yankee Doodle**		**567**
PM0672	Yankee Doodle	1881	254
MBPI2664	**Frontispiece for Yankee Doodle**		**567**
PM0672	Yankee Doodle	1881	254
MBPI2665	**Title page illustration for Yankee Doodle**		**567**
PM0672	Yankee Doodle	1881	254
MBPI2666	**Father and I went down to camp…**		**567**
PM0672	Yankee Doodle	1881	254
MBPI2667	**There was Captain Washington…**		**567**
PM0672	Yankee Doodle	1881	254
MBPI2668	**And then the feathers in his hat…**		**567**
PM0672	Yankee Doodle	1881	254
MBPI2669	**Illustration for Yankee Doodle**		**567**
PM0672	Yankee Doodle	1881	254
PM1274	Ballads of Our Forefathers	1881	326
MBPI2670	**My Jemima.**		**567**
PM0672	Yankee Doodle	1881	254
MBPI2671	**And then they had a swampin gun…**		**567**
PM0672	Yankee Doodle	1881	254
MBPI2672	**And every time they fired it off…**		**567**

PM0672	Yankee Doodle	1881	254
MBPI2673	**Illustration for Yankee Doodle**		**568**
PM0672	Yankee Doodle	1881	254
MBPI2674	**It made a noise like father's gun…**		**568**
PM0672	Yankee Doodle	1881	254
MBPI2675	**I went as near to it myself…**		**568**
PM0672	Yankee Doodle	1881	254
MBPI2676	**Illustration for Yankee Doodle**		**568**
PM0672	Yankee Doodle	1881	254
MBPI2677	**Cousin Simon grew so bold…**		**568**
PM0672	Yankee Doodle	1881	254
MBPI2678	**It scared me so I shrinked off…**		**568**
PM0672	Yankee Doodle	1881	254
MBPI2679	**And there I see a pumpkin shell…**		**568**
PM0672	Yankee Doodle	1881	254
MBPI2680	**Illustration for Yankee Doodle**		**568**
PM0672	Yankee Doodle	1881	254
MBPI2681	**And every time they touched it off…**		**568**
PM0672	Yankee Doodle	1881	254
MBPI2682	**And there I see a little keg…**		**568**
PM0672	Yankee Doodle	1881	254
MBPI2683	**And then they'd fife away like fun…**		**568**
PM0672	Yankee Doodle	1881	254
MBPI2684	**And some had ribbons red as blood…**		**568**
PM0672	Yankee Doodle	1881	254
MBPI2685	**Illustration for Yankee Doodle**		**568**
PM0672	Yankee Doodle	1881	254
MBPI2686	**The troopers, too, would gallop up…**		**568**
PM1578	Selections from Holiday Books	December 14, 1881	103
PM0672	Yankee Doodle	1881	254
MBPI2687	**Old Uncle Sam come then to change…**		**568**
PM0672	Yankee Doodle	1881	254
MBPI2688	**Illustration for Yankee Doodle**		**568**
PM0672	Yankee Doodle	1881	254
MBPI2689	**For 'lasses cake, to carry home…**		**569**
PM0672	Yankee Doodle	1881	254
MBPI2690	**I see another snarl of men…**		**569**
PM0672	Yankee Doodle	1881	254
MBPI2691	**It scared me so, I hooked it off…**		**569**
PM0672	Yankee Doodle	1881	254
MBPI2692	**Nor turned about till I got home…**		**569**
PM0672	Yankee Doodle	1881	254
MBPI2693	**Illustration for Yankee Doodle**		**569**
PM0672	Yankee Doodle	1881	254
MBPI2694	**Back cover design for Yankee Doodle**		**569**
PM0672	Yankee Doodle	1881	254
MBPI2695	**Decorative illustrations for The Lady of Shalott**		**569**
PM0674	The Lady of Shalott	1881	174
MBPI2696	**Decorative illustrations for The Lady of Shalott**		**569**
PM0674	The Lady of Shalott	1881	174
MBPI2697	**Title page decoration for The Lady of Shalott**		**569**
PM0674	The Lady of Shalott	1881	174
MBPI2698	**Decorative illustration for The Lady of Shalott**		**569**
PM0674	The Lady of Shalott	1881	174
MBPI2699	**Part I for The Lady of Shalott**		**569**
PM0674	The Lady of Shalott	1881	174
MBPI2700	**A Description of the Castle**		**569**
PM0674	The Lady of Shalott	1881	174
MBPI2701	**The people passing the Island**		**569**
PM0674	The Lady of Shalott	1881	174

MBPI2702	**The Fairy Lady of Shalott in the Space of Flowers**		**569**
PM0674	The Lady of Shalott	1881	174
MBPI2703	**A Description of the Same**		**569**
PM0674	The Lady of Shalott	1881	174
MBPI2704	**The Boats Passing Along the River**		**569**
PM0674	The Lady of Shalott	1881	174
MBPI2705	**Illustration for The Lady of Shalott**		**570**
PM0674	The Lady of Shalott	1881	174
MBPI2706	**Decorative illustrations for The Lady of Shalott**		**570**
PM0674	The Lady of Shalott	1881	174
MBPI2707	**How the Reapers Hear Her Singing**		**570**
PM0674	The Lady of Shalott	1881	174
MBPI2708	**The Weary Reapers Beneath the Moon Hear Her Singing**		**570**
PM0674	The Lady of Shalott	1881	174
MBPI2709	**Part II for The Lady of Shalott**		**570**
PM0674	The Lady of Shalott	1881	174
MBPI2710	**How the Lady Weaveth Day by Day**		**570**
PM0674	The Lady of Shalott	1881	174
MBPI2711	**What She Sees in the Mirror**		**570**
PM0674	The Lady of Shalott	1881	174
MBPI2712	**Still the Poem Speaketh of the Sights Within the Mirror**		**570**
PM0674	The Lady of Shalott	1881	174
MBPI2713	**All These Things She Weaveth Into the Web**		**570**
PM0674	The Lady of Shalott	1881	174
MBPI2714	**Illustration for The Lady of Shalott**		**570**
PM0674	The Lady of Shalott	1881	174
MBPI2715	**Part III for The Lady of Shalott**		**570**
PM0674	The Lady of Shalott	1881	174
MBPI2716	**In This Verse is Spoken of the Coming of Sir Lancelot the Bold**		**570**
PM0674	The Lady of Shalott	1881	174
MBPI2717	**This Verse Speaketh Also of Lancelot the Bold**		**570**
PM0674	The Lady of Shalott	1881	174
MBPI2718	**The Third Verse Describeth Also the Coming of the Bold Knight**		**570**
PM0674	The Lady of Shalott	1881	174
MBPI2719	**The Fourth Verse Describing the Gallant Knight Sir Lancelot the Bold**		**570**
PM0674	The Lady of Shalott	1881	174
MBPI2720	**Illustration for The Lady of Shalott**		**570**
PM0674	The Lady of Shalott	1881	174
MBPI2721	**Decorative illustration for The Lady of Shalott**		**571**
PM0674	The Lady of Shalott	1881	174
MBPI2722	**The Lady Brings the Curse Upon Her**		**571**
PM0674	The Lady of Shalott	1881	174
MBPI2723	**Illustration for The Lady of Shalott**		**571**
PM0674	The Lady of Shalott	1881	174
MBPI2724	**Part IV for The Lady of Shalott**		**571**
PM0674	The Lady of Shalott	1881	174
MBPI2725	**In Which the Fairy Lady Seeks the River**		**571**
PM0674	The Lady of Shalott	1881	174
MBPI2726	**Illustration for The Lady of Shalott**		**571**
PM0674	The Lady of Shalott	1881	174
MBPI2727	**Decorative illustration for The Lady of Shalott**		**571**
PM0674	The Lady of Shalott	1881	174
MBPI2728	**Illustration and text for The Lady of Shalott**		**571**
PM0674	The Lady of Shalott	1881	174
MBPI2729	**Illustration and text for The Lady of Shalott**		**571**
PM0674	The Lady of Shalott	1881	174
MBPI2730	**The Lady Dieth Floating Adown the Stream**		**571**
PM0674	The Lady of Shalott	1881	174
MBPI2731	**The Dead Lady Floateth Down Ye Stream Toward Camelot**		**571**
PM0674	The Lady of Shalott	1881	174

MBPI2732	**Decorative illustration for The Lady of Shalott**		**571**
PM0674	The Lady of Shalott	1881	174
MBPI2733	**Illustration and text for The Lady of Shalott**		**571**
PM0674	The Lady of Shalott	1881	174
MBPI2734	**Illustration for The Lady of Shalott**		**571**
PM0674	The Lady of Shalott	1881	174
MBPI2735	**Decorative illustration for The Lady of Shalott**		**571**
PM0674	The Lady of Shalott	1881	174
MBPI2736	**Illustration and text for The Lady of Shalott**		**571**
PM0674	The Lady of Shalott	1881	174
MBPI2737	**Illustration for The Lady of Shalott**		**572**
PM0674	The Lady of Shalott	1881	174
MBPI2738	**The end for The Lady of Shalott**		**572**
PM0674	The Lady of Shalott	1881	174
MBPI2739	**Decoration for The Lady of Shalott**		**572**
PM0674	The Lady of Shalott	1881	174
MBPI2740	**Front cover design for Lady of Shalott**		**572**
PM0674	The Lady of Shalott	1881	174
MBPI2741	**Spine design for Lady of Shalott**		**572**
PM0674	The Lady of Shalott	1881	174
MBPI2742	**The Forging of Balmung**		**572**
PM0677	The Story of Siegfried	1882	164, 223
PM1341	Scribner's New List of Books For the Young	1892	266
PM1014	Hero Tales, Told in School	1904	164
MBPI2743	**The Death of Fafnir**		**572**
PM0677	The Story of Siegfried	1882	164, 223
PM0644	Otto of the Silver Hand	1888	197
MBPI2744	**The Awakening of Brunhild**		**572**
PM0677	The Story of Siegfried	1882	164, 223
MBPI2745	**The Trial of Strength**		**572**
PM0677	The Story of Siegfried	1882	164, 223
MBPI2746	**The Quarrel of the Queens**		**572**
PM0677	The Story of Siegfried	1882	164, 223
MBPI2747	**The Death of Siegfried**		**572**
PM0677	The Story of Siegfried	1882	164, 223
MBPI2748	**"Ho, Drummer! quick, silence yon Capet"**		**572**
PM0678	The Chronicle of the Drum	1882	143
MBPI2749	**"Awful, and proud, and erect"**		**572**
PM0678	The Chronicle of the Drum	1882	143
MBPI2750	**"She looked from the bars of her prison"**		**572**
PM0678	The Chronicle of the Drum	1882	143
MBPI2751	**"Aunt Mary Expressing Her Mind"**		**572**
PM0679	Under Green Apple Boughs	1882	105, 240
MBPI2752	**"The Mourning Clam-Man"**		**572**
PM0679	Under Green Apple Boughs	1882	105, 240
MBPI2753	**Grandfather and Little Benny**		**573**
PM0680	New England Bygones	1883	106, 188
MBPI2754	**The Beloved Pastor**		**573**
PM1235	A Sect of Seekers	December 20, 1882	106
PM0680	New England Bygones	1883	106, 188
MBPI2755	**Illustration for Swinton's Fifth Reader and Speaker**		**573**
PM0681	Swinton's Fifth Reader and Speaker	1883	234
PM0714	A School History of the United States	1893	210
PM0992	A Brief History of the City of New York	1899	138
MBPI2756	**Illustration for Swinton's Fifth Reader and Speaker**		**573**
PM0681	Swinton's Fifth Reader and Speaker	1883	234
MBPI2757	**Inaugural Procession**		**573**
PM0682	Building the Nation	1883	138
MBPI2758	**A Kentucky Wedding**		**573**
PM0682	Building the Nation	1883	138

MBPI2759	**Scene in the Theatre in Philadelphia 1794**		**573**
PM0682	Building the Nation	1883	138
PM0761	Harper's Encyclopaedia of United States History	1902	158
PM0954	Harper's Encyclopaedia of United States History from 458 A.D. to 1915	1915	161
MBPI2760	**Dutch and Indians trading**		**573**
PM0683	A History of the United States of America	1884	168
PM1068	A Short History of the United States of America for the use of beginners	1890	211
MBPI2761	**Roger Williams in exile**		**573**
PM0683	A History of the United States of America	1884	168
MBPI2762	**The Indian and the Pioneer**		**573**
PM0683	A History of the United States of America	1884	168
MBPI2763	**Whitman starting for Washington**		**573**
PM0683	A History of the United States of America	1884	168
MBPI2764	**Notes: Descriptive and Biographic**		**573**
PM0684	Art Year Book	1884	132
MBPI2765	**Headpiece, Lexington**		**573**
PM0685	Illustrated Poems of Oliver Wendell Holmes	1885	171
MBPI2766	**The Embarkation**		**573**
PM0685	Illustrated Poems of Oliver Wendell Holmes	1885	171
MBPI2767	**"Blazing and clanging from thicket and wall"**		**573**
PM0685	Illustrated Poems of Oliver Wendell Holmes	1885	171
PM1053	The Poetical Works of James Russell Lowell	1890	203
MBPI2768	**"For they all thought he was dying, as they gathered round him crying"**		**573**
PM0685	Illustrated Poems of Oliver Wendell Holmes	1885	171
MBPI2769	**Illustration for Swinton's Advanced Third Reader**		**574**
PM0689	Swinton's Advanced Third Reader	1886	234
MBPI2770	**"Her native songs for him she sung"**		**574**
PM0690	The Inca Princess	1886	172
MBPI2771	**Headband for A History of New York**		**574**
PM0691	A History of New-York	1886	164
PM1147	The Grolier Club	November, 1889	11
PM0717	Transactions of The Grolier Club of the City of New York. Part II	1894	236
PM0987	Bookbindings, Old And New	1896	136
MBPI2772	**Illustrated initial A for A History of New York**		**574**
PM0691	A History of New-York	1886	164
PM0717	Transactions of The Grolier Club of the City of New York. Part II	1894	236
MBPI2773	**Tailpiece for A History of New York**		**574**
PM0691	A History of New-York	1886	164
PM0717	Transactions of The Grolier Club of the City of New York. Part II	1894	236
MBPI2774	**Sat, like a Fate, and watched the flying thread**		**574**
PM0692	The Closing Scene	1887	144
PM1078	Three Poems	1888	235
MBPI2775	**She heard the stir of his black mantle trailing in the dust**		**574**
PM0692	The Closing Scene	1887	144
PM1078	Three Poems	1888	235
MBPI2776	**While yet her cheek was bright with summer bloom**		**574**
PM0692	The Closing Scene	1887	144
PM1078	Three Poems	1888	235
MBPI2777	**Breathed through her lips a sad and tremulous tune**		**574**
PM0692	The Closing Scene	1887	144
PM1078	Three Poems	1888	235
MBPI2778	**Death and Winter closed the autumn scene**		**574**
PM0692	The Closing Scene	1887	144
PM1078	Three Poems	1888	235
MBPI2779	**Pyrrhus Finds Philoctetes in a Cave**		**574**
PM0693	A Story of The Golden Age	1887	164, 229
MBPI2780	**Odysseus and His Mother**		**574**
PM0693	A Story of The Golden Age	1887	164, 229
PM0744	Odysseus, the Hero of Ithaca	1898	191

MBPI2781	**Apollo Slaying the Python**		**574**
PM0693	A Story of The Golden Age	1887	164, 229
PM1493	Book Reviews	December, 1887	5
PM1343	Scribner's New List of Books for the Young	1895	266
PM1014	Hero Tales, Told in School	1904	164
MBPI2782	**Meleager Refuses to Help in the Defence of the City**		**574**
PM0693	A Story of The Golden Age	1887	164, 229
PM1014	Hero Tales, Told in School	1904	164
MBPI2783	**The Silver-Footed Thetis Rising from the Waves**		**574**
PM0693	A Story of The Golden Age	1887	164, 229
PM0744	Odysseus, the Hero of Ithaca	1898	191
PM1014	Hero Tales, Told in School	1904	164
MBPI2784	**The Swineherd Telling His Story to Odysseus**		**574**
PM0693	A Story of The Golden Age	1887	164, 229
PM0744	Odysseus, the Hero of Ithaca	1898	191
MBPI2785	**Alpheus and Arethusa**		**575**
PM0693	A Story of The Golden Age	1887	164, 229
PM0744	Odysseus, the Hero of Ithaca	1898	191
PM1014	Hero Tales, Told in School	1904	164
MBPI2786	**Odysseus Advises King Tyndareus Concerning Helen's Suitors**		**575**
PM0693	A Story of The Golden Age	1887	164, 229
MBPI2787	**Deianeira and the Dying Centaur Nessus**		**575**
PM0693	A Story of The Golden Age	1887	164, 229
MBPI2788	**Prometheus**		**575**
PM0693	A Story of The Golden Age	1887	164, 229
PM0921	Book Review	December, 1887	9
MBPI2789	**Palamedes Tests the Madness of Odysseus**		**575**
PM0693	A Story of The Golden Age	1887	164, 229
PM0744	Odysseus, the Hero of Ithaca	1898	191
MBPI2790	**Odysseus and Menelaus Persuading Agamemnon to Sacrifice Iphigenia**		**575**
PM0693	A Story of The Golden Age	1887	164, 229
PM0744	Odysseus, the Hero of Ithaca	1898	191
PM1014	Hero Tales, Told in School	1904	164
MBPI2791	**The Boys present the Salmagundi to Heer Governor Stuyvesant**		**575**
PM0694	Storied Holidays	1887	218
MBPI2792	**Washington, the Young Surveyor**		**575**
PM0697	Harper's Fourth Reader	1888	163
PM0788	Founders of Our Country	1912	153
MBPI2793	**"The Sachem's Daughter"**		**575**
PM0706	Works of John Greenleaf Whittier	1892	252
PM0997	The Complete Poetical Works of John Greenleaf Whittier	1904	144
MBPI2794	**"The Vision of Echard"**		**575**
PM0707	Works of John Greenleaf Whittier	1892	252
PM0997	The Complete Poetical Works of John Greenleaf Whittier	1904	144
MBPI2795	**The Deacon**		**575**
PM1222	Notice of The One Hoss Shay	November, 1891	99
PM1118	Book Reviews	December, 1891	6
PM0708	The One Hoss Shay	1892	193, 196
PM0772	The One Hoss Shay	1905	195
MBPI2796	**Headpiece, Preface for The One Hoss Shay**		**575**
PM0708	The One Hoss Shay	1892	193, 196
PM0772	The One Hoss Shay	1905	195
MBPI2797	**Tailpiece, Preface for The One Hoss Shay**		**575**
PM0708	The One Hoss Shay	1892	193, 196
PM0772	The One Hoss Shay	1905	195
MBPI2798	**Headpiece, List of Illustrations for The One Hoss Shay**		**575**
PM0708	The One Hoss Shay	1892	193, 196
PM0772	The One Hoss Shay	1905	195
MBPI2799	**Tailpiece, List of Illustrations for The One Hoss Shay**		**575**
PM0708	The One Hoss Shay	1892	193, 196

PM0772	The One Hoss Shay		1905	195
MBPI2800	**Half-title for The Deacon's Masterpiece**			**575**
PM0708	The One Hoss Shay		1892	193, 196
PM0772	The One Hoss Shay		1905	195
MBPI2801	**The Masterpiece**			**576**
PM0708	The One Hoss Shay		1892	193, 196
PM0772	The One Hoss Shay		1905	195
MBPI2802	**"A chaise breaks down"**			**576**
PM0708	The One Hoss Shay		1892	193, 196
PM0726	Modern Illustration		1895	186
PM0772	The One Hoss Shay		1905	195
MBPI2803	**"The Deacon inquired of the village folk"**			**576**
PM1223	Notice of The One Hoss Shay	December, 1891		99
PM0708	The One Hoss Shay		1892	193, 196
PM0772	The One Hoss Shay		1905	195
MBPI2804	**"Naow she'll dew"**			**576**
PM0708	The One Hoss Shay		1892	193, 196
PM0772	The One Hoss Shay		1905	195
MBPI2805	**"She was a wonder, and nothing less"**			**576**
PM0708	The One Hoss Shay		1892	193, 196
PM0726	Modern Illustration		1895	186
PM0772	The One Hoss Shay		1905	195
PM1012	The Graphic Arts and Crafts Year Book		1907	157
PM1521	The Children's Hour: Myths from Many Lands		1907	142
PM0968	The Riverside Seventh Reader		1913	207
MBPI2806	**"Deacon and deaconess dropped away"**			**576**
PM0708	The One Hoss Shay		1892	193, 196
PM0772	The One Hoss Shay		1905	195
MBPI2807	**"Eighteen Hundred"**			**576**
PM0708	The One Hoss Shay		1892	193, 196
PM0772	The One Hoss Shay		1905	195
PM1360	For The Holidays 1906		1906	271
MBPI2808	**"Fifty-five"**			**576**
PM0708	The One Hoss Shay		1892	193, 196
PM0772	The One Hoss Shay		1905	195
MBPI2809	**"Its hundredth year"**			**576**
PM0708	The One Hoss Shay		1892	193, 196
PM0772	The One Hoss Shay		1905	195
MBPI2810	**"A general flavor of mild decay"**			**576**
PM0708	The One Hoss Shay		1892	193, 196
PM0772	The One Hoss Shay		1905	195
MBPI2811	**"In another hour it will be worn out"**			**576**
PM0708	The One Hoss Shay		1892	193, 196
PM0772	The One Hoss Shay		1905	195
PM1157	The Critic Advertiser: One Hoss Shay	December, 1905		17
PM1484	Advertisements	December, 1905		53
MBPI2812	**"The parson takes a drive"**			**576**
PM0708	The One Hoss Shay		1892	193, 196
PM0772	The One Hoss Shay		1905	195
MBPI2813	**"All at once the horses stood still"**			**576**
PM1118	Book Reviews	December, 1891		6
PM0708	The One Hoss Shay		1892	193, 196
PM0772	The One Hoss Shay		1905	195
MBPI2814	**"Then something decidedly like a spill"**			**576**
PM1136	The One Hoss Shay	November, 1891		9
PM0708	The One Hoss Shay		1892	193, 196
PM0772	The One Hoss Shay		1905	195
MBPI2815	**"Just as bubbles do when they burst"**			**576**
PM0708	The One Hoss Shay		1892	193, 196
PM0772	The One Hoss Shay		1905	195

MBPI2816	"End of the wonderful one-hoss-shay"		**576**
PM0708	The One Hoss Shay	1892	193, 196
PM0772	The One Hoss Shay	1905	195
MBPI2817	**Half-title for How the Old Horse Won the Bet**		**577**
PM0708	The One Hoss Shay	1892	193, 196
PM0772	The One Hoss Shay	1905	195
MBPI2818	"The famous trotting ground"		**577**
PM1118	Book Reviews	December, 1891	6
PM0708	The One Hoss Shay	1892	193, 196
PM0772	The One Hoss Shay	1905	195
MBPI2819	"Many a noted steed"		**577**
PM0708	The One Hoss Shay	1892	193, 196
PM0772	The One Hoss Shay	1905	195
MBPI2820	"The Sunday swell"		**577**
PM0708	The One Hoss Shay	1892	193, 196
PM0772	The One Hoss Shay	1905	195
MBPI2821	"The jointed tandem"		**577**
PM0708	The One Hoss Shay	1892	193, 196
PM0772	The One Hoss Shay	1905	195
MBPI2822	"So shy with us, so free with these"		**577**
PM0708	The One Hoss Shay	1892	193, 196
PM0772	The One Hoss Shay	1905	195
MBPI2823	"The lovely bonnets beamed their smiles"		**577**
PM1118	Book Reviews	December, 1891	6
PM0708	The One Hoss Shay	1892	193, 196
PM0772	The One Hoss Shay	1905	195
MBPI2824	"I'll bet you two to one"		**577**
PM0708	The One Hoss Shay	1892	193, 196
PM0772	The One Hoss Shay	1905	195
MBPI2825	"Harnessed in his one-hoss-shay"		**577**
PM0708	The One Hoss Shay	1892	193, 196
PM0772	The One Hoss Shay	1905	195
MBPI2826	"The sexton…led forth the horse"		**577**
PM0708	The One Hoss Shay	1892	193, 196
PM0772	The One Hoss Shay	1905	195
MBPI2827	"A sight to see"		**577**
PM0708	The One Hoss Shay	1892	193, 196
PM0772	The One Hoss Shay	1905	195
MBPI2828	"They lead him, limping, to the track"		**577**
PM0708	The One Hoss Shay	1892	193, 196
PM0772	The One Hoss Shay	1905	195
MBPI2829	"To limber out each stiffened joint"		**577**
PM0708	The One Hoss Shay	1892	193, 196
PM0772	The One Hoss Shay	1905	195
MBPI2830	"Something like a stride"		**577**
PM0708	The One Hoss Shay	1892	193, 196
PM0772	The One Hoss Shay	1905	195
MBPI2831	"A mighty stride he swung"		**577**
PM0708	The One Hoss Shay	1892	193, 196
PM0772	The One Hoss Shay	1905	195
MBPI2832	"Off went a shoe"		**577**
PM0708	The One Hoss Shay	1892	193, 196
PM0772	The One Hoss Shay	1905	195
MBPI2833	"And now the stand he rushes by"		**578**
PM0708	The One Hoss Shay	1892	193, 196
PM0772	The One Hoss Shay	1905	195
MBPI2834	"And off they spring"		**578**
PM0708	The One Hoss Shay	1892	193, 196
PM0772	The One Hoss Shay	1905	195
MBPI2835	"They follow at his heels"		**578**

PM0708	The One Hoss Shay	1892	193, 196
PM0772	The One Hoss Shay	1905	195
MBPI2836	**"They're losing ground"**		**578**
PM0708	The One Hoss Shay	1892	193, 196
PM0772	The One Hoss Shay	1905	195
MBPI2837	**"He's distanced all the lot"**		**578**
PM0708	The One Hoss Shay	1892	193, 196
PM0772	The One Hoss Shay	1905	195
MBPI2838	**"Some took his time"**		**578**
PM0708	The One Hoss Shay	1892	193, 196
PM0772	The One Hoss Shay	1905	195
MBPI2839	**"Back in the one-hoss-shay he went"**		**578**
PM0708	The One Hoss Shay	1892	193, 196
PM0772	The One Hoss Shay	1905	195
MBPI2840	**"A horse can trot, for all he's old"**		**578**
PM0708	The One Hoss Shay	1892	193, 196
PM0772	The One Hoss Shay	1905	195
MBPI2841	**Half-title for The Broomstick Train**		**578**
PM0708	The One Hoss Shay	1892	193, 196
PM0772	The One Hoss Shay	1905	195
MBPI2842	**"Clear the track"**		**578**
PM0708	The One Hoss Shay	1892	193, 196
PM0772	The One Hoss Shay	1905	195
MBPI2843	**"An Essex Deacon dropped in to call"**		**578**
PM0708	The One Hoss Shay	1892	193, 196
PM0772	The One Hoss Shay	1905	195
MBPI2844	**"The old dwellings"**		**578**
PM0708	The One Hoss Shay	1892	193, 196
PM0772	The One Hoss Shay	1905	195
MBPI2845	**"The small square windows"**		**578**
PM0708	The One Hoss Shay	1892	193, 196
PM0772	The One Hoss Shay	1905	195
MBPI2846	**"Dark, dim, Dante-like solitudes"**		**578**
PM0708	The One Hoss Shay	1892	193, 196
PM0772	The One Hoss Shay	1905	195
MBPI2847	**"Norman's Woe"**		**578**
PM0708	The One Hoss Shay	1892	193, 196
PM0772	The One Hoss Shay	1905	195
MBPI2848	**"The Screeching Woman of Marblehead"**		**578**
PM0708	The One Hoss Shay	1892	193, 196
PM0772	The One Hoss Shay	1905	195
MBPI2849	**"It is n't fair"**		**579**
PM0708	The One Hoss Shay	1892	193, 196
PM0772	The One Hoss Shay	1905	195
MBPI2850	**"You're a good old–fellow–come, let us go"**		**579**
PM0708	The One Hoss Shay	1892	193, 196
PM0772	The One Hoss Shay	1905	195
MBPI2851	**"See how tall they 've grown"**		**579**
PM1136	The One Hoss Shay	November, 1891	9
PM0708	The One Hoss Shay	1892	193, 196
PM0772	The One Hoss Shay	1905	195
MBPI2852	**"They called the cats"**		**579**
PM0708	The One Hoss Shay	1892	193, 196
PM0772	The One Hoss Shay	1905	195
MBPI2853	**"The Essex people had dreadful times"**		**579**
PM0708	The One Hoss Shay	1892	193, 196
PM0772	The One Hoss Shay	1905	195
MBPI2854	**"The withered hags were free"**		**579**
PM0708	The One Hoss Shay	1892	193, 196
PM0772	The One Hoss Shay	1905	195

MBPI2855	**"A strange sea-monster stole their bait"**		**579**
PM0708	The One Hoss Shay	1892	193, 196
PM0772	The One Hoss Shay	1905	195
MBPI2856	**"They could hear him twenty miles"**		**579**
PM0708	The One Hoss Shay	1892	193, 196
PM0772	The One Hoss Shay	1905	195
MBPI2857	**"They came…at their master's call"**		**579**
PM0708	The One Hoss Shay	1892	193, 196
PM0772	The One Hoss Shay	1905	195
MBPI2858	**"You can hear the black cat's purr"**		**579**
PM0708	The One Hoss Shay	1892	193, 196
PM0772	The One Hoss Shay	1905	195
MBPI2859	**"Catch a gleam from her wicked eye"**		**579**
PM0708	The One Hoss Shay	1892	193, 196
PM0772	The One Hoss Shay	1905	195
MBPI2860	**Tailpiece for The Broomstick Train**		**579**
PM0708	The One Hoss Shay	1892	193, 196
PM0772	The One Hoss Shay	1905	195
MBPI2861	**The Last Leaf**		**579**
PM0709	The Works of Oliver Wendell Holmes	1892	253
PM1037	New Library Series, American Authors: Houghton, Mifflin Company	1904	188
MBPI2862	**The One Hoss Shay**		**579**
PM0709	The Works of Oliver Wendell Holmes	1892	253
PM1042	The One-Hoss Shay, The Chambered Nautilus and Other Poems Gay and Grave	1900	196
PM1401	The Copley Prints	1903	269
PM1418	The Deacon's One-Hoss Shay	1903	338
PM1066	Selections From the Riverside Literature Series for Sixth Grade Reading	1913	211
MBPI2863	**Dorothy Q**		**579**
PM0710	The Works of Oliver Wendell Holmes	1892	253
MBPI2864	**The Boston Tea Party**		**579**
PM0710	The Works of Oliver Wendell Holmes	1892	253
PM1084	The War of Independence	1917	241
MBPI2865	**Grandmother's Story of Bunker Hill Battle**		**580**
PM0710	The Works of Oliver Wendell Holmes	1892	253
PM0968	The Riverside Seventh Reader	1913	207
MBPI2866	**Dorothy Q**		**580**
PM1120	Book Reviews	December, 1892	6
PM0713	Dorothy Q	1893	146
MBPI2867	**Half-title for Dorothy Q**		**580**
PM0713	Dorothy Q	1893	146
MBPI2868	**Painting the Picture**		**580**
PM0713	Dorothy Q	1893	146
MBPI2869	**"Girlish bust, but womanly air"**		**580**
PM0713	Dorothy Q	1893	146
MBPI2870	**"Hint and promise of stately mien"**		**580**
PM0713	Dorothy Q	1893	146
MBPI2871	**"The youthful sire"**		**580**
PM0713	Dorothy Q	1893	146
MBPI2872	**"Soft is the breath of a maiden's Yes"**		**580**
PM0713	Dorothy Q	1893	146
MBPI2873	**"Lady and lover"**		**580**
PM0713	Dorothy Q	1893	146
MBPI2874	**"The Boston teapot bubbled"**		**580**
PM0713	Dorothy Q	1893	146
MBPI2875	**Half-title for A Ballad of the Boston Tea-Party**		**580**
PM0713	Dorothy Q	1893	146
MBPI2876	**A cup of Tea**		**580**
PM0713	Dorothy Q	1893	146

MBPI2877	"Many a six foot grenadier–The flattened grass had measured"		580
PM0713	Dorothy Q	1893	146
MBPI2878	"Her tearful memories treasured"		580
PM0713	Dorothy Q	1893	146
MBPI2879	"Behold the guests advancing"		580
PM0713	Dorothy Q	1893	146
MBPI2880	"The lively barber"		580
PM0713	Dorothy Q	1893	146
MBPI2881	"The truant tapster"		581
PM0713	Dorothy Q	1893	146
MBPI2882	"The cooper's boys"		581
PM0713	Dorothy Q	1893	146
MBPI2883	"The lusty young Fort-Hillers"		581
PM0713	Dorothy Q	1893	146
MBPI2884	"The Tories seize the omen"		581
PM0713	Dorothy Q	1893	146
MBPI2885	"The Mohawk band is swarming"		581
PM0713	Dorothy Q	1893	146
MBPI2886	"So gracious, sweet, and purring"		581
PM0713	Dorothy Q	1893	146
MBPI2887	"The quiet dame"		581
PM0713	Dorothy Q	1893	146
MBPI2888	An Old North-Ender		581
PM1120	Book Reviews	December, 1892	6
PM0713	Dorothy Q	1893	146
MBPI2889	Tailpiece for A Ballad of the Boston Tea-Party		581
PM0713	Dorothy Q	1893	146
MBPI2890	Watching the Battle from the Steeple		581
PM0713	Dorothy Q	1893	146
MBPI2891	Title for Grandmother's Story of Bunker Hill Battle		581
PM0713	Dorothy Q	1893	146
PM1479	Hotel Dupont, Wilmington, Delaware	1912	141, 310
MBPI2892	The Grandmother		581
PM0713	Dorothy Q	1893	146
MBPI2893	Half-title for Grandmother's Story of Bunker-Hill Battle		581
PM0713	Dorothy Q	1893	146
MBPI2894	"Lord Percy's hunted soldiers"		581
PM0713	Dorothy Q	1893	146
MBPI2895	"Says grandma, 'What's the matter?'"		581
PM0713	Dorothy Q	1893	146
MBPI2896	"The Mohawks killed her father"		581
PM0713	Dorothy Q	1893	146
PM1479	Hotel Dupont, Wilmington, Delaware	1912	141, 310
MBPI2897	"'Don't you fret and worry any'"		582
PM0713	Dorothy Q	1893	146
MBPI2898	"Down my hair went as I hurried"		582
PM0713	Dorothy Q	1893	146
MBPI2899	"The Corporal marched before"		582
PM0713	Dorothy Q	1893	146
MBPI2900	"We climbed the creaking stair"		582
PM0713	Dorothy Q	1893	146
MBPI2901	"The earthwork hid them from us"		582
PM0713	Dorothy Q	1893	146
MBPI2902	"The cannons' deafening thrill"		582
PM0713	Dorothy Q	1893	146
MBPI2903	"Like a gentleman of leisure"		582
PM0713	Dorothy Q	1893	146
MBPI2904	"The belted grenadiers"		582
PM0713	Dorothy Q	1893	146
MBPI2905	"The barges gliding onward"		582

PM0713	Dorothy Q	1893	146
PM1479	Hotel Dupont, Wilmington, Delaware	1912	141, 310
MBPI2906	**"Again they formed in order"**		**582**
PM0713	Dorothy Q	1893	146
MBPI2907	**"They wait and answer not"**		**582**
PM0713	Dorothy Q	1893	146
MBPI2908	**"The Corporal, our old cripple"**		**582**
PM0713	Dorothy Q	1893	146
MBPI2909	**Dan'l Malcolm's Grave**		**582**
PM0713	Dorothy Q	1893	146
MBPI2910	**"In the hush of expectation"**		**582**
PM0713	Dorothy Q	1893	146
MBPI2911	**"Like a thunder-cloud it breaks"**		**582**
PM0713	Dorothy Q	1893	146
MBPI2912	**"A headlong crowd is flying"**		**582**
PM0713	Dorothy Q	1893	146
MBPI2913	**"Are they beaten?"**		**583**
PM0713	Dorothy Q	1893	146
MBPI2914	**"They are baffled, not defeated"**		**583**
PM0713	Dorothy Q	1893	146
MBPI2915	**"The roofs of Charlestown blazing"**		**583**
PM0713	Dorothy Q	1893	146
MBPI2916	**"We can see each massive column"**		**583**
PM0713	Dorothy Q	1893	146
PM1479	Hotel Dupont, Wilmington, Delaware	1912	141, 310
MBPI2917	**"The ominous calm is broken"**		**583**
PM0713	Dorothy Q	1893	146
PM1479	Hotel Dupont, Wilmington, Delaware	1912	141, 310
MBPI2918	**"The frightened braves of Howe"**		**583**
PM0713	Dorothy Q	1893	146
PM1479	Hotel Dupont, Wilmington, Delaware	1912	141, 310
MBPI2919	**"We looked, poor timid creatures"**		**583**
PM1120	Book Reviews	December, 1892	6
PM0713	Dorothy Q	1893	146
MBPI2920	**"'Have a drop of old Jamaiky'"**		**583**
PM0713	Dorothy Q	1893	146
MBPI2921	**"They were creeping round to four"**		**583**
PM0713	Dorothy Q	1893	146
MBPI2922	**"In close array they come"**		**583**
PM0713	Dorothy Q	1893	146
MBPI2923	**"They surged above the breast-work"**		**583**
PM0713	Dorothy Q	1893	146
MBPI2924	**"They say I fainted"**		**583**
PM0713	Dorothy Q	1893	146
PM1479	Hotel Dupont, Wilmington, Delaware	1912	141, 310
MBPI2925	**"'Here's a soldier bleeding'"**		**583**
PM0713	Dorothy Q	1893	146
PM1479	Hotel Dupont, Wilmington, Delaware	1912	141, 310
MBPI2926	**"Brought him from the battle"**		**583**
PM0713	Dorothy Q	1893	146
MBPI2927	**"I saw his eyes were blue"**		**583**
PM0713	Dorothy Q	1893	146
PM1479	Hotel Dupont, Wilmington, Delaware	1912	141, 310
MBPI2928	**"We came to know each other"**		**583**
PM0713	Dorothy Q	1893	146
MBPI2929	**"His picture Copley painted"**		**584**
PM0713	Dorothy Q	1893	146
MBPI2930	**Headpiece with illustrated initial D, Preface for Dorothy Q**		**584**
PM0713	Dorothy Q	1893	146
MBPI2931	**Tailpiece, Preface for Dorothy Q**		**584**

PM0713	Dorothy Q	1893	146
MBPI2932	**Headpiece, List of Illustrations for Dorothy Q**		**584**
PM0713	Dorothy Q	1893	146
MBPI2933	**Tailpiece, List of Illustrations for Dorothy Q**		**584**
PM0713	Dorothy Q	1893	146
MBPI2934	**Decorative heading for Dorothy Q**		**584**
PM0713	Dorothy Q	1893	146
MBPI2935	**Decorative border for Dorothy Q**		**584**
PM0713	Dorothy Q	1893	146
MBPI2936	**Decorative heading for Dorothy Q**		**584**
PM0713	Dorothy Q	1893	146
MBPI2937	**Decorative border for Dorothy Q**		**584**
PM0713	Dorothy Q	1893	146
MBPI2938	**Decorative heading for Dorothy Q**		**584**
PM0713	Dorothy Q	1893	146
MBPI2939	**Decorative border for Dorothy Q**		**584**
PM0713	Dorothy Q	1893	146
MBPI2940	**Decorative heading for Dorothy Q**		**584**
PM0713	Dorothy Q	1893	146
MBPI2941	**Decorative border for Dorothy Q**		**584**
PM0713	Dorothy Q	1893	146
MBPI2942	**Decorative heading for Dorothy Q**		**584**
PM0713	Dorothy Q	1893	146
MBPI2943	**Decorative border for Dorothy Q**		**584**
PM0713	Dorothy Q	1893	146
MBPI2944	**Decorative border with title for A Ballad of the Boston-Tea Party**		**584**
PM0713	Dorothy Q	1893	146
MBPI2945	**Decorative border for A Ballad of the Boston-Tea Party**		**585**
PM0713	Dorothy Q	1893	146
MBPI2946	**Decorative heading for A Ballad of the Boston-Tea Party**		**585**
PM0713	Dorothy Q	1893	146
MBPI2947	**Tailpiece for A Ballad of the Boston-Tea Party**		**585**
PM0713	Dorothy Q	1893	146
MBPI2948	**Decorative heading for A Ballad of the Boston-Tea Party**		**585**
PM0713	Dorothy Q	1893	146
MBPI2949	**Tailpiece for A Ballad of the Boston-Tea Party**		**585**
PM0713	Dorothy Q	1893	146
MBPI2950	**Decorative heading for A Ballad of the Boston-Tea Party**		**585**
PM0713	Dorothy Q	1893	146
MBPI2951	**Decorative heading for A Ballad of the Boston-Tea Party**		**585**
PM0713	Dorothy Q	1893	146
MBPI2952	**Tailpiece for A Ballad of the Boston-Tea Party**		**585**
PM0713	Dorothy Q	1893	146
MBPI2953	**Decorative heading for A Ballad of the Boston-Tea Party**		**585**
PM0713	Dorothy Q	1893	146
MBPI2954	**Tailpiece for A Ballad of the Boston-Tea Party**		**585**
PM0713	Dorothy Q	1893	146
MBPI2955	**Decorative heading for A Ballad of the Boston-Tea Party**		**585**
PM0713	Dorothy Q	1893	146
MBPI2956	**Tailpiece for A Ballad of the Boston-Tea Party**		**585**
PM0713	Dorothy Q	1893	146
MBPI2957	**Decorative heading for A Ballad of the Boston-Tea Party**		**585**
PM0713	Dorothy Q	1893	146
MBPI2958	**Tailpiece for A Ballad of the Boston-Tea Party**		**585**
PM0713	Dorothy Q	1893	146
MBPI2959	**Decorative heading for A Ballad of the Boston-Tea Party**		**585**
PM0713	Dorothy Q	1893	146
MBPI2960	**Tailpiece for A Ballad of the Boston-Tea Party**		**585**
PM0713	Dorothy Q	1893	146
MBPI2961	**Balboa's Discovery of the Pacific**		**586**

PM0714	A School History of the United States	1893	210
PM1543	Thirty More Famous Stories Retold	1905	235
MBPI2962	**"The Meeting of Cortes and Montezuma"**		**586**
PM0719	Swinton's Primary United States	1894	235
MBPI2963	**Oliver Wendell Holmes at age of 41**		**586**
PM0720	The Autocrat of the Breakfast-Table	1894	132
MBPI2964	**Headpiece, List of Ilustrations for The Autocrat of the Breakfast-Table**		**586**
PM0720	The Autocrat of the Breakfast-Table	1894	132
PM0720	The Autocrat of the Breakfast-Table	1894	132
MBPI2965	**Headpiece with initial T, Preface for The Autocrat of the Breakfast-Table**		**586**
PM0720	The Autocrat of the Breakfast-Table	1894	132
MBPI2966	**Headpiece with initial T for Autocrat's Autobiography**		**586**
PM0720	The Autocrat of the Breakfast-Table	1894	132
MBPI2967	**Tailpiece for Autocrat's Autobiography**		**586**
PM0720	The Autocrat of the Breakfast-Table	1894	132
MBPI2968	**Headpiece with initial I, Part I for The Autocrat of the Breakfast-Table**		**586**
PM0720	The Autocrat of the Breakfast-Table	1894	132
MBPI2969	**The Mutual Admiration Society**		**586**
PM0720	The Autocrat of the Breakfast-Table	1894	132
PM1566	Boswell's Life of Johnson	1917	136
MBPI2970	**Album Verses with initial W**		**586**
PM0720	The Autocrat of the Breakfast-Table	1894	132
MBPI2971	**The Man of Family**		**586**
PM0720	The Autocrat of the Breakfast-Table	1894	132
MBPI2972	**Latter-Day Warnings with initial W**		**586**
PM0720	The Autocrat of the Breakfast-Table	1894	132
MBPI2973	**Tailpiece, Part I for The Autocrat of the Breakfast-Table**		**586**
PM1123	The Autocrat of the Breakfast Table	December, 1893	7
PM0720	The Autocrat of the Breakfast-Table	1894	132
MBPI2974	**Headpiece with initial I, Part II for The Autocrat of the Breakfast-Table**		**586**
PM0720	The Autocrat of the Breakfast-Table	1894	132
MBPI2975	**The Trotting Match**		**586**
PM0720	The Autocrat of the Breakfast-Table	1894	132
PM1342	Houghton, Mifflin and Company's Holiday Bulletin	1894	266
PM1401	The Copley Prints	1903	269
PM1420	The Trotting Match	1903	338
PM1037	New Library Series, American Authors: Houghton, Mifflin Company	1904	188
MBPI2976	**Sun and Shadow with initial A**		**586**
PM0720	The Autocrat of the Breakfast-Table	1894	132
MBPI2977	**This Is It with initial A**		**587**
PM0720	The Autocrat of the Breakfast-Table	1894	132
MBPI2978	**Headpiece with initial T, Part III for The Autocrat of the Breakfast-Table**		**587**
PM1123	The Autocrat of the Breakfast Table	December, 1893	7
PM0720	The Autocrat of the Breakfast-Table	1894	132
MBPI2979	**At the Club**		**587**
PM0720	The Autocrat of the Breakfast-Table	1894	132
MBPI2980	**The Old Man Dreams with initial O**		**587**
PM0720	The Autocrat of the Breakfast-Table	1894	132
MBPI2981	**Tailpiece for The Old Man Dreams**		**587**
PM0720	The Autocrat of the Breakfast-Table	1894	132
MBPI2982	**Headpiece with initial I, Part IV for The Autocrat of the Breakfast-Table**		**587**
PM0720	The Autocrat of the Breakfast-Table	1894	132
MBPI2983	**A Reminiscence of the Marigold**		**587**
PM0720	The Autocrat of the Breakfast-Table	1894	132
MBPI2984	**The Chambered Nautilus with initial T**		**587**
PM0720	The Autocrat of the Breakfast-Table	1894	132
MBPI2985	**Tailpiece for The Chambered Nautilus**		**587**
PM1123	The Autocrat of the Breakfast Table	December, 1893	7
PM0720	The Autocrat of the Breakfast-Table	1894	132
MBPI2986	**Headpiece with initial A, Part V for The Autocrat of the Breakfast-Table**		**587**

PM0720	The Autocrat of the Breakfast-Table	1894	132
MBPI2987	**The Old Violin**		**587**
PM1123	The Autocrat of the Breakfast Table	December, 1893	7
PM1138	A Holiday Autocrat	December, 1893	9
PM0720	The Autocrat of the Breakfast-Table	1894	132
PM1098	Copley Prints	November, 1903	3
PM1401	The Copley Prints	1903	269
PM1419	The Old Violin	1903	338
PM1037	New Library Series, American Authors: Houghton, Mifflin Company	1904	188
MBPI2988	**Mare Rubrum with initial F**		**587**
PM1123	The Autocrat of the Breakfast Table	December, 1893	7
PM0720	The Autocrat of the Breakfast-Table	1894	132
MBPI2989	**Tailpiece for Mare Rubrum**		**587**
PM0720	The Autocrat of the Breakfast-Table	1894	132
MBPI2990	**Headpiece with initial S, Part VI for The Autocrat of the Breakfast-Table**		**587**
PM0720	The Autocrat of the Breakfast-Table	1894	132
MBPI2991	**The Closed Door**		**587**
PM0720	The Autocrat of the Breakfast-Table	1894	132
MBPI2992	**What We All Think with initial T**		**587**
PM0720	The Autocrat of the Breakfast-Table	1894	132
MBPI2993	**Tailpiece for What We All Think**		**588**
PM0720	The Autocrat of the Breakfast-Table	1894	132
MBPI2994	**Oliver Wendell Holmes at the age of 76**		**588**
PM0720	The Autocrat of the Breakfast-Table	1894	132
MBPI2995	**Headpiece with initial T, Part VII for The Autocrat of the Breakfast-Table**		**588**
PM0720	The Autocrat of the Breakfast-Table	1894	132
MBPI2996	**The Last Blossom with initial T**		**588**
PM0720	The Autocrat of the Breakfast-Table	1894	132
MBPI2997	**The Professor in his Boat**		**588**
PM0720	The Autocrat of the Breakfast-Table	1894	132
MBPI2998	**The Living Temple**		**588**
PM0720	The Autocrat of the Breakfast-Table	1894	132
MBPI2999	**Headpiece with initial S, Part VIII for The Autocrat of the Breakfast-Table**		**588**
PM0720	The Autocrat of the Breakfast-Table	1894	132
MBPI3000	**Into the River**		**588**
PM0720	The Autocrat of the Breakfast-Table	1894	132
MBPI3001	**Spring Has Come with initial T**		**588**
PM0720	The Autocrat of the Breakfast-Table	1894	132
MBPI3002	**Headpiece with initial I, Part IX for The Autocrat of the Breakfast-Table**		**588**
PM0720	The Autocrat of the Breakfast-Table	1894	132
MBPI3003	**First Love**		**588**
PM0720	The Autocrat of the Breakfast-Table	1894	132
MBPI3004	**A Good Time Going**		**588**
PM0720	The Autocrat of the Breakfast-Table	1894	132
MBPI3005	**The Two Armies with initial A**		**588**
PM0720	The Autocrat of the Breakfast-Table	1894	132
MBPI3006	**Tailpiece for The Two Armies**		**588**
PM0720	The Autocrat of the Breakfast-Table	1894	132
MBPI3007	**Headpiece with initial T, Part X for The Autocrat of the Breakfast-Table**		**588**
PM0720	The Autocrat of the Breakfast-Table	1894	132
MBPI3008	**The First Walk**		**588**
PM0720	The Autocrat of the Breakfast-Table	1894	132
MBPI3009	**Musa with initial O**		**589**
PM0720	The Autocrat of the Breakfast-Table	1894	132
MBPI3010	**Tailpiece for Musa**		**589**
PM0720	The Autocrat of the Breakfast-Table	1894	132
MBPI3011	**Headpiece with initial T, Part XI for The Autocrat of the Breakfast-Table**		**589**
PM0720	The Autocrat of the Breakfast-Table	1894	132
MBPI3012	**Headpiece for The Deacon's Masterpiece**		**589**
PM0720	The Autocrat of the Breakfast-Table	1894	132

MBPI3013	**Æstivation with initial I**		**589**
PM0720	The Autocrat of the Breakfast-Table	1894	132
MBPI3014	**The Mountain Home**		**589**
PM0720	The Autocrat of the Breakfast-Table	1894	132
PM1037	New Library Series, American Authors: Houghton, Mifflin Company	1904	188
MBPI3015	**Contentment with initial L**		**589**
PM0720	The Autocrat of the Breakfast-Table	1894	132
MBPI3016	**Tailpiece for The Autocrat of the Breakfast-Table**		**589**
PM0720	The Autocrat of the Breakfast-Table	1894	132
MBPI3017	**Headpiece with initial I, Part XII for The Autocrat of the Breakfast-Table**		**589**
PM0720	The Autocrat of the Breakfast-Table	1894	132
MBPI3018	**Headpiece with title for Parson Turell's Legacy**		**589**
PM0720	The Autocrat of the Breakfast-Table	1894	132
MBPI3019	**Parson Turell's legacy**		**589**
PM0720	The Autocrat of the Breakfast-Table	1894	132
MBPI3020	**The Voiceless with initial W**		**589**
PM0720	The Autocrat of the Breakfast-Table	1894	132
MBPI3021	**Tailpiece for The Autocrat of the Breakfast-Table**		**589**
PM0720	The Autocrat of the Breakfast-Table	1894	132
MBPI3022	**Title page decoration for Stops of Various Quills**		**589**
PM0723	Stops of Various Quills	1895	215
MBPI3023	**Title page decoration for Stops of Various Quills**		**589**
PM0723	Stops of Various Quills	1895	215
MBPI3024	**Headpiece, Table of Contents for Stops of Various Quills**		**589**
PM0723	Stops of Various Quills	1895	215
MBPI3025	**Tailpiece for Midway**		**590**
PM0723	Stops of Various Quills	1895	215
MBPI3026	**Tailpiece for The Bewildered Guest**		**590**
PM0723	Stops of Various Quills	1895	215
MBPI3027	**Company**		**590**
PM0723	Stops of Various Quills	1895	215
MBPI3028	**Tailpiece for Company**		**590**
PM0723	Stops of Various Quills	1895	215
MBPI3029	**Twelve P. M.**		**590**
PM0723	Stops of Various Quills	1895	215
MBPI3030	**Tailpiece for In The Dark**		**590**
PM0723	Stops of Various Quills	1895	215
MBPI3031	**Tailpiece for Solitude**		**590**
PM0723	Stops of Various Quills	1895	215
MBPI3032	**Conscience**		**590**
PM0723	Stops of Various Quills	1895	215
MBPI3033	**Illustrated initial J for Conscience**		**590**
PM0723	Stops of Various Quills	1895	215
MBPI3034	**Tailpiece for Conscience**		**590**
PM0723	Stops of Various Quills	1895	215
MBPI3035	**Tailpiece for Reward And Punishment**		**590**
PM0723	Stops of Various Quills	1895	215
MBPI3036	**Illustration for Parable**		**590**
PM0723	Stops of Various Quills	1895	215
MBPI3037	**Tailpiece for Parable**		**590**
PM0723	Stops of Various Quills	1895	215
MBPI3038	**Vision**		**590**
PM0723	Stops of Various Quills	1895	215
MBPI3039	**Decoration for Society**		**590**
PM0723	Stops of Various Quills	1895	215
MBPI3040	**Friends and Foes**		**590**
PM0723	Stops of Various Quills	1895	215
MBPI3041	**Sphinx**		**591**
PM0723	Stops of Various Quills	1895	215
MBPI3042	**Materials of a Story**		**591**

PM0723	Stops of Various Quills	1895	215
MBPI3043	**The King Dines**		**591**
PM0723	Stops of Various Quills	1895	215
MBPI3044	**Illustrated initial T for The King Dines**		**591**
PM0723	Stops of Various Quills	1895	215
MBPI3045	**Labor And Capital**		**591**
PM0723	Stops of Various Quills	1895	215
MBPI3046	**Tailpiece for Labor And Capital**		**591**
PM0723	Stops of Various Quills	1895	215
MBPI3047	**Equality**		**591**
PM0723	Stops of Various Quills	1895	215
MBPI3048	**Judgment Day**		**591**
PM0723	Stops of Various Quills	1895	215
MBPI3049	**Mortality**		**591**
PM0723	Stops of Various Quills	1895	215
MBPI3050	**Another Day**		**591**
PM0723	Stops of Various Quills	1895	215
MBPI3051	**Tailpiece for Another Day**		**591**
PM0723	Stops of Various Quills	1895	215
MBPI3052	**Some One Else**		**591**
PM0723	Stops of Various Quills	1895	215
MBPI3053	**Illustrated initial L for Stops of Various Quills**		**591**
PM0723	Stops of Various Quills	1895	215
MBPI3054	**Life**		**591**
PM0723	Stops of Various Quills	1895	215
MBPI3055	**Tailpiece for Life**		**591**
PM0723	Stops of Various Quills	1895	215
MBPI3056	**Weather-Breeder**		**591**
PM0723	Stops of Various Quills	1895	215
MBPI3057	**Peonage**		**592**
PM0723	Stops of Various Quills	1895	215
MBPI3058	**Race**		**592**
PM0723	Stops of Various Quills	1895	215
MBPI3059	**Tailpiece for Race**		**592**
PM0723	Stops of Various Quills	1895	215
MBPI3060	**Temperament**		**592**
PM0723	Stops of Various Quills	1895	215
MBPI3061	**What Shall It Profit?**		**592**
PM0723	Stops of Various Quills	1895	215
MBPI3062	**Tailpiece for What Shall It Profit?**		**592**
PM0723	Stops of Various Quills	1895	215
MBPI3063	**Illustrated initial B for Stops of Various Quills**		**592**
PM0723	Stops of Various Quills	1895	215
MBPI3064	**Headband for Stops of Various Quills**		**592**
PM0723	Stops of Various Quills	1895	215
MBPI3065	**Vignette for A Maid's Choice**		**592**
PM0130	A Maid's Choice	December, 1891	35
MBPI3066	**Vignette for A Maid's Choice**		**592**
PM0130	A Maid's Choice	December, 1891	35
MBPI3067	**Vignette for A Maid's Choice**		**592**
PM0130	A Maid's Choice	December, 1891	35
MBPI3068	**Vignette for A Maid's Choice**		**592**
PM0130	A Maid's Choice	December, 1891	35
MBPI3069	**Vignette for A Maid's Choice**		**592**
PM0130	A Maid's Choice	December, 1891	35
MBPI3070	**Vignette for A Maid's Choice**		**592**
PM0130	A Maid's Choice	December, 1891	35
MBPI3071	**Vignette for A Maid's Choice**		**592**
PM0130	A Maid's Choice	December, 1891	35
MBPI3072	**Vignette for A Maid's Choice**		**592**

PM0130	A Maid's Choice	December, 1891	35
MBPI3073	**Vignette for A Maid's Choice**		**593**
PM0130	A Maid's Choice	December, 1891	35
MBPI3074	**Vignette for A Maid's Choice**		**593**
PM0130	A Maid's Choice	December, 1891	35
MBPI3075	**Vignette for A Maid's Choice**		**593**
PM0130	A Maid's Choice	December, 1891	35
MBPI3076	**Vignette for A Maid's Choice**		**593**
PM0130	A Maid's Choice	December, 1891	35
MBPI3077	**Vignette for A Maid's Choice**		**593**
PM0130	A Maid's Choice	December, 1891	35
MBPI3078	**Vignette for A Maid's Choice**		**593**
PM0130	A Maid's Choice	December, 1891	35
MBPI3079	**Vignette for A Maid's Choice**		**593**
PM0130	A Maid's Choice	December, 1891	35
MBPI3080	**Vignette for A Maid's Choice**		**593**
PM0130	A Maid's Choice	December, 1891	35
MBPI3081	**Vignette for A Maid's Choice**		**593**
PM0130	A Maid's Choice	December, 1891	35
MBPI3082	**Vignette for A Maid's Choice**		**593**
PM0130	A Maid's Choice	December, 1891	35
MBPI3083	**Vignette for A Maid's Choice**		**593**
PM0130	A Maid's Choice	December, 1891	35
MBPI3084	**Vignette for A Maid's Choice**		**593**
PM0130	A Maid's Choice	December, 1891	35
MBPI3085	**Vignette for A Maid's Choice**		**593**
PM0130	A Maid's Choice	December, 1891	35
MBPI3086	**Vignette for A Maid's Choice**		**593**
PM0130	A Maid's Choice	December, 1891	35
MBPI3087	**Vignette for A Maid's Choice**		**593**
PM0130	A Maid's Choice	December, 1891	35
MBPI3088	**Vignette for A Maid's Choice**		**593**
PM0130	A Maid's Choice	December, 1891	35
MBPI3089	**Vignette for A Maid's Choice**		**594**
PM0130	A Maid's Choice	December, 1891	35
MBPI3090	**Vignette for A Maid's Choice**		**594**
PM0130	A Maid's Choice	December, 1891	35
MBPI3091	**Vignette for A Maid's Choice**		**594**
PM0130	A Maid's Choice	December, 1891	35
MBPI3092	**Vignette for A Maid's Choice**		**594**
PM0130	A Maid's Choice	December, 1891	35
MBPI3093	**Vignette for A Maid's Choice**		**594**
PM0130	A Maid's Choice	December, 1891	35
MBPI3094	**Vignette for A Maid's Choice**		**594**
PM0130	A Maid's Choice	December, 1891	35
MBPI3095	**Vignette for A Maid's Choice**		**594**
PM0130	A Maid's Choice	December, 1891	35
MBPI3096	**Vignette for A Maid's Choice**		**594**
PM0130	A Maid's Choice	December, 1891	35
MBPI3097	**Vignette for A Maid's Choice**		**594**
PM0130	A Maid's Choice	December, 1891	35
MBPI3098	**Vignette for A Maid's Choice**		**594**
PM0130	A Maid's Choice	December, 1891	35
MBPI3099	**Vignette for A Maid's Choice**		**594**
PM0130	A Maid's Choice	December, 1891	35
MBPI3100	**Vignette for A Maid's Choice**		**594**
PM0130	A Maid's Choice	December, 1891	35
MBPI3101	**Father Hennepin Celebrating Mass**		**594**
PM0735	Works of Francis Parkman	1897	251
PM1129	Book Reviews	December, 1898	8

PM1350	New Holiday Publications, Christmas 1898	1898	268
PM1043	Francis Parkman's Works: LaSalle and the Discovery of the Great West	1901	153
PM0760	The Struggle for a Continent	1902	234
PM1046	Francis Parkman's Works: LaSalle and the Discovery of the Great West	1903	153
MBPI3102	**Assassination of LaSalle**		**594**
PM0736	Works of Francis Parkman	1897	252
PM1043	Francis Parkman's Works: LaSalle and the Discovery of the Great West	1901	153
PM0760	The Struggle for a Continent	1902	234
PM0990	The Boy's Parkman	1913	137
MBPI3103	**The Return from Deerfield**		**594**
PM0737	Works of Francis Parkman	1897	252
PM1044	Francis Parkman's Works: A Half-Century of Conflict	1901	153
PM1047	Francis Parkman's Works: A Half-Century of Conflict	1903	153
MBPI3104	**Lygia and Vinicius in the Garden of Aulus**		**594**
PM0740	"Quo Vadis"	1897	204
PM1055	"Quo Vadis"	1897	205
MBPI3105	**The Punishment of Chilo by Vinicius**		**595**
PM0740	"Quo Vadis"	1897	204
MBPI3106	**Nero holding a Golden Lute, with Rome in Flames**		**595**
PM0740	"Quo Vadis"	1897	204
PM1609	Book Reviews	December, 1897	8
PM1056	"Quo Vadis"	1898	205
MBPI3107	**"Peractum est!"**		**595**
PM0740	"Quo Vadis"	1897	204
MBPI3108	**The Conversion of Chilo**		**595**
PM0740	"Quo Vadis"	1897	204
MBPI3109	**"Quo Vadis, Domine!"**		**595**
PM0740	"Quo Vadis"	1897	204
PM1348	New Holiday Publications	1897	268
PM1644	[Frontispiece not identifed with specific article]	November, 1899	11
MBPI3110	**The Fall of Montcalm**		**595**
PM0741	Works of Francis Parkman	1898	252
PM1226	Notice of Francis Parkman's Works	January, 1900	99
PM1045	Francis Parkman's Works: Montcalm and Wolfe	1901	153
PM0760	The Struggle for a Continent	1902	234
PM1048	Francis Parkman's Works: Montcalm and Wolfe	1903	153
PM0990	The Boy's Parkman	1913	137
MBPI3111	**"They scrambled up the parapet and went surging over the crest, pell mell, upon The British"**		**595**
PM0748	Janice Meredith	1899	173
PM1464	Art Institute of Chicago, Chicago, Illinois	1903	130, 297
PM1479	Hotel Dupont, Wilmington, Delaware	1912	141, 310
PM1481	Panama and Pacific International Exhibition, San Francisco, California	1915	315
MBPI3112	**"Why don't you end it?"**		**595**
PM1227	Notice of To Have And To Hold	March, 1900	99
PM0749	To Have and to Hold	1900	236
PM1462	Associated Illustrators, New York, New York	1902	142, 297
PM1625	Catalogue of the First Annual Exhibition of the Associated Illustrators	1902	142, 297
MBPI3113	**Half-title decoration for The Man with the Hoe and Other Poems**		**595**
PM0750	The Man with the Hoe and Other Poems	1900	179
PM0757	Modern Pen Drawings: European and American	1901	187
MBPI3114	**Frontispiece for The Man with the Hoe and Other Poems**		**595**
PM0750	The Man with the Hoe and Other Poems	1900	179
MBPI3115	**Headpiece, Dedication for The Man with the Hoe and Other Poems**		**595**
PM0750	The Man with the Hoe and Other Poems	1900	179
MBPI3116	**Headpiece, Prefatory Note for The Man with the Hoe and Other Poems**		**595**
PM0750	The Man with the Hoe and Other Poems	1900	179
MBPI3117	**Headpiece, The Contents for The Man with the Hoe and Other Poems**		**595**
PM0750	The Man with the Hoe and Other Poems	1900	179
MBPI3118	**The Man With the Hoe**		**595**

PM0750	The Man with the Hoe and Other Poems	1900	179
PM1210	Modern Pen Drawings: European and American	1900	97
MBPI3119	**A Look Into the Gulf**		**595**
PM0750	The Man with the Hoe and Other Poems	1900	179
PM1464	Art Institute of Chicago, Chicago, Illinois	1903	130, 297
MBPI3120	**Brotherhood**		**595**
PM0750	The Man with the Hoe and Other Poems	1900	179
MBPI3121	**Song of the Followers of Pan**		**596**
PM0750	The Man with the Hoe and Other Poems	1900	179
PM1479	Hotel Dupont, Wilmington, Delaware	1912	141, 310
MBPI3122	**Little Brothers of the Ground**		**596**
PM0750	The Man with the Hoe and Other Poems	1900	179
PM1464	Art Institute of Chicago, Chicago, Illinois	1903	130, 297
MBPI3123	**Wail of the Wandering Dead**		**596**
PM0750	The Man with the Hoe and Other Poems	1900	179
MBPI3124	**A Prayer**		**596**
PM0750	The Man with the Hoe and Other Poems	1900	179
PM1464	Art Institute of Chicago, Chicago, Illinois	1903	130, 297
MBPI3125	**The Poet**		**596**
PM0750	The Man with the Hoe and Other Poems	1900	179
PM1094	Art in the Holiday Books	December, 1900	1
MBPI3126	**The Whirlwind Road**		**596**
PM0750	The Man with the Hoe and Other Poems	1900	179
MBPI3127	**The Desire of Nations**		**596**
PM0750	The Man with the Hoe and Other Poems	1900	179
PM1479	Hotel Dupont, Wilmington, Delaware	1912	141, 310
MBPI3128	**Headband I for The Man with the Hoe and Other Poems**		**596**
PM0750	The Man with the Hoe and Other Poems	1900	179
MBPI3129	**The Goblin Laugh**		**596**
PM0750	The Man with the Hoe and Other Poems	1900	179
MBPI3130	**Poetry**		**596**
PM0750	The Man with the Hoe and Other Poems	1900	179
MBPI3131	**A Meeting**		**596**
PM0750	The Man with the Hoe and Other Poems	1900	179
PM1479	Hotel Dupont, Wilmington, Delaware	1912	141, 310
MBPI3132	**Infinite Depths**		**596**
PM0750	The Man with the Hoe and Other Poems	1900	179
PM1464	Art Institute of Chicago, Chicago, Illinois	1903	130, 297
MBPI3133	**A Leaf From the Devil's Jest-Book**		**596**
PM0750	The Man with the Hoe and Other Poems	1900	179
PM1479	Hotel Dupont, Wilmington, Delaware	1912	141, 310
MBPi3134	**The Paymaster**		**596**
PM0750	The Man with the Hoe and Other Poems	1900	179
MBPI3135	**The Last Furrow**		**596**
PM0750	The Man with the Hoe and Other Poems	1900	179
PM1210	Modern Pen Drawings: European and American	1900	97
PM0757	Modern Pen Drawings: European and American	1901	187
PM1464	Art Institute of Chicago, Chicago, Illinois	1903	130, 297
MBPI3136	**In the Storm**		**596**
PM0750	The Man with the Hoe and Other Poems	1900	179
PM1479	Hotel Dupont, Wilmington, Delaware	1912	141, 310
MBPI3137	**After Reading Shakespeare**		**597**
PM0750	The Man with the Hoe and Other Poems	1900	179
PM1464	Art Institute of Chicago, Chicago, Illinois	1903	130, 297
MBPI3138	**Headband II for The Man with the Hoe and Other Poems**		**597**
PM0750	The Man with the Hoe and Other Poems	1900	179
MBPI3139	**The Poets**		**597**
PM0750	The Man with the Hoe and Other Poems	1900	179
PM1479	Hotel Dupont, Wilmington, Delaware	1912	141, 310
MBPI3140	**Love's Vigil**		**597**

PM0750	The Man with the Hoe and Other Poems	1900	179
PM1464	Art Institute of Chicago, Chicago, Illinois	1903	130, 297
MBPI3141	**Two at a Fireside**		**597**
PM0750	The Man with the Hoe and Other Poems	1900	179
MBPI3142	**Headband III for The Man with the Hoe and Other Poems**		**597**
PM0750	The Man with the Hoe and Other Poems	1900	179
MBPI3143	**To William Watson**		**597**
PM0750	The Man with the Hoe and Other Poems	1900	179
MBPI3144	**Man**		**597**
PM0750	The Man with the Hoe and Other Poems	1900	179
MBPI3145	**In High Sierras**		**597**
PM0750	The Man with the Hoe and Other Poems	1900	179
MBPI3146	**The Wharf of Dreams**		**597**
PM0750	The Man with the Hoe and Other Poems	1900	179
MBPI3147	**To Louise Michel**		**597**
PM0750	The Man with the Hoe and Other Poems	1900	179
PM1479	Hotel Dupont, Wilmington, Delaware	1912	141, 310
MBPI3148	**Shepherd Boy and Nereid**		**597**
PM0750	The Man with the Hoe and Other Poems	1900	179
PM1464	Art Institute of Chicago, Chicago, Illinois	1903	130, 297
MBPI3149	**A Song at the Start**		**597**
PM0750	The Man with the Hoe and Other Poems	1900	179
MBPI3150	**My Comrade**		**597**
PM0750	The Man with the Hoe and Other Poems	1900	179
MBPI3151	**Joy of the Morning**		**597**
PM0750	The Man with the Hoe and Other Poems	1900	179
MBPI3152	**A Cry in the Night**		**597**
PM0750	The Man with the Hoe and Other Poems	1900	179
MBPI3153	**Fays**		**598**
PM0750	The Man with the Hoe and Other Poems	1900	179
MBPI3154	**In Death Valley**		**598**
PM0750	The Man with the Hoe and Other Poems	1900	179
MBPI3155	**At Dawn**		**598**
PM0750	The Man with the Hoe and Other Poems	1900	179
PM1479	Hotel Dupont, Wilmington, Delaware	1912	141, 310
MBPI3156	**"Follow Me"**		**598**
PM0750	The Man with the Hoe and Other Poems	1900	179
MBPI3157	**In Poppy Fields**		**598**
PM0750	The Man with the Hoe and Other Poems	1900	179
PM1479	Hotel Dupont, Wilmington, Delaware	1912	141, 310
MBPI3158	**The Joy of the Hills**		**598**
PM0750	The Man with the Hoe and Other Poems	1900	179
MBPI3159	**The Invisible Bride**		**598**
PM0750	The Man with the Hoe and Other Poems	1900	179
MBPI3160	**The Valley**		**598**
PM0750	The Man with the Hoe and Other Poems	1900	179
MBPI3161	**The Climb of Life**		**598**
PM0750	The Man with the Hoe and Other Poems	1900	179
PM1464	Art Institute of Chicago, Chicago, Illinois	1903	130, 297
PM1479	Hotel Dupont, Wilmington, Delaware	1912	141, 310
MBPI3162	**Midsummer Noon**		**598**
PM0750	The Man with the Hoe and Other Poems	1900	179
MBPI3163	**Griefs**		**598**
PM0750	The Man with the Hoe and Other Poems	1900	179
MBPI3164	**An Old Road**		**598**
PM0750	The Man with the Hoe and Other Poems	1900	179
PM1479	Hotel Dupont, Wilmington, Delaware	1912	141, 310
MBPI3165	**Music**		**598**
PM0750	The Man with the Hoe and Other Poems	1900	179
MBPI3166	**Fay Song**		**598**

PM0750	The Man with the Hoe and Other Poems	1900	179
MBPI3167	**The Old Earth**		**598**
PM0750	The Man with the Hoe and Other Poems	1900	179
PM1479	Hotel Dupont, Wilmington, Delaware	1912	141, 310
MBPI3168	**Divine Adventure**		**598**
PM0750	The Man with the Hoe and Other Poems	1900	179
MBPI3169	**To High-born Poets**		**599**
PM0750	The Man with the Hoe and Other Poems	1900	179
PM1464	Art Institute of Chicago, Chicago, Illinois	1903	130, 297
MBPI3170	**The Toilers**		**599**
PM0750	The Man with the Hoe and Other Poems	1900	179
MBPI3171	**On the Gulf of Night**		**599**
PM0750	The Man with the Hoe and Other Poems	1900	179
PM1464	Art Institute of Chicago, Chicago, Illinois	1903	130, 297
MBPI3172	**A Harvest Song**		**599**
PM0750	The Man with the Hoe and Other Poems	1900	179
PM1210	Modern Pen Drawings: European and American	1900	97
PM0757	Modern Pen Drawings: European and American	1901	187
PM1464	Art Institute of Chicago, Chicago, Illinois	1903	130, 297
MBPI3173	**The Man Under the Stone**		**599**
PM0750	The Man with the Hoe and Other Poems	1900	179
MBPI3174	**Song to the Divine Mother**		**599**
PM0750	The Man with the Hoe and Other Poems	1900	179
MBPI3175	**From the Hand of a Child**		**599**
PM0750	The Man with the Hoe and Other Poems	1900	179
MBPI3176	**The Rock-Breaker**		**599**
PM0750	The Man with the Hoe and Other Poems	1900	179
MBPI3177	**These Songs Will Perish**		**599**
PM0750	The Man with the Hoe and Other Poems	1900	179
PM1464	Art Institute of Chicago, Chicago, Illinois	1903	130, 297
MBPI3178	**Assassination of William of Orange**		**599**
PM0751	The Writings of John Lothrop Motley	1900	254
MBPI3179	**A Thousand Miles a Day**		**599**
PM0752	The Complete Writings of Nathaniel Hawthorne	1900	144, 325
PM1263	Illustrations From Hawthorne–Autograph Edition	1900	325, 333
PM1408	A Thousand Miles a Day	1900	333
PM1615	The Children's Hour: Poems & Rhymes	1907	142
MBPI3180	**Vignette for A Wonder Book**		**599**
PM0752	The Complete Writings of Nathaniel Hawthorne	1900	144, 325
MBPI3181	**"Behold it then!" cried Perseus**		**599**
PM0752	The Complete Writings of Nathaniel Hawthorne	1900	144, 325
PM1464	Art Institute of Chicago, Chicago, Illinois	1903	130, 297
PM1466	Kellogg Public Library, Green Bay, Wisconsin	1904	301
PM1470	St. Botolph Club, Boston, Massachusetts	1906	303
PM1521	The Children's Hour: Myths from Many Lands	1907	142
MBPI3182	**Theseus caught the monster off his guard**		**599**
PM0752	The Complete Writings of Nathaniel Hawthorne	1900	144, 325
MBPI3183	**"Who are you?" thundered the giant**		**599**
PM0752	The Complete Writings of Nathaniel Hawthorne	1900	144, 325
PM1464	Art Institute of Chicago, Chicago, Illinois	1903	130, 297
PM1466	Kellogg Public Library, Green Bay, Wisconsin	1904	301
PM1470	St. Botolph Club, Boston, Massachusetts	1906	303
PM1521	The Children's Hour: Myths from Many Lands	1907	142
PM1479	Hotel Dupont, Wilmington, Delaware	1912	141, 310
PM1481	Panama and Pacific International Exhibition, San Francisco, California	1915	315
MBPI3184	**"Let me hasten onward"**		**599**
PM0752	The Complete Writings of Nathaniel Hawthorne	1900	144, 325
MBPI3185	**"'Let me go to him!' she shrieked, in her anguish of soul"**		**600**
PM1228	Notice of Sir Christopher	May, 1901	99
PM1140	Book Review: Sir Christopher	June, 1901	9

PM0753	Sir Christopher	1901	212
PM1002	Desk Book of Fine Papers	1905	146
MBPI3186	**Title page decoration for The Odes & Epodes of Horace**		**600**
PM0754	The Odes & Epodes of Horace	1901	189
PM1077	Tenth Year Book	1911	235
MBPI3187	**The Poet at Twilight**		**600**
PM0754	The Odes & Epodes of Horace	1901	189
MBPI3188	**Subtitle page decoration for The Odes & Epodes of Horace**		**600**
PM0754	The Odes & Epodes of Horace	1901	189
MBPI3189	**"Euterpe"**		**600**
PM0754	The Odes & Epodes of Horace	1901	189
MBPI3190	**Horace Reading to Maecenas**		**600**
PM0754	The Odes & Epodes of Horace	1901	189
MBPI3191	**"There was exchange of thrust and parry"**		**600**
PM0755	Captain Ravenshaw	1901	139
PM0756	A History of American Art	1902	164
MBPI3192	**Lorna Doone**		**600**
PM0758	Character Sketches	1901	142
MBPI3193	**Inauguration of Washington in New York**		**600**
PM0759	A History of the American People	1902	165
PM1479	Hotel Dupont, Wilmington, Delaware	1912	141, 310
PM1481	Panama and Pacific International Exhibition, San Francisco, California	1915	315
PM0795	A History of the American People	1918	166, 170, 273
MBPI3194	**Then the old man's lips began to move**		**600**
PM0762	The Blue Flower	1902	135
MBPI3195	**Illustration for A Report of the truth concerning the last sea-fight of the Revenge**		**600**
PM1132	The Rambler	April, 1902	8
PM0763	A Report of the truth concerning the last sea-fight of the Revenge	1902	206
PM1075	The Strathmore Quality Deckle Edge Book Papers	1906	234
MBPI3196	**Caxton at his Press**		**600**
PM0764	The Bibliomania or Book-Madness	1903	134, 279-280
PM0803	Portfolio of Five Etchings by W. H. W. Bicknell After Original Paintings by Howard Pyle	1903	135, 279, 281
PM0804	Caxton at his Press	1903	279-280
PM0855	Caxton at his Press	1903	134, 280-281
PM1529	St. Louis Universal Exposition, St. Louis, Missouri	1904	303
MBPI3197	**"Friar" Bacon in his Study**		**600**
PM0764	The Bibliomania or Book-Madness	1903	134, 279-280
PM0803	Portfolio of Five Etchings by W. H. W. Bicknell After Original Paintings by Howard Pyle	1903	135, 279, 281
PM0805	Roger Bacon	1903	279-280
PM0856	"Friar" Bacon in his Study	1903	134, 280-281
PM0869	Second Year Book	1903	210
PM1529	St. Louis Universal Exposition, St. Louis, Missouri	1904	303
MBPI3198	**Erasmus reading to Colet And More**		**600**
PM0764	The Bibliomania or Book-Madness	1903	134, 279-280
PM0803	Portfolio of Five Etchings by W. H. W. Bicknell After Original Paintings by Howard Pyle	1903	135, 279, 281
PM0806	Erasmus, Colet and More	1903	279-280
PM0857	Erasmus Reading to Colet and More	1903	134, 280-281
PM0869	Second Year Book	1903	210
PM1529	St. Louis Universal Exposition, St. Louis, Missouri	1904	303
MBPI3199	**"Izaak" Walton**		**600**
PM0764	The Bibliomania or Book-Madness	1903	134, 279-280
PM0803	Portfolio of Five Etchings by W. H. W. Bicknell After Original Paintings by Howard Pyle	1903	135, 279, 281
PM0807	Izaak Walton	1903	279-280
PM0858	"Izaak" Walton	1903	134, 280-281
PM1529	St. Louis Universal Exposition, St. Louis, Missouri	1904	303
MBPI3200	**Richard DeBury and the Young Edward III**		**600**

PM0803	Portfolio of Five Etchings by W. H. W. Bicknell After Original Paintings by Howard Pyle	1903	135, 279, 281
PM0808	Richard DeBury and the Young Edward III	1903	279-280
PM1529	St. Louis Universal Exposition, St. Louis, Missouri	1904	303
MBPI3201	**Illustration for The Eclogues of Vergil**		**601**
PM0765	The Eclogues of Vergil	1904	149
MBPI3202	**Subtitle page decoration for Breviary Treasures**		**601**
PM0991	Odes of Anacreon Anacreontics	1903	150, 191
PM0765	The Eclogues of Vergil	1904	149
MBPI3203	**Hosea and the "cruetin Sarjunt"**		**601**
PM1612	Lowell's Works: The Biglow Papers	1892	178
PM0766	Lowell's Works	1904	178
MBPI3204	**Hosea and the Parson**		**601**
PM1612	Lowell's Works: The Biglow Papers	1892	178
PM0767	Lowell's Works	1904	178
MBPI3205	**Zekle and Huldy**		**601**
PM1612	Lowell's Works: The Biglow Papers	1892	178
PM0767	Lowell's Works	1904	178
MBPI3206	**"Sunthin in the Pastoral Line"**		**601**
PM1612	Lowell's Works: The Biglow Papers	1892	178
PM0767	Lowell's Works	1904	178
PM0774	Snow Bound. A Winter Idyl	1906	212
MBPI3207	**Headpiece, Publisher's Note for The One Hoss Shay**		**601**
PM0772	The One Hoss Shay	1905	195
MBPI3208	**Tailpiece for The One Hoss Shay**		**601**
PM0772	The One Hoss Shay	1905	195
MBPI3209	**Dofobius**		**601**
PM0775	The First Book of the Dofobs	1907	151
PM1065	The Second Book of the Dofobs	1909	210
PM1622	Poems and Letters of Lord Byron	1912	203
MBPI3210	**Cover design for The Tuesday Club**		**601**
PM0811	The Tuesday Club, Wilmington, Delaware, May 29, 1888	1888	341
PM1379	The Lancaster Oratorio Society, Lancaster, Pennsylvania, February 1, 1894	1894	345
MBPI3211	**Headpiece for The Tuesday Club**		**601**
PM0811	The Tuesday Club, Wilmington, Delaware, May 29, 1888	1888	341
PM0812	The Tuesday Club, Wilmington, Delaware, December 18, 1889	1889	342
PM1366	The Tuesday Club, Wilmington, Delaware, June 4, 1889	1889	342
PM1373	The Tuesday Club, Wilmington, Delaware, February 7, 1889	1889	342
PM1370	The Tuesday Club, Wilmington, Delaware, January 21, 1892	1892	343
PM1371	The Tuesday Club, Wilmington, Delaware, May 24, 1892	1892	343
PM1374	The Tuesday Club, Wilmington, Delaware, November 28, 1892	1892	343
PM1372	The Tuesday Club, Wilmington, Delaware, May 22, 1893	1893	344
PM1378	The Tuesday Club, Wilmington, Delaware, January 2, 1893	1893	344
PM1375	The Tuesday Club, Wilmington, Delaware, January 15, 1894	1894	344
PM1377	The Tuesday Club, Wilmington, Delaware, June 4, 1894	1894	345
MBPI3212	**Decoration for The Tuesday Club**		**601**
PM0811	The Tuesday Club, Wilmington, Delaware, May 29, 1888	1888	341
PM0812	The Tuesday Club, Wilmington, Delaware, December 18, 1889	1889	342
PM1373	The Tuesday Club, Wilmington, Delaware, February 7, 1889	1889	342
PM1374	The Tuesday Club, Wilmington, Delaware, November 28, 1892	1892	343
PM1372	The Tuesday Club, Wilmington, Delaware, May 22, 1893	1893	344
PM1375	The Tuesday Club, Wilmington, Delaware, January 15, 1894	1894	344
PM1376	The Tuesday Club, Wilmington, Delaware, March 26, 1894	1894	345
PM1377	The Tuesday Club, Wilmington, Delaware, June 4, 1894	1894	345
MBPI3213	**The Messiah cover design for The Tuesday Club**		**601**
PM0812	The Tuesday Club, Wilmington, Delaware, December 18, 1889	1889	342
PM1378	The Tuesday Club, Wilmington, Delaware, January 2, 1893	1893	344
MBPI3214	**Cover design for The Cecilia Society**		**601**
PM1128	The Cecilia Society, Boston, Massachusetts, December 7, 1898	1898	345-346

PM0813	The Cecilia Society, Boston, Massachusetts, December 6, 1899	1899	345-346
PM1598	The Cecilia Society, Boston, Massachusetts, January 24, 1900	1900	345-346
MBPI3215	**Headpiece for Bi-Centennial Commemoration, Holy Trinity, Old Swedes Church**		**601**
PM0814	Old Swedes' Church, Wilmington, Delaware, May 28, 1899	1899	346
MBPI3216	**Cover design for Twelfth Night at Eagleroost**		**601**
PM0815	The Century Association, New York, January 6, 1906	1906	346
PM1383	The Century Club, New York, January 8, 1917	1917	347
MBPI3217	**Title page decoration for Twelfth Night at Eagleroost**		**602**
PM0815	The Century Association, New York, January 6, 1906	1906	346
PM1383	The Century Club, New York, January 8, 1917	1917	347
MBPI3218	**Headpiece for Twelfth Night at Eagleroost**		**602**
PM0815	The Century Association, New York, January 6, 1906	1906	346
PM1383	The Century Club, New York, January 8, 1917	1917	347
MBPI3219	**Cover design for Centuria's Greetings**		**602**
PM0816	The Century Association invitation for January 6, 1906	1906	346
MBPI3220	**Headpiece for Centuria's Greetings**		**602**
PM0816	The Century Association invitation for January 6, 1906	1906	346
MBPI3221	**Illustrated initial G for Centuria's Greetings**		**602**
PM0816	The Century Association invitation for January 6, 1906	1906	346
MBPI3222	**Poor Richard**		**602**
PM0817	The Franklin Inn Club, Philadelphia, Pennsylvania, January 6, 1906	1906	347
PM1541	Book of the Franklin Inn Club	1914	136
MBPI3223	**Design for The Players bookplate**		**602**
PM0818	The Players, New York	1894	274
PM1156	Some New York Bookplates	April, 1899	17
PM0790	Theatrical Bookplates	1914	235
PM0791	Some American College Bookplates	1915	212
MBPI3224	**Design for The Players bookplate**		**602**
PM0819	The Players, New York	1900	274
MBPI3225	**Design for Frederick Haines Curtiss bookplate**		**602**
PM0820	Frederick Haines Curtiss, Boston	1899	274
MBPI3226	**Design for Howard Pyle bookplate**		**602**
PM0821	Howard Pyle, Wilmington, Delaware	1900	274-275
MBPI3227	**Design for Edith Kermit Roosevelt bookplate**		**602**
PM0822	Edith Kermit Roosevelt, Oyster Bay, New York	1905	275
PM1581	Howard Pyle Designed Bookplate	December, 1913	3
MBPI3228	**Design for The Yale Club of New York City bookplate**		**602**
PM0823	The Yale Club, New York	1905	275
PM0791	Some American College Bookplates	1915	212
MBPI3229	**Design for Keats-Shelley Memorial bookplate**		**602**
PM0824	Keats-Shelley Memorial, Rome, Italy	1908	275
PM1229	Timothy Cole as an Engraver of Book Plates	1914	102
MBPI3230	**The DuPont Powder Wagon**		**602**
PM0941	An Intimate History of the E. I. du Pont de Nemours Powder Co. (part II of III)	November, 1911	102
PM0826	The DuPont Powder Wagon	1912	341
PM0942	Centennial of The Use of Dupont Explosives In An American War	1912	278
PM1017	The History of the E. I. duPont de Nemours Powder Company	1912	167
PM1213	Howard Pyle, Dupont Powder Wagon	December, 1915	97
MBPI3231	**To Have and to Hold**		**602**
PM0827	To Have and to Hold	1900	327-328
PM1280	To Have and To Hold	1900	328
PM1315	To Have and To Hold	1900	272
PM1354	A Holiday Bulletin of Books	1900	269
PM1479	Hotel Dupont, Wilmington, Delaware	1912	141, 310
MBPI3232	**The Genus of Literature**		**602**
PM0828	Mural paintings–Howard Pyle's Home, Wilmington, Delaware	1905	257
MBPI3233	**Shepherd and Girl**		**603**
PM0828	Mural paintings–Howard Pyle's Home, Wilmington, Delaware	1905	257
MBPI3234	**The Genus of Art**		**603**

PM1463	Yale University School of Fine Arts, New Haven, Connecticut	1903	297
PM0828	Mural paintings–Howard Pyle's Home, Wilmington, Delaware	1905	257
PM1469	The Architectural League of New York, New York	1905	303
PM0848	Cleveland Architectural Club, Cleveland, Ohio	1909	141, 257, 308
PM1036	Mural Painting in America	1913	187
MBPI3235	**The Genus of Music**		**603**
PM0828	Mural paintings–Howard Pyle's Home, Wilmington, Delaware	1905	257
MBPI3236	**Young Flowering Trees**		**603**
PM0828	Mural paintings–Howard Pyle's Home, Wilmington, Delaware	1905	257
MBPI3237	**Flowering Tree II**		**603**
PM0828	Mural paintings–Howard Pyle's Home, Wilmington, Delaware	1905	257
MBPI3238	**The Genus of Drama**		**603**
PM0828	Mural paintings–Howard Pyle's Home, Wilmington, Delaware	1905	257
MBPI3239	**The Battle of Nashville**		**603**
PM0829	Mural painting–State Capitol, Saint Paul, Minnesota	1906	257
PM0848	Cleveland Architectural Club, Cleveland, Ohio	1909	141, 257, 308
MBPI3240	**The Landing of Carteret**		**603**
PM0359	Mural painting–Essex County Court House, Newark, New Jersey	February 9, 1907	74
PM1652	Essex County Court House	July, 1907	97
PM0523	Catalogue of theTwenty-second Annual Exhibition of the Architectural League of New York	1907	142, 306
PM0830	Mural painting–Essex County Court House, Newark, New Jersey	1907	257
PM0901	The Landing of Carteret	1907	340
PM0902	The Architectural League of New York	1907	142, 305
PM1004	Essex County Courthouse: Report of Leslie D. Ward, Cass Gilbert and Joseph L. Munn	1908	150
PM0848	Cleveland Architectural Club, Cleveland, Ohio	1909	141, 257, 308
MBPI3241	**Illustration for A Transferred Romance**		**603**
PM0340	A Transferred Romance	April 9, 1892	71
MBPI3242	**The Home-made Press**		**603**
PM1635	How a Comet Struck the Earth	June, 1879	117
PDPI0001	**The Tiger**		**603**
PM0840	McGuffey's Second Eclectic Reader	1879	181
PDPI0002	**Preliminary study for proposed mural for Soldiers and Sailors Memorial Hall of Allegheny County, Pennsylvania**		**603**
PM0848	Cleveland Architectural Club, Cleveland, Ohio	1909	141, 257, 308
PM0914	Mural preliminary study for proposed Lincoln Memorial	1909	141, 257, 308
PM1591	Catalogue of the Architectural Exhibition of the Cleveland Architectural Club	1909	141, 257, 308
PDPI0003	**Birthday Tribute to Theodore Roosevelt**		**603**
PM0847	Birthday Tribute to Theodore Roosevelt	1908	
PDPI0004	**Howard Pyle self portrait painting**		**603**
PM0853	Howard Pyle self portrait painting	1905	
PDPI0005	**Howard Pyle script book label**		**603**
PM1526	Howard Pyle	1885	274
PDPI0006	**The portrait of a young gentleman who always says "Thank you!"**		**603**
PM1268	The portrait of a young gentleman who always says "Thank you!"	1904	
PDPI0007	**The Escape**		**604**
PM1532	The Escape	1910	
PDPI0008	**Preliminary study for MBPI2501 Peter Stuyvesant and the English Fleet**		**604**
PM0918	Mural preliminary study for MBPI2501 Peter Stuyvesant and the English Fleet	1910	258
PM0903	The Architectural League of New York	1911	131, 309
PM1624	Architectural League of New York Year Book and Catalogue	1911	130, 309
PDPI0009	**Preliminary study for MBPI2500 Hendryk Hudson and the Half-Moon**		**604**
PM0919	Mural preliminary study for MBPI2500 Hendryk Hudson and the Half-Moon	1910	258
PM0903	The Architectural League of New York	1911	131, 309
PM1624	Architectural League of New York Year Book and Catalogue	1911	130, 309
PDPI0010	**Preliminary study for MBPI2502 Life in an Old Dutch Town**		**604**

PM0920	Mural preliminary study for MBPI2502 Life in an Old Dutch Town	1910	258
PM0903	The Architectural League of New York	1911	131, 309
PM1624	Architectural League of New York Year Book and Catalogue	1911	130, 309
PDPI0011	**Strip of Green for mural panel**		**604**
PM0828	Mural paintings–Howard Pyle's Home, Wilmington, Delaware	1905	257
PDPI0012	**Flowering Tree I**		**604**
PM0828	Mural paintings–Howard Pyle's Home, Wilmington, Delaware	1905	257
PDPI0013	**General Prescott**		**604**
PM1544	General Prescott	1893	
PDPI0014	**Ye Queen of Hearts**		**604**
PM1537	Ye Queen of Hearts	1904	
PDPI0015	**A Matter of Fate**		**604**
PM1067	A Matter of Fate	1901	
PDPI0016	**A view in Jamaica**		**604**
PM1539	A View in Jamaica	1906	
PDPI0017	**Suspicious Strangers**		**604**
PM1440	American Water Color Society, New York, New York	1881	282
PM1531	Suspicious Strangers	1881	
PDPI0018	**Ye Pirate Bold, as imagined by a Quaker Gentleman**		**604**
PM0846	Ye Pirate Bold, as imagined by a Quaker Gentleman	1903	
PDPI0019	**Illustrated initial F with decoration for The Captain's Well**		**604**
PM0500	The Captain's Well	January 11, 1890	104
PDPI0020	**Vignette for newspaper head**		**604**
PM1288	Our Head	September 4, 1871	19, 114, 116
PDPI0021	**Cavalier with sword**		**604**
PM0962	To Have and To Hold–Bookmark	1900	277
PDPI0022	**The Inquisitive Peasant**		**604**
PM1307	Wooden puzzle	1909	348
PDPI0023	**Design for drinking mug**		**605**
PM1649	The Salmagundi Mug Sale/Annual Auction of Pottery Painted by Members of the Club	March 22, 1902	99, 347
PM1305	Salmagundi Club Drinking Mug	1902	100, 209, 347
PDPI0024	**Tailpiece design and verse for drinking mug**		**605**
PM1305	Salmagundi Club Drinking Mug	1902	100, 209, 347
PDPI0025	**Decoration and illustrated initial T for Quill and Grill Club Invitation**		**605**
PM1324	Quill and Grill Club Invitation, Wilmington, Delaware	1883	278
PDPI0026	**Seal decoration for Quill and Grill Club Invitation**		**605**
PM1324	Quill and Grill Club Invitation, Wilmington, Delaware	1883	278
PDPI0027	**Design for unused Howard Pyle bookplate**		**605**
PM1284	Howard Pyle	1885	274
PDPI0028	**Unused color design for Howard Pyle bookplate**		**605**
PM1286	Howard Pyle, Wilmington, Delaware	1900	275
PDPI0029	**Angel of Death**		**605**
PM0848	Cleveland Architectural Club, Cleveland, Ohio	1909	141, 257, 308
PM1262	Stained Glass Window, Hotchkiss School	1909	348
PM1591	Catalogue of the Architectural Exhibition of the Cleveland Architectural Club	1909	141, 257, 308
PDPI0030	**Spine design for Twilight Land**		**605**
PM0651	Twilight Land	1895	237
PDPI0031	**The Indians Aiming at the Loop-Holes**		**605**
PM0671	Old Times in the Colonies	1881	193
PM0686	Indian History For Young Folks	1885	172
PM0929	Indian History For Young Folks	1919	172
PDPI0032	**Bugler at Fort Macon**		**605**
PM1062	A Popular History of the United States	1880	203
PM1064	Scribner's Popular History of the United States	1896	210
PDPI0033	**Vignette, woman on a houseboat**		**605**
PM0905	Vignette, woman on a houseboat	1896	
PDPI0034	**Young woman standing under tree**		**605**
PM1264	Untitled Etching	1884	279

PDPI0035	**Pennsylvania Avenue**		**605**
PM1190	The Flood at Washington, D.C.	March 5, 1881	66
PDPI0036	**Illustration for Odes of Anacreon Anacreontics**		**605**
PM0991	Odes of Anacreon Anacreontics	1903	150, 191
PDPI0037	**"The Serenade"**		**605**
PM1236	Wood-Engraving as an Occupation for Women	July 4, 1883	16
PDPI0038	**Something Fresh**		**605**
PM1060	The Salmagundi Club	1918	100, 209, 347
PDPI0039	**A Very Merry Christmas In The "Good Old Times"**		**606**
PM1300	A Very Merry Christmas In The "Good Old Times"	December 25, 1880	103
PDPI0040	**Illustrated initial A for A Very Merry Christmas in The "Good Old Times"**		**606**
PM1300	A Very Merry Christmas In The "Good Old Times"	December 25, 1880	103
PDPI0041	**"A Study"**		**606**
PM1478	Los Angeles Architectural Club, Los Angeles, California	1911	178, 310
PM1626	Los Angeles Architectural Club Year Book and Catalogue	1911	178, 310
PDPI0042	**Design for The Grolier Club bookplate**		**606**
PM1285	The Grolier Club, New York	1887	274
PDPI0043	**Theatrical costumes designed by Howard Pyle**		**606**
PM0971	Designs for theatrical costumes	1909	
PDPI0044	**Renaissance Couple**		**606**
PM0972	Renaissance Couple	1902	
PDPI0045	**Portrait of Joshua Clayton**		**606**
PM0973	Portrait of Joshua Clayton	1898	
PDPI0046	**Design for punch bowl**		**606**
PM0974	Design for punch bowl	1909	
PDPI0047	**Design for centerpiece**		**606**
PM0975	Design for centerpiece	1909	
PDPI0048	**Design for candelabra–candlestick–electrolier**		**606**
PM0976	Design for candelabra, candelstick, electrolier	1909	
PDPI0049	**Medieval Scene**		**606**
PM0980	Medieval scene	1875	
PDPI0050	**Soldier with spear**		**606**
PM0978	Soldier with spear	1900	
PDPI0051	**The Sly Fox**		**606**
PM0979	The Sly Fox	1876	
PDPI0052	**The Flute Player**		**606**
PM0977	The Flute Player	1890	
PDPI0053	**Illustrated initial T for The Star Bearer**		**606**
PM0633	The Star Bearer	December, 1887	127
PM0695	The Star Bearer	1888	214
PDPI0054	**Tailpiece for The Star Bearer**		**606**
PM0633	The Star Bearer	December, 1887	127
PM0695	The Star Bearer	1888	214
PDPI0055	**"All eyes were turned to Abraham Davenport. He rose, slow cleaving with his steady voice the intolerable hush."**		**607**
PM1034	Monroe's New Fifth Reader	1884	187
PM1035	Monroe's New Readers	1884	265
PDPI0056	**The Garfield Ambulance Train on its way to Elberon, N.J.**		**607**
PM1064	Scribner's Popular History of the United States	1896	210
PDPI0057	**Cover design for Report of the Board of Park Commissioners, Wilmington, Delaware**		**607**
PM1270	Report of Board of Park Commissioners, Wilmington, Delaware for the year 1896	1897	206
PM1271	Report of Board of Park Commissioners, Wilmington, Delaware for the year 1897	1898	206
PM1272	Report of Board of Park Commissioners, Wilmington, Delaware for the year 1898	1899	206
PM1273	Report of Board of Park Commissioners, Wilmington, Delaware for the year 1899	1900	206
PDPI0058	**Woman at a Spinning Wheel**		**607**
PM0926	Woman at a Spinning Wheel	1879	

PDPI0059 **The Deacon's Masterpiece: or the Wonderful "One-Hoss-Shay" with initial H** **607**

PM0927 The Deacon's Masterpiece: or, the Wonderful "One Hoss-Shay" with 1891
initial H

PDPI0060 **Peter Rugg Ye Bostonian** **607**

PM0928 Peter Rugg Ye Bostonian 1891

PDPI0061 **Young Woman in Elizabethan Dress** **607**

PM1281 To Have and To Hold 1900 328

PDPI0062 **Design for Howard Pyle School of Art lapel pin** **607**

PM1306 Howard Pyle School of Art lapel pin 1903 348

PDPI0063 **Woman carrying urn** **607**

PM1319 The Calendar of Famous Artists 1904 277

PDPI0064 **Design for 1908 Christmas Seal** **607**

PM1322 1908 Christmas Seal, First and Second Printings 1908 278

PM1567 Cartoons By Halladay 1914 140

PM1564 Achievements of the Past October, 1915 1

PDPI0065 **Design for 1908 Christmas Seal–Rounded corners** **607**

PM1323 1908 Christmas Seal, Third Printing 1908 278

PDPI0066 **Cover design without border for Tuesday Club** **607**

PM1366 The Tuesday Club, Wilmington, Delaware, June 4, 1889 1889 342

PM1367 The Tuesday Club, Wilmington, Delaware, May 15, 1890 1890 342

PM1368 The Tuesday Club, Wilmington, Delaware, May 21, 1891 1891 343

PM1370 The Tuesday Club, Wilmington, Delaware, January 21, 1892 1892 343

PM1371 The Tuesday Club, Wilmington, Delaware, May 24, 1892 1892 343

PM1372 The Tuesday Club, Wilmington, Delaware, May 22, 1893 1893 344

PDPI0067 **Headpiece with title, A Relay Tavern** **607**

PM1495 Old Coaching Days June 6, 1891 71

PDPI0068 **A Race for Life** **607**

PM1496 A Race For Life October 20, 1881 128

PDPI0069 **Front cover decorative border for McClure's Magazine** **607**

PM1497 Front cover decorative border July, 1907 101

PDPI0070 **The Burning of the Guillotine Before the Statue of Voltaire** **607**

PM1498 The Seige and Commune of Paris March, 1887 108

PM0700 Recollections of a Minister to France 1887 205

PDPI0071 **The Frightful Accident** **608**

PM1499 The Frightful Accident March 24, 1877 21

PDPI0072 **And we kept those fellows alee, astern** **608**

PM1500 A Ballad of The Constitution October 8, 1895 63

PDPI0073 **For many a mile we sailed** **608**

PM1500 A Ballad of The Constitution October 8, 1895 63

PM1650 Harper's Round Table for 1898 1898 268

PDPI0074 **Her decks are red with her gallant dead** **608**

PM1500 A Ballad of The Constitution October 8, 1895 63

PDPI0075 **River Rocks** **608**

PM0904 River Rocks 1910

PDPI0076 **The Sea Fight** **608**

PM0907 The Sea Fight 1900

PM1466 Kellogg Public Library, Green Bay, Wisconsin 1904 301

PDPI0077 **Spine design for Pepper & Salt** **608**

PM0641 Pepper & Salt 1886 76-82, 200

PDPI0078 **Headband for The Gods of the Copybook Maxims** **608**

PM1178 The Gods of the Copybook Maxims January, 1920 62

PDPI0079 **Tailpiece for The Painted Pitcher** **608**

PM0273 The Painted Pitcher November, 1911 61

PDPI0080 **Beach Scene** **608**

PM0983 Beach Scene 1891

PDPI0081 **Illustrated initial M for Invitation** **608**

PM1563 Bohemian Card Party 1904 279

PDPI0082 **Tailpiece for Invitation** **608**

PM1563 Bohemian Card Party 1904 279

PDPI0083 **Ocean View** **608**

PM1573	Ocean View	1904	261
PDPI0084	**"May I have the pleasure for the next"**		**608**
PM1576	"May I have the pleasure for the next"	1883	103
PDPI0085	**Bust profile with chalice**		**608**
PM0754	The Odes & Epodes of Horace	1901	189
PDPI0086	**Bust profile arm extended**		**608**
PM0754	The Odes & Epodes of Horace	1901	189
PDPI0087	**Head I**		**609**
PM0754	The Odes & Epodes of Horace	1901	189
PDPI0088	**Head II**		**609**
PM0754	The Odes & Epodes of Horace	1901	189
PDPI0089	**Head III**		**609**
PM0754	The Odes & Epodes of Horace	1901	189
PDPI0090	**Head I with wings**		**609**
PM0754	The Odes & Epodes of Horace	1901	189
PDPI0091	**Head II with wings**		**609**
PM0754	The Odes & Epodes of Horace	1901	189
PDPI0092	**Head III with wings**		**609**
PM0754	The Odes & Epodes of Horace	1901	189
PDPI0093	**Head IV with wings**		**609**
PM0754	The Odes & Epodes of Horace	1901	189
PDPI0094	**Wings**		**609**
PM0754	The Odes & Epodes of Horace	1901	189
PDPI0095	**Subtitle decoration I**		**609**
PM0754	The Odes & Epodes of Horace	1901	189
PDPI0096	**Subtitle decoration II**		**609**
PM0754	The Odes & Epodes of Horace	1901	189
PDPI0097	**Old Fire-Place, Aunt Saber's Kitchen**		**609**
PM0065	A Peninsular Canaan. I	May, 1879	24
PDPI0098	**Marooned**		**609**
PM1618	Marooned	1909	
PDPI0099	**Night Haul of The Seine**		**609**
PM0066	A Peninsular Canaan. II	June, 1879	24
PDPI0100	**Cover border design for The Ladies' Home Journal**		**609**
PM0492	Cover Design	May, 1897	98
PDPI0101	**Sea Battle between Two Frigates**		**609**
PM0802	Sea Battle between Two Frigates	1903	
PDPI0102	**Cor Cordia: A Christmas Greeting from Thy Husband**		**609**
PM1362	Cor Cordia: A Christmas Greeting from Thy Husband	1881	
PDPI0103	**Illustration for The Adventure of a Mouse**		**610**
PM1255	The Adventure of a Mouse	December, 1885	118
PDPI0104	**"But the Proudest and Grandest of All the Flock Was Gobble, Our Gorgeous Turkey-Cock."**		**610**
PM1638	The Reformer	November, 1875	19, 114-115
PDPI0105	**Theatrical costumes designed by Howard Pyle**		**610**
PM1639	The Pecuniary Rewards of Playwriting	December, 1909	18, 20, 125
MBOP0001	**Howard Pyle photo portrait**		**610**
PM0866	Harper's Magazine for 1896	November, 1895	41
PM1148	Advertisement: Century Co's publications	November, 1895	12
PM1604	Howard Pyle photo portrait	1895	322
PM0871	Harper's Bookshelf	July, 1907	54
PM0865	Harper's Bookshelf	February, 1909	57
PM0867	Howard Pyle–An Appreciation	November 18, 1911	74
PM0636	When I Was a Little Boy	April, 1912	127
PM0936	Howard Pyle–Maker of Pictures and Stories	May, 1915	124
MBOP0002	**Howard Pyle photo portrait**		**610**
PM0868	Howard Pyle	October, 1888	5, 329
PM1605	Howard Pyle photo portrait	1888	322
PM1494	Howard Pyle photo portrait	1890	328
PM0801	American Illustrators	1892	130
PM1251	"Artist-Authors"	May 26, 1894	106

MBOP0003	**Howard Pyle photo portrait**		**610**
PM0931	Great American Illustrators: Howard Pyle, Illustrator	September, 1907	99, 106
PM1606	Howard Pyle photo portrait	1907	324
PM0839	Celebrities	January, 1908	96
PM0965	Howard Pyle, Illustrator	May 2, 1909	10, 74, 107
PM0964	Talented Howard Pyle: Man of Various Parts	1909	10, 74, 107
PM0809	Catalogue of Pictures by Howard Pyle	1912	141, 310
PM1479	Hotel Dupont, Wilmington, Delaware	1912	141, 310
PM0944	An Evening With Howard Pyle	November, 1919	18
MBOP0004	**Howard Pyle photo portrait**		**610**
PM1097	Howard Pyle	January, 1903	2
PM0869	Second Year Book	1903	210
PM1607	Howard Pyle photo portrait	1903	324
PM0966	The Founder of an American School of Art	February 23, 1907	106
PM0794	American Art by American Artists	1915	130
PDOP0001	**Howard Pyle photo portrait**		**610**
PM0912	Young Folks Authors a game of cards	1897	277
PM1600	Howard Pyle photo portrait	1897	323
PM0849	Fifty Years of Harper's Magazine	May, 1900	47
PM0870	Books and Bookmen	July 25, 1903	74
PM0864	Harper's Bookshelf	August, 1903	50
PM0863	A Group of Harper Authors and Artists	December 19, 1903	74
PM0005	Fairy Tales	December, 1904	10
PM1218	Book Review: Stolen Treasure	July 6, 1907	99
PM1292	Tributes to Howard Pyle	November 10, 1911	127
PM1293	Tributes to Howard Pyle	November 13, 1911	102
PM0940	Delaware's Great Men	November, 1911	102
PM0873	Howard Pyle	December, 1911	1
PDOP0002	**Howard Pyle photo portrait**		**610**
PM1159	Some Illustrators of the Day	April, 1897	18
PM0850	The Rambler	May, 1897	8
PM1601	Howard Pyle photo portrait	1897	323
PM1643	Eccentric	1897	149
PDOP0003	**Howard Pyle photo portrait**		**610**
PM0915	Howard Pyle photo portrait	1883	322
PDOP0004	**Howard Pyle photo portrait**		**610**
PM0874	Harper & Brothers' Descriptive List of Publications with Trade-List Prices	1896	266
PM1599	Howard Pyle photo portrait	1896	322-323
PM1595	Howard Pyle photo portrait	1900	333, 337
PM1611	My Dear Young Friend	March 25, 1902	338
PM0876	Howard Pyle	August, 1903	99
PM1217	A Revolutionary Force In American Art	March 23, 1907	98
PM0943	The Foremost American Illustrator	November 25, 1911	99
PM0851	The Late Howard Pyle	January, 1912	10
PDOP0005	**Howard Pyle photo portrait**		**610**
PM0875	Howard Pyle photo portrait	1896	323
PDOP0006	**Howard Pyle photo portrait**		**610**
PM0861	Howard Pyle photo portrait	1896	322
PDOP0007	**Howard Pyle photo portrait**		**610**
PM0878	Howard Pyle photo portrait	1910	324
PDOP0008	**Howard Pyle photo portrait**		**610**
PM0916	Howard Pyle photo portrait	1910	324
PDOP0009	**Howard Pyle photo portrait**		**610**
PM0917	Howard Pyle photo portrait	1903	324
PDOP0010	**Howard Pyle photo portrait**		**611**
PM1487	Howard Pyle photo portrait	1898	323
PDOP0011	**Howard Pyle photo portrait**		**611**
PM1488	Howard Pyle photo portrait	1856	322
PDOP0012	**Howard Pyle photo portrait**		**611**

PM1489	Howard Pyle photo portrait	1910	325
PDOP0013	**Howard Pyle photo portrait**		**611**
PM1602	Howard Pyle photo portrait	1906	324
PM0966	The Founder of an American School of Art	February 23, 1907	106
PDOP0014	**Howard Pyle silhouette photo portrait**		**611**
PM0854	Howard Pyle silhouette photo portrait	1901	324
PDOP0015	**Howard Pyle photo portrait**		**611**
PM1490	Howard Pyle photo portrait	1906	324
PDOP0016	**Howard Pyle photo portrait**		**611**
PM1491	Howard Pyle photo portrait	1884	322
PDOP0017	**Howard Pyle photo portrait**		**611**
PM1492	Howard Pyle photo portrait	1892	322
PDOP0018	**Howard Pyle photo portrait**		**611**
PM0877	Howard Pyle	November, 1899	8
PM1603	Howard Pyle photo portrait	1899	323
PDOP0019	**Howard Pyle photo portrait**		**611**
PM0963	Howard Pyle photo portrait	1896	323
PDOP0020	**Howard Pyle photo portrait**		**611**
PM0967	Howard Pyle photo portrait	1896	323
PDOP0021	**Howard Pyle portrait likeness**		**611**
PM0841	Howard Pyle Cigar Box Label	1902	278
MBOI0001	**Arrivals at the Creamery**		**611**
PM1629	A Creamery	1882	318
MBOI0002	**Receiving Milk**		**611**
PM1629	A Creamery	1882	318
MBOI0003	**Making Cheese**		**611**
PM1629	A Creamery	1882	318
MBOI0004	**Early Morning on the Ferries**		**611**
PM1629	A Creamery	1882	318
MBOI0005	**Assorting the Peaches**		**612**
PM1630	Assorting the Peaches	1879	318
MBOI0006	**Headpiece with title for The Sea Man**		**612**
PM1631	Headpiece with Title for the Sea Man	1901	319
MBOI0007	**The storm of 1821**		**612**
PM1632	The Storm of 1821	1877	318
MBOI0008	**The Tile House, New Castle, Delaware**		**612**
PM1633	The Tile House, New Castle, Delaware	1882	319
MBOI0009	**Wayne Homestead**		**612**
PM1634	Wayne Homestead	1880	318
MBOI0010	**Tailpiece for Gretelein and Her Queer Stove**		**612**
PM1636	Tailpiece for Gretelein and Her Queer Stove	1879	318